Secondary School

MATHEMATICS

Grade Eleven

W. B. MacLEAN
D. L. MUMFORD
R. W. BOCK
D. N. HAZELL
G. A. KAYE

SECONDARY SCHOOL
Mathematics
GRADE ELEVEN

THE COPP CLARK PUBLISHING CO. LIMITED

VANCOUVER   TORONTO   MONTREAL

AUTHORS

W. B. MacLEAN
Professor of Methods in Mathematics
Ontario College of Education
University of Toronto

D. L. MUMFORD
Associate Professor of Methods in Mathematics
Ontario College of Education
University of Toronto

R. W. BOCK
Head, Department of Mathematics
Royal York Collegiate Institute
Etobicoke, Ontario

D. N. HAZELL
Head, Department of Mathematics
Don Mills Collegiate Institute
Don Mills, Ontario

G. A. KAYE
Head, Department of Mathematics
Downsview Secondary School
Downsview, Ontario

CONSULTANT

DR. D. B. DeLURY
Chairman, Department of Mathematics
University of Toronto

[1408]

PREFACE

Secondary School Mathematics Grade Eleven is the fifth text in the Copp Clark Modern Mathematics series from Grade 7 through Grade 12. The text, which follows the requirements of the Ontario Department of Education Grade 11 curriculum, is designed to provide a thorough course in essential mathematical concepts, as well as a body of practical, precise, mathematical knowledge.

Organized so that it can be readily adapted to classes of differing aptitudes and to future program developments, this text makes possible a two-stage introduction to the Modern Mathematics program. Classes beginning new mathematics at this grade can acquire the necessary vocabulary and basic ideas quickly from the comprehensive review chapters which form part of the Grade 11 course. Classes which began the new program in earlier grades will be able to complete many of the supplementary topics which, at present, follow in more advanced courses.

With the emphasis in this text on discovery and on understanding of the general principles and processes of mathematics, many discovery exercises and pre-assignment practice examples are included which students can work independently and then compare with models provided at the back of the book.

The introduction to logic, which was begun in *Secondary School Mathematics Grade Ten*, is continued and developed more fully here in the deductive geometry chapters, and the analysis of deductions is also given a key place in the development of geometry. The introduction to trigonometry and coordinate geometry is organized so that the student can make fundamental discoveries himself about the new ideas and principles of modern mathematics.

v

The authors wish to express their appreciation to the Copp Clark Publishing Company and to all who have helped in the preparation of this book. They acknowledge with gratitude the close co-operation of Mr. F. L. Barrett, the editorial supervision and labour of Mrs. Ruth Kerpneck, and the assistance of Miss Linda Taylor in reading and correcting copy during the production of *Secondary School Mathematics Grade Eleven*. They wish, as well, to thank Mr. O. Hall, Head of the Department of Mathematics, Richview Collegiate Institute, and Mrs. Daphne Kaye for their careful preparation of the diagrams.

W.B.M.
D.L.M.
R.W.B.
D.N.H.
G.A.K.

Contents

IV GENERAL PRINCIPLES OF GEOMETRY, DEDUCTIVE REASONING, FUNDAMENTAL ANGLE PAIR THEOREMS

V CONGRUENCE, PARALLELISM

VI POLYGONS, AREAS OF POLYGONS

VII RATIO AND PROPORTION, SIMILAR FIGURES

VIII TRIGONOMETRY

IX RELATIONS

X SYSTEMS OF LINEAR EQUATIONS

XI COORDINATE GEOMETRY OF THE STRAIGHT LINE

XI COORDINATE GEOMETRY OF
THE STRAIGHT LINE (cont.)

MATHEMATICAL SYMBOLS

$\because$	since; because
$\therefore$	therefore
$\ldots$	and so on
$.$	decimal point
$.\dot{3}$ or $.\overline{3}$	repeating decimal
$+$	plus; add; positive
$-$	minus; subtract; negative
$\pm$	plus or minus; positive or negative
$\times$ or $\cdot$	multiplied by
$\div$	divided by
$=$	is equal to
$\neq$	is not equal to
$\doteqdot$ or $\simeq$	is approximately equal to
$\cong$	is congruent to; is identical to
$\sim$	is similar to (as in $\triangle ABC \sim \triangle DEF$)
$>$	is greater than
$\not>$	is not greater than
$<$	is less than
$\not<$	is not less than
$\geqq$	is greater than or equal to
$\ngeqq$	is not greater than or equal to
$\leqq$	is less than or equal to
$\nleqq$	is not less than or equal to
$\cup$	cup; the union of
$\cap$	cap; the intersection of
$\leftrightarrow$	corresponds to; is equivalent to; if and only if
$\rightarrow$	implies; only if
$\sim A$	not A; the negation of A
$A \times B$	the Cartesian product of A and B
$a : b$	the ratio of a to b
$|\ |$	the absolute value of
$\sqrt{\ }$	the square root of
$\sqrt[n]{\ }$	the nth root of

$\parallel$	is parallel to
$\not\parallel$	is not parallel to
$\perp$	is perpendicular to
$\angle$	angle
$\triangle$	triangle
$\parallel^{\text{gm}}$	parallelogram
$^\circ$	degree
$'$	minute; foot
$''$	second; inch
π	$\frac{22}{7}$ (3 sig. digits); 3.1416 (5 sig. digits)
$\%$	per cent
( )	round brackets
[ ]	square brackets
{ }	brace brackets; the set
$\overline{a+b}$	bar bracket
{ | }	the set builder
$\in$	belongs to; is a member of; is an element of
$\notin$	is not a member of
$\emptyset$	null set
$\subset$	is a proper subset of
$\subseteq$	is a subset of
N	the set of natural numbers
N_0	the set of natural numbers and zero
I	the set of integers
^{+}I	the set of positive integers
^{-}I	the set of negative integers
Q	the set of rational numbers
R	the set of real numbers
^{+}R	the set of positive real numbers
^{-}R	the set of negative real numbers
(ClA)	Closure Law for Addition
(ClM)	Closure Law for Multiplication
(CA)	Commutative Law for Addition
(CM)	Commutative Law for Multiplication
(AA)	Associative Law for Addition
(AM)	Associative Law for Multiplication
(D)	Distributive Law

Review A

SETS

A·1 The concept of a set. From the earliest times people have thought in terms of sets or collections of objects: for example,

> a collection of books,
> a collection of coins,
> the members of a family,
> the set of fingers on one's hand.

A set is a well-defined collection of objects.

Each object in a set is called a *member* or *element* of the set. The words *well-defined* mean that it is clearly established whether or not an object is included in a particular set. In mathematics, the members of sets are generally mathematical objects, such as counting numbers, fractions, points, lines, angles.

Membership in a set may be indicated in several ways:

(a) by stating a *rule of membership* such as

  (i) the set of all odd whole numbers;

  (ii) the set of all boys in a school;

(b) by using a *capital letter* which suggests the defining rule of the set: for example, E might be used to represent the set of all even whole numbers;

(c) by *listing* the members of the set in *brace brackets*: for example, the set of all prime numbers between 1 and 20 may be written

$$P = \{2, 3, 5, 7, 11, 13, 17, 19\}$$

which presents a complete list of all the members of the set. The statement is read, "P is the set 2, 3, 5, 7, 11, 13, 17, 19"; the brace brackets symbol $\{\ \}$ is read, "the set of".

In the preceding example, P represents the set whose members are 2, 3, 5, 7, 11, 13, 17, 19. The fact that 3 is a member of this set is expressed

$$3 \in P.$$

The symbol $\in$ (the Greek letter epsilon) is read, "is a member of" or "is an element of" or "belongs to".

Write a solution for each of the following problems; compare your solutions with those on page 437.

1. If $A = \{2, 4, 6, 8, 10\}$
    (i) describe the set in words;
    (ii) express in symbols the fact that 6 is a member of the set.

2. State a defining rule for membership in each of the following sets:

    (i) $\{3, 5, 7, 9\}$ (ii) $\left\{\dfrac{1}{2}, \dfrac{3}{2}, \dfrac{5}{2}, \dfrac{7}{2}\right\}$

3. The concept of a set implies that the members are different from each other. How many members are there in each of the following sets? Rewrite each set listing each element only once.
    (i) $\{1, 2, 4, 9\}$ (ii) $\{a, b, c, d, a\}$
    (iii) $\{1, 1, 1, 2, 2, 2, 2\}$ (iv) $\{0\}$
    (v) $\{0, 2, 3, 4, 3, 2, 0\}$ (vi) $\{a, m, a\}$

A·2 Finite sets, infinite sets, null set. A set may consist of any number of elements. If there is a counting number which represents the number of elements in a set, then the set is a finite set ("finite" from the Latin *finitus* meaning "finished" or "ended"). Thus, *a finite set is a set with a limited number of elements.*

The following are examples of finite sets:

(i) $\{x_1, x_2, x_3\}$ is a finite set with three members;

(ii) $\{2, 4, 6, 8, \ldots, 100\}$ is a finite set with fifty members;

(iii) $\{a_1, a_2, a_3, \ldots, a_n\}$, where n represents some counting number, is a finite set with n members.

The three dots $\ldots$ are used to indicate the continuing nature of the set and in example (ii) imply the even numbers between 8 and 100.

The set of all even numbers between 10 and 12 contains no members. The set of all prime factors of 27 which are greater than 6 also has no members. Sets with no members are said to be *empty* sets, and each is referred to as the *null* set. The null set is represented by the Greek letter $\emptyset$. Thus,

(i) the set of all even numbers between 10 and 12 is $\emptyset$;

(ii) the set of all prime factors of 27 greater than 6 is $\emptyset$.

Sets which are neither finite nor null are called *infinite* sets (not finished, unlimited) and are usually designated by a rule of membership or verbal description. The membership of an infinite set may be implied by listing some members in brace brackets and using three dots (read, "and so on") to indicate that the membership suggested by the listing is unending.

The following are examples of infinite sets:

(i) the set of all counting numbers is $\{1, 2, 3, 4, \ldots\}$;

(ii) the set of all odd numbers is $\{1, 3, 5, 7, \ldots\}$;

(iii) the set of all even numbers is $\{2, 4, 6, 8, \ldots\}$.

A·3 Identical sets and equivalent sets. Two or more sets are said to be identical if they have exactly the same members. Thus, the sets

$$A = \{x, y, z\} \text{ and } B = \{x, z, y\}$$

are *identical*. The members are not written in the same order, but this is not important since membership is not concerned with the order of listing. To express the idea that set A is identical to set B, we write

$$\{x, y, z\} = \{x, z, y\}$$
$$\text{or} \qquad A = B.$$

Each of the sets

$$A = \{a, b, c\} \text{ and } B = \{m, n, p\}$$

has the *same number* of elements, but the elements are different. Such sets are said to be *equivalent*. If the symbol $n\{\quad\}$ is defined to mean the number of elements in the set, then we may write

$$n\{a, b, c\} = n\{m, n, p\}$$
$$\text{or} \qquad n(A) = n(B)$$

where A and B represent the two sets respectively.

Exercise A-1

(A)

State the members of each of the following sets:

1. The set of all even numbers between 3 and 9.
2. The set of all natural number divisors of 12.
3. The set of all prime numbers between 23 and 29.
4. The set whose members belong to both $\{-3, -2, -1, 0\}$ and $\{0, 1, 2, 3\}$.

State the number of elements in each of the following sets:

5. $\{1, 2, 2, 3, 4, 3, 3, 1, 2\}$ **6.** $\{7, 7, 7, 6\}$ **7.** $\{0\}$

8. $\{a, a, b, b, b, c\}$ **9.** $\{a, a^2, b, b, b, b^2\}$ **10.** $\{\quad\}$

State a rule which describes the set in each of the following:

11. $\{2, 4, 6, 8, 10\}$ **12.** $\left\{\dfrac{1}{2}, \dfrac{2}{3}, \dfrac{3}{4}, \dfrac{4}{5}, \ldots\right\}$ **13.** $\{3, 6, 9, 12, \ldots\}$

14. $\{1, 4, 9, 16, 25, 36, 49, 64, 81\}$ **15.** $\left\{\dfrac{1}{2}, \dfrac{1}{3}, \dfrac{2}{3}\right\}$

16. Classify the following sets as finite, infinite, or null:

    (i) all odd natural numbers less than 25;

    (ii) the natural numbers;

    (iii) all squares between 50 and 60;

    (iv) the set of all factors of 120;

    (v) the set of all multiples of 5;

    (vi) the set of all words printed in this book;

    (vii) the set of all four-sided triangles.

(B)

17. List (i) equivalent sets (ii) identical sets from the following:

    $A = \{4, 5, 6, 7, 8\}$ $B = \{a, b\}$ $C = \{2, 4\}$

    $D = \{7\}$ $E = \{0\}$ $F = \{100, 101\}$

    $G = \emptyset$ $H = \left\{\dfrac{3}{4}\right\}$ $I = \{6, 4, 7, 5, 8\}$

List the members of the following sets in brace brackets:

18. The set of all prime numbers less than 24.

19. The set of all multiples of 9 between 30 and 35.

20. The set of all natural number divisors of 60.

21. The set of all proper fractions whose numerators and denominators are chosen from $U = \{3, 4, 7, 11\}$.

22. A circle divides all the points on a page into three sets. Describe these point sets in words.

23. In the accompanying figure, the circle and the rectangle divide all points on the page into sets indicated by the letters $A, B, C, D, E,$ and F. Give a description:

    (i) for the set A;

    (ii) for the set F;

    (iii) for the set which includes the sets C and B only;

    (iv) for the set which includes the sets D and E only.

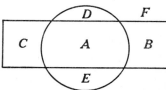

A·4 Subsets. If $A = \{2, 3\}$ and $B = \{1, 2, 3, 4, 5\}$, then A is said to be a *subset* of B because *every member of set A is also a mem'er of set B.* This is expressed by the symbols $A \subseteq B$ read, "*A* is a subset of *B*".

Using this definition of a subset, do the following problem and compare your solution with that on page 437.

1. List all the subsets of the set $A = \{a, b, c, d\}$ and thereby determine the number of subsets of A.

A·5 Venn diagrams. Sets are sometimes represented pictorially by the type of diagram illustrated in *Figures A-1 to A-5*. In considering two sets A and B, all the members of set A may be represented by points within or on the circle marked A, and all the members of set B by points on or within the circle B.

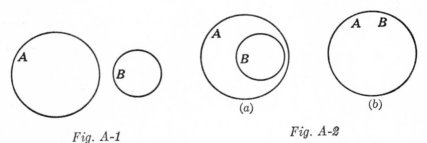

Fig. A-1   Fig. A-2

Any relationship that may exist between the members of A and B can be indicated by the positioning of the circles with respect to each other. In *Fig. A-1*, the two circles are completely separate or distinct from each other. This signifies that the two sets A and B have *no members in common*. Such sets are said to be *disjoint* sets.

In *Fig. A-2 (a)*, the circle B is entirely within circle A, which signifies that B is a proper subset of A: that is, $B \subset A$. In *Fig. A-2 (b)*, the circles A and B coincide, which signifies that A and B are identical: that is $A = B$.

In *Fig. A-3*, the circles A and B partially overlap. This signifies that some, but not all, the members of B are also members of A, and vice-versa. The shaded portion of the diagram corresponds to those members which belong to both set A and set B. This set of elements is called the *intersection* or *intersection set* of A and B and is indicated symbolically by $A \cap B$ read, "A intersect B".

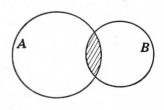

Fig. A-3

or "A cap B" or the "intersection of A and B". The word "and" is also used to imply the intersection of two sets. Thus, $A \cap B$ may also be written "A and B".

> The intersection of two sets, A and B, is the set of all elements which belong to both set A and set B.

Write a solution to the following problem; compare your solution with that on page 437.

1. $A = \{a, b, c, d, e\}, \quad B = \{c, d, e, f, g, h\}, \quad C = \{f, g, h\}$
   - (i) Draw a diagram to illustrate how the sets A and B are related.
   - (ii) List the elements in $A \cap B$ and shade the diagram to illustrate this set.
   - (iii) Draw a diagram to illustrate how sets A and C are related.
   - (iv) What is meant by "A and B"?
   - (v) List the elements in $B \cap C$.
   - (vi) How is C related to B? Draw a diagram to illustrate your answer.

In *Fig. A-4*, the circles A and B also partially overlap. The shaded portion includes:

- (i) the members of set A;
- (ii) the members of set B;
- (iii) the members belonging both to A and B.

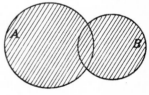

Fig. A-4

This set is called the *union* or *union set* of sets A and B and is designated symbolically by $A \cup B$ which is read, "A union B" or "A cup B" or "the union of A and B". The word "or" is also used to imply the union of two sets. Thus $A \cup B$ may also be written "A or B".

> The union of two sets is the set of all elements which belong to at least one of the two sets.

Write a solution to the following problem; compare your solution with that on page 438.

2. $A = \{1, 2, 3, 4\}, \quad B = \{3, 4, 5, 6\}, \quad C = \{7, 8, 9\}$
   - (i) Draw a diagram to illustrate how set A and set B are related.
   - (ii) List the elements in $A \cup B$. (Remember, elements are listed only once.)
   - (iii) Shade the diagram to indicate "A or B".
   - (iv) Draw a diagram to illustrate how set B and set C are related.
   - (v) List the elements in "B or C".
   - (vi) Shade the diagram to illustrate $B \cup C$.

(vii) Under what circumstances is $n(B \cup C) = n(B) + n(C)$?

(viii) Find $n(A \cup B)$.

Two sets A and B in some particular situation may be subsets of some general set. For example, the sets

$$A = \{2, 4, 6, 8\} \text{ and } B = \{1, 3, 5, 7, 10\}$$

are subsets of the general set, the set of all counting numbers,

$$U = \{1, 2, 3, 4, \ldots\}.$$

The general set contains all the objects being considered in a particular situation and is referred to as the *universal* set U. It is usually represented in a diagram by a rectangle. The sets A and B are usually represented by circles within the rectangle.

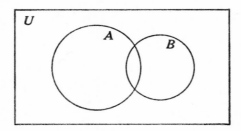

Fig. A-5

For example, in *Fig. A-5*,

U might represent all the boys in your school;

A might represent all the boys in your class;

B might represent all the boys who play hockey in your school.

Since the circles A and B overlap, the figure illustrates that some of the boys in your class play hockey. These boys are the members of the intersection set $A \cap B$.

This use of circles originated with an eighteenth-century Swiss mathematician named Leonhard Euler (1707-1783). The circles are often referred to as *Euler circles*. John Venn, an English mathematician (1834-1923), made use of the same type of figure in his writings on logic. He did not restrict himself to circles but used any closed figure. These diagrams are often referred to as *Venn diagrams*.

Write solutions to the following problems; compare your solutions with those on page 438.

3. Make a Venn diagram to illustrate how the following sets are related; list the members of (i) $A \cap B$ (ii) $A \cup B$:

$U = \{$ all letters in the alphabet $\}$,

$A = \{a, c, e, g, i\}, \qquad B = \{a, b, c, d, e, f\}$

4. Given the following sets: $A = \{1, 2, 3, 4, 5, 6, 7, 8, 9\}$,
   $B = \{1, 3, 5, 7, 9\}$, $C = \{2, 4, 6, 8\}$, $D = \{2, 3, 5, 7\}$

   (i) Which of the following relations are true?

   (a) $B \subseteq A$ (b) $C \subseteq A$
   (c) $D \subseteq A$ (d) $\emptyset \subseteq A$

   (ii) List the sets described below:

   (a) $A \cup B$; $A \cap B$ (b) $A \cup C$; $A \cap C$
   (c) $B \cup C$; $B \cap C$ (d) $A \cup D$; $A \cap D$
   (e) $C \cup D$; $C \cap D$ (f) $(B \cup C) \cup D$

   (iii) State the number of subsets of:

   (a) A (b) B (c) C (d) D

Exercise A-2

(B)

Draw Venn diagrams to illustrate how the following sets are related:

1. Given the following sets
   $A = \{$all boys taking Grade 10 Latin$\}$,
   $B = \{$all Grade 10 boys on the football team$\}$,
   $U = \{$all Grade 10 boys$\}$,
   draw a Venn diagram to illustrate each of the following possibilities:

   (i) No football player takes Latin.

   (ii) All Grade 10 football players also take Latin.

   (iii) Some, but not all, boys taking Latin also play football.

2. Given the following sets
   U is the set of all students in your high school,
   G is the set of all students in your grade,
   B is the set of all students who play basketball,
   draw Venn diagrams to illustrate each of the following:

   (i) All students who play basketball are in your grade.

   (ii) No students who play basketball are in your grade.

   (iii) Some students who play basketball are in your grade.

   (iv) Only those students who are in your grade play basketball.

   (v) All students in your grade play basketball.

Use Venn diagrams to solve the following problems:

3. In a class of 32 students, each of whom must take English or History, 20 take English, 9 take both English and History. How many take History?

4. There are 38 cars on a dealer's lot: 25 have automatic transmission, and 20 have power steering. How many of these cars have both automatic transmission and power steering?

5. In a certain university, all freshmen must take English or Philosophy. If 180 take English and 152 take Philosophy, how many freshmen are there for each of the following situations?
    (i)   No freshman can take both English and Philosophy.
    (ii) Both courses may be taken, and 32 freshmen take both English and Philosophy.

6. If 28 girls belong to the basketball team, 19 girls belong to the swimming team, and of these, 6 girls belong to both the basketball team and the swimming team, how many box lunches would be required to feed both teams?

7. The area of rectangle A is 20 sq. ft.; the area of rectangle B is 10 sq. ft.; the area of rectangle C is 16 sq. ft. The area of the part common to rectangles A and B is 3 sq. ft.; the area common to rectangles A and C is 6 sq. ft.; the area common to rectangles B and C is 4 sq. ft. The area common to all three rectangles is 2 sq. ft. Find the total area of the whole figure.

8. The Mathematics Club in a school held an open house on three afternoons. 115, 100, and 135 students attended on the first, second, and third afternoons, respectively. 25 attended just the first day; 30 attended both the first and second days; 80 attended both the first and third days; and 60 attended both the second and third days. How many attended (i) all three days (ii) just the second day (iii) just the third day?

9. In one high school, each boy is required to take part in at least one of basketball, track, or swimming. A student reporter for the local paper reported that in a class of 50 there were 25 participating in basketball, 15 in track, 35 in swimming, 4 in both basketball and track, 10 in both track and swimming, 8 in both basketball and swimming, and 3 who took part in all three activities. Show that the reporter could not count.

10. Four football games were to be played on Saturday. Three sports-writers made predictions regarding the winner of each of the four games. Sportswriter A picked {Hamilton, Edmonton, Winnipeg, Ottawa} . Sportswriter B picked {Winnipeg, Toronto, B.C. Lions, Edmonton} . Sportswriter C picked {Ottawa, Calgary, Toronto, Winnipeg} . None of these sportswriters picked Montreal. Determine which teams played each other.

NATURAL NUMBERS AND ZERO

INTEGERS

RATIONAL NUMBERS

B·1 The set of natural numbers. The set of natural numbers, invented for counting purposes, is represented symbolically by

$$N = \{1, 2, 3, 4, \ldots\}.$$

The following are the properties or laws of the natural number system.

If a, b, c ∈ N, then

	ADDITION		MULTIPLICATION	
Closure Law	$a + b$ *represents one and only one natural number*	(ClA)	ab *represents one and only one natural number*	(ClM)
Commutative Law	$a + b = b + a$	(CA)	$ab = ba$	(CM)
Associative Law	$(a+b)+c = a+(b+c)$	(AA)	$(ab)c = a(bc)$	(AM)
Distributive Law			$a(b + c) = ab + ac$	(D)
Identity Element			*Unity*	

The set of natural numbers is closed under the operations of addition and multiplication. This means that the sum or product of any two natural numbers is a unique natural number.

Commutativity of addition and multiplication of natural numbers means that the sum or product of any two natural numbers obtained by adding or multiplying in either order is the same.

Associativity of addition and multiplication of natural numbers is the basis for adding or multiplying more than two natural numbers. The law states that the sum (or product) of three natural numbers is the same whether the sum (or product) of the first two is added to (multiplied by) the third, or the first is added to (multiplied by) the sum (or product) of the second and third.

The *Distributive Law* links multiplication and addition directly. It states that multiplication may be distributed over addition.

The number 1 (or unity) has the special property with respect to multiplication that:

$$\text{If } a \in N, \text{ then } a \times 1 = 1 \times a = a.$$

Thus, 1 is called the *identity* (or *neutral*) *element for multiplication.*

The *inverse* (undoing) operations of subtraction and division are defined in terms of addition and multiplication, respectively.

If a, b, $x \in N$, then

$$a - b = x \text{ if and only if } a = b + x,$$
$$\text{and}$$
$$a \div b = x \text{ if and only if } a = b \times x.$$

The set N is not closed under subtraction or division, and these operations are neither commutative nor associative.

B·2 The set of natural numbers and zero. The natural numbers together with zero form the set of *whole numbers* (N_0).

$$N_0 = \{0, 1, 2, 3, 4, \ldots\}.$$

Operations involving zero are defined as follows:

a. *Addition and subtraction.*

If $a \in N_0$, then

$$a + 0 = 0 + a = a.$$

Since the sum of zero and any whole number is that number itself, zero is called the *identity* or *neutral element for addition.*

Since subtraction is the inverse of addition,

$$a - 0 = a, \text{ and } a - a = 0.$$

b. *Multiplication.*

If a, b, $\in N_0$, then

$$b + 0 = b. \qquad \text{(Definition)}$$

If N_0 is to be closed under multiplication, then

$$a(b + 0) = a \cdot b.$$

If multiplication is to be distributive over addition, then

$$a \cdot b + a \cdot 0 = a \cdot b.$$

$$\therefore \quad a \cdot 0 \text{ is the identity element for addition.}$$

$$\therefore \quad a \cdot 0 = 0$$

If multiplication is to be commutative, then
$$0 \cdot a = 0.$$
Thus, $$a \cdot 0 = 0 \cdot a = 0.$$
Also,   **if $ab = 0$, then $a = 0$ or $b = 0$.**

c. *Division*.

There are three cases of division involving zero. Consider the quotient $a \div b$, where $a, b \in N_0$.

(i) *If $a = 0$, $b \neq 0$, then*
$$0 \div b = x, \; x \in N_0 \text{ if and only if } 0 = b \times x.$$
This is true if and only if $x = 0$, since $b \neq 0$.
Therefore, $0 \div b = 0$ if $b \in N_0$, $b \neq 0$.

(ii) *If $a \neq 0$, $b = 0$, then*
$$a \div 0 = x \text{ if and only if } a = 0 \cdot x.$$
This is not true for any whole number represented by x.
Therefore the quotient $a \div 0$, $a \neq 0$ is meaningless.

(iii) *If $a = 0$, $b = 0$, then*
$$0 \div 0 = x \text{ if and only if } 0 = 0 \cdot x.$$
This is true for every whole number represented by x.
Thus, there is no unique whole number which represents $0 \div 0$.
Therefore, the quotient $0 \div 0$ is indeterminate.

Division by zero is not defined.

The number 1 (or unity) has the special property with respect to multiplication that:
$$\text{If } a \in N_0, \text{ then } a \times 1 = 1 \times a = a.$$
Thus, 1 is called the *identity* or *neutral element for multiplication*.

N_0 is closed under the operations of addition and multiplication. These operations are commutative and associative, and multiplication is distributive over addition. N_0 is not closed under the operations of subtraction and division. These operations are neither commutative nor associative, and division by zero is not defined.

B·3 The N-line and the N_0-line. The set of natural numbers N may be represented geometrically on a number line called the *N-line* (*Fig. B-1*). Two points are selected on a line, and the numerals 1 and 2 are associated with them, as indicated in *Fig. B-1*. Using this line segment as a unit, other points to the right of these points are selected by marking off unit distances in succession. The numerals 3, 4, 5, ... are associated with these points as shown. The numerals are called the *coordinates* (names) of the points. The number line also illustrates the idea of order or magnitude that is inherent in the set of whole numbers. This is discussed in detail in section *B*·7.

If the coordinates 0 and 1 are given to the first two points selected, the number line pictures the set of whole numbers and is called the *N₀-line*.

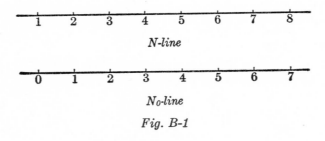

N-line

N₀-line

Fig. B-1

B·4 **Solution sets and graphs.** Sentences such as (i) $2x + 5 = 11$, $x \in N$ (ii) $5z - 2 < 13$, $z \in N$ (iii) $3y \geq 2y + 3$, $x \in N_0$ each define a set of numbers which is a subset of the set of natural numbers N or of the whole numbers N_0.

The letter symbol in each of the *equations* or *inequations*

(i) $2x + 5 = 11$ (ii) $5z - 2 < 13$ (iii) $3y \geq 2y + 3$

may be replaced by any member of its indicated *replacement set N* or N_0. For some replacements the given sentence may be true, and for some it may be false. The set of numbers whose elements are the members of the replacement set for which the given sentence is true is called the *solution set*.

The solution set of $2x + 5 = 11$, $x \in N$ is $\{3\}$; its graph is shown in *Fig. B-2*.

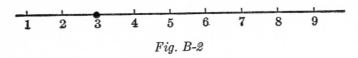

Fig. B-2

The solution set defined by $5z + 2 < 13$, $z \in N$ is $\{1, 2\}$; its graph is shown in *Fig. B-3*.

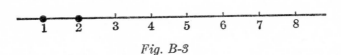

Fig. B-3

The solution set defined by $3y \geq 2y + 3$, $x \in N_0$ is $\{3, 4, 5, \ldots\}$; its graph is shown in *Fig. B-4.* The arrow indicates the continuing nature of the graph.

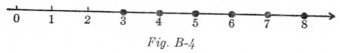

Fig. B-4

The set whose defining sentence is $2x + 5 = 11$, $x \in N$ may be expressed in *set-builder notation* as follows:

$$\{x \mid 2x + 5 = 11,\ x \in N\}$$

This is read, "the set of all x such that $2x + 5 = 11$ and x belongs to N".
The brace brackets symbol $\{ \quad \}$ is read, "the set of".
The solidus $\mid$ is read, "such that" or "defined by".
The comma is read, "and".

Thus, $\{x \mid 2x + 5 = 11,\ x \in N\} = \{3\}$.

Similarly,

$$\{z \mid 5z - 2 < 13,\ z \in N\} = \{1, 2\} \text{ and}$$
$$\{y \mid 3y \geq 2y + 3,\ y \in N_0\} = \{3, 4, 5, \ldots\} \ .$$

Example. Find $A = \{x \mid 2x - 5 < 11,\ x \in N_0\} \cap \{x \mid 3x + 1 \geq 7,\ x \in N_0\}$.

Solution: A is the intersection set of two sets

$A_1 = \{x \mid 2x - 5 < 11,\ x \in N_0\}$ and $A_2 = \{x \mid 3x + 1 \geq 7,\ x \in N_0\}$.

If	$2x - 5 = 11$		If	$3x + 1 = 7$
then	$2x = 16$		then	$3x = 6$
and	$x = 8$.		and	$x = 2$.

$\therefore A_1 = \{0, 1, 2, \ldots, 7\}$ $\therefore A_2 = \{2, 3, 4, \ldots\}$

$$A = \{2, 3, 4, 5, 6, 7\}$$

The graphs of A_1, A_2, and A are shown in *Fig. B-5.*

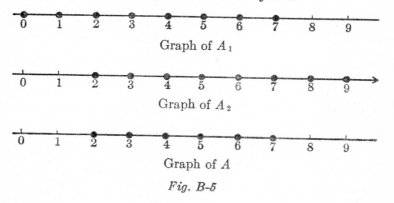

Graph of A_1

Graph of A_2

Graph of A

Fig. B-5

Write solutions for the following problems and compare them with those on page 439.

1. Find $\{x \mid 0 \leq x < 5, x \in N_0\}$ and draw its graph.
2. Find the solution set defined by $3(4 + y) \geq 2(y + 7) + 3, \ y \in N$ and draw its graph.
3. Find $\{x \mid 3 < x \leq 5, x \in N\} \cup \{x \mid 9 > x > 6, x \in N\}$.
4. Find $\{x \mid 1 < x \leq 8, x \in N_0\} \cap \{x \mid 8 > x > 0, x \in N_0\}$.

Exercise B-1

(A)

Read each of the following and state the members of the solution set:

1. $\{x \mid x + 2 = 7, x \in N\}$
2. $\{x \mid x < 9, x \in N, x$ is an even number.$\}$
3. $\{x \mid x \leq 1, x \in N_0\}$
4. $\{x \mid x < 5$ or $x > 8, x \in N\}$
5. $\{x \mid x > 4, x \in N_0\}$
6. $\{x \mid 10 > x \geq 5, x \in N\}$
7. $\{x \mid 2x - 3 < 7, x \in N\}$
8. $\{x \mid 3x - 1 \geq 11, x \in N_0\}$
9. $\{x \mid 3(x - 2) = 2x - 6, x \in N\}$
10. $\{x \mid x + 3 < 3, x \in N_0\}$

(B)

List the members of each of the following sets:

11. $\{x \mid 7 \geq x \geq 6, x \in N\}$
12. $\{x \mid 3x + 1 \geq 10, x \in N_0\}$
13. $\{x \mid x < 5, x \in N\}$
14. $\{x \mid x < 5$ or $x \geq 8, x \in N\}$
15. $\{x \mid x - 5 = 8 - (2x + 4), x \in N_0\}$
16. $\{x \mid (10x + 6) - (11 - 15x) \neq 20x, x \in N_0\}$
17. $\{x \mid 7x - 4 > 2x + 21, x \in N\}$
18. $\left\{x \mid \dfrac{3x - 2}{5} + \dfrac{x + 2}{3} = \dfrac{5x - 4}{4}, \ x \in N\right\}$

Find and draw the graph of each of the following sets:

19. $\{x \mid 2(3x - 1) - 3(x + 3) \neq 7, x \in N\}$
20. $\{x \mid 2x > x + 5, x \in N_0\}$ or $\{x \mid 3x - 1 \leq 8, x \in N_0\}$
21. $\{x \mid 2x - 1 = 7, x \in N\}$ and $\{x \mid x + 3 = 2x - 1, x \in N\}$
22. $\{x \mid 0 \leq x < 3, x \in N_0\} \cup \{x \mid 5 \leq x < 8, x \in N_0\}$
23. $\{x \mid 3x + 2 = 11, x \in N\} \cap \{x \mid 2 = 3x - 1, x \in N\}$

B·5 The set of integers. As civilization progressed, the natural numbers and the whole numbers proved to be inadequate:

(i) to represent opposites, such as profit and loss;

(ii) to provide a solution to equations such as $x + 3 = 0$ (that is, the set of whole numbers is not closed under subtraction).

The integers or signed numbers were invented to indicate oppositeness in sense or quality. The set of all integers, designated by I, is represented as follows:

$$I = \{\ldots, -3, -2, -1, 0, +1, +2, +3, \ldots\}$$

or $\quad I = \{\pm a \mid a \in N\} \cup \{0\}.$

The $+$ and $-$ signs are called *signs of quality*.

The properties of (i) magnitude and (ii) oppositeness in sense or direction with respect to zero are indicated on the *integer-line* or *I-line* in *Fig. B-6*. It should be noted that zero is neither positive nor negative.

The whole number line starts with a point whose coordinate is zero and extends endlessly to the right with certain points, a unit distance apart, having natural number coordinates. If the extension of the line to the left has unit distances marked off in succession from the zero point (origin), then corresponding to each marked point to the right of the origin there is a point an equal distance to the left from the origin. If the points to the right of the origin are given coordinates $+1$ (read, "positive one"), $+2, +3, \ldots$, then, to indicate their oppositeness in sense or direction, the selected points on the left of the origin may be given co-ordinates -1 (read, "negative one"), $-2, -3, \ldots$, as indicated. Note that all distances are measured to the right or left from the origin.

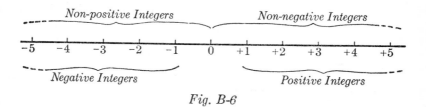

Fig. B-6

Fig. B-6 also indicates the following important subsets of the set of integers:

(i) the set of positive integers, $\{+1, +2, +3, \ldots\}$;

(ii) the set of negative integers, $\{-1, -2, -3, \ldots\}$;

(iii) the set of non-positive integers, $\{0, -1, -2, -3, \ldots\}$;

(iv) the set of non-negative integers, $\{0, +1, +2, +3, \ldots\}$.

B·6 Addition in the set of integers.

If $a, b \in N$, then

(i) $(+a) + (+b) = (+b) + (+a) = +(a+b);$

(ii) $(-a) + (-b) = (-b) + (-a) = -(a+b);$

(iii) $(+a) + (-b) = (-b) + (+a) = +(a-b)$ if $a > b$
$$= -(b-a) \text{ if } a < b.$$

(iv) Zero is the identity element for addition for the set of whole numbers. To extend this concept to the set of integers, we define addition involving zero as follows:

If $a \in I$, then
$$a + 0 = 0 + a = a.$$

Zero is the identity or neutral element for addition.

If $b = a$, then

from (iii) $(+a) + (-a) = (-a) + (+a) = +(a-a) = 0.$

Thus, the integers may be paired off $(+1)$ and (-1), $(+2)$ and (-2), $(+3)$ and (-3), and so on, in such a way that the sum of each pair of integers is zero. The members of these pairs are called *additive inverses* or *negatives* of each other. The additive inverse of zero is zero.

The set of integers is closed under addition, and addition is commutative and associative.

B·7 Subtraction of integers.
Since subtraction is the inverse operation of addition, it is defined as follows:

If $a, b, c \in I$, then
$$a - b = c \text{ if and only if } c + b = a.$$

That is, the difference $a - b$ exists if and only if an integer c can be found whose sum with b is a. The following examples suggest that the integer c always exists and indicate how it may be determined.

ADDITION	SUBTRACTION (INVERSE)	ADDITION PRODUCING THE SAME RESULT
Since $(+6)+(+2)=(+8)$	$\therefore (+8)-(+2)=(+6)$	$(+8)+(-2)=(+6)$
Since $(+6)+(-2)=(+4)$	$\therefore (+4)-(-2)=(+6)$	$(+4)+(+2)=(+6)$
Since $(-6)+(+2)=(-4)$	$\therefore (-4)-(+2)=(-6)$	$(-4)+(-2)=(-6)$
Since $(-6)+(-2)=(-8)$	$\therefore (-8)-(-2)=(-6)$	$(-8)+(+2)=(-6)$

The third column suggests:

To subtract an integer, add its negative (additive inverse).

B·8 **Multiplication in the set of integers.**

If a, b ∈ *N, then*

$$\text{(i) } (+a)(+b) = (+b)(+a) = +(ab) ;$$
$$\text{(ii) } (-a)(-b) = (-b)(-a) = +(ab) ;$$
$$\text{(iii) } (+a)(-b) = (-b)(+a) = -(ab) .$$

A discussion similar to that in section *B*·2 leads to the statement:
If *a, b* ∈ *I*, then (i) $a \cdot 0 = 0 \cdot a = 0$; (ii) if $ab = 0$, then $a = 0$ or $b = 0$.

The product of any integer and zero is zero. If the product of two integers is zero, then at least one of them is zero.

If *a* is replaced by 1, then

from   (i) $(+1)(+b) = (+b)(+1) = +(1 \times b) = +b$;
from (iii) $(+1)(-b) = (-b)(+1) = -(1 \times b) = -b$.

The product of any integer and $(+1)$ is that integer.

$(+1)$ *is the identity or neutral element for multiplication.*

If *b* is replaced by 1, then

from   (ii) $(-a)(-1) = (-1)(-a) = +(a \times 1) = +a$;
from (iii) $(+a)(-1) = (-1)(+a) = -(a \times 1) = -a$.

The product of any integer and (-1) *is the negative of the integer.*

The set of integers is closed under multiplication; multiplication is commutative, associative, and distributive over addition.

B·9 **Division in the set of integers.** Since division is the inverse operation of multiplication, it must be defined as follows:

If *a, b* ∈ *N*, then

$$\because (+a)(+b) = +ab \quad \therefore \frac{+ab}{+b} = +a$$

$$\because (+a)(-b) = -ab \quad \therefore \frac{-ab}{-b} = +a$$

$$\because (-a)(-b) = +ab \quad \therefore \frac{+ab}{-b} = -a .$$

Since there is no integer whose product with $(+3)$ is $(+13)$
$$\therefore (+13) \div (+3) \text{ is not an integer.}$$
Therefore the set of integers is not closed with respect to division.

A discussion similar to that of section *B*·2 leads to the statement:
Division by zero is not defined in the set of integers.

B·10 Summary of the properties of the integer number system.

If a, b, c ∈ I, then

	ADDITION	MULTIPLICATION
Closure Law	$(a + b)$ *represents one and only one integer* (*ClA*)	(ab) *represents one and only one integer* (*ClM*)
Commutative Law	$a + b = b + a$ (*CA*)	$ab = ba$ (*CM*)
Associative Law	$(a+b)+c=a+(b+c)$ (*AA*)	$(ab)c = a(bc)$ (*AM*)
Distributive Law		$a(b + c) = ab + ac$	
Identity Element	0 (*Zero*)	1 (*Unity*)
Inverse Element	$-a$	

Since the positive integers behave, under addition or multiplication, in exactly the same way as the natural numbers, we use the natural number symbols to represent the positive integers unless otherwise specified.

B·11 **Order relation in the set of integers.** The idea of order is inherent in the set of natural numbers. Since they were invented to count the number of objects in various sets, it is natural when thinking of any two counting numbers to say that one of these is *equal to*, or is *greater than* ($>$), or is *less than* ($<$) the other and that only one of these can be true. In this sense, the natural numbers are ordered, and this order is precisely defined as follows:

$$\text{If } a, b \in N, \text{ then } a > b, \text{ if } (a - b) \in N .$$

To have the ordering of the positive integers correspond to the ordering of the natural numbers it is necessary to say:

If a, b are positive integers, then
$a > b$ if $a - b$ is a positive integer, or
$a > b$ if $a = b + c$, where c is a positive integer.

If we extend this definition to include all integers, then the definition of order in the set of integers is:

If $a, b \in I$, then
$a > b$ if $a - b$ is a positive integer, or
$a > b$ if $a = b + c$, where c is a positive integer.

The consequents of this definition are illustrated in the following examples:

(i) all positive integers are greater than zero,
   $(+ 5)$ is greater than zero since $(+ 5) = 0 + (+ 5)$;
(ii) all negative integers are less than zero,
   0 is greater than $(- 5)$ since $0 = (- 5) + (+ 5)$;

(iii) all positive integers are greater than all negative integers,
$(+5)$ is greater than (-5) since $(+5) = (-5) + (+10)$;

(iv) $(+5)$ is greater than $(+2)$ since $(+5) = (+2) + (+3)$. This corresponds to the ordering of the corresponding natural numbers.

(v) (-2) is greater than (-5) since $(-2) = (-5) + (+3)$.

Since the set I is closed under addition and subtraction, the following *trichotomy assumption* of order is made:

$$\text{If } a, b \in I, \text{ then } a < b \text{ or } a = b \text{ or } a > b .$$

The geometric interpretation of this definition on a number line is as follows:

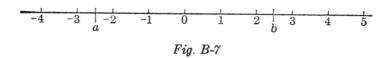

Fig. B-7

if $a > b$, then the point with coordinate a lies to the right of the point with coordinate b;

if $a = b$, then a and b are coordinates of the same point;

if $a < b$, then the point with coordinate a lies to the left of the point with coordinate b (*Fig. B-7*) .

A further consequent of the definition of order is the *transitive property* of order:

$$\text{If } a, b, c \in I, \text{ and } a < b \text{ and } b < c, \text{ then } a < c .$$

Geometrically, this means that if a point with coordinate a lies to the left of a point with coordinate b, which lies to the left of a point with coordinate c, then the point with coordinate a lies to the left of the point with coordinate c.

Exercise B-2

(*The variables are integers.*)

(A)

1. Find the following sums:

(i) $\begin{array}{r} +32 \\ -37 \\ \hline \end{array}$ (ii) $\begin{array}{r} -16 \\ -8 \\ \hline \end{array}$ (iii) $\begin{array}{r} -12 \\ +19 \\ \hline \end{array}$ (iv) $\begin{array}{r} +25 \\ -45 \\ \hline \end{array}$

(v) $(+35)+(+16)$ (vi) $(-15)+(+15)$ (vii) $(-46)+(-64)$

2. Find the following differences:

   (i) $+17$ (ii) -18 (iii) -27 (iv) -10
       $\underline{-14}$ $\underline{-\ 5}$ $\underline{+16}$ $\underline{-20}$

   (v) $(-32)-(-37)$ (vi) $(-17)-(-17)$ (vii) $(+27)-(-35)$

3. Simplify:

   (i) $(-4)(+7)$ (ii) $(-10)(-1)$ (iii) $(4)(-3y^2)$

   (iv) $(-5xy)(2xy)$ (v) $(3)(-4)(-6)$ (vi) $(-16)\div(-4)$

   (vii) $(-225b)\div(25)$ (viii) $(-1)^4$ (ix) $(-1)^7$

   (x) $(-2a^2b)(-3ab^2)$ (xi) $\dfrac{+16x^2y}{-8xy}$, $x,\ y \neq 0$

   (xii) $\dfrac{(+6a)(0)(-3a^3)}{(-2a^2)(-9a^4)}$, $a\neq 0$ (xiii) $\dfrac{-42a^5b^4c^3}{-7a^4b^3c^3}$, $a,\ b,\ c\neq 0$

(B)

4. Show that each of the following indicated sums is associative:

   (i) $(-16)+(-10)+(+12)$

   (ii) $(+12)+(-11)+(+13)$

   (iii) $(+3a)+(-10a)+(-6a)$

   (iv) $(-6b^2)+(+15b^2)+(-9b^2)$

5. Expand, using the distributive property:

   (i) $(+5)[(+x)+(-y)]$ (ii) $(-2)[(+a)+(+b)]$

   (iii) $(-3)[(-c)+(+d)]$ (iv) $(+6)[(-m)+(-n)]$

   (v) $(-1)[(-a)+(+b)]$ (vi) $(-1)[(-3)+(+2)]$

   (vii) $(-1)[(-p)+(-q)+(-c)]$

6. Show that each of the following indicated products is associative:

   (i) $(-3a)(+2b)(-5c)$ (ii) $(+3mn)(-2mn)(-4mn)$

   (iii) $(-1)(-x^2a)(ax)$ (iv) $(-x^2)(4x^3)(-1)$

If the variables represent integers, find the following sets and draw their graphs:

7. $\{x\mid 2x+8=-8-2x\}$ **8.** $\{y\mid 3y+16=-6y-11\}$

9. $\{x\mid 3(2x+4)+5\neq 41\}$

10. $\{a\mid 4a+3+2(3a-6)=a-9\}$

11. $\left\{x\mid\dfrac{3x-3}{8}+\dfrac{x+5}{2}=-4\right\}$ **12.** $\{x\mid \tfrac{1}{10}(7x+1)-1\neq\tfrac{1}{4}(x-9)$

13. $\{x\mid .3(5-x)=.1(x+31)\}$ **14.** $\{x\mid 3x+7<-5\}$

15. $\{x \mid 3(x + 1) > x - 5\}$ **16.** $\{x \mid 7 - 2x \leqq 11\}$

(C)

Draw the graph of each of the following sets, if the variables are integers:

17. $\{x \mid 5x - 7 = 18\} \cup \{x \mid 3x + 5 = 26\}$

18. $\{x \mid 2x + 1 \geqq -5\} \cap \{x \mid 1 - 3x \geqq -8\}$

19. $\{x \mid 3(2 - x) < 9\} \cap \{x \mid 3(x - 1) < 2(2 + x) - 3\}$

20. $\{x \mid x + \frac{3}{2} \geqq 5\frac{1}{2}\} \cup \{x \mid \frac{2}{5}x - 1 < -3\}$

B·12 Absolute value. Integers represent ideas involving both magnitude and sense or direction. $+3$ indicates a magnitude of 3 in one sense, and -3 indicates a magnitude of 3 in the opposite sense. The magnitude of a number is referred to as its *absolute value.* It is indicated by placing the numeral between vertical bars.

Thus: $|+3|$ represents the absolute value of $+3$;
                   $|-3|$ represents the absolute value of -3 .

The natural number 3 indicates the magnitude involved in the integers $+3$ and -3, and we might be inclined to define $|+3|$ and $|-3|$ as the natural number 3. But we are interested in operating in the set of integers; thus, it is customary to define the absolute value of an integer as the corresponding positive integer.

Thus: $|+3| = +3$ $|-3| = +3$

The above examples suggest the following precise definition of absolute value.

If $x \in I$, and

$\qquad$ (i) if $x > 0$, then $|x| = x$;

$\qquad$ (ii) if $x = 0$, then $|x| = 0$;

$\qquad$ (iii) if $x < 0$, then $|x| = -x$.

Example 1. Write the absolute value of (i) $+15$ (ii) -15 .

Solution.   (i) $|+15| = +15$ (ii) $|-15| = -(-15) = +15$

Example 2. Find: (i) $|12 - 4|$ (ii) $|12 - (-4)|$
                    (iii) $|-3 + (-4)|$ (iv) $|(-3) - (-4)|$

Solution.   (i) $|12 - 4| = |+8| = 8$

$\qquad$ (ii) $|12 - (-4)| = |12 + 4| = |+16| = 16$

$\qquad$ (iii) $|-3 + (-4)| = |-3 - 4| = |-7| = 7$

$\qquad$ (iv) $|(-3) - (-4)| = |-3 + 4| = |+1| = 1$

Exercise B-3

(A)

Find:

1. $|-5|$ **2.** $|\frac{6}{7}|$ **3.** $|8-5|$

4. $|5-8|$ **5.** $|6-5-4|$ **6.** $|-5|^2$

7. $|6|-|-5|+|-4|$ **8.** $|-2a|, a>0$

9. $\left|\frac{y-4}{4-y}\right| \cdot 3, y \neq 4$ **10.** $|x-3|, x<0$

11. $-(|-5|-2)$ **12.** $(-3)(|-5|+5)$

13. $|0|$ **14.** $|y^2|, y<0$ **15.** $|3a-9|, a<3$

(B)

Evaluate or simplify:

16. $|-8|+|5|$ **17.** $|-7|-|-12|+|-16|$

18. $|4x|-|-4x|, x>0$ **19.** $|-5| \cdot |-2|-|-1|$

20. $|-8|-|-2|+|-3|)$ **21.** $|20-2|-|21-23|$

22. $\dfrac{|-24+3|}{3}$ **23.** $|-2|(|-4|)^2$

24. $|4x+3|, x>1$ **25.** $|x^2+2x+1|, x \in R$

Using the symbols $>$, $=$, $<$, *complete the following to make true sentences:*

26. $|15-9|$? $|15|-|9|$ **27.** $|9-15|$? $|9|-|15|$

28. $|(-8)+(-5)|$? $|-8|-|5|$ **29.** $|(-5)-(-8)|$? $|-5|-|-8|$

30. $|(-8)-(-5)|$? $|-8|-|-5|$ **31.** $|(-5)-7|$? $|-5|-|-7|$

Evaluate the following, if $a=-1, b=2, c=-3$:

32. $|a|+|b|-|c|$ **33.** $|a-c|-|b-c|$ **34.** $|b^2|+|c^2|-|a^2|$

35. $|b^2+c^2-a^2|+|-b|$ **36.** $|(b+c)^2|-|(a+c)^2|$

B·13 Polynomials. The symbols 2, 3, 0, $4+7$, $\dfrac{8+2}{5}$, 6×7 are *numerals* or *expressions* which represent number ideas. In the expression $4+7$ the numerals 4 and 7 are called the *terms* of the expression. In the expression 4×7 the numerals 4 and 7 are called *factors* of the expression.

Similarly, if the symbols x, y, z represent integers, then

$$3x, \quad 4y, \quad \frac{x}{y}, \quad 3x+4y, \quad 5x-z+3, \quad \frac{x+z}{y+z}, \quad x^2+2x-7$$

are expressions which represent number ideas. These expressions which involve variables are called *algebraic expressions*. In these expressions, the set of integers I is the *replacement set* for the symbols x, y, z which represent variables, since they are placeholders for the integer number ideas. An expression like $3x + 4y$ is meaningless without a given replacement set for x and y.

Algebraic expressions of the form

$$\tfrac{3}{2}x, \quad 3x + 4y, \quad 5x - y + 2z + 3, \quad \tfrac{4}{3}x + \tfrac{1}{2}y$$

in which the variables do not appear as denominators are called *polynomial expressions* or simply *polynomials*.

The expression $(+1) + (-2) + (+3)$ is an expression whose three terms are the integers $(+1)$, (-2), $(+3)$. Because it is cumbersome to write the expression in the manner indicated, including parentheses to separate the $+$ and $-$ signs of operation and quality, it is customary to write the expression

$$1 - 2 + 3$$

leaving out the operation signs of addition. Although the addition signs are not written, they are understood, and the terms of the expression are considered to be $(+1)$, (-2), and $(+3)$. This expression may be read, "positive one plus negative two plus positive three" or "one plus negative two plus three".

Also, $(+2) - (+5) = (+2) + (-5)$
                                    $= 2 - 5$.

In the expression $2 - 5$, the addition sign of operation is understood. The expression $2 - 5$ may be read, "two minus five" which is understood to mean "positive two minus positive five" or "positive two plus negative five".

Similarly, in the algebraic expression

$$3a - 4b + 2c - 4d, \text{ where } a, b, c, d \in I,$$

the terms of the expression are understood to be

$$+ 3a, - 4b, + 2c, - 4d$$

and it is understood that these terms are to be added. Thus, for the purpose of applying the laws of addition and multiplication, the expression is considered to be (or mean)

$$(+3a) + (-4b) + (+2c) + (-4d).$$

This means that every expression is considered to be a sum, and thus the commutative law of addition and the distributive law may always be applied.

For ease in reference, polynomials with one, two, and three terms are referred to as *monomials*, *binomials*, and *trinomials*, respectively.

B·14 **Addition and subtraction of polynomials.** In the following examples the variables are integers.

Example 1. Simplify $(5a + 3b - c) + (4a + 5b - 6c)$.

Solution. This expression is read, "the expression $5a$ plus $3b$ minus c plus the expression $4a$ plus $5b$ minus $6c$".

$$(5a + 3b - c) + (4a + 5b - 6c)$$
$$= 5a + 3b - c + 4a + 5b - 6c$$
$$= 5a + 4a + 3b + 5b - c - 6c \qquad (CA)$$
$$= (5 + 4)a + (3 + 5)b + (-1 - 6)c \qquad (D)$$
$$= 9a + 8b + (-7)c$$
$$= 9a + 8b - 7c$$

With practice the commutative and distributive properties may be applied as follows:

$$(5a + 3b - c) + (4a + 5b - 6c) = 5a + 3b - c + 4a + 5b - 6c$$
$$= 5a + 4a + 3b + 5b - c - 6c$$
$$= 9a + 8b - 7c$$

In the worked examples of the text the authorities which are most significant in the development are given in brackets. When writing a solution you should think the authorities for the steps, but it is not necessary to include them in your solution.

The study of subtraction of integers led to the working rule:

To subtract an integer, add its negative.

The following example illustrates how the negative of an integer represented by a polynomial may be determined.

Example 2. Determine the negative of the following algebraic expressions:
(i) $3a + 4b$ (ii) $-4x + 3y - 2$ (iii) $-(2a - 3b + 4c)$

Solution. Since the negative of an integer may be obtained by multiplying the integer by (-1):
(i) the negative of $3a + 4b$ is $(-1)(3a + 4b) = -3a - 4b$; (D)
(ii) the negative of $-4x + 3y - 2$ is $(-1)(-4x + 3y - 2)$
    $= 4x - 3y + 2;$ (D)
(iii) the negative of $-(2a - 3b + 4c)$ is $(-1)(-1)(2a - 3b + 4c)$
    $= 2a - 3b + 4c$. (D)

The negative of an algebraic expression may be obtained by replacing each term by its negative.

Example 3. Simplify $(5x - 2y + 6x^2) - (4x^2 - 3x + 2y)$.

Solution.

$$(5x - 2y + 6x^2) - (4x^2 - 3x + 2y)$$
$$= 5x - 2y + 6x^2 + (- 4x^2 + 3x - 2y)$$
$$= 5x - 2y + 6x^2 - 4x^2 + 3x - 2y$$
$$= 6x^2 - 4x^2 - 2y - 2y + 5x + 3x \qquad (CA)$$
$$= (6 - 4)x^2 + (- 2 - 2)y + (5 + 3)x \quad (D)$$
$$= 2x^2 + (- 4)y + 8x$$
$$= 2x^2 - 4y + 8x$$

With practice, simplification may be carried out as follows:
$$(5x - 2y + 6x^2) - (4x^2 - 3x + 2y) = 5x - 2y + 6x^2 - 4x^2 + 3x - 2y$$
$$= 8x - 4y + 2x^2$$

The simplification of a polynomial is sometimes referred to as the *collection of like terms* or terms containing the same variable or literal coefficient. By means of the distributive law, the specific numerical coefficient of this variable in the simplified expression is obtained.

Write a solution for each of the following and compare your solutions with those on page 439.

1. Add $7x^2 - x + 2$, $3x - 10x^2 - 5$, $x^2 - 2x + 7$.

2. Simplify $(5x + 3y - 2) + (3x - 4y + 3) - (6x + 3y - 6)$.

Exercise B-4

(The variables are integers.)

(A)

1. State the negative of each of the following:

    (i) $-3a$ (ii) $2a - 3b + 4c$ (iii) $- 5y + 4z - 2c$

    (iv) $- (3a - 2b + c)$ (v) $- 3n + 4p - 5c$

    (vi) $3a + 5m - 2q$ (vii) $- (7m - 4q + 5r)$

(B)

Simplify:

2. $2a - 3b + (- a + 2b)$ **3.** $(x - 4y) - (2y - x)$

4. $6x^2 + x - 2 - (4x^2 - 3x + 1) + (x^2 - 7x + 2)$

5. $(3a - b + 2c) - (2a + 5b - 4c)$

6. $(6n - 2m + 4p) - (- m - 2n + 3p) + (3m + 2p - 4n)$

7. $(a + 2b - 3c) - (3a - 5b + c) - (4a + 6b - 2c)$

If $x = -3$, $y = -2$, find the number represented by each of the following:

8. $6x - 3y + (-6x + y) - (3x - 5y)$
9. $(x^2 - 6xy + y^2) - (-3x^2 + xy - y^2)$
10. $(x - 2y) - (2x + 3y) - (-2x - 3y)$

Simplify:

11. $0 - (a - 5b) - [(5b - a) + (2a - 3b)]$
12. $[(-x - 2y) - (-3x + 4y)] - [(x + 4y) - (2x + y)]$
13. $[-(m + n) - (3m - 4n)] - [(5m - n) - (9m - 4n)]$
14. If $x = 2a - b$, and $y = a - 3b$, express $(x - 2y) - (2x - y)$ in terms of a and b.

Write as expressions in x and y:

15. $a(x + y) + b(3x + 2y) - c(2y - 3x)$
16. $p(3x - y) - q(2y - x) - r(x - y)$
17. $x(m - n) + y(n - m) - p(x - y)$

Arrange each of the following in descending powers of x:

18. $ax - dx^2 + cx^3 + bx^2 - 2x + 8 - 3x^3$
19. $px^2 - hx + ax^2 - kx^3 + x^3 - bx$
20. $p(x^2 - x) - qx^2 - 2(x - x^3) + mx^3 - n(x^3 - 1)$
21. Write the coefficient of x^2 in $6x^3 + 4ax + bx^2 - cx - dx^2 + x^2$.
22. Write the coefficient of x in $mx^2 - 8 + ax - x^2 - bx - 4cx$.
23. Write the coefficient of y in $3a(1 - y) - 2b(y - 2) - y$.

B·15 Multiplication of polynomials. In each of the following examples the variables are integers.

Example 1. Expand: (i) $3(a + 2b)$ (ii) $3a(2a - 4b)$
$\qquad\qquad\qquad$ (iii) $3a\,(2a + 3b - 4c + 5d)$

Solution. (i) $\quad 3(a + 2b)$
$\qquad\qquad = 3a + 6b$ (D)

(ii) $\quad 3a(2a - 4b)$
$\qquad = 3a[(2a) + (-4b)]$
$\qquad = 6a^2 + (3a)(-4b)$ (D)
$\qquad = 6a^2 - 12ab$

(iii) $\quad 3a(2a + 3b - 4c + 5d)$
$\qquad = 3a[(2a + 3b) + (-4c + 5d)]$ (AA)
$\qquad = 3a\,(2a + 3b) + 3a(-4c + 5d)$ (D)
$\qquad = 6a^2 + 9ab - 12ac + 15ad$ (D)

In practice, the intermediate steps shown in (ii) and (iii) may be omitted.

Example 2. Factor $8ab - 12ac$ and evaluate if $a = -3$, $b = +2$, $c = -2$.

Solution. $8ab - 12ac = 4a(2b - 3c)$ (D)

$$= 4(-3)[2(+2) - 3(-2)]$$
$$= (-12)(+4 + 6)$$
$$= (-12)(10)$$
$$= -120$$

Example 3. Expand the product $(2x + 3y)(x - 2y)$.

Solution.

$$(2x + 3y)(x - 2y)$$

$= (2x + 3y)x + (2x + 3y)(-2y)$ (D) $2x + 3y$

$= 2x^2 + 3xy - 4xy - 6y^2$ (D) $\underline{x - 2y}$

$= 2x^2 + (3 - 4)xy - 6y^2$ (D) $2x^2 + 3xy$ (D)

$= 2x^2 - xy - 6y^2$ $\underline{\quad - 4xy - 6y^2}$ (D)

$\qquad\qquad\qquad\qquad\qquad\qquad\qquad\quad 2x^2 - xy - 6y^2$ (D)

Exercise B-5

(Variables are integers.)

(A)

1. Expand the following:
   - (i) $3(2a + 3b)$ (ii) $(-4)(2x - 5y)$ (iii) $(-1)(-3m - 5n)$
   - (iv) $5(3a - 2b + 4c - 5d)$ (v) $(-6)(2x - 4y + 6z - 2q)$

2. Factor the following:
   - (i) $4m + 8p$ (ii) $6ab - 4ac$ (iii) $-3a - 12b$
   - (iv) $16a^2 - 4ab - 8ac$ (v) $-7mp - 14mq - 21mr$

3. State the negative of each of the following:
   - (i) $4m + 5n$ (ii) $3a - 2b$ (iii) $-(2x + y)$
   - (iv) $-4m - 2n + p$ (v) $x^2 - 5x + 6$ (vi) $-(-2x^2 - x + 1)$

4. Read the following with the brackets removed:
   - (i) $3(a + b) + 4(c + d)$ (ii) $2(3a - 4b) - 5(2c - 3d)$
   - (iii) $(-3)(a - 4b + 2c) + 5(-2c - 5d + 4e)$
   - (iv) $xy(-3 + 4a) - yz(4 - 2a) - xz(-7 + 6a)$

5. Expand each of the following:
   - (i) $(x + 1)(x + 1)$ (ii) $(a - 2)(a - 2)$
   - (iii) $(m + 5)(m - 5)$ (iv) $(3x - 2)(3x + 2)$
   - (v) $(1 - a)(1 - b)$ (vi) $(a - b)(c + d)$

(B)

6. Simplify:
   (i) $2(a + b - c) + 3(2a - b + 3c)$
   (ii) $(3x + 2y) - 2(x + 4y) + 3(2x - 3y)$
   (iii) $0 - 2(3x + 2y) + (-4)(2x - 8y)$
   (iv) $(-3)(2a - 4b) + 2(3a - 6b) - 4(a + b - 3c)$
   (v) $4m(2m + 3n) - 4n(3m - 2n) + 3(m^2 - n^2)$

7. If $a = 2, b = -4, c = -1$, compare:
   (i) $a^2 - b^2$ and $(a - b)(a + b)$
   (ii) $a^3 + b^3 + c^3 - 3abc$ and $(a+b+c)(a^2+b^2+c^2-ab-ac-bc)$

8. If $x = 3, y = -2, z = 4$, find $\dfrac{2x + 3y}{z} + \dfrac{4x - 5z}{-2y}$.

9. Factor:
   (i) $a^2 + ab$ (ii) $3a + 6b - 12c$ (iii) $-4mp - 8p - 12pq$
   (iv) $-12x + 3a - 15b$

10. Expand and simplify:
    (i) $m - n[(x + y) - 5z]$ (ii) $(x + y)(3a + 2b)$
    (iii) $(4a + b)(a - 3b)$ (iv) $(x - 2y)(2x - y)$

11. Expand each of the following:
    (i) $(3x + 2)(2x + 3)$ (ii) $(5m + 2)(5m + 2)$
    (iii) $(9a + 5b)(9a - 5b)$ (iv) $(2a + b)(3a - b + 2c)$
    (v) $(m - 3n)(6m - 2n + 7)$ (vi) $(2x + 3)(4x^2 + 12x + 9)$

12. Expand and simplify:
    (i) $(3a - 2b)(3a + 2b) + (4a - 3b)(2a + b) - (a - 7b)(a + b)$
    (ii) $(2m-1)(m^2+m+1) - (m-2)(m^2+2m+4) + (2m-3)(m^2-1)$

B.16 **The set of rational numbers** (Q). The extension of the number system to the set of integers provides a set of numbers closed under the operations of addition, subtraction, and multiplication, but *not closed under division*. Since there is no integer whose product with $(+2)$ is $(+7)$, the quotient $(+7) \div (+2)$ does not exist in this set. To overcome this deficiency a further extension of the number system has been made, and a set of numerals of the form

$$\frac{-3}{+2}, \frac{-4}{-7}, \frac{+5}{-11}$$

has been invented to represent quotients of every integer divided by a non-zero integer.

In general, for every pair of integers represented by a and b, $b \neq 0$, there is a numeral of the form $\dfrac{a}{b}$ (read, "a over b") which represents the quotient $a \div b$. The set of numbers thus represented is called the set of *rational (ratio)* numbers. It is designated by Q (*quotient*) and is defined to be the set of all numbers represented by $\dfrac{a}{b}$ such that a and b represent integers and $b \neq 0$.

In set-builder notation,

$$Q = \left\{ \frac{a}{b} \mid a, b \in I, b \neq 0 \right\}.$$

The symbol $\dfrac{a}{b}$, $b \neq 0$ is called a *fraction*; a is the *numerator*, and b is the *denominator* of the fraction; a and b are the *terms* of the fraction.

If $a, b \in I, b \neq 0$

$$\because \frac{a}{b} = a \div b \qquad \therefore (a \div b)(b) = a. \quad \text{(Definition of division)}$$

$$\therefore \frac{a}{b} \times b = a$$

Since multiplication is to be commutative, this property is expressed as follows:

If $a, b \in I$, then $\dfrac{a}{b} \times b = b \times \dfrac{a}{b} = \bar{a}.$

B·17 Multiplication in the set of rational numbers. If the set of rational numbers is to be an extension of the set of integers, it is necessary that the operations of addition and multiplication be consistent with those of the integers. The set should be closed under the operations, and the operations should be commutative and associative, and multiplication should be distributive over addition.

a. *Product of any two rational numbers.*

If $\dfrac{a}{b}, \dfrac{c}{d} \in Q$, *then* $\dfrac{a}{b} \times b = a$

and $\dfrac{c}{d} \times d = c.$

$$\therefore \left(\frac{a}{b} \times b \right)\left(\frac{c}{d} \times d \right) = a \times c$$

If multiplication is to be commutative and associative, then

$$\left(\frac{a}{b} \times \frac{c}{d}\right)(b \times d) = a \times c.$$

$$\therefore \quad \frac{a}{b} \times \frac{c}{d} = (a \times c) \div (b \times d) \quad \text{(Definition of division)}$$

or

$$\frac{a}{b} \times \frac{c}{d} = \frac{a \times c}{b \times d}$$

Thus, if $\dfrac{a}{b}$, $\dfrac{c}{d}$ $\in Q$, *then*

$$\frac{a}{b} \times \frac{c}{d} = \frac{a \times c}{b \times d}.$$

Since $a, c, b, d \in I$, therefore ac and $bd \in I$, and therefore $\dfrac{ac}{bd} \in Q$.

Thus, the set of rational numbers is closed under multiplication. The definition was developed on the assumption that multiplication is commutative and associative.

b. *Identity element for multiplication.*

If $\dfrac{a}{b} \in Q$, then

(i) $\quad \dfrac{a}{b} \times \dfrac{(+1)}{(+1)} = \dfrac{a(+1)}{b(+1)} = \dfrac{a}{b}$

(ii) $\quad \dfrac{-a}{b} \times \dfrac{(+1)}{(+1)} = \dfrac{(-a)(+1)}{b(+1)} = \dfrac{-a}{b}.$

These examples illustrate that $\dfrac{+1}{+1}$ or 1 is the *identity element* for multiplication.

c. *Reciprocal (multiplicative inverse).*

If $a, b \in I$, $a, b \neq 0$, then

$$\frac{a}{b} \times \frac{b}{a} = \frac{ab}{ba}$$

$$= \frac{ab}{ab} \quad (CM)$$

$$= 1.$$

Two numbers whose product is 1 are called *reciprocals* or *multiplicative inverses* of each other. Division by zero is not defined; zero has no reciprocal.

Example. State the reciprocals of:

(i) $\dfrac{3}{-2}$ (ii) $\dfrac{-4}{-5}$ (iii) $\dfrac{-6}{7}$ (iv) 7   (v) 1   (vi) 0

Solution.

(i) $\dfrac{-2}{3}$ (ii) $\dfrac{-5}{-4}$ (iii) $\dfrac{7}{-6}$ (iv) $\dfrac{1}{7}$ (v) 1

(vi) Zero has no reciprocal.

B·18 The principle of equivalent fractions. Since 1 is the identity element for multiplication and

$$1 = \frac{1}{1} = \frac{x}{x}, \quad x \in I, \; x \neq 0,$$

then if $\dfrac{a}{b} \in Q,$

$$\frac{a}{b} = \frac{a}{b} \times \frac{1}{1} = \frac{a \times 1}{b \times 1}$$

$$= \frac{a}{b} \times \frac{x}{x} = \frac{ax}{bx}, \quad x \in I, \; x \neq 0.$$

Thus, there are many fractions which represent the same rational number. This fact is expressed in the following principle.

Principle of equivalent fractions (PEF)

$$\textbf{If } \frac{a}{b} \in Q \textbf{ and } x \in I, \; x \neq 0, \textbf{ then } \frac{a}{b} = \frac{ax}{bx}.$$

In the following exercises, symbols of the form $\dfrac{a}{b}$ represent rational numbers.

B·19 Alternate form of numerals for rational numbers. Since

$$\frac{-2}{+3} = \frac{(-1)}{(+1)} \times \frac{(+2)}{(+3)} = (-1) \times \frac{(+2)}{(+3)}$$

$$\therefore \; \frac{-2}{+3} \text{ is equivalent to } -\frac{+2}{+3} \text{ or } -\frac{2}{3}.$$

Similarly, $\dfrac{-2}{-3} = \dfrac{(-1)}{(-1)} \times \dfrac{(+2)}{(+3)} = (+1) \times \dfrac{(+2)}{(+3)}$

$$\therefore \; \frac{-2}{-3} \text{ is equivalent to } +\frac{2}{3} \text{ or } \frac{2}{3}.$$

Also, $\dfrac{+2}{-3} = \dfrac{(+1)}{(-1)} \times \dfrac{(+2)}{(+3)} = (-1) \times \dfrac{(+2)}{(+3)}$

$$\therefore \ \dfrac{+2}{-3} \ \text{is equivalent to} \ -\dfrac{2}{3}.$$

In general, if a, b $\in$ ^+I, *then*

$$\dfrac{-a}{+b} = -\dfrac{a}{b}, \quad \dfrac{+a}{-b} = -\dfrac{a}{b}, \quad \dfrac{-a}{-b} = \dfrac{a}{b}.$$

A rational number is positive if the product of its terms is positive and is negative if the product of its terms is negative.

B·20 Division in the set of rational numbers. Since division is the inverse operation of multiplication:

If $a, b, c \in Q$, then $a \div b = c$ if and only if $bc = a$.

The following illustrates how the quotient may be determined.

MULTIPLICATION	DIVISION	MULTIPLICATION WHICH PRODUCES THE SAME RESULT
If $\dfrac{a}{b}, \dfrac{c}{d} \in Q$, then $\dfrac{a}{b} \times \dfrac{c}{d} = \dfrac{ac}{bd}.$	$\dfrac{ac}{bd} \div \dfrac{c}{d} = \dfrac{a}{b}$	$\dfrac{ac}{bd} \times \dfrac{d}{c} = \dfrac{acd}{bdc}$ $= \dfrac{a}{b}$

To divide by a fraction, multiply by its reciprocal.

In general, if $\dfrac{a}{b}, \dfrac{c}{d} \in Q$, *then*

$$\dfrac{a}{b} \div \dfrac{c}{d} = \dfrac{a}{b} \times \dfrac{d}{c} = \dfrac{ad}{bc}, \ c \neq 0.$$

Since $\dfrac{ad}{bc}$, $(b, c \neq 0)$, is a rational number, the set of rational numbers is closed under division, except for division by zero which is not defined.

Exercise B-6

(A)

1. State two equivalent forms of:

    (i) $\dfrac{-4}{5}$ (ii) $\dfrac{-3}{-8}$ (iii) $-\dfrac{5}{9}$ (iv) $\dfrac{9}{16}$

2. Express the following products in simplest form:

    (i) $\dfrac{-5}{8} \times \dfrac{3}{-4}$ (ii) $3 \times \dfrac{-5}{6}$ (iii) $\dfrac{-6}{15} \times -\dfrac{10}{18}$

    (iv) $\left(-\dfrac{3}{4}\right) \times \left(\dfrac{10}{-9}\right) \times \dfrac{1}{5}$ (v) $\dfrac{3x^2}{-2a} \times \left(-\dfrac{2}{3}\right) \times \dfrac{x}{5}$

3. State the reciprocals of:

    (i) $\dfrac{-7}{8}$ (ii) $\dfrac{4}{-3}$ (iii) 5 (iv) $\dfrac{-9}{-10}$

    (v) $\dfrac{0}{-1}$ (vi) -1 (vii) $-\dfrac{1}{2}$ (viii) $\dfrac{c}{-c}$

4. Using the principle of equivalent fractions, reduce the following rational numbers to lowest terms:

    (i) $\dfrac{-27}{36}$ (ii) $\dfrac{+36a^2}{-180a}$ (iii) $\dfrac{5 \times 0}{-10}$ (iv) $\dfrac{-34abc}{-85b^2c}$

    (v) $\dfrac{(-3)(-10)}{24}$ (vi) $\dfrac{60x^2y}{25xy^2}$ (vii) $\dfrac{(3)(-4)(-5)}{(-6)(-8)}$ (viii) $\dfrac{-14pq}{91q}$

5. Simplify:

    (i) $-\dfrac{-5}{-6} \div \dfrac{-15}{4}$ (ii) $\dfrac{-4a}{3} \div \dfrac{12b}{-5}$ (iii) $-\dfrac{x^2}{4y} \div \dfrac{-5x^2}{-28y}$

    (iv) $\dfrac{-\dfrac{x}{y}}{\dfrac{-p}{q}}$ (v) $\dfrac{-3}{\dfrac{x}{6}}$ (vi) $\dfrac{-2f}{\dfrac{g}{\dfrac{3}{fg}}}$

(B)

6. Reduce to lowest terms:

    (i) $\dfrac{5p + 15q}{-10}$ (ii) $\dfrac{-24a^3b^3r}{-10a^2br^2}$ (iii) $\dfrac{-4a + 10a^2 - 6a^3}{-8a^3}$

    (iv) $\dfrac{(-3x)(-10x^2y)(-6xy)}{(-5y^2)(-12xy^2)}$ (v) $-\dfrac{-6a}{-(3a^2 + 6a)}$

7. Express the following products in simplest form:

    (i) $\dfrac{6x}{-2(-y)} \times \dfrac{by}{-3x}$ (ii) $\dfrac{(4x)(-y)}{(-3x)(z)} \times \dfrac{(3y)(-3z)}{2xyz}$

    (iii) $\dfrac{2a}{-3b} \times -\dfrac{6b}{5c} \times \dfrac{-15c}{18a^2}$ (iv) $6(-a) \times \dfrac{1}{-12ac} \times \dfrac{5c^2}{-1}$

(v) $\dfrac{3}{2} \times \dfrac{-6a - 18ab}{12a^2}$

(vi) $\left(-\dfrac{-1}{2}\right)\left(-8\right)\left(\dfrac{1}{-2a}\right)$

8. Simplify:

(i) $\dfrac{t^2}{4} \div \dfrac{5st}{-12}$

(ii) $\dfrac{-1}{a^2b^2c} \div \dfrac{-1}{-abc^2}$

(iii) $-5 \div \dfrac{-14a^2b}{-35b}$

(iv) $\dfrac{-2c^2}{(3c)(-d)} \div \dfrac{(-8c)(-d)^2}{c^3d}$

(v) $\dfrac{\dfrac{-5x}{4y^2}}{\dfrac{-15x^3}{-8y^3}}$

(vi) $\dfrac{(2)(-3a)}{-\dfrac{12c}{7b}}$

(vii) $\dfrac{\dfrac{-1}{xy^2z}}{\dfrac{-1}{xyz}}$

9. If $p = \dfrac{-3}{4}$ and $q = \dfrac{2}{3}$, find:

(i) $4p^2q$ (ii) $8p^2 - pq - 9q^2$ (iii) $\dfrac{-3p}{q}$

10. Write the negative reciprocal of:

(i) $\dfrac{-15a}{30b}$ (ii) $-\dfrac{3}{4}$ (iii) $\dfrac{9x}{3x}$ (iv) $\dfrac{0}{-4}$

11. Show that $\left(\dfrac{2}{-3} \times \dfrac{-5}{-7}\right) \times \dfrac{-4}{13} = \dfrac{2}{-3}\left(\dfrac{-5}{-7} \times \dfrac{-4}{13}\right)$.

12. Show that $\left(\dfrac{-a}{b} \times \dfrac{x}{-y}\right) \times \left(-\dfrac{p}{q}\right) = \dfrac{-a}{b} \times \left[\dfrac{x}{-y} \times \left(-\dfrac{p}{q}\right)\right]$.

B·21 Addition in the set of rational numbers.

a. *Addition of rational numbers with the same denominator.*

If $\dfrac{a}{b},\ \dfrac{c}{b} \in Q$, then $\dfrac{a}{b} + \dfrac{c}{b} = \dfrac{a}{1} \times \dfrac{1}{b} + \dfrac{c}{1} \times \dfrac{1}{b}$

$$= a \times \dfrac{1}{b} + c \times \dfrac{1}{b}$$

$$= (a + c)\dfrac{1}{b} \quad (D)$$

$$= \dfrac{a + c}{b}.$$

b. *Addition of any two rational numbers.* The sum of any two rational numbers may be related to the sum of two rational numbers with the same denominator by means of the principle of equivalent fractions.

If $\dfrac{a}{b}$, $\dfrac{c}{d} \in Q$, then

$$\frac{a}{b} + \frac{c}{d} = \frac{ad}{bd} + \frac{bc}{bd} = \frac{ad + bc}{bd}.$$

The set of rational numbers is closed under addition; addition is commutative and associative, and multiplication is distributive over addition.

c. *Identity element for addition.*

$$\frac{a}{b} + 0 = \frac{a}{b} + \frac{0}{b}$$

$$= \frac{a}{b}$$

Thus, zero is the identity element for addition.

d. *Additive inverse or negative of a rational number.*

Since
$$\frac{a}{b} + \frac{-a}{b} = \frac{a + (-a)}{b}$$

$$= \frac{0}{b}$$

$$= 0$$

$\therefore \; \dfrac{-a}{b}$ is the additive inverse or negative of $\dfrac{a}{b}$, and

$\dfrac{a}{b}$ is the additive inverse or negative of $\dfrac{-a}{b}$.

$\therefore$ *the product of any rational number (except zero) and* **(− 1)** *is the negative of the rational number.*

$$\because \; \frac{-a}{b} = -\frac{a}{b} = \frac{a}{-b}$$

$\therefore$ the negative of $\dfrac{a}{b}$ may be written $\dfrac{-a}{b}$ or $-\dfrac{a}{b}$ or $\dfrac{a}{-b}$.

B·22 Subtraction in the set of rational numbers. Since subtraction is the inverse operation of addition, therefore if a, b, $c \in Q$, then

$$a - b = c \text{ if and only if } c + b = a.$$

The following illustrates subtraction of rational numbers.

ADDITION	SUBTRACTION	ADDITION WHICH PRODUCES THE SAME RESULT
If $\dfrac{a}{b}$, $\dfrac{c}{d} \in Q$, then $$\dfrac{a}{b}+\dfrac{c}{d}=\dfrac{ad+bc}{bd}\,.$$	$\therefore \dfrac{ad+bc}{bd}-\dfrac{c}{d}$ $=\dfrac{a}{b}$	$\dfrac{ad+bc}{bd}+\dfrac{-c}{d}=\dfrac{ad+bc+(-bc)}{bd}$ $=\dfrac{ad}{bd}$ $=\dfrac{a}{b}$

To subtract a rational number, add its negative.

If $\dfrac{a}{b}$, $\dfrac{c}{d} \in Q$, then

$$\frac{a}{b}-\frac{c}{d}=\frac{a}{b}+\frac{-c}{d}=\frac{ad}{bd}+\frac{-bc}{bd}=\frac{ad-bc}{bd}\,.$$

Since $a, b, c, d \in I$,

$$\therefore\ ad, bc, bd, ad-bc \in I \text{ and } \frac{ad-bc}{bd} \in Q\,.$$

Thus, the set of rational numbers is closed under subtraction.

B·23 Order relations in the set of rational numbers. If the same idea of order as that established for the integers is to be extended to the rational numbers, it is necessary to make the following definition:

If $a, b \in Q$, then

$a > b$ *if* $a - b$ *is a positive rational number, or*

$a > b$ *if* $a = b + c$, *where c is a positive rational number.*

It follows from this definition that:

(i) all positive rational numbers are greater than zero;

(ii) all negative rational numbers are less than zero;

(iii) all positive rational numbers are greater than all negative rational numbers;

(iv) $-\dfrac{1}{4}$ is greater than $-\dfrac{3}{2}$

since $-\dfrac{1}{4}-\left(-\dfrac{3}{2}\right)=\dfrac{-1}{4}+\dfrac{3}{2}=\dfrac{-1+6}{4}=\dfrac{5}{4}$ (a positive rational number).

The following are the two fundamental properties of this order relation.

(i) *The trichotomy property:*

   If $a, b \in Q$, then $a < b$ or $a = b$ or $a > b$.

(ii) *The transitive property:*

   If $a, b \in Q$ and $a < b$ and $b < c$, then $a < c$.

Exercise B-7

(A)

State the negative of:

1. $\dfrac{3}{-2}$

2. $\dfrac{-5}{6}$

3. $\dfrac{-4}{-7}$

4. $-\dfrac{-3}{2xy}$

5. $\dfrac{2a}{-3b}$

6. $-\dfrac{-a}{-2b}$

Simplify:

7. $\left(-\dfrac{3}{4}\right) + \left(-\dfrac{3}{4}\right)$

8. $\dfrac{3}{5} + \dfrac{-3}{5}$

9. $\dfrac{5}{6} - \dfrac{2}{3}$

10. $3 + \dfrac{-2}{3}$

11. $\dfrac{2}{-3} + \dfrac{-3}{4}$

12. $\dfrac{3a}{4} - \dfrac{-a}{8}$

(B)

Simplify:

13. $\dfrac{-5}{6} + \dfrac{1}{3} - \dfrac{-2}{9}$

14. $\dfrac{3}{-a} - \dfrac{4}{-2a} + \dfrac{-3}{-3a}$

15. $\dfrac{4}{xy} - \dfrac{5}{2xy} - \dfrac{-3}{-xy}$

16. $\dfrac{x^2}{y^2z^2} - \dfrac{2y^2}{x^2z^2} + \dfrac{3z^2}{x^2y^2}$

17. $\dfrac{5p}{3qr} - \dfrac{6q}{9pq}$

18. $1 - \dfrac{2}{b+c}$

19. $\dfrac{3}{x+y} - 2$

20. $m + \dfrac{1}{n} + n + \dfrac{1}{m}$

21. $\dfrac{x}{y} - \dfrac{-y}{x} - \dfrac{-1}{-2}$

22. $\dfrac{2}{x-y} - \dfrac{-3}{x+y}$

23. $\dfrac{1}{r_1} + \dfrac{1}{r_2} + \dfrac{1}{r_3}$

24. $\dfrac{1}{-\frac{1}{2}} - \dfrac{1}{-\frac{1}{3}} - \dfrac{1}{-\frac{1}{4}}$

Arrange the elements of the following sets in increasing order of magnitude:

25. $\left\{\dfrac{-3}{7}, \dfrac{-3}{-7}, \dfrac{2}{-7}, \dfrac{-2}{-7}\right\}$

26. $\left\{-\dfrac{5}{-8}, \dfrac{-5}{-4}, \dfrac{-5}{4}, -\dfrac{-5}{-8}\right\}$

27. $\left\{\dfrac{1}{-4}, -\dfrac{1}{3}, \dfrac{5}{-6}, -\dfrac{-2}{3}, \dfrac{-7}{-12}\right\}$

28. $\left\{-\dfrac{2}{7}, \dfrac{4}{-15}, -\dfrac{-9}{-35}\right\}$

Simplify:

29. $\left(-3 \div \dfrac{-9}{-xy}\right) + \dfrac{5xy}{-6}$

30. $\dfrac{\frac{2}{pq}}{-3p} - \dfrac{-5q}{q^3}$

31. $\left(\dfrac{-2}{ab} + \dfrac{3}{-2ab}\right) - \left(\dfrac{-3c}{2abc} - \dfrac{-3}{ab}\right)$

Chapter I

THE REAL NUMBER SYSTEM

***1·1* Rational numbers in decimal notation.** In decimal notation:

$$\frac{3}{4} = .75 \qquad \frac{3}{8} = .375 \qquad \frac{5}{2} = 2.5$$

In changing the rational numerals $\frac{3}{4}$, $\frac{3}{8}$, $\frac{5}{2}$ to their decimal equivalents, the division process is complete or terminates. The decimals are called *terminating decimals*.

In decimal notation:

$$\frac{1}{3} = .3333\ldots \text{ or } \frac{1}{3} = .\dot{3}$$

$$\frac{2}{7} = .285714285714\ldots \text{ or } \frac{2}{7} = .\dot{2}8571\dot{4}$$

In attempting to change the rational numerals $\frac{1}{3}$, $\frac{2}{7}$ to their decimal equivalents, the division does not terminate but has recurring sets of digits. These decimals are referred to as *non-terminating recurring decimals*.

It is also customary to write the repeating decimals $.\dot{3}$ and $.\dot{2}8571\dot{4}$ in the form $.\overline{3}$ and $.\overline{285714}$.

THEOREM A. *Any rational number may be represented by either a terminating or a non-terminating recurring decimal.*

Two particular examples illustrate the plausibility of this theorem. (i) To find the decimal equivalent of a fraction which represents a rational number, the numerator is divided by the denominator. At each step of the division, a remainder occurs. If at one stage of the division the remainder is zero, the division is complete, and the decimal terminates.

(ii) If 2 is divided by 7, the only possible remainders which can occur are 0, 1, 2, 3, 4, 5, 6. If the remainder zero does not occur, then, as the division continues, some remainder must occur again. The division then repeats itself.

Either (i) or (ii) is true for all rational numbers.

The division of 2 by 7 has been completed by the long division method only to display the remainders.

THEOREM B. *Any terminating or non-terminating recurring decimal represents a rational number.*

The following examples illustrate the plausibility of this theorem.

```
        .375                    .2857142
    8 | 3.0000            7 | 2.0000000
        2 4                    1 4
        ----                   ----
         60                     60
         56                     56
         ----                   ----
          40                     40
          40                     35
          ----                   ----
           0                     50
                                 49
                                 ----
                                  10
                                   7
                                  ----
                                   30
                                   28
                                  ----
                                   20
                                   14
                                  ----
                                   60
```

(i) Any terminating decimal may be written as a fraction with denominator 10 or a power of 10 and, therefore, represents a rational number.

$$.5 = \frac{5}{10} \qquad\qquad .34 = \frac{34}{10^2}$$

$$= \frac{1}{2} \qquad\qquad = \frac{17}{50}$$

(ii) Any non-terminating recurring decimal may be expressed as a fraction by using the method shown in the following example.

Example 1. Show that the following non-terminating recurring decimals represent rational numbers:

(i) $.\dot{6}$ (ii) $.\dot{1}\dot{8}$ (iii) $.2\dot{3}\dot{5}$ (iv) $.2\dot{3}\dot{5}$

Solution.

(i) Let $x = .\dot{6} = .6666\ldots$

$10x = 6.66666\ldots$

$x = .66666\ldots$

$\therefore 9x = 6$

$\therefore x = \dfrac{6}{9}$

$\therefore .\dot{6} = \dfrac{2}{3}$

(ii) Let $y = .\dot{1}\dot{8} = .181818\ldots$

$100y = 18.18181818\ldots$

$y = .18181818\ldots$

$\therefore 99y = 18$

$\therefore y = \dfrac{18}{99}$

$\therefore .\dot{1}\dot{8} = \dfrac{2}{11}$

(iii) Let $m = .2\dot{3}\dot{5} = .235235\ldots$ (iv) Let $n = .2\dot{3}\dot{5} = .2353535\ldots$

$1000m = 235.235235\ldots$ $1000n = 235.353535\ldots$

$\underline{m = .235235\ldots}$ $\underline{10n = 2.353535\ldots}$

$\therefore\ 999m = 235$ $\therefore\ 990n = 233$

$\therefore\ m = \dfrac{235}{999}$ $\therefore\ n = \dfrac{233}{990}$

$\therefore\ .2\dot{3}\dot{5} = \dfrac{235}{999}$ $\therefore\ .2\dot{3}\dot{5} = \dfrac{233}{990}$

Each of the above results may be checked by division. The decimal fraction .375 is often referred to as a non-terminating recurring decimal, the repeating digit being zero, that is, $.375\dot{0}$. Thus, all rational numbers may be represented by non-terminating recurring decimals which are referred to as *periodic decimals*.

It is interesting to note that some rational numbers have *two decimal equivalents*. This is illustrated in the following example.

Example 2. Show that (i) .5 and (ii) $.4\dot{9}$ are each equivalent to $\frac{1}{2}$.

Solution.   (i) $.5 = \dfrac{5}{10} = \dfrac{1}{2}$ (ii) Let $x = .499\ldots$

then $100x = 49.999\ldots$

$\underline{10x = 4.999\ldots}$

$\therefore\ 90x = 45$

$\therefore\ x = \dfrac{1}{2}$

Similarly it may be shown that the numerals 5 and $4.\dot{9}$ represent the same rational number.

Write a solution for the following problem and compare it with that on page 439.

1. Show that (i) $.374\dot{9}$ and (ii) .375 are each equivalent to $\frac{3}{8}$.

It should be noted that the decimal part of any periodic decimal can be expressed in fraction form by the following procedure:

The *numerator* is obtained by subtracting the number formed by the non-repeating digits from the number formed by all the digits.

The *denominator* is formed by writing a 9 for each repeating digit, followed by a zero for each non-repeating digit following the decimal point.

For example: $.2\dot{3}\dot{5} = \dfrac{235 - 2}{990} = \dfrac{233}{990}.$

Exercise 1-1

(A)

State each of the following periodic decimals in fraction form:

1. (i) $.6$ (ii) $.75$ (iii) $.7\dot{2}$ (iv) $.15$
2. (i) $.\dot{2}$ (ii) $.\dot{2}\dot{4}$ (iii) $.30\dot{5}$ (iv) $.\dot{4}7\dot{2}$
3. (i) $.2\dot{7}$ (ii) $.1\dot{3}$ (iii) $.3\dot{2}\dot{4}$ (iv) $.09\dot{2}$
4. (i) $.2\dot{3}\dot{3}$ (ii) $.4\dot{5}6\dot{2}$ (iii) $3.\dot{3}\dot{2}$ (iv) $3.4\dot{2}$

(B)

Show by the process of division that the following are equivalent to periodic decimals:

5. $3\frac{1}{5}$ 6. $6\frac{2}{3}$ 7. $\dfrac{1}{11}$ 8. $\dfrac{11}{27}$

9. $\dfrac{19}{9}$ 10. $\dfrac{95}{7}$ 11. $-11\frac{1}{10}$ 12. $-\dfrac{13}{31}$

Show that the following represent rational numbers:

13. $.\dot{5}$ 14. $.\dot{1}\dot{5}$ 15. $2.\dot{3}$ 16. 1.414
17. $3.\dot{7}82\dot{5}$ 18. $0.23\dot{2}\dot{7}$ 19. $0.3634\dot{1}$ 20. $2.\dot{5}83\dot{7}$

Show that the following pairs of periodic decimals represent the same rational number:

21. $.4$ and $.3\dot{9}$ 22. $.32$ and $.319\dot{9}$

1·2 The density of rational numbers. The rational numbers may be considered as coordinates of points on a number line. Such a number line may be called a *rational number line* (*Fig. 1-1*). It is both interesting and

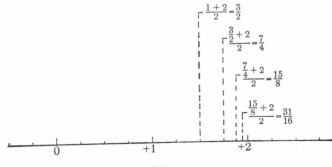

Fig. 1-1

essential to note that between any two rational numbers there is another rational number, and hence between any two points on a rational number line there is another point with a rational coordinate. This is suggested by the following examples.

Between 1 and 2 is the rational number $\dfrac{1 + 2}{2} = \dfrac{3}{2}$.

Between $\dfrac{3}{2}$ and 2 is the rational number $\dfrac{\dfrac{3}{2} + 2}{2} = \dfrac{7}{4}$,

and so on without limit.

If $a, b \in Q$ and $a < b$, then between a and b lies the rational number
$$\frac{a + b}{2}.$$

Between $\dfrac{a + b}{2}$ and b lies the rational number
$$\frac{\dfrac{a + b}{2} + b}{2} = \frac{a + 3b}{4},$$
and so on without limit.

To describe mathematically the fact that between any two rational numbers there is another rational number, we say the rational numbers are *dense*.

It might appear from this discussion that not only is there a distinct point on a line corresponding to each rational number, but that to each point on that line there corresponds a rational number coordinate. In other words, it appears that there is a one-to-one correspondence between the points on a line and the rational numbers. But this is not so. The points on a line which have rational coordinates are only a small portion of all the points on that line.

1·3 **The set of irrational numbers.** In section 1·2 it was stated that although there is a point on a line which corresponds to each rational number, there is not a rational coordinate for each point on that line. The rational number system is not complete in this sense. It was also observed, although not proved, that each rational number could be represented in the form of a periodic decimal and that each periodic decimal represents a rational number.

It is easy, however, to make up a decimal form which is not periodic in nature. For example, such a number form may be constructed by starting with the periodic decimal
$$.32323232\ldots$$
If the digit 5 is inserted after the first period .32, 55 after the second period, 555 after the third period, 5555 after the fourth period, and so on, the resulting numeral
$$.325325532555325555\ldots$$

neither terminates nor repeats and is called a *non-periodic decimal.*

Similarly, by inserting different digits in this way, an unlimited number of non-periodic decimals may be produced from one periodic decimal. Since the numbers represented by these non-periodic decimals are not rational numbers, they are called *irrational numbers.*

Numerals such as the following represent irrational numbers:

$$\sqrt{2} = 1.4142136\ldots$$
$$\sqrt{3} = 1.73205080\ldots$$
$$\sqrt[3]{1001} = 10.00333222283909464\ldots$$
$$\pi = 3.14159265358979323846264633832\ldots$$

The following examples illustrate that the irrational numbers are coordinates of definite points on a number line.

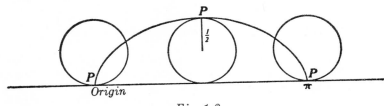

Fig. 1-2

A circle with radius $\frac{1}{2}$ unit (*Fig. 1-2*) has a circumference of $(2\pi \times \frac{1}{2})$ units $= \pi$ units. If such a circle is rolled, without slipping, for one complete revolution along a number line starting with a point P on the circumference coinciding with the zero point on the line, then a point corresponding to π units is determined. This point has the irrational coordinate π.

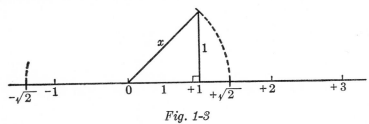

Fig. 1-3

The Pythagorean Theorem states, "the area of the square on the hypotenuse of a right triangle is equal to the sum of the areas of the squares on the other two sides".

Thus, in the right triangle of *Fig. 1-3*,

$$x^2 = 1^2 + 1^2$$
$$\text{or} \quad x^2 = 2$$

and, hence, by definition x is a square root of 2, and the length of the hypotenuse may be designated $\sqrt{2}$ units. As illustrated in *Fig. 1-3*, there is a segment of the number line congruent to the hypotenuse with one end point the origin. The other end point, to the right of the origin, must have coordinate $\sqrt{2}$. Similarly, to the left of the origin is a point with coordinate $-\sqrt{2}$.

1·4 $\sqrt{2}$ **does not represent a rational number (supplementary).** One proof of this statement depends upon an understanding of the relationship between the square of an integer and the integer itself. This relationship may be observed in the following.

An integer is *even* if and only if it is of the form
$$2n, \; n \in I,$$
and an integer is *odd* if and only if it is of the form
$$2n + 1, \; n \in I.$$
The square of any even integer may be expressed as
$$(2n)^2 = 4n^2, \; n \in I,$$
and the square of any odd integer may be expressed as
$$(2n + 1)^2 = 4n^2 + 4n + 1, \; n \in I.$$

From this it may be observed that if the square of an integer is divisible by 2 (i.e. even), then the integer itself is divisible by 2 (i.e. even).

The method of proof is indirect. We will assume that $\sqrt{2}$ represents a rational number and show that this leads to a contradiction.

Proof: Either $\sqrt{2}$ does or does not represent a rational number. Suppose $\sqrt{2}$ represents a rational number.

Then,
$$\sqrt{2} \in \left\{ \frac{a}{b} \,\middle|\, a, b \in I, \; b \neq 0 \right\}.$$

That is, $\sqrt{2}$ may be expressed in the form of a fraction

$$\frac{a}{b} \text{ where } a, b \in I, \; b \neq 0.$$

Since this fraction, if not in lowest terms, may be reduced to lowest terms, let

$$\sqrt{2} = \frac{a}{b} \text{ where } a, b \text{ have no common factor except 1.}$$

Then
$$2 = \frac{a^2}{b^2}$$

$$\therefore 2b^2 = a^2$$

or
$$a^2 = 2b^2 \qquad (1)$$

$\because 2b^2$ is an even integer $\therefore a^2$ is even and $\therefore a$ *is even.*

∵ a is an even integer, let $a = 2c$, $c \in I$.

Then $\qquad\qquad a^2 = 4c^2$ and,

substituting in equation (1),

$$4c^2 = 2b^2.$$
$$\therefore \ b^2 = 2c^2$$

∵ $2c^2$ is even ∴ b^2 is even and b *is even.*

Since a and b are both even, then a and b have a common factor 2, and $\frac{a}{b}$ is not in its lowest terms.

But it was given that $\frac{a}{b}$ is in its lowest terms.

Thus, the assumption that $\sqrt{2}$ represents a rational number leads to a contradiction.

∴ $\sqrt{2}$ does not represent a rational number.

Another proof that $\sqrt{2}$ is not rational depends upon the *Unique Factorization Theorem* which states:

A positive integer can be resolved into prime factors in only one way.

Let p represent a positive integer, and suppose that p is equivalent to the following two products of prime factors:

$$p = a_1 \, a_2 \, a_3 \, \dots$$
$$p = b_1 \, b_2 \, b_3 \, \dots$$

Then $\qquad\qquad a_1 \, a_2 \, a_3 \dots = b_1 \, b_2 \, b_3 \dots$

$\qquad\qquad\qquad a_1$ divides the product $a_1 \, a_2 \, a_3 \dots$

and $\qquad\qquad\quad b_1$ divides the product $b_1 \, b_2 \, b_3 \dots$.

Each factor of $b_1 \, b_2 \, b_3 \dots$ is a prime factor; ∴ a_1 must divide into one of them, say b_1. But a_1 and b_1 are both prime numbers; ∴ a_1 must equal b_1.

$$\therefore \ a_2 \, a_3 \dots = b_2 \, b_3 \dots$$

Similarly, a_2 may be shown to be equal to b_2, and so on.

∴ the factors in $a_1 \, a_2 \, a_3 \dots$ are the same as those in $b_1 \, b_2 \, b_3 \dots$.

∴ p can be resolved into prime factors in only one way.

Proof: Either $\sqrt{2}$ does or does not represent a rational number.

Suppose $\sqrt{2}$ represents a rational number and

$$\sqrt{2} = \frac{a}{b} \text{ where } a, b \in I, b \neq 0.$$

Then $\qquad 2 = \frac{a^2}{b^2}$ or $a^2 = 2b^2$.

We may consider a and b to be positive integers.

Either a and b are prime numbers or have a unique prime factorization.

Let $\quad\quad a = a_1\, a_2\, a_3 \ldots a_h \quad$ and $\quad b = b_1\, b_2\, b_3 \ldots b_k$.

Then $\quad\quad a^2 = a_1\, a_1\, a_2\, a_2\, a_3\, a_3 \ldots a_h\, a_h$

and $\quad\quad b^2 = b_1\, b_1\, b_2\, b_2\, b_3\, b_3 \ldots b_k\, b_k$

where a_1, a_2, ... and b_1, b_2, ... are prime numbers.

Each factor a_1, a_2, ... appears twice in the factorization of a^2, and each factor b_1, b_2, ... appears twice in the factorization of b^2.

Some of the factors a_1, a_2, ... may be identical, but every factor in the factorization of a^2 appears an even number of times, and the same is true for the factors of b^2.

$$\because\ a^2 = 2b^2$$

$\therefore\ a_1\, a_1\, a_2\, a_2 \ldots a_h\, a_h = 2 \cdot b_1\, b_1\, b_2\, b_2 \ldots b_k\, b_k$

$\therefore$ 2 appears as a factor on the left side an even number of times, if it appears at all, and an odd number of times on the right side.

Thus, the prime factorization on the left is not identical to that on the right. This contradicts the prime factorization theorem.

$$\therefore\ \sqrt{2} \text{ does not represent a rational number.}$$

1·5 Finding the point corresponding to an infinite decimal. Theoretically, we may determine the point corresponding to

$$\pi \text{ or } 3.1415926535 \ldots$$

by considering rational approximations to this number. For example, 3.14 is a *rational approximation* to the infinite decimal because:

(i) it represents a rational number (a terminating decimal);

(ii) it is an approximation obtained by rounding off the infinite decimal to two decimal places.

Evidently π lies between 3.1 and 3.2, both of which represent rational numbers and are the coordinates of points which can be determined on the rational number line.

Similarly, $\quad\pi$ lies between 3.14 and 3.15;

$\quad\quad\quad\quad\quad\pi$ lies between 3.141 and 3.142;

$\quad\quad\quad\quad\quad\pi$ lies between 3.1415 and 3.1416;

$$\cdots$$

$\quad\quad\quad\pi$ lies between 3.141592 and 3.141593.

Each of these pairs of numbers determines a segment of the number line, and each successive segment lies within the previous one and is $\frac{1}{10}$ as long. This is illustrated in *Fig. 1-4*. It seems likely that if this process is continued without limit there is just *one point common to all these segments, and this point corresponds to the number* π. The same procedure could be carried out for any infinite decimal. The nature of the method makes us feel certain there is a definite point corresponding to each infinite decimal, and to each point there corresponds an infinite decimal. We assume that this is true.

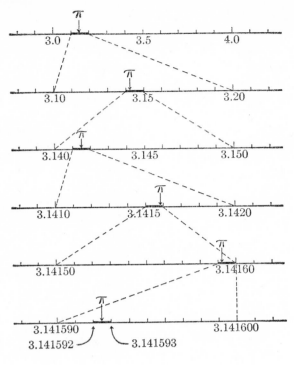

Fig. 1-4

1·6 The set of real numbers (R). The set of all decimals (the union of the periodic and non-periodic decimals) represents a set of numbers which is called the *set of real numbers*. This set is complete in the sense that there is a one-to-one correspondence between its elements and the points on a number line. Its composition is shown in *Fig. 1-5*.

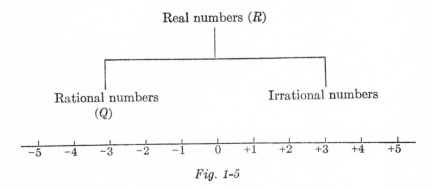

Fig. 1-5

The real number line in *Fig. 1-5* draws attention to the fact that the set of real numbers contains all positive and negative decimals. Each decimal may be paired with its negative: for example, the real number represented by a may be paired with its negative $- a$.

Whenever operations with irrational numbers in decimal form are required, rational approximations are used. For example, to find the area of a circle (πr^2), useful rational approximations to the area of the circle are obtained by using $\frac{22}{7}$, or 3.14, or 3.142, or 3.1416 as rational approximations for π. Similarly, any infinite decimal is rounded off to provide a suitable rational approximation for use under given circumstances, according to the following procedure.

> *In rounding off, discard all unnecessary digits and add 1 to the last retained digit whenever the next digit on its right is 5 or more, except when a single digit 5 is being discarded, in which case it is customary to round off to the nearest even digit.*

It is assumed that the definitions and properties of addition and multiplication of rational numbers are extended to the real numbers.

1·7 Summary. The set of real numbers R, which consists of the set of rational numbers Q and the set of irrational numbers, has subsets which, under addition and multiplication, behave in exactly the same manner as the integers and the natural numbers. In this sense, the set of real numbers is an extension of each of these sets, retaining the basic properties of them and providing a set of numbers closed under addition, multiplication, subtraction, and division.

The steps in the development from the natural numbers to the real numbers are listed below:

(i) $N = \{1, 2, 3, \ldots\}$

(ii) $N_0 = \{0, 1, 2, 3, \ldots\}$

(iii) $I = \{\ldots, -2, -1, 0, +1, +2, \ldots\}$

$\quad = \{\pm a \mid a \in N\} \cup \{0\}$

(iv) $Q = \left\{\dfrac{a}{b} \mid a, b \in I, b \neq 0\right\}$

(v) R is the union set of Q and the set of irrational numbers: that is, the set of all decimals.

The *laws of the real number system* are listed below:

If a, b, c ∈ R, then

	ADDITION		MULTIPLICATION	
Closure Law	$a + b$ represents one and only one real number	(ClA)	ab represents one and only one real number	(ClM)
Commutative Law	$a + b = b + a$	(CA)	$ab = ba$	(CM)
Associative Law	$(a+b)+c=a+(b+c)$	(AA)	$(ab)c = a(bc)$	(AM)
Distributive Law		$a(b + c) = ab + ac$	(D)	
Identity Element	*Zero*		*Unity*	
Inverse Element	$-a$		$\dfrac{1}{a}, a \neq 0$	

Order: If $a, b \in R$, then

$\qquad a > b$ if $a - b$ is a positive real number, or

$\qquad a > b$ if $a = b + c$ where c is a positive real number.

Trichotomy property: $a < b$ or $a = b$ or $a > b$.

Transitive property: If $a > b$ and $b > c$ then $a > c$.

Completeness: The real number system is complete: that is, each point on the number line corresponds to a real number, and each real number corresponds to a point on the number line.

Unless otherwise specified, it will be understood that the variables are real numbers in the remainder of this text.

Exercise 1-2

(A)

1. Describe in set notation the sets N, N_0, I, Q, R.
2. Name two important subsets of R.
3. From the periodic decimal $2.\dot{3}\dot{4}$ form four different non-periodic decimals. Discuss the statement: "There are infinitely more irrational numbers than rational numbers".
4. Of what elements is the set of real numbers composed?
5. What is a periodic decimal?
6. What assumption was made concerning (i) the real numbers and points on a number line (ii) points on a number line and real numbers?
7. How are the real numbers ordered? What is meant by saying $a > b$ where a, b represent real numbers?

8. State one rational number and one irrational number between the irrational numbers: $a = 6.3274108\ldots$ and $b = 5.3725038\ldots$.

9. State one rational number and one irrational number between the rational numbers: $c = 0.32323232\ldots$ and $d = 0.65372372\ldots$.

(B)

State rational approximations for the following real numbers correct to 2, 3, *and* 4 *decimal places:*

10. $3.14159\ldots$ **11.** $1.41426\ldots$ **12.** $15.345726\ldots$

13. $17.432768\ldots$ **14.** $2.1\dot{5}$ **15.** $18.\dot{2}\dot{3}$

16. $15.2\dot{3}\dot{5}$ **17.** $3.\dot{6}72\dot{5}$ **18.** $2.71828\ldots$

19. Copy the table below and check off the properties possessed by the indicated number sets.

PROPERTY		N_0	I	Q	R
Addition:	(1) Closed				
	(2) Commutative				
	(3) Associative				
	(4) Identity				
	(5) Inverse				
Multiplication:	(6) Closed				
	(7) Commutative				
	(8) Associative				
	(9) Identity				
	(10) Inverse				
	(11) Distributive				

Chapter II

EQUATIONS AND INEQUATIONS

2·1 Solving equations of the first degree in one variable. Sentences like $x - 4 = -2$ are called *equations of the first degree in one variable* because the exponent of the variable is unity. The variable, represented by x, is the element from a replacement set which is always specified (R, unless otherwise indicated). To solve such an equation means to determine the number (or numbers) from the replacement set which makes the sentence true: that is, makes the number represented by $x - 4$ (Left side, L.S.) equal to -2 (Right side, R.S.). In this example, the replacement which makes the sentence true is 2; 2 is called the *root* of the equation, and $\{2\}$ the *solution set*.

It may be observed by inspection that in the following set of equations

(i) $x = 2$ (ii) $4x = 8$ (iii) $x + 3 = 5$ (iv) $x - 4 = -2$ (v) $\dfrac{x}{2} = 1$

each has the same root 2 and the same solution set $\{2\}$.

Since each equation has the same root 2, we should be able to obtain one equation from the other using the number properties.

The closure property (law) of the set of real numbers under multiplication states:

If $a, b \in R$, then $a \cdot b$ is a *unique* real number .

Thus, in equation (ii), if $x \in R$, then $4x$ is a *unique* real number. Also, since $2 \in R$, then $4 \cdot 2$ is the unique real number 8. But equation (i) states that x equals 2, and hence by the uniqueness property of closure under multiplication, $4x$ and 8 represent the same real number.

Thus, if $x = 2$, then $4x = 8$.   (*ClM*)

Similarly, the closure property of the set of real numbers under addition, subtraction, and division allows (iii), (iv), and (v) to be obtained from equation (i).

Thus, if $x = 2$, then $x + 3 = 2 + 3$, or $x + 3 = 5$; (ClA)

if $x = 2$, then $x - 4 = 2 - 4$, or $x - 4 = -2$; (ClS)

if $x = 2$, then $\dfrac{x}{2} = \dfrac{2}{2}$, or $\dfrac{x}{2} = 1$. (ClD)

The same properties permit the reverse steps to be taken:

if $4x = 8$, then $\dfrac{4x}{4} = \dfrac{8}{4}$, or $x = 2$; (ClD)

if $x + 3 = 5$, then $x + 3 - 3 = 5 - 3$, or $x = 2$; (ClS)

if $x - 4 = -2$, then $x - 4 + 4 = -2 + 4$, or $x = 2$; (ClA)

if $\dfrac{x}{2} = 1$, then $2 \cdot \dfrac{x}{2} = 2 \cdot 1$, or $x = 2$. (ClM)

Thus, it can be said, for example,

if $x = 2$, then $4x = 8$, and

if $4x = 8$, then $x = 2$.

Since both *if . . . then* statements can be made, the two statements $x = 2$ and $4x = 8$ are *equivalent*. This implies, in the case of equations, that they have the same solution set.

Similarly, by applying the uniqueness property of closure under the four operations in the set of real numbers, each of the equations (i) to (v) may be shown to be *equivalent* to each of the others. Such equations are called *equivalent equations*. They have the same solution set.

In solving equations, the solution set may be obtained by inspection in simple cases, but usually the solution set is obtained by forming a succession of equivalent equations leading to an equation, such as $x = 2$, from which the solution set is obtained.

To solve the equation $2x - 3 = 9$, $x \in R$, we note:

if $2x - 3 = 9$

(add 3 to each side)   then $2x = 12$ (ClA)

(divide each side by 2)   then $x = 6$. (ClD)

Thus   (i) if $2x - 3 = 9$,   then $x = 6$.

It remains to be shown that

(ii) if $x = 6$,   then $2x - 3 = 9$.

Statement (ii) is proved by showing that the steps taken in proving (i) are *reversible* as follows:

if $x = 6$

(multiply each side by 2)   then $2x = 12$ (ClM)

(subtract 3 from each side)   then $2x - 3 = 9$. (ClS)

Thus,   if $x = 6$, then $2x - 3 = 9$.

It has now been shown that $2x - 3 = 9$ and $x = 6$ are equivalent equations. Therefore 6 is the root, and $\{6\}$ the solution set of the equation $2x - 3 = 9,\ x \in R$.

When the closure property of the set of real numbers under addition, subtraction, multiplication, and division is used to write a sequence of equations, the steps are always reversible, and thus the equations formed are always equivalent. Thus, it is not necessary to write the second part of the solution. It is customary to verify the number (or numbers) obtained as follows:

Verification.   L.S. $= 2 \times 6 - 3$ R.S. $= 9$
$$= 12 - 3$$
$$= 9$$

The verification shows that 6 *satisfies* the equation.

In general, given an equation
$$a = b,$$
equivalent equations may be formed by applying the closure property of the set of real numbers under addition, subtraction, multiplication, and division.

Thus, $a = b$ and

     (i) $a + c = b + c$ (Addition property)

     (ii) $a - c = b - c$ (Subtraction property)

     (iii) $a \times c = b \times c$ (Multiplication property)

     (iv) $a \div c = b \div c,\ c \neq 0$ (Division property)

are equivalent equations.

These properties are properties of the equality relation between two real numbers.

Example. Solve $7x - 4 = 2x + 21,\ x \in R$, and verify.

Solution.
$$7x - 4 = 2x + 21$$

(add 4 to each side) $7x = 2x + 25$ (Addition property)

(subtract $2x$ from each side) $7x - 2x = 25$ (Subtraction property)

(by distributive property) $5x = 25$ (D)

(divide each side by 5) $x = 5$ (Division property)

The root is 5, and the solution set is $\{5\}$.

Verification.   L.S. $= 7 \times 5 - 4$ R.S. $= 2 \times 5 + 21$
$$= 35 - 4 \qquad\qquad\qquad = 10 + 21$$
$$= 31 \qquad\qquad\qquad\quad = 31$$

In the worked examples of the text, the authorities which are most significant in the development are given in brackets. When writing a solution you should think the authorities for the steps, but it is not necessary to include them in your solution.

In this text it is understood that the variables are real numbers unless otherwise specified. Thus, $\{x \mid 3x + 2 = 8, x \in R\}$ is written $\{x \mid 3x + 2 = 8\}$.

Write solutions to the following problems and compare them with those on page 440. In question 1 show that the steps are reversible, and in question 2 and 3 verify by substitution.

1. Solve $(10x + 6) - (11 - 15x) = 20x$.

2. Find $\{x \mid 8x + (x - 7) + 3 = 2x - (3 + x)\}$.

3. Find the solution set defined by
$3(x - 5) - 2(3 + 4x) = 8 - 6(2x - 1)$.

2·2 Alternative form of solution. In the example, page 55, the application of the addition, subtraction, and division properties of the equality relation allowed the conclusion:

$$\text{If } 7x - 4 = 2x + 21, \text{ then } x = 5.$$

If only the addition, subtraction, multiplication, and division properties of the equality relation are used in such a development, then each step is reversible and the converse proposition

$$\text{if } x = 5, \text{ then } 7x - 4 = 2x + 21$$

is also true, and the two equations are equivalent.

The statement

$$7x - 4 = 2x + 21 \text{ if and only if } x = 5$$

is the mathematical way of stating the two converse propositions in one sentence and implies the equivalence of the two equations.

The abbreviation "iff" is often used to imply the phrase "if and only if".

The following form of solution to the above equation implies that at each step the reversibility of the step has been considered and is possible.

$$
\begin{aligned}
&& 7x - 4 &= 2x + 21 \\
\text{iff} && 7x &= 2x + 25 \\
\text{iff} && 7x - 2x &= 25 \\
\text{iff} && 5x &= 25 && (D \text{ is reversible.}) \\
\text{iff} && x &= 5
\end{aligned}
$$

$\therefore$ the solution set is $\{5\}$.

Although verification by substitution is not an integral part of the solution, it does provide a check against possible mechanical errors.

Unless otherwise stated, the number symbols in the exercises which follow represent real numbers.

Exercise 2-1

(A)

In each of the following, the given equations are equivalent. State how each equation has been obtained from the preceding equation:

1. $7x = 9x + 8, -2x = 8, x = -4$

2. $6x - 5 = 2x + 7, 4x = 12, x = 3$

3. $4 - \dfrac{x}{3} = 5, -\dfrac{x}{3} = 1, x = -3$

4. $\dfrac{x}{2} - 2 = \dfrac{x}{3}, 3x - 12 = 2x, x = 12$

Form equivalent equations for each of the following by performing the indicated operation:

5. $2x + 8 = 0$, addition of -8 **6.** $\frac{2}{3}x = 8$, division by $\frac{2}{3}$

7. $\dfrac{x}{5} + \dfrac{x}{3} = 2\frac{1}{3}$, multiplication by 15

8. $2x = 3x - 7$, addition of $-3x$

9. $3x - 7 = 4x + 2$, subtraction of $4x - 7$

Solve the following equations orally, stating the equivalent equations formed in the process and the authority for each statement:

10. $3x + 4 = 28$ **11.** $5y = 2y + 12$

12. $7 - 3x = 13$ **13.** $2(2x + 1) = 2$

14. $y + 5 = 2 - 2y$ **15.** $11m + 2 = 26 + 7m$

16. $4a - a = 6 - a$ **17.** $5x + 3 = 2x + 9$

18. $2y - 7 = -(y - 1)$ **19.** $3(x + 2) = 2x - 6$

(B)

Solve and verify:

20. $3a - 2 - (a + 1) = 5$ **21.** $y - 7 = 3 - (3y + 2)$

22. $x^2 + x + 4 = x(x + 2)$ **23.** $(x-1)(2x+1) = (2x+3)(x-3)$

Solve:

24. $6x - (x - 3) - 11 = x + 5 - (x - 7)$

25. $4(3x + 6) - 14 = 5(2x - 4)$

26. $3(y - 10) = -5(3y - 4) - 14$

27. $-12y + 6(y + 1) = 3 - 4(2y + 1)$

28. $5x - (3x - 7) + 2x - (2x - 3) = 14$

29. $2(x + 1) - 2(x^2 - 4x + 4) = 16 - 2x^2 - x$

Find the solution set defined by each of the following:

30. $10(2y - 4) - 6(3y + 1) = 5 + 5(1 - y)$

31. $7x + 7(4 + x) - 6(3 + 4x) = 0$

32. Find $\{x \mid 6x - 4(5x + 9) = 4(2x - 9)\}$.

33. Find $\{x \mid 352 - 11(x - 9) = 4x - 44\}$.

2·3 Equations with fractional coefficients.

Write solutions to the following problems; compare them with those on page 440.

1. Solve $\frac{1}{3}(2x - 1) - \frac{1}{5}(4x - 6) = \frac{7}{15}$.

2. Find $\left\{ x \mid \dfrac{x - 2}{2} + \dfrac{x + 3}{3} = \dfrac{3x + 4}{4} - 2 \right\}$ and verify.

2·4 Equations involving products.

Write a solution to the following problem and compare it with that on page 441.

1. Find $\{x \mid 3(x + 2)(x - 1) - 2(x - 4)^2 = x^2 + 19, x \in I\}$; verify.

Exercise 2-2

(A)

Solve:

1. $\frac{2}{3}x = -4$ **2.** $\frac{1}{2}y = 6$ **3.** $-\frac{3}{2}m = 3$

4. $1\frac{2}{13}a = 0$ **5.** $\frac{1}{4}x = -1$ **6.** $\frac{3}{5}y = 9$

7. $\dfrac{x}{4} = -\dfrac{2}{3}$ **8.** $\dfrac{3x}{5} = \dfrac{8}{3}$ **9.** $\frac{1}{2}x + \frac{3}{4}x = 1$

(B)

Solve:

10. $\frac{1}{2}x + \frac{1}{3}x = 10$ **11.** $\dfrac{x}{2} - 2 = \frac{2}{3}x - 1$

12. $\frac{1}{4}(x - 5) - \frac{1}{3}(2x + 1) = 3$ **13.** $\frac{1}{2}x - \frac{1}{4} = \dfrac{x}{4} + \dfrac{3}{2}$

14. $\dfrac{2x - 4}{3} - \dfrac{3x + 1}{5} = \dfrac{2 - x}{6}$ **15.** $\dfrac{x + 5}{2} + \dfrac{3x - 3}{8} + 4 = 0$

16. $2(x - 1)(x - 3) + 4 = (2x - 1)(x + 3)$

17. $(x - 1)^2 - (x + 1)^2 = 4$

18. $(a - 5)^2 + 3(a + 2)^2 = 4(a^2 - 1) - 9$

19. $9y(y + 3) - (3y - 1)^2 = 32$

20. $3(x - 1)^2 - 3(x^2 - 1) = x - 15$

Solve and verify:

21. $\frac{1}{4}(2x - 2) - \frac{1}{2}(3x + 1) = \frac{1}{6}(x + 1)$

22. $\dfrac{2x - 2}{8} - \dfrac{5x + 2}{6} = -\dfrac{8x - 1}{9} + \dfrac{3x + 5}{12}$

23. $\dfrac{a - 10}{5} + \dfrac{a - 8}{6} - \dfrac{a - 5}{10} = \dfrac{a - 11}{3} - \dfrac{5}{2}$

24. $(2x - 1)(3x + 2) = 15 + (3x - 1)(2x + 5)$

25. $r + 7 + 2(2r - 1)^2 = (1 - 2r)(1 - 4r)$

26. $(3m - 1)(3m + 1) - (3m + 2)^2 = 7$

Find the solution set defined by each of the following:

27. $\frac{1}{3}(x + 1) - \frac{1}{2}(x - 1) = \frac{1}{4}(2x - 1) - \frac{1}{6}(3x - 1)$

28. $\dfrac{2(x + 2)}{3} - \dfrac{3(x - 7)}{7} = 6$

29. $(5x + 7)(6x - 2) - 15x(x - 3) = 35 + 15x^2$

Find:

30. $\left\{ x \mid \frac{3}{16}(x - 1) - \frac{5}{12}(x - 4) = \frac{2}{5}(x - 6) + \frac{5}{48} \right\}$

31. $\left\{ y \mid (2y - 3)^2 + 3(y + 5) = 4(y + 6)(y + 1) \right\}$

32. $\left\{ x \mid \dfrac{(x + 1)^2}{3} - \dfrac{(x + 2)^2}{2} = \dfrac{2 - x^2}{6} \right\}.$

2·5 Graphs of solution sets.

Example 1. Find the solution set defined by
$$(2x - 7)(3x + 1) = 7 + 6(x - 3)^2.$$
Verify and draw the graph of the solution set.

Solution. $(2x - 7)(3x + 1) = 7 + 6(x - 3)^2$

$\therefore\ 6x^2 - 19x - 7 = 7 + 6(x^2 - 6x + 9)$ *(D)*

$\therefore\ 6x^2 - 19x - 7 = 7 + 6x^2 - 36x + 54$ *(D)*

$\therefore\ 17x = 68$

$\therefore\ x = 4$ (Division property)

The solution set is $\{4\}$.

Verification.   L.S. $= (2x - 7)(3x + 1)$ R.S. $= 7 + 6(x - 3)^2$
                       $= (1)(13)$ $= 7 + 6(1)^2$
                       $= 13$ $= 13$

The graph is the point with coordinate 4 in *Fig. 2-1.*

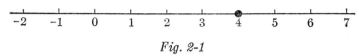

Fig. 2-1

Example 2. Determine the solution set defined by
$(2x - 7)(3x + 1) \neq 7 + 6(x - 3)^2$ and draw its graph.

Solution. $\{x \mid (2x - 7)(3x + 1) = 7 + 6(x - 3)^2\} = \{4\}$
                   $\therefore \; \{x \mid (2x - 7)(3x + 1) \neq 7 + 6(x - 3)^2\} = \{x \mid x \neq 4\}$

Thus the graph of $\{x \mid (2x - 7)(3x + 1) \neq 7 + 6(x - 3)^2\}$ includes all
points on the real number line except the point with coordinate 4, *Fig. 2-2.*

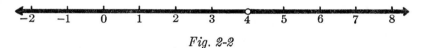

Fig. 2-2

The continuous nature of the graph is indicated by the solid line.
The arrows indicate that the graph extends indefinitely.

Example 3. Find $\left\{x \mid \dfrac{3x - 4}{2} - \dfrac{x - 6}{4} \neq \dfrac{5x}{6} - 3, x \in I\right\}$ and draw its graph.

Solution. To solve this inequation, first solve the equality

$$\frac{3x - 4}{2} - \frac{x - 6}{4} = \frac{5x}{6} - 3 .$$

Multiply each term by 12:   (L.C.D.)
$\therefore \; 6(3x - 4) - 3(x - 6) = 2(5x) - 36$ (Multiplication property)
$\therefore \; 18x - 24 - 3x + 18 = 10x - 36$ (D)
$\therefore \; 5x = -30$
$\therefore \; x = -6$ (Division property)

$$\therefore \left\{x \mid \frac{3x - 4}{2} - \frac{x - 6}{4} = \frac{5x}{6} - 3, x \in I\right\} = \{-6\}$$

$$\therefore \left\{x \mid \frac{3x - 4}{2} - \frac{x - 6}{4} \neq \frac{5x}{6} - 3, x \in I\right\} = \{\ldots, -8, -7, -5, -4, \ldots\}$$

The graph is shown in *Fig. 2-3.*

Fig. 2-3

Exercise 2-3

(A)

Use set-builder notation to define the sets illustrated by each of the following graphs:

1.

2.

3.

4.

5.

6.

7.

8.

(B)

Find the solution set defined by each of the following and draw its graph:

9. $5(5 - 2x) - 3(8 - 2x) = 0$

10. $5(x - 3) - 21 + 7(x - 6) = 3(x - 8),\ x \in N$

11. $\dfrac{x + 11}{6} - \dfrac{4 - x}{3} \neq -1,\ x \in I$

12. $\dfrac{x - 1}{10} - \dfrac{2 - x}{5} - \dfrac{5 - x}{2} = 0$

13. $5x + 12 \neq [(x - 3) - (5x - 4)] - 7,\ x \in I$

14. $(3x + 8)(x - 5) \neq (x - 4)(3x - 2) + 8,\ x \in I$

15. $\dfrac{-7x}{8} + \frac{1}{6}x \neq \frac{5}{6} - \frac{1}{2}x$

16. $-8 \neq 2(x + 3)(x + 1) - (2x + 1)(x + 5),\ x \in N$

17. $\dfrac{4 - 3x}{8} + x \neq \dfrac{x - 5}{4} - 2,\ x \in N$

18. $3(x - 4)^2 - 2(x - 2)^2 \neq x^2 - 8$
    (i) for $x \in R$ (ii) for $x \in I$ (iii) for $x \in N$

2·6 The inequality relation. The solving of equations is based on the properties of the equality relation outlined in section 2·1.

The solving of inequations, such as
$$3x - 12 > 0, \; x \in R,$$
is based on properties of the *inequality relation*: that is, *greater than*, $>$, or *less than*, $<$, for the set of numbers involved.

The definition of inequality (order) for real numbers and the trichotomy and transitive properties are as follows.

(i) *Definition of inequality:*

If a, $b \in R$ and $a > b$, then

$a - b$ is a positive real number, or

$a = b + c$ where c is a positive real number (i.e. $c \in {}^+R$).

(ii) *Trichotomy property:*

If a, $b \in R$, then $a < b$ or $a = b$ or $a > b$.

(iii) *Transitive property:*

If a, b, $c \in R$ and $a > b$ and $b > c$, then $a > c$.

Further properties of the inequality relation for real numbers may be obtained by examining the following three cases.

a. *Addition (or subtraction) of the same real number to (or from) each member of an inequality.*

Examples.

(i) $5 > 3$

If 3 is added to each side:

L.S. $= 5 + 3$ R.S. $= 3 + 3$

$\qquad = 8 \qquad\qquad = 6$

But $8 > 6$

$\therefore \; 5 + 3 > 3 + 3$

(ii) $-2 > -6$

If -3 is added to each side:

L.S. $= -2 + (-3)$ R.S. $= -6 + (-3)$

$\qquad = -5 \qquad\qquad = -9$

But $-5 > -9$

$\therefore \; -2 + (-3) > -6 + (-3)$

(iii) $8 > 4$

If 3 is subtracted from each side:

L.S. $= 8 - 3$ R.S. $= 4 - 3$

$\qquad = 5 \qquad\qquad = 1$

But $5 > 1$

$\therefore \; 8 - 3 > 4 - 3$

(iv) $6 > -2$

If -3 is subtracted from each side:

L.S. $= 6 - (-3)$ R.S. $= (-2) - (-3)$

$\qquad = 9 \qquad\qquad = 1$

But $9 > 1$

$\therefore \; 6 - (-3) > -2 - (-3)$

These examples suggest the following theorem.

THEOREM. *The sense of an inequality is not changed if the same real number is added to, or subtracted from, each member.*

That is, if a, b, $c \in R$ and $a > b$, then

(i) $a + c > b + c$ (Addition property)

(ii) $a - c > b - c$.   (Subtraction property)

Proof of the theorem (supplementary).

Given: $a, b, c \in R$ and $a > b$

Prove: (i) $a + c > b + c$ (Addition property)

(ii) $a - c > b - c$ (Subtraction property)

Proof: $a > b$

$a = b + d, d \in {}^+R$	(Definition)
$a + c = b + d + c$	(Equality addition property)
$a + c = (b + c) + d$	(CA) (AA)
$a + c > b + c$	(Definition)
Similarly, $a - c = b + d - c$	(Equality subtraction property)
$a - c = (b - c) + d$	(CA) (AA)
$a - c > b - c$	(Definition)

Since each step in the proof is reversible, the converse theorem is also true.

b. *Multiplication (or division) of each member of an inequality by a positive real number.*

Examples.

(i) $5 > 3$

If each side is multiplied by 3:

L.S. $= 5 \times 3$ R.S. $= 3 \times 3$
$= 15$ $= 9$

But $15 > 9$

$\therefore\ 5 \times 3 > 3 \times 3$

(ii) $-2 > -6$

If each side is multiplied by 3:

L.S. $= (-2)(3)$ R.S. $= (-6)(3)$
$= -6$ $= -18$

But $-6 > -18$

$\therefore\ (-2)(3) > (-6)(3)$

(iii) $8 > 4$

If each side is divided by 3:

L.S. $= \dfrac{8}{3}$ R.S. $= \dfrac{4}{3}$

But $\dfrac{8}{3} > \dfrac{4}{3}$

$\therefore\ 8 \div 3 > 4 \div 3$

(iv) $6 > -2$

If each side is divided by 3:

L.S. $= \dfrac{6}{3}$ R.S. $= \dfrac{-2}{3}$

But $\dfrac{6}{3} > \dfrac{-2}{3}$

$\therefore\ 6 \div 3 > (-2) \div 3$

These examples suggest the following theorem.

THEOREM. *The sense of an inequality is not changed if each member is multiplied, or divided, by the same positive real number.*

That is, if $a, b, c \in R$ and $c > 0$ (i.e. $c \in {}^+R$) and $a > b$, then

(i) $ac > bc$ (Multiplication property)

(ii) $a \div c > b \div c$.   (Division property)

Proof of the theorem (supplementary).

Given: $a, b \in R, c \in {}^{+}R$ and $a > b$

Prove: (i) $ac > bc$ (ii) $\dfrac{a}{c} > \dfrac{b}{c}$

Proof: $\because \; a > b$

$\therefore \; a = b + d, d \in {}^{+}R$ (Definition)

$\therefore \; ac = (b + d)c$ (Equality multiplication property)

$\therefore \; ac = bc + dc$ (D)

But $dc \in {}^{+}R$

$\therefore \; ac > bc$ (Definition)

Similarly, $\dfrac{a}{c} = \dfrac{b + d}{c}$ (Equality division property)

$\therefore \; \dfrac{a}{c} = \dfrac{b}{c} + \dfrac{d}{c}$ (Definition)

$\therefore \; \dfrac{a}{c} > \dfrac{b}{c} \; \because \; \dfrac{d}{c} \in {}^{+}R$ (Definition)

Since the steps in the proof are reversible, the converse theorem is true.

c. *Multiplication (or division) of each member of an inequality by a negative real number.*

Examples.

(i) $5 > 3$

If each side is multiplied by -3:

L.S. $= 5 \times (-3)$ R.S. $= 3 \times (-3)$

$\qquad = -15 \qquad\qquad = -9$

But $-15 < -9$

$\therefore \; 5 \times (-3) < 3 \times (-3)$

(ii) $-2 > -6$

If each side is multiplied by -3:

L.S. $= (-2)(-3)$ R.S. $= (-6)(-3)$

$\qquad = +6 \qquad\qquad = +18$

But $(+6) < (+18)$

$\therefore \; (-2) \times (-3) < (-6)(-18)$

(iii) $8 > 4$

If each side is divided by -3:

L.S. $= \dfrac{8}{-3}$ R.S. $= \dfrac{4}{-3}$

$\qquad = -\dfrac{8}{3} \qquad\qquad = -\dfrac{4}{3}$

But $-\dfrac{8}{3} < -\dfrac{4}{3}$

$\therefore \; 8 \div (-3) < 4 \div (-3)$

(iv) $6 > -2$

If each side is divided by -3:

L.S. $= \dfrac{6}{-3}$ R.S. $= \dfrac{-2}{-3}$

$\qquad = -\dfrac{6}{3} \qquad\qquad = \dfrac{2}{3}$

But $-\dfrac{6}{3} < \dfrac{2}{3}$

$\therefore \; 6 \div (-3) < (-2) \div (-3)$

These examples suggest the following theorem.

THEOREM. *The sense of an inequality is reversed if each member is multiplied, or divided, by the same negative real number.*

That is, if $a, b, c \in R$ and $c < 0$ (i.e. $c \in {}^{-}R$), and $a > b$, then

      (i) $ac < bc$ (Multiplication property)

      (ii) $a \div c < b \div c$.   (Division property)

Proof of the theorem (supplementary).

Given: $a, b \in R$, $c \in {}^{-}R$ and $a > b$

Prove: (i) $ac < bc$ (ii) $\dfrac{a}{c} < \dfrac{b}{c}$

Proof: $\because$ $a > b$

        $\therefore$ $a = b + d, d \in {}^{+}R$ (Definition)

        $\therefore$ $ac = (b + d)c$ (Equality multiplication property)

        $\therefore$ $ac = bc + dc$ (D)

But $dc \in {}^{-}R$

        $\therefore$ $ac < bc$ (Definition)

Similarly, $\dfrac{a}{c} = \dfrac{b + d}{c}$ (Equality division property)

        $\therefore$ $\dfrac{a}{c} = \dfrac{b}{c} + \dfrac{d}{c}$ (Definition)

But $\dfrac{d}{c} \in {}^{-}R$

        $\therefore$ $\dfrac{a}{c} < \dfrac{b}{c}$ (Definition)

Since the steps in the proof are reversible, the converse theorem is true.

2.7 Summary of the properties of the inequality relation for real numbers used in forming equivalent inequations.

(a) If $a, b \in R$ and $a > b$, then
$$a = b + d, \; d \in {}^{+}R .$$

(b) If $a, b, c \in R$ and $a > b$, then

      (i) $a + c > b + c$ (Addition property)

      (ii) $a - c > b - c$ (Subtraction property)

     (iii) $\left. \begin{array}{l} ac > bc \text{ if } c \in {}^{+}R \\ ac < bc \text{ if } c \in {}^{-}R \end{array} \right\}$ (Multiplication property)

     (iv) $\left. \begin{array}{l} \dfrac{a}{c} > \dfrac{b}{c} \text{ if } c \in {}^{+}R \\[2mm] \dfrac{a}{c} < \dfrac{b}{c} \text{ if } c \in {}^{-}R . \end{array} \right\}$ (Division property)

(c) If $a, b, c \in R$, then $a < b$ or $a = b$ or $a > b$.   (Trichotomy property)

(d) If $a, b \in R$, then if $a > b$ and $b > c$ then $a > c$.   (Transitive property)

2·8 **Solution of inequations.** The pattern of solution of inequations is parallel to that of equations except that the properties of the inequality relation must be used. It is a process of writing simpler and simpler equivalent inequations based on the proper number properties. For example:

$$\text{if} \quad 3x - 12 > 0$$

(add 12 to each side)	$3x > 12$	(Addition property)
(divide each side by 3)	$x > 4$	(Division property)

This discussion discloses the following:

$$\text{if } 3x - 12 > 0, \quad \text{then } x > 4 .$$

The converse statement,

$$\text{if } x > 4, \quad \text{then } 3x - 12 > 0 ,$$

is proved by showing that the steps of the first development are reversible as follows:

$$\text{if} \quad x > 4$$

(multiply each side by 3)	$3x > 12$	(Multiplication property)
(subtract 12 from each side)	$3x - 12 > 0$	(Subtraction property)

It has now been shown that $3x - 12 > 0$ and $x > 4$ are *equivalent inequations*, and therefore the solution set is $\{x \mid x > 4\}$.

When the properties of the inequality relation listed in section 2·7 are applied to determine the roots or the solution set of an inequation of the first degree in one variable, the steps are always reversible. Thus, it is not necessary to write the second part of the solution. The solution set may be checked or verified by substitution as follows.

Verification.

Since $x > 4$, let $x = 4 + d$ where $d \in {}^+R$.

L.S. $= 3(4 + d) - 12$ R.S. $= 0$
      $= 12 + 3d - 12$
      $= 3d$ (a positive number)

$\therefore$ for all $x > 4$,   L.S. is greater than zero, or $3x - 12 > 0$.

$\therefore$ the solution set is $\{x \mid x > 4\}$.

Example Find the solution set defined by $-12 - 3x > 2x + 3$ and draw its graph.

Solution. $-12 - 3x > 2x + 8$

$\therefore \quad -3x - 2x > 8 + 12$ (Addition and subtraction properties)

$\therefore \quad -5x > 20$ (D)

$\therefore \quad x < -4$ (Division property)

The solution set is $\{x \mid x < -4\}$.

Note that in applying the division property that division by -5 has reversed the sense of the inequality.

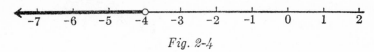

Fig. 2-4

Write solutions to the following problems and compare your solutions with those on page 441.

1. Find $\{x \mid 21 - 8x \leqq 9 - 5x\}$ and draw its graph.

2. Find the solution set defined by
$3(-4 - y) \geqq 2(2y + 3) - 11,\ y \in I$ and draw its graph.

Exercise 2-4

(A)

Solve:

1. $x + 4 > 7$	**2.** $x + 1 < 4$	**3.** $5x < 15$
4. $2x > 8$	**5.** $4x < -12$	**6.** $-3x > 9$
7. $x - 3 \leqq 5$	**8.** $x + 4 \geqq -3$	**9.** $2x + 1 < 4$
10. $4x > 3x - 2$	**11.** $3x > 4x - 2$	**12.** $4x < -2 + 4x$

Find:

13. $\{x \mid 3x > 15\}$ **14.** $\{x \mid 3x < 13\}$
15. $\{x \mid x + 6 \geqq 10\}$ **16.** $\{x \mid 3x - 4 \leqq 2x\}$
17. $\{x \mid 2x > 4x - 3\}$ **18.** $\{x \mid -4x \leqq -16\}$

(B)

Solve:

19. $x - 5 \leqq 8$ **20.** $6 = 5 + x$ **21.** $4 > 3 + x$
22. $4x - 2 > 6$ **23.** $4y - 1\frac{4}{5} = y$ **24.** $7x + 2 \leqq -12$
25. $3 + 5x \geqq 7x - 7$ **26.** $10x - 30 < 20 - 15x$
27. $4 - (8y - 12) \leqq 2y + 16$ **28.** $4(x - 3) - 13 > 6(x - 2)$
29. $(6x - 2) + 10 - (8x + 6) > 4x + 1 - 2(x - 4)$

Find the solution set defined by each of the following and draw its graph:

30. $5x + 2x \geqq 18 - 2x,\ x \in I$ **31.** $7x + 5 \leqq 3x - 7,\ x \in I$
32. $3(3y - 3) > 10y + 10$
33. $10x + 16 \geqq 6(x + 2) + 2x$
34. $3(x - 2) - 2(x + 1) + (3 + x) \leqq 0$
35. $5(-x + 2) - 2(1 - 2x) < 4 + 2x$
36. $5(x - 3) + 9 > 3(x - 2),\ x \in I$

37. $3(2x - 5) - 5(2x + 1) \geq -3$

38. $10y - 5(y - 4) \geq 7y + 3(9 - y),\ y \in N$

39. $(x - 5)(x + 5) - x(x - 1) < -x + 3$

40. $x(x - 5) \leq (x + 4)(x - 5)$

Find:

41. $\{x \mid 4x - 6 \geq 5x - 13\}$

42. $\{x \mid 2(3x - 5) \geq 3 - 4(x + 2)\}$

43. $\{y \mid (2y - 1)(y - 2) + 2y(y + 2) \geq y(4y - 2)\}$

2·9 Inequations involving products and fractional coefficients. The questions in Exercise 2-5 are more difficult than those of the previous exercise because the expressions involved require more simplification.

Write solutions to the following problems and compare them with those on page 442.

1. Solve $2x^2 \geq 2(2x - 3)^2 - 3(2x - 5)(x + 1)$.

2. Find $\left\{ x \mid 1 - \dfrac{1 - 2x}{4} > \dfrac{x - 2}{6},\ x \in I \right\}$ and draw the graph of the solution set.

Exercise 2-5

(B)

Solve each of the following:

1. $\dfrac{2x + 1}{5} - 6 < \dfrac{1 - 8x}{3}$

2. $\dfrac{13}{3} - \dfrac{5y + 3}{6} > \dfrac{3y - 5}{3}$

3. $(2x + 1)^2 - 2(x - 2)^2 > 2x^2 + 1$

4. $2(3x + 4)^2 - 11x \geq 4(x + 2)(2x - 1) - 5x(3 - 2x)$

Find the solution set defined by each of the following and draw the graph:

5. $4(3y + 2) - 5(2y - 1) - 2[2(y + 2) - 3(y - 1) - 6] > 0$

6. $(y + 1)(y + 2) - 16 - (y + 4)(y - 3) > 0,\ y \in I$

7. $\dfrac{x - 3}{2} - (x - 5) - \dfrac{x - 7}{5} > 0,\ x \in N$

8. $2y(y + 4) - 3(y - 2)(y + 2) \leq -(y - 2)^2,\ y \in I$

9. $4(1 - x)(x + 2) - 2x(3x - 5) \geq 2x(x - 1) - 3(2x - 1)^2$

10. $\dfrac{x + 1}{7} - \dfrac{x - 3}{6} - \dfrac{2}{3} \neq 0,\ x \in I$

Find:

11. $\{y \mid 3[1 - y(4y - 1)] \leqq - (3y + 2)(4y - 3)\}$

12. $\left\{x \mid \dfrac{1 - 2x}{2} < \dfrac{2x - 4}{5} - x\right\}$

13. $\left\{x \mid \dfrac{x + 2}{3} + \dfrac{x + 1}{2} - \dfrac{x + 6}{4} \leqq 6\frac{2}{3}\right\}$

14. $\{a \mid 2(a - 3)(a + 1) - 3a(a + 2) < - 20 - a^2\}$

2·10 Graphs of sets defined by compound sentences.   In Review *A* the intersection and union of sets were discussed. If *A* and *B* are two sets of objects, then:

(a) *A* and *B*, $(A \cap B)$. represents the intersection set of *A* and *B*. It contains those elements which are in both *A* and *B*.

(b) *A* or *B*, $(A \cup B)$, represents the union set of *A* and *B*. It contains the elements in at least one of *A* and *B*.

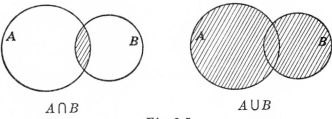

$A \cap B$ $A \cup B$

Fig. 2-5

In the following examples, sets are defined by algebraic sentences or conditions connected by *and* or *or*, implying the intersection and union, respectively, of the sets defined by the individual sentences or conditions.

Example 1. Draw the graph of $\{x \mid 4x - 5 < 7 \text{ and } 2x + 1 > - 3\}$.

Solution. $\{x \mid 4x - 5 < 7 \text{ and } 2x + 1 > - 3\}$ is the intersection set of the two sets $A = \{x \mid 4x - 5 < 7\}$, $B = \{x \mid 2x + 1 > - 3\}$.

$$A \cap B = \{x \mid 4x - 5 < 7\} \cap \{x \mid 2x + 1 > - 3\}$$

Solving the two defining sentences:

$$4x - 5 < 7 \qquad\qquad\qquad 2x + 1 > - 3$$
$$\therefore\ 4x < 12 \qquad\qquad\qquad \therefore\ 2x > - 4$$
$$\therefore\ \ x < 3 \qquad\qquad\qquad \therefore\ \ x > - 2$$
$$A = \{x \mid x < 3\} \qquad\qquad B = \{x \mid x > - 2\}$$

The graphs of (i) *A* (ii) *B* and (iii) $A \cap B$ are shown in *Fig. 2-6.*

(i)
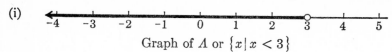
Graph of A or $\{x \mid x < 3\}$

(ii)
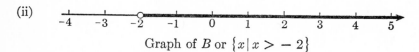
Graph of B or $\{x \mid x > -2\}$

(iii)
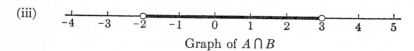
Graph of $A \cap B$

Fig. 2-6

Example 2. Draw the graph of $\{x \mid 3x + 5 \leqq 2 \text{ or } 5x + 2 \geqq 17\}$.

Solution. $\{x \mid 3x + 5 \leqq 2 \text{ or } 5x + 2 \geqq 17\}$ is the union set of the two sets $A = \{x \mid 3x + 5 \leqq 2\}$, $B = \{x \mid 5x + 2 \geqq 17\}$.

$A \cup B = \{x \mid 3x + 5 \leqq 2\} \cup \{x \mid 5x + 2 \geqq 17\}$

Solving the two defining sentences:

$$3x + 5 \leqq 2 \qquad\qquad\qquad 5x + 2 \geqq 17$$
$$\therefore 3x \leqq -3 \qquad\qquad\qquad \therefore 5x \geqq 15$$
$$\therefore x \leqq -1 \qquad\qquad\qquad \therefore x \geqq 3$$
$$A = \{x \mid x \leqq -1\} \qquad\qquad B = \{x \mid x \geqq 3\}$$

The graphs of (i) A (ii) B (iii) $A \cup B$ are shown in *Fig. 2-7*.

(i)
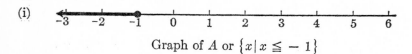
Graph of A or $\{x \mid x \leqq -1\}$

(ii)
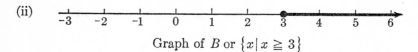
Graph of B or $\{x \mid x \geqq 3\}$

(iii)
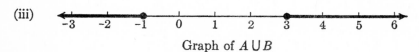
Graph of $A \cup B$

Fig. 2-7

Exercise 2-6

(A)

List the members of the following sets where $x \in I$:

1. $\{x \mid x > -2 \text{ and } x < 2\}$
2. $\{x \mid x \leq -3 \text{ and } x \geq -6\}$
3. $\{x \mid x > -2 \text{ or } x < 2\}$
4. $\{x \mid x = -1 \text{ or } x < -1\}$
5. $\{x \mid x < -4\} \cap \{x \mid x > -7\}$
6. $\{x \mid x \leq -4\} \cup \{x \mid x \leq -7\}$
7. $\{x \mid x < -4\} \cap \{x \mid x < -7\}$
8. $\{x \mid x \neq -3\} \cup \{x \mid x < 0\}$

(B)

Draw the graph of each of the following sets:

9. $\{x \mid 3x - 1 \leq 5\}$ and $\{x \mid 2x + 1 \geq -1\}$
10. $\{x \mid 3(x - 1) \geq 2x - 3\}$ and $\{x \mid 5x - 4 \leq 2x - 1\}$
11. $\{x \mid 4x + 5 \geq 5x + 6\}$ or $\{x \mid 2x - 3 > 1\}$
12. $\{x \mid 2(5x + 2) - (5x + 9) < 0\}$ or $\{x \mid 9x - 5(x + 2) = 2\}$
13. $\{x \mid -5(x - 2) > 0\} \cap \{x \mid 3(2 - x) \leq 15\}$
14. $\{x \mid 3(4x - 5) - 5(2x + 1) < -3x\} \cup \{x \mid 4(3x + 2) < 4x\}$
15. $\{x \mid 8 - (x + 1) \neq 4 + (5 - 2x), x \in I\} \cup$
    $\{x \mid 9x - 4 \geq 2x + 17, x \in I\}$
16. $\{x \mid 10 + 7x < 2(3x + 4), x \in I\} \cap \{x \mid 3(x - 1) \neq -12, x \in I\}$
17. $\{x \mid -x > 1 \text{ and } -6 < x\}$ or $\{x \mid -x < -1 \text{ and } 3 > x\}$
18. $\{x \mid -x \not< -2 \text{ and } -x \geq -5, x \in I\}$ and
    $\{x \mid -x \leq 2 \text{ and } x \neq 0, x \in I\}$

(C)

Draw the graph of each of the following sets:

19. $\{x \mid (2x-3)^2 \leq 4(x-2)^2 + 1 \text{ or } x(3x-1) - (3x-1)(x+2) \leq -22\}$
20. $\{x \mid (x - 5)(x - 4) > (x - 2)(x - 6) \text{ and } 4x^2 - (2x - 1)^2 + 5 > 0\}$
21. $\left\{x \mid \dfrac{x + 2}{2} + \dfrac{x + 4}{3} \geq x + 1, x \in I\right\} \cap \left\{x \mid \dfrac{x + 3}{2} + 8 \leq x + 7, x \in I\right\}$
22. $\{x \mid (x + 1)(3x - 7) + 5 > 3x(x - 3) + 8, x \in I\} \cup$
    $\{x \mid (x - 1)(3x - 5) + 32 > 3(x - 3)^2, x \in I\}$

2·11 The quadratic equation. If $a, b \in R$ and $a = 0$ or $b = 0$, then $a \cdot b = 0$.

Thus, if $x + 2 = 0$ or $x - 3 = 0$, then

$$(x + 2)(x - 3) = 0 \text{ and } x^2 - x - 6 = 0.$$

The equation $(x + 2)(x - 3) = 0$ (or $x^2 - x - 6 = 0$) is called the *joint equation* of the equations $x + 2 = 0$ and $x - 3 = 0$.

Also if $a, b \in R$ and $ab = 0$, then $a = 0$ or $b = 0$.

Thus, if $x^2 - x - 6 = 0$, or $(x + 2)(x - 3) = 0$, then $x + 2 = 0$ or $x - 3 = 0$.

Thus, the statements

(i) $x + 2 = 0$ or $x - 3 = 0$
(ii) $(x + 2)(x - 3) = 0$
(iii) $x^2 - x - 6 = 0$

are equivalent.

Since $x + 2 = 0$ or $x - 3 = 0$ is equivalent to

$$x = -2 \quad \text{or } x = 3$$

∴ the solution set of the equation $x^2 - x + 6 = 0$ is $\{-2, 3\}$.

The equations $x^2 - x + 6 = 0$ and $(x + 2)(x - 3) = 0$ are called *quadratic equations in one variable* since the highest power in which the variable appears is the second.

Other examples of quadratic equations are:

$$3b^2 - 4 = 0, \quad 7a^2 - 2a = 0, \quad \sqrt{3}y^2 - \sqrt{2}y + 3.14 = 0$$

Example. By factoring, solve $4x^2 - 25 = 0$.

Solution.

$$4x^2 - 25 = 0$$
$$\therefore (2x - 5)(2x + 5) = 0$$
$$\therefore 2x - 5 = 0 \text{ or } 2x + 5 = 0$$
$$\therefore x = \frac{5}{2} \quad \bigg| \quad x = -\frac{5}{2}$$

The solution set is $\left\{ \frac{5}{2}, -\frac{5}{2} \right\}$.

Verification.

L.S. $= 4\left(\dfrac{5}{2}\right)^2 - 25$ R.S. $= 0$ $\quad\bigg|\quad$ L.S. $= 4\left(-\dfrac{5}{2}\right)^2 - 25$ R.S. $= 0$

$= 25 - 25$ $\qquad\qquad\qquad\quad\bigg|\quad = 25 - 25$

$= 0$ $\qquad\qquad\qquad\qquad\qquad\bigg|\quad = 0$

Write solutions for the following problems and compare them with those on page 442.

1. Solve $2x^2 + 3x - 2 = 0$ and verify.

2. Solve $x^2 - 6 = x$.

Exercise 2-7

(A)

By factoring, state an equivalent quadratic equation for each of the following:

1. $4a^2 - 25 = 0$

2. $y^2 - y - 2 = 0$

3. $x^2 - x - 12 = 0$

4. $b^2 - 6b + 9 = 0$

5. $3y^2 + 2y - 1 = 0$

6. $2x^2 - 8 = 0$

(B)

Solve and verify:

7. $x^2 - x - 20 = 0$

8. $a^2 + 15 = 8a$

9. $y^2 = 3y + 10$

10. $p^2 - 100 = 0$

11. $x^2 - \dfrac{9}{16} = 0$

12. $2x^2 - 18x = 0$

13. $2c^2 + 3c - 5 = 0$

14. $m^2 - 16m + 64 = 0$

15. $5y^2 - 5y = 280$

16. $3t^2 - 14 = t$

17. $7b^2 = 343$

18. $7x^2 = -36x - 5$

19. $6y^2 = 5y + 6$

20. $5 - 14x = 3x^2$

21. $6a^2 - 5 = 7a$

22. $21y^2 = 4(2y + 1)$

23. $3p^2 - 4 = 7p + 2$

24. $6x^2 + 6 = 13x$

25. $4y^2 + 12y = 27$

26. $3(x^2 + 4) = -20x$

27. $a(a + 4) - 12(3 - a) = 0$

(C)

Solve for x:

28. $x^2 + 4cx - 21c^2 = 0$

29. $14x^2 - bx = 4b^2$

30. $x^2 - ax - bx + ab = 0$

31. $2mx^2 + mx - 2x - 1 = 0$

32. $(x - p)(x - q) - pq = 0$

33. $x^2 + 2x(c + d) + 4cd = 0$

2·12 Equations involving absolute value (supplementary). The idea of absolute value as defined for the integers is extended to the real numbers by the following definition:

If $x \in R$, and

(i) if $x > 0$, then $|x| = x$;

(ii) if $x = 0$, then $|x| = 0$;

(iii) if $x < 0$, then $|x| = -x$.

Thus, to solve the equation $|x| = 3$, we consider the following cases.

(i) If $x > 0$, then $|x| = x$.

∴ the equation $|x| = 3$ is equivalent to $x = 3$

(ii) If $x = 0$, then $|x| = 0$.

∴ the equation $|x| = 3$ becomes $0 = 3$ which is not true.

(iii) If $x < 0$, then $|x| = -x$.

∴ the equation $|x| = 3$ is equivalent to $-x = 3$ or $x = -3$.

Thus the equation $|x| = 3$ is equivalent to

$$x = 3 \quad \text{or} \quad x = -3.$$

∴ the solution set is $\{3, -3\}$.

By a similar argument, the equation $|x - 3| = 2$ is equivalent to:

$$x - 3 = 2 \qquad \text{or} \qquad x - 3 = -2$$
$$\therefore \quad x = 5 \qquad\qquad \therefore \quad x = 1$$

The solution set is $\{1, 5\}$. The roots of the equation are 1 and 5.

Verification.

If $x = 5$,   L.S. $= |5 - 3|$ R.S. $= 2$

                $= |2|$

                $= 2$

If $x = 1$,   L.S. $= |1 - 3|$ R.S. $= 2$

                $= |-2|$

                $= 2$

The graph of the solution set is shown in *Fig. 2-8.*

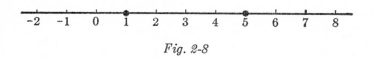

Fig. 2-8

Write solutions for the following problems and compare them with those on page 442.

1. Solve $|2x + 1| = 1$ and verify.

2. Find the solution set of $|3y - 2| = -3$.

Exercise 2-8

(A)

Solve:

1. $|x| = 3$ **2.** $|y| = -2$ **3.** $-|r| = -1$

4. $|x + 2| = 5$ **5.** $|2x| = 0$ **6.** $|-2x| = 4$

7. $|-3x| = -3$ **8.** $|2x + 1| = 3$ **9.** $-|-x| = 2$

(B)

Find the solution set:

10. $|2x - 1| = 7$

11. $2|3x + 2| = 8$

12. $|3x - 1| = -1$

13. $-2|3x - 2| = -8$

14. $-2|3x - 2| = 2$

15. $|4x + 3| = 5$

Find the solution set and verify:

16. $3 = \dfrac{|2x + 1|}{2}$

17. $|2(x-1)+3| = 4$

18. $|x + 4| = |-2|$

19. $4\left|\dfrac{2x}{3}\right| = 14$

20. $\left|\dfrac{3x + 1}{2}\right| = 2$

21. $\left|\dfrac{3x - 1}{2}\right| = 2$

Solve and draw the graph of the solution set:

22. $|2x| = \dfrac{3}{2}$

23. $|-3x| = 3$

24. $2|x - 2| = 2$

25. $|x - (2x - 1)| = 2$

26. $\left|\dfrac{2x + 3}{3}\right| = |-2|$

27. $|+3| = |-2x + 1|$

28. $|3x - 4| = |-3| - |2|$

29. $|3x - 4| = \left|\dfrac{-3}{-2}\right|$

30. $|3x - 4| = \dfrac{|-3|}{-2}$

Review Exercise 2-9

(A)

Name the property which justifies each of the following statements (letter symbols represent real numbers):

1. $ba + bc = b(a + c)$

2. $3(2 \cdot 7) = (3 \cdot 2)7$

3. $p + q \in R$

4. $m + (n + r) = (m + n) + r$

5. $2(x + y) + a(x + y) = (x + y)(2 + a)$

6. $5a$ is a real number.

7. $ab = ba$

8. $(x + 2) + (3 + 2x) = (3 + 2x) + (x + 2)$

State the solution set of each of the following:

9. $\{x \mid 5x + 2 \geq -8, x \in I\}$

10. $\{x \mid 2 > x \geq -2, x \in I\}$

11. $\{x \mid x + 2 \geq 0 \text{ and } 3x - 4 \leq 5\}$

12. $\{x \mid |x| \leq 3, x \neq 0, x \in I\}$

13. $\{x \mid 4x - 3(x + 2) > -x + 4\}$

14. $\{x \mid |2x - 1| = 0, x \in I\}$

(B)

15. Find $\{x \mid \frac{1}{2}(5 - x) - 6(x - 2) < 7x - 26, x \in I\}$ and draw its graph.

16. Draw the graph of the solution set defined by:

$$\frac{x-1}{3} - \frac{x-1}{2} \leq \frac{x+2}{-3}$$

17. Draw the graph of each of the following:

(i) $\{x \mid 2x - 5 > -1\}$ or $\{x \mid 4(x-1) - (12x+7) < 0\}$

(ii) $\{x \mid 5 - (x-2)^2 < -(x-1)^2, x \in I\} \cap$

$$\{x \mid 2 + \frac{3x}{5} > \frac{x-1}{2}, x \in I\}$$

18. Solve the equations given below, and draw the graph of each solution set:

(i) $|y - 2| > 4$ (ii) $|2x + 1| \leq 3$

19. Draw the graph of the solution set defined by:

$9(8 - x) + 4(x - 3) \leq 3(3 - x) + 5(x + 2) + 20$

20. Find the solution set defined by:

$(3x - 2)(x + 1) - 2(x - 1)^2 = 7 + (x + 7)(x - 5)$

Simplify the following:

21. $|10| - (-3)(+7) - |-36|$ **22.** $|4a| + (-4)| - 3b|, a, b > 0$

23. $|4 - 7| - 3|16 - 32| + (-6)$ **24.** $|3b - 4c|, b > 0, c < 0$

Draw the graph of each of the following:

25. $\{x \mid -(x+2) \leq 0 \text{ and } 2x - 3 \leq 3\}$

26. $\{x \mid 3x - 6 \geq 0 \text{ or } 4x + 3 \leq -5\}$

27. $\{x \mid x - 5 \geq 1 - 2x, x \in I\}$ or $\{x \mid 6 + 5x < x - 2, x \in I\}$

28. $\{x \mid 2(x - 3) < 7x + 9\}$ and $\{x \mid 2x - 3 \leq 6x + 5\}$

29. Show that $(a - 2b)(3b - 2c) = a(3b - 2c) - 2b(3b - 2c)$ when $a = 2, b = -3, c = -1$.

Find the solution set of the following:

30. $4b^2 - .25 = 0$ **31.** $8x^2 - 14x - 15 = 0$

32. $7x^2 = 19x$ **33.** $x^2 - \frac{23}{6}x - 3 = 0$

Chapter III

EXPONENTS
SQUARE ROOTS
RADICALS

3·1 Definition of a^n, $n \in {}^+I$. In earlier studies the definition

$$2^5 = 2 \cdot 2 \cdot 2 \cdot 2 \cdot 2$$

or, in general terms,

$$a^n = a \cdot a \ldots a \; (n \text{ factors}, n \in {}^+I, a \in R)$$

provided a very useful shorthand for expressing the products of equal factors where the factors were real numbers.

The exponent n indicates the number of times the *base* a is taken as a factor. The expression a^n is read, "a to the exponent n". a^n is referred to as a *power*, called the nth power of a.

In the sections which immediately follow, the laws for operating with integral exponents are derived from particular examples. Unless otherwise indicated, the base is considered to be a real number.

3·2 The law of a product involving integral exponents.

$$\text{The product } a^2 \cdot a^3 = (a \cdot a)(a \cdot a \cdot a) \qquad \text{(Definition)}$$
$$= a^5 \qquad \text{(Definition)}$$
$$= a^{2+3}.$$

This and similar examples suggest the general law:

$$a^n \times a^m = a^{n+m}, n, m \in {}^+I$$

This law, called the *law of a product,* may be extended to any number of factors. Thus:

$$a^n \cdot a^m \cdot a^p \ldots = a^{n+m+p+\cdots}$$

If we wish to extend this law to include zero as an exponent, then it must be true that:

$$(-3)^3(-3)^0 = (-3)^{3+0} \qquad \text{or in general} \qquad a^n \times a^0 = a^{n+0}$$
$$= (-3)^3 \qquad\qquad\qquad\qquad\qquad\qquad = a^n$$

and a^0 must be 1, the neutral element for multiplication. Therefore, we extend the law to a zero exponent by defining

$$a^0 = 1 .$$

If we replace a by zero in the statement $a^n \times a^0 = a^n$, then

$$0^n \times 0^0 = 0^n .$$

Since zero to any positive integral exponent is zero, this statement is equivalent to

$$0 \times 0^0 = 0 .$$

Since the product of any real number and zero is zero, this statement is true if 0^0 is any real number. Consequently, we will not attempt to define 0^0 but will restrict the definition of a^0 so that $a \neq 0$. Thus,

$$a^0 = 1, a \neq 0 .$$

If we wish to extend this law to include negative integral exponents, then it must be true that:

$$2^2 \times 2^{-2} = 2^{2+(-2)} \qquad \text{or in general} \qquad a^n \times a^{-n} = a^{n+(-n)}$$
$$= 2^0 \qquad\qquad\qquad\qquad\qquad\qquad = a^0, \quad a \neq 0$$
$$= 1 \qquad\qquad\qquad\qquad\qquad\qquad = 1$$

Since the product of *reciprocals* is 1, the law of a product involving exponents may be extended to include negative integral exponents if and only if we define a^n and a^{-n} to be reciprocals; that is:

$$a^{-n} = \frac{1}{a^n} \quad \textit{for all } n \in I, a \neq 0$$

Simplify each of the following and compare your solutions with those on page 443.

1. $2^2 \cdot 2^4$ **2.** $(-3)^4 \cdot (-3)^0$ **3.** $5^3 \times 5^{-2}$

4. $(-16)^3(-16)^{-3}$ **5.** $x^3 \cdot x^{-4}$ **6.** $x^{-2} \cdot x^{-3}$

3·3 The law of a quotient involving integral exponents. Since division is the inverse operation of multiplication:

(i) the quotient

$$(-3)^5 \div (-3)^2 = x \text{ if and only if } (-3)^5 = (-3)^2 \cdot x, \; x \in R.$$

Since $(-3)^2(-3)^3 = (-3)^5$ (Law of a product)

$$\therefore \; (-3)^5 \div (-3)^2 = (-3)^3$$
$$= (-3)^{5-2}$$

(ii) the quotient

$$2^3 \div 2^{-4} = x \text{ if and only if } 2^3 = 2^{-4} \cdot x, \; x \in R.$$

Since $2^{-4} \times 2^7 = 2^3$ (Law of a product)

$$\therefore \; 2^3 \div 2^{-4} = 2^7$$
$$= 2^{3-(-4)}$$

(iii) the quotient

$$5^{-3} \div 5^{-2} = x \text{ if and only if } 5^{-3} = 5^{-2} \cdot x, \; x \in R.$$

Since $5^{-2} \times 5^{-1} = 5^{-3}$ (Law of a product)

$$\therefore \; 5^{-3} \div 5^{-2} = 5^{-1}$$
$$= 5^{-3-(-2)}$$

(iv) In general, if $n, m \in I$, the quotient

$$a^n \div a^m = x \text{ if and only if } a^n = a^m \cdot x, \; x \in R, \; a \neq 0.$$

Since $a^m \cdot a^{n-m} = a^{m+n-m}$ (Law of a product)

$$= a^n$$
$$\therefore \; a^n \div a^m = a^{n-m}, \quad a \neq 0$$

Thus, the law of a quotient involving integral exponents is

$$a^n \div a^m = a^{n-m}, \; a \neq 0.$$

The base a cannot be zero because division by zero is not defined.

Simplify each of the following and compare your solutions with those on page 443. Assume $x, y, z \neq 0$.

1. $3^5 \div 3^2$ **2.** $(-2)^3 \div (-2)^0$ **3.** $(-5)^2 \div (-5)^{-3}$

4. $x^0 \div x^{-2}$ **5.** $y^{-2} \div y^{-4}$ **6.** $z^0 \div z^0$

3·4 Summary.

If $n, m \in I$, $a \neq 0$, then

(i) *Law of a product:* $a^n \cdot a^m = a^{n+m}$;

(ii) *Zero exponent:* $a^0 = 1$;

(iii) *Negative exponent:* $a^{-n} = \dfrac{1}{a^n}$;

(iv) *Law of division:* $a^n \div a^m = a^{n-m}$.

Obtain simpler equivalent expressions for each of the following and compare your solutions with those on page 443.

1. $(a^2b^3c^4)(a^0b^{-2}c^2)$ **2.** $3m^{-2}p^0q^2 \times 4m^4p^{-3}q^{-4}$

3. $x^4y^2z^0 \div x^{-2}y^4z^3$ **4.** $12r^4s^{-5} \div 3r^{-2}s^5$

Exercise 3-1

(The variables are real numbers for which the expressions are defined.)

(A)

Simplify each of the following:

1. $a^3 \times a^5$ **2.** $a^8 \div a^2$ **3.** $a^2 \div a^6$ **4.** $\dfrac{a^2b^5c^2}{a^6bc^2}$

5. $(3m^2b)(2mb^4)$ **6.** $3x^2 \times 4x^3$ **7.** $\dfrac{b^{5n}}{b^{2n}}$ **8.** x^0y^0

9. $b^n \cdot b^3$ **10.** $x^2 \cdot y^3 \cdot x \cdot y$ **11.** $(-3)^5$ **12.** $(-2)^4(-2)^{-3}$

Express with positive exponents:

13. a^{-3} **14.** a^2b^{-4} **15.** $\dfrac{a^2b^{-1}}{c}$ **16.** $\dfrac{m^{-1}n^{-2}}{c^{-3}}$

17. $\dfrac{7}{a^{-4}}$ **18.** $x^{-2}y^{-3}$ **19.** $5b^{-10}$ **20.** $\dfrac{m^{-3}}{p^{-2}}$

21. $\dfrac{2x^{-4}}{3y^{-2}}$ **22.** $a^{-1}+b^{-1}$ **23.** $\dfrac{1}{a^{-1}}-\dfrac{1}{b^{-2}}$ **24.** $\dfrac{1}{a^{-1}+b^{-1}}$

Simplify:

25. 7^0 **26.** $(-5)^0$ **27.** $\dfrac{1}{(-3)^0}$ **28.** $\dfrac{2^0}{3^0}$

29. 5^{-3} **30.** $\dfrac{2^{-1}}{3^{-1}}$ **31.** $6^0 \cdot 2$ **32.** $5 \div 8^0$

33. $5 \cdot z^0$ **34.** $\dfrac{4}{3^{-1}}$ **35.** $6 \cdot 8^0$ **36.** $\dfrac{4}{2x^0}$

37. $7^0 \cdot 3^0$ **38.** $(-4)^{-2}$ **39.** $\dfrac{1+a^0}{2}$ **40.** $32 \cdot 4^{-2}$

41. $32 \cdot 2^{-4}$ **42.** $3 \cdot 10^{-4}$ **43.** $x^{-3} \div x^{-3}$ **44.** $\dfrac{1}{2^0+b^0}$

45. $10^{-3} \cdot 10^4$ **46.** $10{,}000 \times 10^{-4}$ **47.** $(25)^{-2}$ **48.** $(-4)^{-2}$

49. $a^3b^4 \times a^{-2}b^{-5}$ **50.** $\dfrac{x^3y^4}{x^2y^5}$ **51.** $\dfrac{12m^{-2}p^3}{3m^3p^{-2}}$

52. $\dfrac{x^4y^0z^6}{x^2y^{-2}z^4}$

53. $\dfrac{36a^3b^4c^5}{72a^{-3}b^{-4}c^{-5}}$

54. $\dfrac{125m^{-3}p^0q^5}{75p^0q^5}$

55. $13a^2b^3c^{-3} \times 4a^{-2}b^{-4}c^3$

56. $\dfrac{(x-1)^2(y-3)^0}{(x-1)^3(y-3)^{-2}}$

57. $\dfrac{(a+b+c)^3(a-b+c)^4}{(a+b+c)^0(a-b+c)^4}$

3·5 The power law for integral exponents.

The power $(a^2)^4 = a^2 \cdot a^2 \cdot a^2 \cdot a^2$ (Definition)

$ = a^{2+2+2+2}$ (Law of a product)

$ = a^8$

$ = a^{2\times 4}$

This and similar examples suggest the general **law:**

$$(a^n)^m = a^{nm}, \quad n, m \in I,$$

called the *power law.*

3·6 The law of the power of a product for integral exponents.

The power $(a \cdot b)^3 = (a \cdot b)(a \cdot b)(a \cdot b)$ (Definition)

$ = (a \cdot a \cdot a)(b \cdot b \cdot b)$ (CM) (AM)

$ = a^3b^3$ (Definition)

This and similar examples suggest the general law:

$$(a \cdot b)^n = a^n \cdot b^n, n \in I,$$

called the *power of a product.*

3·7 The law of the power of a quotient for integral exponents.

The power $\left(\dfrac{a}{b}\right)^4 = \left(\dfrac{a}{b}\right)\left(\dfrac{a}{b}\right)\left(\dfrac{a}{b}\right)\left(\dfrac{a}{b}\right), \; b \neq 0$ (Definition)

$\phantom{The power \left(\dfrac{a}{b}\right)^4} = \dfrac{a^4}{b^4}$ (Definition)

This and similar examples suggest the general law:

$$\left(\dfrac{a}{b}\right)^n = \dfrac{a^n}{b^n}, b \neq 0, n \in I,$$

called the *power of a quotient.*

3·8 Summary of the laws of exponents for integral exponents.

If $n, m \in I$ and $a \neq 0$, then

(i)   *Law of a product:* $a^n \times a^m = a^{n+m}$;

(ii) *Zero exponent:* $a^0 = 1$;

(iii) *Negative exponent:* $a^{-n} = \dfrac{1}{a^n}$;

(iv) *Law of a quotient:* $a^n \div a^m = a^{n-m}$;

(v)   *Power law:* $(a^n)^m = a^{nm}$;

(vi) *Power of a product:* $(a \cdot b)^n = a^n b^n$;

(vii) *Power of a quotient:* $\left(\dfrac{a}{b}\right)^n = \dfrac{a^n}{b^n}$.

Obtain simpler equivalent expressions for each of the following and compare your solutions with those on page 443.

1. $3(a^2)^{10}$ **2.** $(3m^2 n^3 p^4)^3$ **3.** $(4x^{-2} z^0 y^2)^{-3}$

4. $\left(\dfrac{r^2}{t^3}\right)^3$ **5.** $\left(\dfrac{6s^3 t^{-4}}{3mn^2}\right)^{-1}$ **6.** $\left(\dfrac{a^0}{b^0}\right)^3$

Exercise 3-2

(The variables are real numbers for which the expressions are defined.)

(A)

State simpler equivalent expressions for each of the following:

1. $(a^2)^3$ **2.** $(a^{-2})^3$ **3.** $(a^{-2})^{-3}$

4. $(x^2 y^3)^0$ **5.** $(x^2 y^3)^2$ **6.** $(x^2 y^3)^{-1}$

7. $(a^0 b^0 c^0)^0$ **8.** $(a^2)^2 (b^3)^3$ **9.** $(-2)^3$

10. $(-12x^3)^2$ **11.** $(5ab^2 c^3)^2$ **12.** $(-3xy^2)^4$

13. $\left(\dfrac{x}{y}\right)^{10}$ **14.** $\dfrac{x^{23}}{x^{12}}$ **15.** $\left(\dfrac{2a}{b}\right)^3$

16. $\left(\dfrac{2m}{5n}\right)^4$ **17.** $\dfrac{a^3}{b^3}$ **18.** $\left(\dfrac{p}{q}\right)^2 \left(\dfrac{q}{p}\right)^3$

19. $(-x)^{3021}$ **20.** $(-y)^{3022}$ **21.** $-(-3x)^3$

22. $(3^2)^2$ **23.** $(2x^2)^2$ **24.** $(2x)^3 (2x)^3$

25. $(-6a^2 b^2)^2$ **26.** $-\tfrac{1}{2}(-\tfrac{1}{2})^3$ **27.** $(-2a^4)^3$

28. $\dfrac{b^{25}}{b^{35}}$ **29.** $\dfrac{3a^3}{9a^8}$ **30.** $(-3ab^2)^{-3}$

31. $2^5 \cdot 2^{-8}$ **32.** $3^5 \cdot 3^7 \cdot 3^{-10}$ **33.** $\dfrac{(3a-b)^4}{(3a-b)^2}$

34. $\dfrac{(2a)^{12}}{(2a)^{10}}$ **35.** $(x^{2y})^y$ **36.** $(a^{3p})^{2p}$

37. $\dfrac{3^6 \cdot 2^4}{3^3 \cdot 2^3}$ **38.** $\dfrac{-(mn)^4}{(-mn)^4}$ **39.** $\left(\dfrac{a^3}{2}\right)^3$

40. $\left(\dfrac{2p}{m}\right)^2$ **41.** $8a^3 \div 4a^2$ **42.** $(\tfrac{1}{4}pq^2)^2$

43. $(2a)^2 - 3a^2$ **44.** $ab \cdot 3a^2b \cdot 2a^3b$ **45.** $6a^5 + 2a^3$

46. $2a^2$ is a factor of $16a^3b$.   What is the other factor?

47. $5m^2n^3$ is a factor of $35mn^4$.   What is the other factor?

48. $6x^0y^5$ is a factor of $30x^4y^2$.   What is the other factor?

49. $3x^{-2}y^{-3}$ is a factor of $9x^{-4}y^0$. What is the other factor?

Obtain as simple a form as possible for each of the following:

50. $ab + 2ab$ **51.** $3abc \cdot 2b^2 \cdot 3a^0c^2d$

52. $a^4 + a^3$ **53.** $6a^5b^5 \div 3a^2b^3$

54. $2r^3 \cdot 2p^5$ **55.** $-20pq^4 \div -5p^2q^3$

56. $ab + a$ **57.** $4a^2 \div 4a$

58. $4a^2 + 4a$ **59.** $xy \cdot x$

60. $xy \div x$ **61.** $(5a)(6a)$

62. $\dfrac{45a^4b^3}{-5a^3b^4}$ **63.** $2b^2 + 2b^2 + 4b$

64. $2b^2 \cdot 2b^2 \cdot 4b$ **65.** $\dfrac{6mnp^2}{9m^4np}$

66. $(4c^2d^3)^2$ **67.** $\left(\dfrac{a^2}{3}\right)^3$

68. $4a^2 \cdot \dfrac{9}{4a}$ **69.** $(4x^2yz^3)(-3x^{-2}y^{-1}z^{-3})$

3.9 The principal square root of a non-negative real number. The *square* of any real number is a non-negative real number. For example:

(i) $(-5)^2 = 25$ (ii) $0^2 = 0$ (iii) $(+5)^2 = 25$

Any positive real number has two *square roots*. For example:

(i) $25 = (-5)^2$ and (ii) $25 = (+5)^2$

and hence both $+5$ and -5 are square roots of 25. Zero has only one square root, zero.

In general,

$$if\ a,\ b \in R,\ a \geqq 0,$$
$$b\ is\ called\ a\ square\ root\ of\ a\ if\ and\ only\ if\ b^2 = a.$$

The example illustrates that b may be positive, negative, or zero, but a must be positive or zero.

The *positive square root* of any positive real number a is called the *principal square root* of a and is designated $\sqrt{a}$. The *radical sign* (or square root sign), $\sqrt{\ }$, always implies the principal square root. The indicated square root of a positive real number, $\sqrt{a}$, $a \in {}^{+}R$, is called *a radical* or a *surd of the second order*. The number a is called the *radicand*. The cube root of 5, $\sqrt[3]{5}$, and the fourth root of 5, $\sqrt[4]{5}$, are examples of radicals or surds of the third and fourth order, respectively. The numeral written above the radical sign to indicate the order of the root is called the *index* of the radical. The negative square root of a positive real number a is indicated by $-\sqrt{a}$. Our discussions will be concerned only with radicals of the second order.

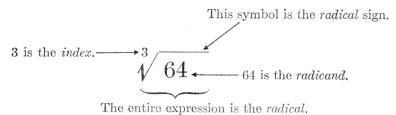

This symbol is the *radical* sign.

3 is the *index.* ⟶ 3

$\sqrt{64}$ ⟵ 64 is the *radicand.*

The entire expression is the *radical.*

In the following sections, methods of operating with radicals involving square roots and the simplification of expressions involving such radicals are discussed.

3·10 The product of two square roots. It should be recalled that the (principal) square root of any non-negative real number is a real number; hence, in combining radicals of the second order, the laws of addition and multiplication for real numbers and the laws of exponents apply.

(i) By definition, $(\sqrt{a})^2 = a$ or $\sqrt{a} \times \sqrt{a} = \sqrt{a^2} = a$ if $a \geqq 0$.

(ii) $\qquad (\sqrt{2} \times \sqrt{3})^2 = (\sqrt{2})^2(\sqrt{3})^2 \qquad$ (Power of a product)

$\qquad\qquad\qquad = 2 \times 3 \qquad\qquad$ (Definition)

$\qquad\qquad\qquad = 6$

Thus $\sqrt{2} \times \sqrt{3} = \sqrt{2 \times 3} = \sqrt{6} \qquad$ (Definition)

Similarly, if $a, b \geqq 0$, then

$\qquad (\sqrt{a} \times \sqrt{b})^2 = (\sqrt{a})^2(\sqrt{b})^2 \qquad$ (Power of a product)

$\qquad\qquad\qquad = a \cdot b. \qquad\qquad$ (Definition)

$\qquad \therefore \ \sqrt{a} \times \sqrt{b} = \sqrt{ab}$

Example 1. Simplify the following:

$\qquad$ (i) $\sqrt{3} \times \sqrt{7} \qquad$ (ii) $\sqrt{5} \times \sqrt{11} \qquad$ (iii) $\sqrt{12} \qquad$ (iv) $\sqrt{75}$

Solution. $\quad$ (i) $\sqrt{3} \times \sqrt{7} = \sqrt{3 \times 7} \qquad\qquad$ (ii) $\sqrt{5} \times \sqrt{11} = \sqrt{5 \times 11}$

$\qquad\qquad\qquad\qquad = \sqrt{21} \qquad\qquad\qquad\qquad\qquad\qquad = \sqrt{55}$

$$\text{(iii) } \sqrt{12} = \sqrt{4 \times 3}$$
$$= \sqrt{4} \times \sqrt{3}$$
$$= 2\sqrt{3}$$

$$\text{(iv) } \sqrt{75} = \sqrt{25 \times 3}$$
$$= \sqrt{25} \times \sqrt{3}$$
$$= 5\sqrt{3}$$

In parts (iii) and (iv), each of the radicands has a factor which is a perfect square. Since in general, $\sqrt{ab} = \sqrt{a} \times \sqrt{b}$, such a factor may be separated as the examples indicate. Numerals such as $2\sqrt{3}$, $5\sqrt{3}$ are called *mixed radicals* or *mixed surds*. Mixed radicals may be written as *entire radicals* or *entire surds* by reversing this process. For example:

$$2\sqrt{3} = \sqrt{4}\sqrt{3} \quad \text{and} \quad 5\sqrt{3} = \sqrt{25}\sqrt{3}$$
$$= \sqrt{12} \qquad\qquad = \sqrt{75}$$

Example 2. Simplify: (i) $5\sqrt{2} \times 3\sqrt{3}$ (ii) $7\sqrt{5} \times 6\sqrt{7}$
              (iii) $m\sqrt{n} \times p\sqrt{q}$, $n, q \geq 0$

Solution.

(i) $5\sqrt{2} \times 3\sqrt{3}$
    $= 5 \times 3 \times \sqrt{2} \times \sqrt{3}$ *(CM)*
    $= 15\sqrt{6}$ *(AM)*

(ii) $7\sqrt{5} \times 6\sqrt{7}$
    $= 7 \times 6 \times \sqrt{5} \times \sqrt{7}$ *(CM)*
    $= 42\sqrt{35}$ *(AM)*

(iii) $m\sqrt{n} \times p\sqrt{q} = m \times p \times \sqrt{n} + \sqrt{q}$ *(CM)*
            $= mp\sqrt{nq}$

Example 3. Simplify: (i) $\sqrt{x^2}$ (ii) $\sqrt{x^2 + 2x + 1}$

Solution. In each example the principal square root is required, and this is a positive number or zero. Thus:

     (i) $\sqrt{x^2} = |x|$ (ii) $\sqrt{x^2 + 2x + 1} = \sqrt{(x + 1)^2}$
                                            $= |x + 1|$

The absolute value signs ensure that, whatever number x represents, the root is positive or zero.

In the worked examples of the text, the authorities which are most significant in the development are given in brackets. When writing a solution, you should think the authorities for the steps, but it is not necessary to include them in your solution.

Exercise 3-3

(The variables are real numbers for which the expressions are defined.)

(A)

1. In $b^2 = a$ how many numbers does b represent?
2. If b is the principal square root of a, what quality does it possess?

3. What is the name of the symbol $\sqrt{}$ and what does it imply?

4. How is the negative square root of a positive real number indicated?

5. What is the radicand in the symbol $-\sqrt{3a}$?

6. What is the order of the following radicals or surds?

(i) $\sqrt{3}$ (ii) $\sqrt[5]{6}$ (iii) $\sqrt[10]{7}$ (iv) $\sqrt[n]{64}$

State the principal square root of each of the following:

7. 36   **8.** 64   **9.** 81   **10.** 0

11. $16x^2$ **12.** $4(x-1)^2$ **13.** $a^2 - 2ab + b^2$

14. $x^2 + 4x + 4$ **15.** $(2a - 3b)^4$ **16.** $a^2b^4c^6$

State each of the following as entire surds or radicals:

17. $2\sqrt{3}$ **18.** $3\sqrt{5}$ **19.** $4\sqrt{a}$

20. $a\sqrt{b}$ **21.** $b^2\sqrt{c}$ **22.** $b^4\sqrt{x^2y}$

23. $6\sqrt{6}$ **24.** $2^2\sqrt{3}$ **25.** $3a^4b^2\sqrt{x}$

State each of the following as mixed radicals or surds:

26. $\sqrt{8}$ **27.** $\sqrt{12}$ **28.** $\sqrt{18}$

29. $\sqrt{32}$ **30.** $\sqrt{24}$ **31.** $\sqrt{48}$

32. $\sqrt{54}$ **33.** $\sqrt{68}$ **34.** $\sqrt{44}$

35. $\sqrt{72}$ **36.** $\sqrt{125}$ **37.** $\sqrt{80}$

38. $\sqrt{52}$ **39.** $\sqrt{75}$ **40.** $\sqrt{75x}$

41. $\sqrt{18b^2}$ **42.** $\sqrt{98}$ **43.** $\sqrt{8a^2}$

44. $\sqrt{90y^3}$ **45.** $\sqrt{\dfrac{12y}{5}}$ **46.** $\sqrt{\frac{8}{49}}$

47. $\sqrt{\frac{3}{4}}$ **48.** $\sqrt{\frac{4}{81}}$ **49.** $\sqrt{\frac{200}{16}}$

50. $\sqrt{2a^2b^4}$ **51.** $\sqrt{60x^4y}$ **52.** $\sqrt{x^3}$

53. $\sqrt{2a^2 + 4a + 2}$ **54.** $\sqrt{5(b-2)^2}$ **55.** $\sqrt{(a-b)(a+b)^2}$

Expand the indicated products:

56. $\sqrt{3} \times \sqrt{3}$ **57.** $2\sqrt{5} \cdot \sqrt{3}$ **58.** $\sqrt{6} \cdot \sqrt{2}$

59. $\sqrt{6} \times \sqrt{\frac{2}{3}}$ **60.** $\sqrt{2xy} \cdot \sqrt{3x^2y^2}$ **61.** $\sqrt{b} \cdot \sqrt{2b^2}$

62. $\sqrt{5} \times \sqrt{\frac{3}{5}}$ **63.** $\sqrt{5} \cdot \sqrt{2}$ **64.** $\sqrt{2a} \cdot \sqrt{3b}$

65. $\sqrt{2} \times \sqrt{18}$ **66.** $3\sqrt{5} \times 4\sqrt{2}$ **67.** $4\sqrt{7} \cdot 3\sqrt{8}$

68. $\sqrt{\frac{5}{7}} \cdot \sqrt{\frac{5}{7}}$ **69.** $\sqrt{2x} \cdot \sqrt{5x}$ **70.** $x\sqrt{a} \cdot \sqrt{b}$

(B)

Write the principal square root of each of the following:

71. $x^2 + 6x + 9$ **72.** $(x-3)^2$ **73.** $4x^2 + 4x + 1$

74. $9x^2 + 12x + 4$ **75.** $4x^2 - 20x + 25$ **76.** $\dfrac{x^2}{4} - \dfrac{x}{4} + \dfrac{1}{16}$

77. $25 + 30x + 9x^2$ **78.** $49x^2 - 14x + 1$ **79.** $64x^2 + 48x + 9$

Write each of the following as an entire surd or radical (assume that the coefficients of the radicals are positive):

80. $a\sqrt{b}$ **81.** $3\sqrt{c}$ **82.** $3x\sqrt{3y}$

83. $(a-b)\sqrt{3}$ **84.** $(a+b)\sqrt{2}$ **85.** $(x+3)\sqrt{y}$

86. $(a-b)\sqrt{(a+b)}$ **87.** $(2x+4)\sqrt{5}$ **88.** $(3x+y)\sqrt{z}$

Write each of the following as a mixed radical or surd:

89. $\sqrt{99}$ **90.** $\sqrt{3a^2}$ **91.** $\sqrt{2(x-1)^2}$

92. $\sqrt{3(x^2+16x+64)}$ **93.** $\sqrt{5x^2+10x+5}$ **94.** $\sqrt{b^2a-8ba+16a}$

95. $\sqrt{\dfrac{(a-b)^2}{(a+b)^2}}$ **96.** $\sqrt{12(a+ab)^2}$ **97.** $\sqrt{3x^2+6x+3}$

Multiply as indicated and write the result with simplest radicand:

98. $\sqrt{2xy} \cdot \sqrt{3xy}$ **99.** $\sqrt{x^3} \cdot \sqrt{x^2}$ **100.** $2\sqrt{3} \cdot 3\sqrt{4}$

101. $\sqrt{18} \times \sqrt{32}$ **102.** $\sqrt{b} \cdot \sqrt{3b}$ **103.** $\sqrt{45} \cdot \sqrt{80}$

104. $\sqrt{8} \times \sqrt{6} \times \sqrt{3}$ **105.** $\sqrt{2} \cdot \sqrt{18}$ **106.** $\sqrt{10} \cdot \sqrt{4}$

107. $3\sqrt{6} \cdot 5\sqrt{5} \cdot 2\sqrt{15}$ **108.** $6\sqrt{14} \cdot 2\sqrt{7}$ **109.** $20\sqrt{20} \cdot 5\sqrt{5}$

110. $\sqrt{\frac{14}{27}} \cdot \sqrt{\frac{4}{21}}$ **111.** $\sqrt{\frac{96}{25}} \cdot \sqrt{\frac{125}{54}}$ **112.** $\sqrt{\frac{10}{11}} \cdot \sqrt{\frac{33}{15}}$

3·11 Addition of second order radicals. The mixed radicals $3\sqrt{2}$ and $5\sqrt{2}$ are said to be similar, since they have the same radical coefficient. The indicated sum of two or more such radicals may be simplified by applying the distributive property of multiplication over addition. For example:

(i) $\begin{aligned} 3\sqrt{2} + 5\sqrt{2} &= (3+5)\sqrt{2} \\ &= 8\sqrt{2} \end{aligned}$

(ii) $\begin{aligned} 7\sqrt{5} + 3\sqrt{5} &- 2\sqrt{5} \\ &= (7+3-2)\sqrt{5} \\ &= 8\sqrt{5} \end{aligned}$

Simplify each of the following and compare your solutions with those on page 444.

1. $3\sqrt{2} + 4\sqrt{8} - 5\sqrt{18}$ **2.** $3\sqrt{8} + 5\sqrt{32} - 2\sqrt{72}$

3. $\sqrt{75} - \sqrt{27} + \sqrt{200}$

Exercise 3-4

(The variables are real numbers for which the expressions are defined.)

(A)

State the sum in simplified form:

1. $2\sqrt{3} + 3\sqrt{3}$ **2.** $4\sqrt{5} + 6\sqrt{5}$ **3.** $3\sqrt{2} - 2\sqrt{2}$

4. $3\sqrt{6}+5\sqrt{6}-2\sqrt{6}$ **5.** $2\sqrt{7}-3\sqrt{7}+5\sqrt{7}$ **6.** $2\sqrt{3}+4\sqrt{3}-10\sqrt{3}$

7. $3\sqrt{x} + 2\sqrt{x} - 4\sqrt{x}$ **8.** $11\sqrt{y} + 2\sqrt{y} - 3\sqrt{y}$

9. $12\sqrt{6} - 7\sqrt{6} + 2\sqrt{2} - 3\sqrt{2}$ **10.** $7\sqrt{a} - 4\sqrt{b} + 2\sqrt{a} - 3\sqrt{b}$

11. $3\sqrt{c} - 4\sqrt{d} + 3\sqrt{2} - 6\sqrt{c}$ **12.** $3\sqrt{b} - \sqrt{b} + \sqrt{c}$

13. $5\sqrt{x} - 3\sqrt{y} + 2\sqrt{x}$ **14.** $6\sqrt{a} + 7\sqrt{b} - 4\sqrt{a} - 5\sqrt{b}$

15. $5\sqrt{ab} - 2\sqrt{ab} + 3\sqrt{ab}$

(B)

Simplify the following expressions:

16. $4\sqrt{2} - 2\sqrt{2}$ **17.** $\sqrt{98} + \sqrt{32}$ **18.** $2\sqrt{50} + 4\sqrt{18}$

19. $7\sqrt{3} + 3\sqrt{3}$ **20.** $\sqrt{45} - \sqrt{245}$ **21.** $2\sqrt{27} - \sqrt{12}$

22. $\sqrt{28} + 2\sqrt{7}$ **23.** $x\sqrt{2} - x$ **24.** $2\sqrt{50} + \sqrt{98}$

25. $\sqrt{\frac{4}{5}} + 2\sqrt{\frac{4}{5}}$ **26.** $\frac{3}{4}\sqrt{45} - \frac{1}{3}\sqrt{20}$ **27.** $\sqrt{40} - \sqrt{90}$

28. $\sqrt{8} + \frac{1}{2}\sqrt{2}$ **29.** $\sqrt{b} + \sqrt{4b}$ **30.** $\sqrt{2a^2} + \sqrt{8a^2}$

31. $\sqrt{6} + 2\sqrt{24} - \sqrt{54}$ **32.** $6\sqrt{24} + 2\sqrt{18} - 3\sqrt{50}$

33. $\sqrt{72} - \sqrt{32} + \sqrt{8}$ **34.** $\sqrt{32} + \sqrt{128} - \sqrt{18} + \sqrt{50}$

35. $2\sqrt{128} + 3\sqrt{32} - \sqrt{18}$ **36.** $\sqrt{32} + 3\sqrt{8} - 2\sqrt{18}$

37. $\sqrt{6} + 3\sqrt{6} + 5\sqrt{6}$ **38.** $4\sqrt{20}+2\sqrt{45}-3\sqrt{80}+\sqrt{32}$

39. $3\sqrt{32} - 2\sqrt{8} + 5\sqrt{72}$ **40.** $\frac{\sqrt{4}}{2} + \frac{\sqrt{12}}{3} + \frac{2\sqrt{3}}{3}$

3·12 Square roots of fractions.

(i) $$\left(\frac{\sqrt{3}}{\sqrt{2}}\right)^2 = \frac{(\sqrt{3})^2}{(\sqrt{2})^2}$$ (Power of a quotient)

$$= \frac{3}{2}$$ (Definition)

Thus, $$\frac{\sqrt{3}}{\sqrt{2}} = \sqrt{\frac{3}{2}}$$ (Definition)

Similarly, if $a \geqq 0$, $b > 0$

$$\left(\frac{\sqrt{a}}{\sqrt{b}}\right)^2 = \frac{(\sqrt{a})^2}{(\sqrt{b})^2} \qquad \text{(Power of a quotient)}$$

$$= \frac{a}{b}. \qquad \text{(Definition)}$$

Thus, in general if $a \geqq 0$, $b > 0$, then $\dfrac{\sqrt{a}}{\sqrt{b}} = \sqrt{\dfrac{a}{b}}$.

Write solutions to the following problems and compare them with those on page 444.

1. Write each of the following in the form $\sqrt{\dfrac{a}{b}}$:

(i) $\dfrac{\sqrt{3}}{\sqrt{7}}$ (ii) $\dfrac{\sqrt{5}}{\sqrt{10}}$ (iii) $\dfrac{2\sqrt{7}}{\sqrt{3}}$ (iv) $\dfrac{3\sqrt{5}}{2\sqrt{11}}$

2. Perform each of the following divisions:

(i) $\sqrt{12} \div \sqrt{3}$ (ii) $4\sqrt{15} \div 2\sqrt{5}$

3·13 Rationalizing a denominator. The expression $\dfrac{\sqrt{3}}{\sqrt{2}}$ may be simplified to the form $\sqrt{\dfrac{3}{2}}$ or $\sqrt{1.5}$. It may also be simplified in another manner.

$$\frac{\sqrt{3}}{\sqrt{2}} = \frac{\sqrt{3} \cdot \sqrt{2}}{\sqrt{2} \cdot \sqrt{2}} = \frac{\sqrt{6}}{2} \qquad \text{(Principle of equivalent fractions)}$$

The latter simplification has produced a form involving a rational denominator and a radical numerator. If the radicand in such a denominator is a rational number, this process will always produce a rational denominator and is sometimes referred to as *rationalizing the denominator*. This procedure facilitates further simplification by division as follows:

$$\frac{\sqrt{6}}{2} \div \frac{2.449}{2} \div 1.225$$

Exercise 3-5

(The variables are real numbers for which the expressions are defined.)

(A)

Simplify by division:

1. $\dfrac{\sqrt{6}}{\sqrt{3}}$ **2.** $\dfrac{\sqrt{8}}{\sqrt{2}}$ **3.** $\dfrac{\sqrt{15}}{\sqrt{5}}$ **4.** $\dfrac{21\sqrt{14}}{2\sqrt{7}}$

Simplify by division:

5. $\dfrac{5\sqrt{18}}{3\sqrt{3}}$

6. $\dfrac{\sqrt{8x^3}}{\sqrt{2x^2}}$

7. $\dfrac{3\sqrt{a^2 - b^2}}{2\sqrt{a + b}}$

8. $\dfrac{\sqrt{250x^4y^2z^3}}{\sqrt{25x^2y^2z^2}}$

State the simplest number necessary to multiply numerator and denominator in order to rationalize the denominator:

9. $\dfrac{1}{\sqrt{2}}$

10. $\dfrac{\sqrt{3}}{\sqrt{5}}$

11. $\dfrac{3\sqrt{2}}{2\sqrt{3}}$

12. $\dfrac{3}{\sqrt{7}}$

13. $\dfrac{4}{a\sqrt{2}}$

14. $\dfrac{3\sqrt{2}}{\sqrt{3}}$

15. $\dfrac{11}{\sqrt{12}}$

16. $\dfrac{7}{\sqrt{8}}$

17. $\dfrac{5}{\sqrt{50}}$

18. $\dfrac{7}{\sqrt{18}}$

19. $\dfrac{2}{\sqrt{8a}}$

20. $\dfrac{6b}{\sqrt{b}}$

State an equivalent expression in the form $\sqrt{\dfrac{a}{b}}$ *for each of the following:*

21. $\dfrac{\sqrt{2}}{\sqrt{3}}$

22. $\dfrac{2\sqrt{2}}{\sqrt{5}}$

23. $\dfrac{a\sqrt{b}}{\sqrt{c}}$

24. $\dfrac{3\sqrt{x}}{2\sqrt{y}}$

25. $\dfrac{a\sqrt{b}}{b\sqrt{a}}$

26. $\dfrac{\sqrt{11}}{\sqrt{3}}$

27. $\dfrac{(a - b)\sqrt{3}}{\sqrt{a - b}}$

28. $\dfrac{3x\sqrt{y}}{5\sqrt{x}}$

(B)

Rationalize the denominators of the following expressions:

29. $\dfrac{2}{\sqrt{2}}$

30. $\dfrac{\sqrt{5}}{\sqrt{3}}$

31. $\dfrac{\sqrt{2}}{\sqrt{3}}$

32. $\dfrac{b}{\sqrt{b}}$

33. $\dfrac{2\sqrt{3}}{5\sqrt{2}}$

34. $\dfrac{8x}{\sqrt{x}}$

35. $\dfrac{2}{\sqrt{5}}$

36. $\dfrac{\sqrt{11}}{\sqrt{7}}$

37. $\dfrac{4}{\sqrt{8}}$

38. $\dfrac{\sqrt{45}}{\sqrt{12}}$

39. $\dfrac{\sqrt{3}}{5\sqrt{20}}$

40. $\dfrac{\sqrt{5}}{\sqrt{14}}$

41. $\dfrac{15}{\sqrt{50}}$

42. $\dfrac{3}{\sqrt{18}}$

43. $\dfrac{6\sqrt{5}}{3\sqrt{2}}$

44. $\dfrac{48}{5\sqrt{32}}$

If $\sqrt{2} = 1.414$, $\sqrt{3} = 1.732$, $\sqrt{5} = 2.236$, *find correct to two decimal places the numerical value of:*

45. $\dfrac{1}{\sqrt{2}}$

46. $\dfrac{2}{\sqrt{5}}$

47. $\dfrac{2}{5\sqrt{2}}$

48. $\dfrac{15}{\sqrt{45}}$

49. $\dfrac{3}{\sqrt{8}}$

3·14 The product of radical expressions. Since second order radicals represent real numbers, if the radicand is positive or zero, the laws of addition and multiplication apply.

Write solutions to the following problems and compare them with those on page 444. Consider the radicands to be positive or zero.

1. Expand each of the following using the distributive law:

(i) $\sqrt{2}(\sqrt{3} + \sqrt{5})$ (ii) $3\sqrt{2}(\sqrt{7} + 5\sqrt{11})$

2. Expand the indicated product by means of the distributive law and simplify: $(3\sqrt{2} + 5\sqrt{3})^2$

3. Expand the following squares:

(i) $(3\sqrt{2} + 5\sqrt{3})^2$ (ii) $(\sqrt{5} - 2\sqrt{7})^2$

4. Expand the indicated product: $(\sqrt{2} + \sqrt{3})(2\sqrt{2} - \sqrt{3})$

5. Expand using the distributive law: $(\sqrt{2} - \sqrt{3})(\sqrt{2} + \sqrt{3})$

6. Expand:

(i) $(\sqrt{2} - \sqrt{3})(\sqrt{2} + \sqrt{3})$ (ii) $(3\sqrt{2} + 4\sqrt{5})(3\sqrt{2} - 4\sqrt{5})$

(iii) $(\sqrt{x} + \sqrt{y})(\sqrt{x} - \sqrt{y})$ (iv) $(a\sqrt{x} + b\sqrt{y})(a\sqrt{x} - b\sqrt{y})$

Two radical expressions of the form $\sqrt{x} + \sqrt{y}$ and $\sqrt{x} - \sqrt{y}$ or $a\sqrt{x} + b\sqrt{y}$ and $a\sqrt{x} - b\sqrt{y}$ are called *conjugate radicals*. If a, b, x, y represent rational numbers, then the product of these conjugate radical expressions represent a rational number. Thus:

(i) $(\sqrt{x} + \sqrt{y})(\sqrt{x} - \sqrt{y}) = x - y$

(ii) $(a\sqrt{x} + b\sqrt{y})(a\sqrt{x} - b\sqrt{y}) = a^2x - b^2y$

and $x - y$ and $a^2x - b^2y$ represent rational numbers.

Exercise 3-6

(The variables are real numbers for which the expressions are defined.)

(B)

Expand the indicated products:

1. $\sqrt{2}(\sqrt{2} + 2)$ **2.** $\sqrt{3}(2\sqrt{3} - 2)$

3. $\sqrt{5}(1 + 2\sqrt{5})$ **4.** $\sqrt{2}(5 + \sqrt{2})$

5. $2\sqrt{3}(\sqrt{2} + \sqrt{5})$ **6.** $\sqrt{2}(2\sqrt{5} - 3\sqrt{8})$

7. $(\sqrt{12} + \sqrt{5})\sqrt{5}$ **8.** $(\sqrt{2} + 1)(\sqrt{2} - 1)$

9. $(2 + \sqrt{3})(2 - \sqrt{3})$ **10.** $(\sqrt{2} + 3)^2$

11. $(\sqrt{3} - \sqrt{2})^2$ **12.** $(\sqrt{2} + 2)(\sqrt{2} - 2)$

13. $(2 + \sqrt{3})^2$ **14.** $(\sqrt{6} + \sqrt{2})^2$

15. $(\sqrt{6} + \sqrt{3})(\sqrt{6} - \sqrt{3})$ **16.** $\dfrac{\sqrt{7} + 2}{3} \cdot \dfrac{\sqrt{7} - 2}{3}$

17. $\left(\dfrac{\sqrt{11} + 1}{2}\right)^2$ **18.** $\left(\dfrac{2 - \sqrt{3}}{2}\right)^2$

Expand the indicated products:

19. $(2\sqrt{7} - 5\sqrt{2})(2\sqrt{7} + 5\sqrt{2})$ **20.** $(\sqrt{3} + 3\sqrt{2})(4\sqrt{3} - 2\sqrt{2})$

21. $(3\sqrt{2} - 4\sqrt{3})^2$ **22.** $(3\sqrt{x} - \sqrt{y})^2$

23. $(5\sqrt{3} - 3\sqrt{2})^2$ **24.** $2\sqrt{7}(1 - 2\sqrt{7})$

25. $(\sqrt{x} - 1)^2$ **26.** $(3\sqrt{5} - 1)(3\sqrt{5} + 1)$

27. $(\sqrt{x} - \sqrt{y})^2$ **28.** $(\sqrt{a} + \sqrt{b})^2$

29. $\sqrt{5 + 3\sqrt{2}} \ \sqrt{5 - 3\sqrt{2}}$ **30.** $\dfrac{-3 + \sqrt{2}}{3} \cdot \dfrac{-3 - \sqrt{2}}{3}$

31. $(\sqrt{2} + \sqrt{5})(2\sqrt{2} + 3\sqrt{5})$ **32.** $(3\sqrt{x} - \sqrt{y})(2\sqrt{x} + 3\sqrt{y})$

33. $(4\sqrt{5} - 2\sqrt{7})(3\sqrt{5} - \sqrt{7})$ **34.** $(\sqrt{a} + \sqrt{b})(\sqrt{c} + \sqrt{d})$

35. $(3\sqrt{5} - \sqrt{11})(2\sqrt{5} + 3\sqrt{11})$ **36.** $(3\sqrt{2} + \sqrt{10})(2\sqrt{2} + \sqrt{10})$

3·15 Rationalizing a denominator which is a binomial containing radicals. The fact that the product of two conjugate (binomial) radicals, $(\sqrt{a} + \sqrt{b})(\sqrt{a} - \sqrt{b})$, is a rational number, $a - b$, if a, $b \in Q$, may be used to rationalize the denominator of a fraction when it is a binomial containing radicals.

Example. Simplify by multiplying both terms of the fraction by the conjugate of the denominator: (i) $\dfrac{3}{3 + \sqrt{2}}$ (ii) $\dfrac{5}{\sqrt{5} - \sqrt{3}}$

Solution. (i) $\dfrac{3}{3 + \sqrt{2}}$ (ii) $\dfrac{5}{\sqrt{5} - \sqrt{3}}$

$= \dfrac{3(3 - \sqrt{2})}{(3 + \sqrt{2})(3 - \sqrt{2})}$ $= \dfrac{5(\sqrt{5} + \sqrt{3})}{(\sqrt{5} - \sqrt{3})(\sqrt{5} + \sqrt{3})}$

$= \dfrac{9 - 3\sqrt{2}}{9 - 2}$ $= \dfrac{5\sqrt{5} + 5\sqrt{3}}{5 - 3}$

$= \dfrac{9 - 3\sqrt{2}}{7}$ $= \dfrac{5\sqrt{5} + 5\sqrt{3}}{2}$

Write solutions for each of the following and compare them with those on page 445.

Simplify:

1. $\dfrac{\sqrt{2}}{3\sqrt{7} - \sqrt{5}}$ **2.** $\dfrac{3\sqrt{3}}{3\sqrt{5} - 4\sqrt{2}}$

3. $\dfrac{3 + \sqrt{11}}{2\sqrt{7} + 3\sqrt{6}}$ **4.** $\dfrac{5\sqrt{2} - 3\sqrt{3}}{2\sqrt{5} + 3\sqrt{2}}$

Exercise 3-7

(The variables are real numbers for which the expressions are defined.)

(B)

Simplify by multiplying both terms of the fraction by the conjugate of the denominator:

1. $\dfrac{1}{\sqrt{2}+1}$

2. $\dfrac{3}{3-\sqrt{3}}$

3. $\dfrac{6}{2+\sqrt{5}}$

4. $\dfrac{5}{3-\sqrt{7}}$

5. $\dfrac{2}{x-\sqrt{y}}$

6. $\dfrac{\sqrt{5}}{2-\sqrt{6}}$

7. $\dfrac{\sqrt{7}}{\sqrt{5}-3}$

8. $\dfrac{2\sqrt{3}}{\sqrt{7}+2}$

9. $\dfrac{1}{2\sqrt{2}-3}$

10. $\dfrac{3}{\sqrt{2}+\sqrt{3}}$

11. $\dfrac{\sqrt{5}}{\sqrt{5}+\sqrt{2}}$

12. $\dfrac{\sqrt{3}}{2\sqrt{2}-\sqrt{7}}$

13. $\dfrac{\sqrt{2}+\sqrt{3}}{\sqrt{2}-\sqrt{3}}$

14. $\dfrac{4-\sqrt{5}}{4+\sqrt{5}}$

15. $\dfrac{\sqrt{5}+\sqrt{3}}{\sqrt{5}-\sqrt{3}}$

16. $\dfrac{\sqrt{3}-2\sqrt{2}}{\sqrt{3}+2\sqrt{2}}$

17. $\dfrac{\sqrt{6}-\sqrt{5}}{\sqrt{5}-\sqrt{6}}$

18. $\dfrac{2\sqrt{2}-3\sqrt{5}}{\sqrt{5}+\sqrt{7}}$

19. $\dfrac{4\sqrt{7}-5\sqrt{3}}{4\sqrt{7}+5\sqrt{3}}$

20. $\dfrac{2\sqrt{2}-3\sqrt{3}}{2\sqrt{2}+3\sqrt{3}}$

21. $\dfrac{4\sqrt{3}-3\sqrt{5}}{\sqrt{5}+\sqrt{3}}$

(C)

22. $\dfrac{x+y\sqrt{z}}{x-y\sqrt{z}}$

23. $\dfrac{\sqrt{a^2+3}-2}{\sqrt{a^2+3}+2}$

24. $\dfrac{\sqrt{a}-\sqrt{b}}{\sqrt{a}+\sqrt{b}}$

25. $\dfrac{\sqrt{x+1}+\sqrt{x-1}}{\sqrt{x+1}-\sqrt{x-1}}$

26. $\dfrac{ay-by}{\sqrt{a}+\sqrt{b}}$

27. $\dfrac{a-3\sqrt{b}}{\sqrt{b}+a}$

28. $\dfrac{1+\sqrt{2}+\sqrt{3}}{1+\sqrt{2}-\sqrt{3}}$

3·16 Radical equations in one variable. A radical equation is one in which the variable occurs in a radicand. For example:

(i) $\sqrt{x}=3$ (ii) $\sqrt{2x-5}+2=3$ (iii) $\sqrt{4y^2-7}+3=2y$

are each radical equations.

Our method of solving equations has been to write simpler equivalent equations until the solution set has been obtained. To do this, we used the uniqueness property of closure for real numbers under addition, multiplication, subtraction, and division.

Consider the equation:

(i) $\sqrt{4y^2 - 7} + 3 = 2y$

The equation may be written:

(ii) $\sqrt{4y^2 - 7} = 2y - 3$ (Subtraction property)

To obtain the solution set, it is necessary to obtain an equation not involving a radical. This may be done by squaring both sides of the equation.

(iii) $\therefore\ 4y^2 - 7 = 4y^2 - 12y + 9$ (Squaring)

(iv) $\therefore\ 12y = 16$ (Subtraction, addition)

(v) $\therefore\ y = \dfrac{4}{3}$ (Division property)

Verification.

$$\text{L.S.} = \sqrt{4(\tfrac{4}{3})^2 - 7} + 3 \qquad\qquad \text{R.S.} = 2 \cdot \tfrac{4}{3}$$

$$= \sqrt{\frac{64 - 63}{9}} + 3 \qquad\qquad = \frac{8}{3}$$

$$= \frac{1}{3} + 3$$

$$= \frac{10}{3}$$

Upon verification we see that $\tfrac{4}{3}$ does not satisfy the equation and is, therefore, *not* a root of the equation. In fact, the given equation has no root.

The fact that $\tfrac{4}{3}$ is not a root of the equation means that

$$\sqrt{4y^2 - 7} + 3 = 2y \text{ and } y = \tfrac{4}{3}$$

are not equivalent equations. Which step in the procedure of solving is not reversible? To get from step (ii) to (iii) it was necessary to square both sides of the equation. Is squaring and taking square roots a reversible operation? If not, then equations (ii) and (iii) are not equivalent.

Consider the following example. The only root of the equation $x = 3$ is 3. If both sides are squared, then $x^2 = 9$. This equation has the two roots 3 and -3. That is, taking the square root of both sides produces the result, $x = \pm\, 3$, which is not the original equation.

Thus, the squaring of both sides of an equation may not produce an equivalent equation. The equation produced will contain among its roots the root or roots of the original equation, if it has any. It may, however, be satisfied by numbers which are not roots of the original equation. Thus, when the squaring process is introduced, it is necessary to verify or check the numbers obtained to determine the roots, if any, of the original equation.

In the previous example, $\frac{4}{3}$ is a root of the equation $4y^2 - 7 = 4y^2 - 12y + 9$, determined by squaring both members of the original equation, $\sqrt{4y^2 - 7} + 3 = 2y$. $\frac{4}{3}$ is said to be *extraneous* to the equation $\sqrt{4y^2 - 7} + 3 = 2y$ and has been introduced by the squaring process.

Example. Solve $\sqrt{a + 3} - 4 = 0$.

Solution.
$$\sqrt{a + 3} - 4 = 0$$
$$\therefore \sqrt{a + 3} = 4$$
$$\therefore a + 3 = 16 \qquad \text{(Squaring both sides)}$$
$$\therefore a = 13$$

Verification.

$$\text{L.S.} = \sqrt{13 + 3} - 4 \qquad\qquad \text{R.S.} = 0$$
$$= 4 - 4$$
$$= 0$$

$\therefore$ 13 is the root of the equation, and the solution set is $\{13\}$.

Exercise 3-8

(B)

Solve:

1. $\sqrt{2a} - 6 = 0$

2. $\sqrt{b} + 1 = 0$

3. $\sqrt{y + 3} - 5 = 0$

4. $3\sqrt{m + 1} - 8 = 0$

5. $\sqrt{a^2 + 11} - 1 = a$

6. $\sqrt{2p + 1} - 3 = 0$

7. $\sqrt{y^2 + 6} - y + 3 = 0$

8. $\sqrt{x - 2} = 3$

9. $\sqrt{x + 1} = -3$

10. $\sqrt{x^2 + 5} + x = 5$

11. $\dfrac{4}{\sqrt{y - 5}} - \sqrt{y - 5} = 0$

12. $\dfrac{6}{\sqrt{a + 5}} = \sqrt{a + 5}$

3·17 Radical equations in one variable (continued).

Example. Solve $\sqrt{x + 3} + \sqrt{x - 2} = 5$.

Solution. $\sqrt{x + 3} + \sqrt{x - 2} = 5$

We may square both sides as they stand, but trial will show that the arithmetic is simpler if one radical occurs in each side. Therefore, write:

$$\sqrt{x+3} = 5 - \sqrt{x-2} \qquad \text{(Subtraction property)}$$

$$\therefore \ x+3 = 25 - 10\sqrt{x-2} + x - 2 \quad \text{(Squaring)}$$

$$\therefore \ 10\sqrt{x-2} = 20$$

$$\therefore \ \sqrt{x-2} = 2$$

$$\therefore \ x - 2 = 4 \qquad \text{(Squaring)}$$

$$\therefore \ x = 6$$

Verification.

$$\text{L.S.} = \sqrt{6+3} + \sqrt{6-2} \qquad \text{R.S.} = 5$$

$$= 3 + 2 = 5$$

$$\therefore \ \text{the solution set is } \{6\} \ .$$

Note that both sides were squared twice in the process of solving the equation.

Solve the following equations and compare your solutions with those on page 445.

1. $\sqrt{b+5} + \sqrt{b} - \sqrt{4b+9} = 0$

2. $\sqrt{x^2 + 7x + 17} - \sqrt{x^2 + 3x + 5} = 2$

Exercise 3-9

(B)

Solve:

1. $\sqrt{3b+1} = 5$

2. $\sqrt{x-5} - 5 = \sqrt{x}$

3. $\sqrt{y-9} + \sqrt{y} = 1$

4. $\sqrt{4a+5} = \sqrt{7a+2}$

5. $\sqrt{9m^2 + 4} - 3m = 2$

6. $\sqrt{y-3} - 3 = -\sqrt{y}$

7. $\sqrt{5a+34} - \sqrt{5a+6} = 2$

8. $\sqrt{25y-29} - 3\sqrt{y} = \sqrt{4y-11}$

9. $\sqrt{a-3} + \sqrt{a+4} = 7$

10. $\sqrt{x^2+12} - x = 2$

(C)

11. $\sqrt{2-y} - \dfrac{3}{\sqrt{3-y}} = -\sqrt{3-y}$

12. $\sqrt{b+60} - 2\sqrt{b+5} = \sqrt{b}$

13. $\sqrt{m-5} + 2\sqrt{4m-15} = \sqrt{9m-5}$

14. $\dfrac{a}{\sqrt{a-y}} - \sqrt{a-y} = \sqrt{b-y}, \ a, b > 0$

Chapter IV

GENERAL PRINCIPLES OF GEOMETRY
DEDUCTIVE REASONING
FUNDAMENTAL ANGLE PAIR THEOREMS

4.1 **Basic ideas of geometry.** The basic element in geometry is the *point*. A point is a concept or idea which exists only in the mind and is associated with the notion of position in space. It has no dimensions. The set of all points is called *space*. A *plane* is a special subset of the points in space. This subset is thought of as having the property of flatness, like a table top, but extending in all directions without limit. A *line* is a special subset of points in a plane. Although there are many types of lines, for example, straight, curved, and broken, when the word "line" is used in this text it means *straight line*.

Geometry is the study of relations between points and sets of points, a study of ideas existing only in the mind. Representations of geometric figures, called *models* or *diagrams*, are drawn to represent the geometric concepts. The student of geometry must be aware constantly of the distinction between the physical model or diagram and the idea it represents.

4.2 **Undefined terms and definitions.** In any study, certain ideas must be accepted to provide a starting point for discussion. These ideas are fundamental, so much so that they defy description in simpler terms. In geometry, *point* and *line* are two such ideas. The meaning of these fundamental terms is accepted without definition; they are referred to as *undefined terms*. Some other undefined terms in geometry are *set, space, belongs to, lies on, on one side of, is equal to,* and *between.*

When defining a term we attempt to express its meaning by using other terms which have been previously defined or accepted as undefined.

The characteristics of a correct definition are listed below.

1. A definition is expressed in a sentence.
2. The subject of the sentence is the name of the thing being defined.
3. The predicate of the sentence:
    (i) places the thing in a known set to which it belongs;
    (ii) states the property which distinguishes the thing from the other members of the set in which it has been placed.
4. The sentence uses only terms which have already been defined or accepted as undefined.
5. The sentence is reversible.

In section 4·3 the definitions for some basic geometric figures are given. These definitions should be tested to see that each of the above requirements is satisfied.

4·3 Some basic geometric figures. Geometric figures are sets of points related in some particular way. The definition of a plane geometric figure tells how these points are selected from the set of all points in a plane.

a. *Line.* Straight line is an undefined term. It is a special set of points in a plane. It extends without limit and has no end points. These properties are indicated by the arrows in *Fig. 4-1*.

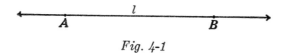

Fig. 4-1

It is customary to name a line either (i) by associating a letter l with it and calling it "line l" (*Fig. 4-1*) or (ii) by selecting two points on it, naming them with capital letters, such as A and B, and calling it "line AB" or "line BA" (*Fig. 4-1*).

The following definitions of basic geometric figures are based on the undefined terms "line" and "point". Other definitions will be introduced when necessary.

b. *Line segment.* A line segment is the point set consisting of two distinct points on a line and all the points between them.

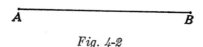

Fig. 4-2

c. *Half-line.* A half-line is the point set consisting of all the points on one side of a given point on a line. The given point is called the *boundary* point of the half-line.

d. *Ray.* A ray is the point set consisting of a point on a line and all the points on the line on one side of the given point.

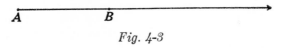

Fig. 4-3

Fig. 4-3 is a diagram of a ray from point *A*. If a second point *B* is selected on the ray, then the ray is named "ray *AB*".

In *Fig. 4-4*, the ray *AB* on line *l* is illustrated. The ray *AC* is also shown. In naming a ray, the first letter indicates the end point. Rays *AB* and *AC* are called *opposite rays*.

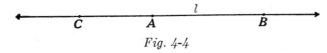

Fig. 4-4

e. *Angle* An angle is the set of all points on two distinct rays with a common end point.

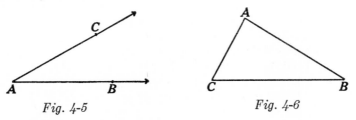

Fig. 4-5   *Fig. 4-6*

In *Fig. 4-5*, the rays *AB* and *AC* *compose* the angle. The common end point of the two rays is called the *vertex* of the angle.

f. *Triangle.* A triangle is the set of all points on the line segments determined by three points which are not all on one line.

In *Fig. 4-6*, line segments *AB*, *BC*, and *CA* are called the *sides* of the triangle, and the points *A*, *B*, and *C* are called the *vertices* of the triangle.

4·4 Postulates. Just as the development of definitions depends on the acceptance of certain undefined terms or ideas, the development and proof of conclusions in geometry depend on basic accepted properties called *assumptions* or *postulates*. Postulates make possible a precise starting point for discussion and also describe the basic properties of points, lines, and planes. A list of postulates is given on page 421.

Discovery Exercise 4-1

Compare your statements of postulates and definitions formed in this exercise with those found in the list of postulates on page 421 and in the list of definitions on page 417.

(B)

1.   (i) How many half-lines are shown in the diagram at the left below? Name them.
     (ii) How many rays? Name them.
     (iii) How many line segments? Name them.
     (iv) On the ray on B for which A is the end point, there are represented several sets of points. Name them.

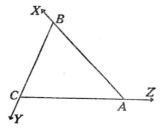 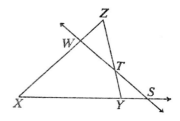

2.   (i) Name the triangles in the diagram at the right above.
     (ii) What is the intersection set of:
          (a) line WS and line segment ZY?
          (b) half-line TS and ray YS?
          (c) half-line TS and line segment XY?
          (d) line WS and triangle XYZ?
          (e) triangle XYZ and triangle TYS?
          (f) triangle XYZ and triangle ZWT?
          (g) triangle ZWT and triangle TYS?

3.   Make a diagram of a circle and a quadrilateral for which the intersection set consists of:
     (i) no points   (ii) 1 point   (iii) 2 points   (iv) 4 points
     (v) 6 points   (vi) the largest number of points possible

4.   If two distinct lines l_1 and l_2 intersect on a point A, state the number of other points of intersection of l_1 and l_2. Formulate a postulate to express this basic property of two intersecting lines.

5.   Draw a diagram of two distinct lines which do not have any point in common.
     (i) What term is used to describe these lines?
     (ii) Write a definition of this term.

6. In the accompanying diagram, lines l_1, l_2, l_3, and l_4 intersect on point A.

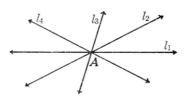

   (i) Name six pairs of lines which determine the point A.
   (ii) The lines l_1, l_2, l_3, and l_4 are *concurrent*. Write a definition for the term "concurrent lines".

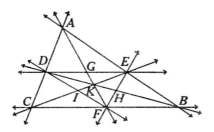

7. Draw a line l and name five points A, B, C, D, and E on it.
   (i) Name 5 pairs of points which determine line l.
   (ii) The points A, B, C, D, and E are *collinear* points. Write a definition for the term "collinear points".

8. For the accompanying diagram:
   (i) list sets of collinear points;
   (ii) list sets of concurrent lines.

4·5 Measuring a line segment.

a. *Measuring a physical model of a line segment.* This is done by first associating the number one, 1, with a line segment which is taken as the unit of length; then, the length of any given line segment is obtained by counting the number of times the unit length is contained in it.

Fig. 4-7

A length involves two things: a number and a unit. If the length of line segment CD is 7 inches, we say:

$$CD = 7 \text{ inches;}$$

   or the length of CD is 7 inches;
   or the measurement of CD is 7 inches;
   or the measure of CD in inches is 7;
   or the distance between C and D is 7 inches.

In *Fig. 4-7*, if the line segment AB is the unit of length, then the length of line segment CD is obtained by determining the number of times AB is contained in CD. The symbol CD will be considered to represent:

   (i) the line segment CD (the set of points), or
   (ii) the length of the line segment CD (a number of units).

Since the choice of unit determines the number of units which is the length of the segment, it is essential in practical applications to have standard units of length. Those in common usage are the *yard* and the *metre*. In order to determine the length of a line segment more precisely, the yard is divided into sub-units: the *foot*, the *inch*, $\frac{1}{10}$-*inch*, and so on. The metre is divided into sub-units: the *centimetre* (cm.), the *millimetre* (mm.), and so on.

Regardless of the unit selected, it is impossible to measure a line segment exactly, and so every physical measurement is only an approximation.

b. *The length of a line segment.* In theoretical geometry, line segments are sets of points which cannot be physically measured, but with which we associate the idea of length.

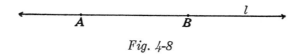

Fig. 4-8

Any line segment AB, *Fig. 4-8*, determines a line l. If a unit length is chosen and the number zero associated with the point A, then the points on the ray AB may be placed in *one-to-one correspondence* with the positive real numbers. Since B is a point on ray AB, then a real number corresponds to point B. This number is the coordinate of point B and is defined to be the length of the line segment AB in terms of the unit used.

Thus, because there is a one-to-one correspondence between the points on a line and the real numbers (postulate), there is a unique positive real number associated with a unit which corresponds to any line segment. This is important because it means that line segments may be added or subtracted according to the properties of the real numbers: for example,

$$\text{if } AB = 6 \text{ in., } BC = 10 \text{ in.}$$
$$\therefore \ AB + BC = (6 + 10) \text{ in.} = 16 \text{ in.}$$

LENGTH OF A LINE SEGMENT POSTULATE

To every line segment there corresponds a unique positive real number of units called the length of the line segment, or the distance between its end points.

On some diagrams, for convenience, we express a length simply as a positive real number, and it is understood to be a number of linear units.

4·6 Betweeness. In *Fig. 4-9*, point B is between A and C.

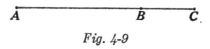

Fig. 4-9

To say that a point B is between any two other points, A and C, means that:

(i) all three points lie on the same line;

(ii) they are arranged as in *Fig. 4-9* (or with A and C interchanged).

> B *is between* A *and* C *if*
> (i) A, B, C *are distinct points on a line, and*
> (ii) $AB + BC = AC$.

The following completion postulate for line segments results from the idea of betweeness and the properties of the real numbers.

COMPLETION POSTULATE FOR LINE SEGMENTS

If B is a point between A and C on a line segment, then
$$AC = AB + BC.$$

It follows that
(i) $AB = AC - BC$
(ii) $BC = AC - AB$
(iii) $AC > AB$
(iv) $AC > CB$.

4.7 The measurement of an angle. The measurement of an angle is obtained in a manner similar to that of obtaining the length of a line segment. A unit angle is selected, and, on the basis of this unit, a positive real number may be associated with each angle.

In measuring models of angles, the protractor is used, and the unit is based on the straight angle, *Fig. 4-10*, in which the two arms of the angle are opposite rays.

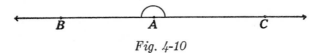

$$\overset{\bullet}{B} \qquad\qquad \overset{\bullet}{A} \qquad\qquad \overset{\bullet}{C}$$

Fig. 4-10

The unit angle is called a *degree* and is defined to be $\frac{1}{180}$ of a straight angle.

The symbol $\angle ABC$, *Fig. 4-11*, will be used:

(i) to name the angle ABC (the set of points) or

(ii) to indicate the measurement of the angle (a number of degrees) according to the context.

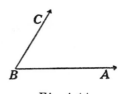

Thus, if $\angle ABC = 60°$, we say that the measurement of $\angle ABC$ is 60 degrees, or the degree measure of $\angle ABC$ is 60.

Fig. 4-11

It is accepted intuitively (postulated) that to each geometric angle there corresponds a unique positive real number of degrees; the degree measure of an angle is greater than zero and equal to, or less than, 180.

Since the definition of angle in geometry involves two distinct rays, there can be no zero angle.

In *Fig. 4-12*, ∠ABC has a degree measure between zero and 180. We may associate with ∠ABC the measurement (360° − measurement of ∠ABC) which is indicated by the double-headed arrow. When we are concerned with this latter measurement, we speak of *reflex angle* ABC.

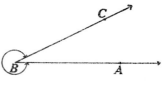

Fig. 4-12

The idea of an angle as a point set consisting of the union of two distinct rays having a common end point is sufficient for the purposes of this study of geometry. Later, however, you will think of an angle in other ways. For example, an angle may be thought of in terms of the rotation of a ray from an initial position to a terminal position. In this context, angles may have measurements greater than 180° and equal to 0°.

Since the measurement of an angle is a positive real number, measurements of angles may be added and subtracted according to the properties of the real numbers: for example,

$$\text{if } \angle ABC = 70°, \ \angle DEF = 50°, \text{ then}$$
$$\angle ABC + \angle DEF = (70 + 50)° = 120°.$$

Also, 120° is said to be the *angle sum* of ∠ABC and ∠DEF.

In *Fig. 4-13*, since D is on the same side of ray BA as C, and D is on the same side of ray BC as A, then ray BD is between ray BA and ray BC. D is said to be in the interior of ∠ABC.

COMPLETION POSTULATE FOR ANGLES

If D is a point in the interior of ∠ABC, then ∠ABC = ∠ABD + ∠DBC.

It follows that

   (i) ∠ABD = ∠ABC − ∠DBC

   (ii) ∠DBC = ∠ABC − ∠ABD

   (iii) ∠ABC > ∠ABD

   (iv) ∠ABC > ∠DBC.

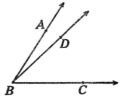

Fig. 4-13

Discovery Exercise 4-2

(B)

Compare your definitions with the definitions on page 417, and your postulates with those on page 421.

1. Examine the diagram representing each of the following geometric figures:

(a)   (b)   (c)

Isosceles triangle   *Scalene triangle*   *Equilateral triangle*

(i) State a set to which each figure belongs.

(ii) State the characteristic which distinguishes the figure from the other members of the set.

(iii) Formulate a definition for each figure.

2. M, N, and P are three points on a line.

(i) Express the following conditions in terms of lengths of line segments: N is between M and P; M is between N and P.

(ii) Show that the statements in (i) are not consistent.

(iii) Formulate a betweeness postulate which expresses this idea.

3. In the diagram at the left below, ABC is a straight angle. BD is any other ray drawn on B.

(i) What is the angle sum of $\angle ABD$ and $\angle DBC$?

(ii) What term is used to describe two such angles?

(iii) Which of the following pairs are measurements of supplementary angles?

(a) $60°$, $30°$ (b) $72°$, $30°$ (c) $90°$, $90°$
(d) $120°$, $50°$ (e) $35°$, $145°$ (f) $110°$, $60°$

(iv) State the measurement of the angle supplementary to each of the following:

$$35°, \quad 72°, \quad 105°, \quad 84°, \quad 92°, \quad 115°, \quad 130°$$

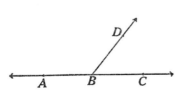 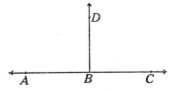

4. (i) How many rays bisect a straight angle?

(ii) In the diagram at the right above, what is the measurement of each of the angles ABD and DBC, if BD is a ray bisecting straight angle ABC?

(iii) Define a right angle.

5. In the diagram at the left below, $\angle ABC$ is a right angle and BD is a ray such that D is in the interior of $\angle ABC$.

  (i) What is the angle sum of $\angle ABD$ and $\angle DBC$?

  (ii) What term is used to describe two such angles?

  (iii) Which of the following pairs are measurements of complementary angles?

  (a) $45°, 45°$ (b) $30°, 60°$ (c) $40°, 60°$

  (d) $72°, 38°$ (e) $25°, 65°$ (f) $80°, 9°$

  (iv) State the measurement of the angle complementary to each of the following:

$$70°, \quad 62°, \quad 54°, \quad 42°, \quad 72°, \quad 36°, \quad 18°$$

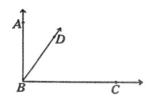

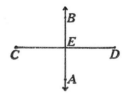

6. In the diagram at the right above, CD is a line segment, and the line AB is on the midpoint of CD, and $\angle AED = 90°$.

  (i) What term is applied to a line such as AB?

  (ii) Write a definition of this term.

  (iii) How many right bisectors does a line segment have?

  (iv) Formulate a postulate to this effect.

7. (i) Write definitions for the terms "acute angle" and "obtuse angle". By examining the diagram which represents the indicated classification of triangles according to angles:

  (ii) state a set to which each figure belongs;

  (iii) state the characteristic which distinguishes the figure from the other members of the set;

  (iv) formulate a definition for each figure.

  (a)   *(b)*   *(c)*

Acute triangle   *Right triangle*   *Obtuse triangle*

4·8 Logic in geometry. Deductive geometry is concerned with the proof of statements of the properties of geometric figures. Mathematical proof requires a type of reasoning known as *deductive reasoning* or *logical deduction*. A logical argument is a series of statements, each of which "follows logically" from previously accepted statements. Logic, then, is a way of thinking expressed in precise language. To understand proof, it is necessary first to become acquainted with the language of logic and its use.

4·9 Sentences and sentential connectives. In logic, each English sentence has a form which is given an identifying name. For example, the sentence:

It is a quadrilateral.

is a basic type of sentence. In logic, such a sentence is called a *simple sentence* or an *atomic sentence*.

If we combine two simple sentences by a connecting word, the resulting sentence is called a *compound sentence* or a *molecular sentence*. For example, the sentence:

It is a quadrilateral and it is a square.

is a compound sentence in which the word *and* combines the two simple sentences:

1. *It is a square.*
2. *It is a quadrilateral.*

It should be noted that the word *and* is not a part of either simple sentence but merely connects the simple sentences to produce a compound sentence. Thus, the word *and* in logic is called a *sentential connective*.

The basic sentential connectives are *and, or, if . . . then . . . , not*.

The use of each of these connectives in combining the simple sentences

1. *It is a square.*
2. *It is a quadrilateral.*

to produce a compound sentence is illustrated in the following:

(i) Connective: *and*

It is a square *and* it is a quadrilateral.

(ii) Connective: *or*

It is a square *or* it is a quadrilateral.

(iii) Connective: *if . . . then . . . ,*

If it is a square, *then* it is a quadrilateral.

The sentence in (iii) is called a *conditional sentence* or *implication*.

It should be noted that the connectives *and, or, if . . . then . . .* control or modify two sentences.

(iv) Connective: *not*

It is *not* a square.

It should be noted that the connective *not* controls or modifies one sentence.

The basic forms of compound sentences are:

        (i) (   ) *and* (   ).

       (ii) (   ) *or* (   ).

     (iii) *If* (   ), *then* (   ).

     (iv) *not* (   ).

The parentheses may be filled by simple or compound sentences.

In logic, capital letters are used to represent sentences. Thus, if P represents, *It is a square,* and Q represents, *It is a quadrilateral,* the compound sentence

               (It is a square) and (it is a quadrilateral),

may be represented symbolically by

               (P) and (Q)

or simply, P and Q.

In general, if A and B represent any two sentences, the basic compound sentences may be represented symbolically as follows:

        (i) A and B.

       (ii) A or B.

     (iii) If A then B; (or) A implies B; (or) $A \rightarrow B$.

     (iv) Not A; (or) $\sim A$.

Exercise 4-3

(A)

Classify each of the following sentences as simple or compound:

1. January is a winter month.

2. Mathematics is the Queen of Sciences.

3. Gauss was a brilliant mathematician.

4. Mathematics is not a difficult subject.

5. John collects stamps, and he has a large collection.

6. The football team plays today and on Wednesday.

7. $6x - 2 < 2x + 5$

8. $5x \neq 3y$

9. $x = 2$ or $x = -2$

10. If two lines are parallel, then they do not have a common point.

11. 2 is rational, and $\sqrt{2}$ is irrational.

12. An integer is positive or it is negative or it is zero.

13. $a < b$ or $a = b$ or $a > b$, $a, b \in N$

14. $+6 \in I$

(B)

In each of the following sentences, make a list of the connectives, if there are any; write each sentence in symbolic form:

15. Today is Monday, and tomorrow is Tuesday.

16. $4x + 6 > 2$ or $3x - 4 = 7$

17. $\{0\}$ is not a null set.

18. If $a, b \in N$, then $\dfrac{a}{b} \in Q$.

19. If $3x + 2 < 5$, then $x < 1$.

20. The length of a line segment is a real number of units.

21. A triangle has three sides and three vertices.

22. If $x, y, z \in N$ and $x > y$ and $y > z$, then $x > z$.

23. An angle is a geometric figure; therefore it is a set of points.

Form a compound sentence by combining the simple sentences in each of the following using the connective indicated:

24. A triangle is isosceles. It has two equal sides. (*if . . . then . . .*)

25. An angle is acute. An angle is obtuse. (*and*)

26. A triangle is a quadrilateral. (*not*)

27. A figure has four equal sides. It is a square. It is a rhombus. (*if . . . then . . .*) (*or*)

4·10 Deductive reasoning. The process of making necessary conclusions from accepted statements by applying accepted rules of logical inference is called *deductive reasoning.*

Given the following statements:

    1. *If the measurement of $\angle ABC$ is 90°, then $\angle ABC$ is a right angle.*

    2. *The measurement of angle ABC is 90°.*

The inescapable consequent of these two statements is the conclusion:

$$\angle ABC \text{ is a right angle.}$$

The two given statements are the *premises* of the argument, and the conclusion is the *logical consequent* of the premises.

The rule of logical inference which permits us to make this conclusion from these statements is called the *Law of Detachment.* By this law, if we are given any implication and precisely the "if clause" of this implication, we can detach the "then clause" and state it as a logical consequent.

If P represents the statement, "The measurement of $\angle ABC$ is 90°", and Q represents the statement, "$\angle ABC$ is a right angle", the complete argument may be arranged as follows:

Premises: 1. $P \rightarrow Q$
                       2. P

Logical consequent: Q (Law of Detachment)

It should be noted that the Law of Detachment ensures that if P and $P \rightarrow Q$ are true statements, that is, assumed or previously proved statements, then Q is a true statement.

The implication $P \rightarrow Q$ and the statement P are referred to as the *premises;* together the two premises form the *hypothesis* of the argument.

Example. State the logical consequent, if there is one, for each of the following.

   (i) **Hypothesis:** 1. If $\triangle ABC$ is equilateral, then $AB = BC = CA$.
                       2. $\triangle ABC$ is equilateral.
  (ii) **Hypothesis:** 1. If $\triangle DEF \cong \triangle XYZ$, then $\angle DEF = \angle XYZ$.
                       2. $\angle DEF = \angle XYZ$
 (iii) **Hypothesis:** 1. If $AB = CD$ and $AB \parallel CD$, then $ABCD$ is a parallelogram.
                       2. $AB \parallel CD$

Solution.

  (i) Logical consequent: $AB = BC = CA$
 (ii) No logical consequent, since we are given the "then clause", rather than the "if clause".
(iii) No logical consequent, since we are given only part of the "if clause" and we must be given precisely the "if clause".

Exercise 4-4

(A)

In each of the following, deduce a logical consequent, where possible:

1. *Hypothesis:* (i) If I study, I will learn mathematics.
                   (ii) I study.
2. *Hypothesis:* (i) $(A \text{ and } B) \rightarrow C$
                   (ii) $(A \text{ and } B)$
3. *Hypothesis:* (i) $(A \text{ or } B) \rightarrow C$
                   (ii) $(A \text{ or } B)$
4. *Hypothesis:* (i) If the measurement of $\angle A$ is less than 90°, then $\angle A$ is an acute angle.
                   (ii) The measurement of $\angle A$ is less than 90°.
5. *Hypothesis:* (i) If $a \in I$, then $(a - 3) \in I$.
                   (ii) $a \in N$

6. *Hypothesis:* (i) If $b \in A$ and A is a subset of B, then $b \in B$.
   (ii) A is a subset of B.

7. *Hypothesis:* (i) If $AB = BC = CD = DA$, then $ABCD$ is a rhombus.
   (ii) $ABCD$ is a rhombus.

8. *Hypothesis:* (i) $\sim A \rightarrow B$ 9. *Hypothesis:* (i) $P \rightarrow (Q$ or $R)$
   (ii) $\sim A$ (ii) $(Q$ or $R)$

10. *Hypothesis:* (i) P
    (ii) $P \rightarrow Q$

11. *Hypothesis:* (i) $(A$ and $B) \rightarrow \sim (P$ or $Q)$
    (ii) $(A$ and $B)$

12. *Hypothesis:* (i) If $a, b, c \in I$, then $a > b$ or $a = b$ or $a < b$.
    (ii) $a, b, c \in Q$

13. *Hypothesis:* (i) $(\angle ADC + \angle CDB = 180°) \rightarrow (\angle ADB$ is a straight angle).
    (ii) $(\angle ADC + \angle CDB = 180°)$

14. *Hypothesis:* (i) $ABCD$ is a parallelogram.
    (ii) $(ABCD$ is a $||^{gm}) \rightarrow (AB = CD$ and $BC = AD)$.

15. *Hypothesis:* (i) $($In $\triangle ABC, AB > AC) \rightarrow (\angle ACB > \angle ABC)$.
    (ii) In $\triangle ABC, AB > AC$.

16. *Hypothesis:* (i) $B \rightarrow \sim A$
    (ii) $\sim A$

4·11 Deductive proofs involving several steps. Most deductive arguments consist of more than one application of the Law of Detachment. This is illustrated in the following example.

Hypothesis: 1. If the measurement of $\angle ABC = 90°$, then $\angle ABC$ is a right angle.
          2. The measurement of $\angle ABC = 90°$.
          3. If $\angle ABC$ is a right angle, then $AB \perp BC$.

Conclusion: $AB \perp BC$

This conclusion may be shown to be a logical consequent of the premises by applying the Law of Detachment twice. Thus, from statements (1) and (2) we obtain the conclusion, "$\angle ABC$ is a right angle", by a first application of the law. Then, by combining this conclusion with statement (3), the Law of Detachment brings us to the logical consequent, $AB \perp BC$.

A formal deductive proof involving more than one application of the Law of Detachment follows:

Hypothesis: 1. $A \rightarrow \sim B$
          2. A
          3. $\sim B \rightarrow D$

Conclusion: D

Proof:

STATEMENTS	AUTHORITIES
1. $A \to \sim B$	1. Hypothesis
2. A	2. Hypothesis
3. $\sim B$	3. Law of Detachment 1, 2
4. $\sim B \to D$	4. Hypothesis
5. D	5. Law of Detachment 3, 4

A formal deductive proof is a succession of statements leading to the desired conclusion. Each statement is either a premise or a statement derived directly by a rule of inference. The proof is arranged in two columns: STATEMENTS in the first column, and AUTHORITIES for these statements in the second column. The process of building a formal deductive proof is called *synthesis*.

Example 1. Complete the following formal deductive proof; compare your proof with that on page 446.

Hypothesis: $R \to \sim S,\ \sim S \to Q,\ T \to R,\ T$

Conclusion: Q

Proof:

STATEMENTS	AUTHORITIES
1. $T \to R$	1.
2. T	2.
3. R	3.
4. $R \to \sim S$	4.
5. $\sim S$	5.
6. $\sim S \to Q$	6.
7. Q	7.

Exercise 4-5

(A)

State the authorities required to complete each of the following formal deductive proofs:

1. *Hypothesis: $A,\ A \to (\sim B),\ (\sim B) \to C$*
   Conclusion: C

Proof:

STATEMENTS	AUTHORITIES
1. A	1.
2. $A \rightarrow (\sim B)$	2.
3. $(\sim B)$	3.
4. $(\sim B) \rightarrow C$	4.
5. C	5.

2. *Hypothesis:* $(AB = AC) \rightarrow (\angle B = \angle C)$, $(\angle B = \angle C) \rightarrow (\angle B = 72°)$
$(\angle B = 72°) \rightarrow (\angle A = 36°)$, $AB = AC$

Conclusion: $\angle A = 36°$

Proof:

STATEMENTS	AUTHORITIES
1. $AB = AC$	1.
2. $(AB = AC) \rightarrow (\angle B = \angle C)$	2.
3. $\angle B = \angle C$	3.
4. $(\angle B = \angle C) \rightarrow (\angle B = 72°)$	4.
5. $\angle B = 72°$	5.
6. $(\angle B = 72°) \rightarrow (\angle A = 36°)$	6.
7. $\angle A = 36°$	7.

(B)

Write complete formal deductive proofs for each of the following:

3. *Hypothesis:* $P \rightarrow Q$, $\sim R \rightarrow S$, $Q \rightarrow \sim R$, P
   Conclusion: S

4. *Hypothesis:* $A \rightarrow (B \text{ or } C)$, $\sim N \rightarrow M$, $(B \text{ or } C) \rightarrow \sim N$, A
   Conclusion: M

5. *Hypothesis:* $\sim (A \text{ and } B) \rightarrow C$, $D \rightarrow \sim (A \text{ and } B)$, D, $C \rightarrow (F \text{ and } G)$
   Conclusion: F and G

6. *Hypothesis:* $S \rightarrow T$, $S \rightarrow R$, S, $T \rightarrow \sim V$, $\sim V \rightarrow W$
   Conclusion: W

7. *Hypothesis:* $(l_1 \| l_2) \rightarrow (\angle y = \angle w)$, $\angle x = \angle y$, $(\angle y = \angle w) \rightarrow (l_2 \| l_3)$,
   $(\angle x = \angle y) \rightarrow (l_1 \| l_2)$
   Conclusion: $l_2 \| l_3$

8. *Hypothesis:* R, $(P \rightarrow Q) \rightarrow (R \rightarrow S)$, $B \rightarrow (P \rightarrow Q)$, B
   Conclusion: S

4.12 The syllogism. Examination of the following statements:

　　　　1. *All persons who live in Toronto live in Ontario.*
　　　　2. *John lives in Toronto.*

leads to the conclusion: *John lives in Ontario.*

This conclusion appears to be a necessary consequent of statements 1 and 2. However, the Law of Detachment cannot be used to justify a conclusion unless we are given an implication and precisely its "if clause".

In logic, the statement, *All persons who live in Toronto live in Ontario*, has the meaning, *For all persons, if a person lives in Toronto, then the person lives in Ontario*, which is an implication. The statement, *John lives in Toronto*, is not precisely the "if clause" of the implication; it is a particular case of the "if clause". Thus, it is not possible to go directly to the conclusion, *John lives in Ontario*, by simply applying the Law of Detachment. To reach the conclusion logically we must first agree that if an implication applies to all members of a set it applies to any specified member.

An argument of this form, called a *syllogism*, involves three steps, as follows:

(a) *Major premise:* a general implication which gives the characteristic property of a set.
(b) *Minor premise:* a particular subset of the set in (a).
(c) *Logical consequent:* the particular subset has the characteristic property of the set.

It should be noted that if the major and minor premises are true (accepted) statements, the logical consequent is a true statement.

Example. State the logical consequent, if there is one, in each of the following; compare your answers with those on page 446.

(i) **Hypothesis:** 1. All straight angles are equal angles.
　　　　　　　　2. A and B are straight angles.
(ii) **Hypothesis:** 1. All straight angles are equal angles.
　　　　　　　　2. A and B are equal angles.
(iii) **Hypothesis:** 1. If an angle is less than 90°, then it is an acute angle.
　　　　　　　　2. $\angle P$ is less than 90°.
(iv) **Hypothesis:** 1. All triangles have an angle sum of 180°.
　　　　　　　　2.

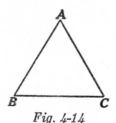

Fig. 4-14

(v) **Hypothesis:** 1. If two angles of a triangle are equal, then the sides opposite these angles are equal.

           2.

Fig. 4-15

(vi) **Hypothesis:** 1. If a point is equidistant from the end points of a line segment, then it is on the right bisector of the line segment.

           2.

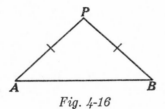

Fig. 4-16

Exercise 4-6

(A)

State the logical consequent, if there is one, in each of the following:

1. *Hypothesis:* 1. If a person is 21 years of age, then he may vote.
           2. John is 21 years of age.

2. *Hypothesis:* 1. If it is about to rain, then my rheumatism bothers me.
           2. My rheumatism bothers me.

3. *Hypothesis:* 1. If $a, b, c \in I$, then $(a \cdot b) \cdot c = a \cdot (b \cdot c)$.
           2. $-2, -3, +4 \in I$

4. *Hypothesis:* 1. If $x, y, z \in N$, then
             $(x + y) + z = x + (y + z)$.
           2. $(3 + 2) + 8 = 3 + (2 + 8)$

5. *Hypothesis:* 1. If an angle has a measurement of 90°, then it is a right angle.
           2. $\angle PQR$ is a right angle.

6. *Hypothesis:* 1. If an angle has a measurement of 180°, then it is a straight angle.
           2. $\angle DEF = 180°$

Restate each of the following conditional statements in "if . . . then . . ."
form:

7. An acute angle is an angle whose degree measurement is less than 90.

8. Points on the same straight line are collinear points.

9. A red sky at night indicates fair weather.

10. Deductive reasoning is the process of applying a rule of inference.

11. A rolling stone gathers no moss.

12. The logical consequent of two accepted premises is called a deduction.

(B)

In each of the following, state the logical consequent, if there is one:

13. *Hypothesis:* (i) All right angles are equal.
(ii) $\angle ABC$ and $\angle PQR$ each equal 90°.

14. *Hypothesis:* (i) All straight angles are equal.
(ii) $\angle M = \angle R$

15. *Hypothesis:* (i) All obtuse angles have measurements greater than 90°.
(ii) $\angle A$ is obtuse.

16. *Hypothesis:* (i) If a quadrilateral has one pair of opposite sides parallel, then it is a trapezoid.
(ii) $ABCD$ is a trapezoid.

17. *Hypothesis:* (i) A parallelogram has both pairs of opposite sides parallel.
(ii) $PQRS$ is a parallelogram.

18. *Hypothesis:* (i) An equilateral triangle has all sides equal.
(ii) $\triangle RST$ is equilateral.

19. *Hypothesis:* (i) Coplanar points are points in the same plane.
(ii) P, Q, R, and S are coplanar points.

20. *Hypothesis:* (i) If points are in the same plane, they are coplanar.
(ii) X, Y, and Z are in plane p.

21. *Hypothesis:* (i) If angles are supplements of the same angle, then they are equal.
(ii) $\angle B = \angle C$

22. *Hypothesis:* (i) All obtuse triangles have one angle an obtuse angle.
(ii) $\triangle DEF$ has $\angle E = 100°$.

23. *Hypothesis:* (i) Perpendicular lines intersect to form a right angle.
(ii) Line $MN \perp$ line ST.

24. *Hypothesis:* (i) If angles are complements of the same angle, then they are equal.
(ii) $\angle 1$ and $\angle 2$ are each complements of $\angle 3$.

4·13 A logical system of geometry. Now that the basic principles of deductive reasoning have been studied, it is possible to organize our geometric knowledge into a logical system in which each statement is derived from preceding statements by deductive reasoning. The initial ideas and statements in this system are undefined terms, definitions, postulates, and number axioms. Conclusions deduced by deductive reasoning from these statements are called *deductions*. The generalizations expressed in these deductions may be used in turn as the premises from which further conclusions can be deduced. The conclusions of some deductions are used so frequently that they are given special status and are called *theorems*. The following diagram illustrates the structure of this logical (deductive) system of geometry.

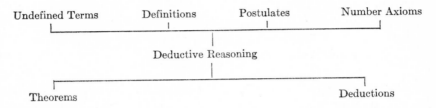

The following is a list of postulates and number axioms used frequently as premises for geometric deductions.

a. *Existence Postulates.*

    (i) There exists one and only one midpoint of a line segment.

    (ii) There exists one and only one bisector of an angle.

    (iii) There exists an unlimited number of line segments equal to a given line segment.

    (iv) There exists an unlimited number of angles equal to a given angle.

    (v) There exists a real number for each line segment which represents in some unit the length of the line segment.

    (vi) There exists a unique real number x for each angle which represents the number of degrees in the angle where $0 < x \leq 180$.

b. *Completion Postulates.*

    (i) If B is between A and C, then

$$AB + BC = AC$$
$$AC - BC = AB$$
$$AC - AB = BC$$
$$AC > AB$$
$$AC > BC.$$

Fig. 4-17

(ii) If ray AC is between rays AB and AD, then

$$\angle BAD = \angle BAC + \angle CAD$$
$$\angle BAD - \angle CAD = \angle BAC$$
$$\angle BAD - \angle BAC = \angle CAD$$
$$\angle BAD > \angle BAC$$
$$\angle BAD > \angle CAD.$$

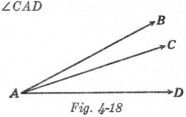

Fig. 4-18

c. *Number Axioms.*

(i) Properties of the real number system:

If a, b, c $\in$ R,

	ADDITION		MULTIPLICATION	
Closure Law	$a + b$ *represents one and only one real number*	*(ClA)*	*ab represents one and only one real number*	*(ClM)*
Commutative Law	$a + b = b + a$	*(CA)*	$ab = ba$	*(CM)*
Associative Law	$(a+b)+c = a+(b+c)$	*(AA)*	$(ab)c = a(bc)$	*(AM)*
Distributive Law		$a(b + c) = ab + ac$		*(D)*
Identity Element	*Zero*		*Unity*	
Inverse Element	$- a$		$\dfrac{1}{a}, a \neq 0$	

(ii) Properties of the equality relation:

$a = a.$	(Reflexive property)
If $a = b$, then $b = a.$	(Symmetric property)
If $a = b$ and $b = c$, then $a = c.$	(Transitive property)

(iii) Properties resulting from the closure law:

If $a = b$, then $a + c = b + c.$	(Addition property)
If $a = b$, then $a - c = b - c.$	(Subtraction property)
If $a = b$, then $ac = bc.$	(Multiplication property)
If $a = b$, then $\dfrac{a}{c} = \dfrac{b}{c}, c \neq 0.$	(Division property)
If $a = b$, then a may be replaced by $b.$	(Replacement property)

(iv) Order properties:

Either $a = b$ or $a \neq b.$	(Dichotomy property)
Either $a < b$ or $a = b$ or $a > b.$	(Trichotomy property)
If $a > b$ and $b > c$, then $a > c.$	(Transitive property)

4·14 **Fundamental angle pair theorems.**

Complementary Angle Theorem

If angles are complements of equal angles, then they are equal.

Hypothesis: $\angle ABC = \angle EFG = 90°$, $\angle 2 = \angle 4$, $\angle 1$ is the complement of $\angle 2$, $\angle 3$ is the complement of $\angle 4$ (*Fig. 4-19*).

Conclusion: $\angle 1 = \angle 3$

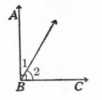

Fig. 4-19

Proof:

STATEMENTS	AUTHORITIES
1. $\angle ABC = \angle EFG$	1. Hypothesis
2. $\angle 2 = \angle 4$	2. Hypothesis
3. $\angle ABC - \angle 2 = \angle EFG - \angle 4$	3. Subtraction
4. $\angle 1 = \angle 3$	4. Completion

Corollary: If angles are complements of the same angle, then they are equal.

Supplementary Angle Theorem

If angles are supplements of equal angles, then they are equal.

Hypothesis: $\angle ABC = \angle DFG = 180°$, $\angle 2 = \angle 4$, $\angle 1$ is the supplement of $\angle 2$, $\angle 3$ is the supplement of $\angle 4$ (*Fig. 4-20*).

Conclusion: $\angle 1 = \angle 3$

Fig. 4-20

Proof: Write a proof for this theorem and compare it with that on page 446.

Corollary: If angles are supplements of the same angle, then they are equal.

Vertical Angle Theorem

If two lines intersect, then the vertical angles are equal.

Hypothesis: Lines AB and CD intersect on E, forming vertical angle pairs
$(\angle 1,\ \angle 3),\ (\angle 2,\ \angle 4)$, Fig. 4-21.

Conclusion: $\angle 1 = \angle 3,\ \angle 2 = \angle 4$

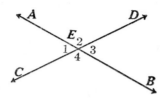

Fig. 4-21

Proof: Copy and complete the following proof:

STATEMENTS	AUTHORITIES
1. $\angle CED$ is a straight angle.	1.
2. $\angle 1$ is the supplement of $\angle 2$.	2.
3. $\angle AEB$ is a straight angle.	3.
4. $\angle 3$ is the supplement of $\angle 2$.	4.
5. $\angle 1 = \angle 3$	5.
6. Similarly, $\angle 2$ and $\angle 4$ are each supplements of $\angle 1$.	6.
7. $\angle 2 = \angle 4$.	7.

Exercise 4-7

(A)

1. State the measurement of the angle which is the complement of each of the following:

(i) 60°   (ii) 37°   (iii) 40°   (iv) 8°   (v) 82°

2. State the measurement of the angle which is the supplement of each of the following:

(i) 60°   (ii) 37°   (iii) 40°   (iv) 120°   (v) 143°

3. Name pairs of equal angles in each of the following diagrams and state the authority which justifies each conclusion:

(i) 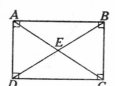 (ii)   (iii)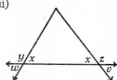

4. State the authorities which are necessary to complete the proof of the following deduction:

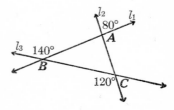

Hypothesis: Lines l_1, l_2, l_3 intersecting on A, B, C, as shown, so that the angles have the measurements indicated

Conclusion: $\angle BAC + \angle ABC + \angle ACB = 180°$

Proof:

STATEMENTS	AUTHORITIES
1. $\quad \angle BAC = 80°$	1.
2. $\quad \angle ABC = 40°$	2.
3. $\quad \angle ACB = 60°$	3.
4. $\quad \angle BAC + \angle ABC + \angle ACB$ $= (80 + 40 + 60)°$	4.
5. $\quad \angle BAC + \angle ABC + \angle ACB$ $= 180°$	5.

(B)

Write a complete proof for each of the following deductions:

5. In the diagram at the left below, XA and XE are opposite rays, and $XB \perp XD$. Prove $\angle AXB$ and $\angle DXE$ are complementary.

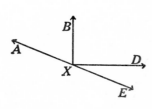

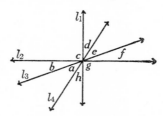

6. In the diagram at the right above, l_1, l_2, l_3, and l_4 intersect as shown, and $l_1 \perp l_2$. The angles have the measurements indicated. Prove $d + a + f = g$.

7. In the accompanying diagram, $\angle 2 = \angle 3$.
Prove $\angle 1 + \angle 4 = 180°$.

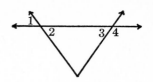

4·15 Summary.

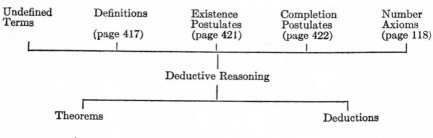

Chapter V

CONGRUENCE PARALLELISM

5.1 Triangle congruence postulates.

TRIANGLE CONGRUENCE POSTULATE (sas)

If two triangles have two sides and the contained angle of one respectively equal to two sides and the contained angle of the other, then the triangles are congruent.

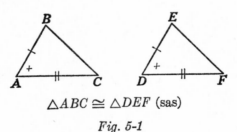

$\triangle ABC \cong \triangle DEF$ (sas)

Fig. 5-1

TRIANGLE CONGRUENCE POSTULATE (sss)

If two triangles have three sides of one respectively equal to three sides of the other, then the triangles are congruent.

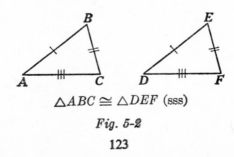

$\triangle ABC \cong \triangle DEF$ (sss)

Fig. 5-2

123

TRIANGLE CONGRUENCE POSTULATE (asa)

If two triangles have two angles and the contained side of one respectively equal to two angles and the contained side of the other, then the triangles are congruent.

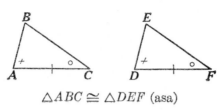

$$\triangle ABC \cong \triangle DEF \text{ (asa)}$$

Fig. 5-3

5·2 Analysis of a deduction. Analysis is the method used to discover the plan for writing a formal proof. It works in reverse order to synthesis. We begin with what we are trying to prove and work back to the given conditions, as illustrated in the following example.

Hypothesis: $A \to \sim B,\ C,\ \sim D \to F,\ \sim B \to \sim D,\ C \to A$

Conclusion: F

Analysis:

I CAN PROVE	IF I CAN PROVE	
1. F	1. $\sim D$	$(\because \sim D \to F)$.
2. $\sim D$	2. $\sim B$	$(\because \sim B \to \sim D)$.
3. $\sim B$	3. A	$(\because A \to \sim B)$.
4. A	4. C	$(\because C \to A)$.
5. C by hypothesis.		

The statements contained in the analysis are used in reverse order to build the proof.

Proof:

STATEMENTS	AUTHORITIES
1. $C \to A$	1. Hypothesis
2. C	2. Hypothesis
3. A	3. Law of Detachment 1, 2
4. $A \to \sim B$	4. Hypothesis
5. $\sim B$	5. Law of Detachment 3, 4
6. $\sim B \to \sim D$	6. Hypothesis
7. $\sim D$	7. Law of Detachment 5, 6
8. $\sim D \to F$	8. Hypothesis
9. F	9. Law of Detachment 7, 8

Analysis becomes increasingly valuable as the number of steps in the proof and the number of premises increase. When a given hypothesis contains many statements, analysis enables us to recognize those which are relevant to the proof.

Example 1. If in quadrilateral $ABCD$ (*Fig. 5-4*), $AD = CB$ and $\angle ADB = \angle CBD$, then $AB = CD$.

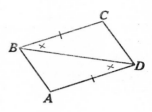

Hypothesis: $ABCD$ is a quadrilateral with $AD = CB$ and $\angle ADB = \angle CBD$.

Conclusion: $AB = CD$

Fig. 5-4

Analysis:

I CAN PROVE	IF I CAN PROVE
1. $AB = CD$	1. Two triangles congruent with AB and CD as corresponding sides.
2. Two triangles congruent with AB and CD as corresponding sides	2. $\triangle ABD \cong \triangle CDB$.
3. $\triangle ABD \cong \triangle CDB$	3. $AD = CB$, $BD = DB$, $\angle ADB = \angle CBD$.
4. $AD = CB$ by hypothesis.	
5. $BD = DB$ by reflexive property.	
6. $\angle ADB = \angle CBD$ by hypothesis.	

Proof:

STATEMENTS		AUTHORITIES
1. In $\triangle$'s ABD and CDB $\Big\{$ $AD = CB$		1. Hypothesis
2. $BD = DB$		2. Reflexive
3. $\angle ADB = \angle CBD$		3. Hypothesis
4. $\triangle ABD \cong \triangle CDB$		4. sas
5. $AB = CD$		5. Definition

Example 2. In *Fig. 5-5*, if A and B are the centres of two intersecting circles, then line segment AB bisects $\angle PAQ$.

Hypothesis: Two circles with centres A and B intersecting on P and Q

Conclusion: $\angle PAB = \angle QAB$

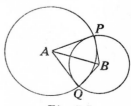

Fig. 5-5

Analysis:

I CAN PROVE	IF I CAN PROVE
1. $\angle PAB = \angle QAB$	1. Two triangles congruent with $\angle PAB$, $\angle QAB$ corresponding angles.
2. Two triangles congruent with $\angle PAB$, $\angle QAB$ corresponding angles	2. $\triangle PAB \cong \triangle QAB$.
3. $\triangle PAB \cong \triangle QAB$	3. $PA = QA$, $AB = AB$, $PB = QB$.
4. $PA = QA$ by definition.	
5. $AB = AB$ by reflexive property.	
6. $PB = QB$ by definition.	

Proof: Write a complete proof; compare it with that on page 447.

Example 3. Write a complete analysis and proof of the following deduction and compare them with those on page 447.

Hypothesis: In *Fig. 5-6*, $AB = AD$ and $BC = DC$.

Conclusion: $BE = ED$

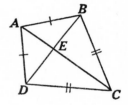

Fig. 5-6

Exercise 5-1

(A)

1. In the following pairs of triangles, name the equal sides or angles sufficient for the congruence of each pair:

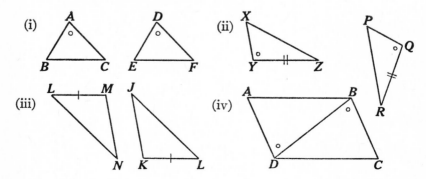

Give an oral analysis of each of the following:

2. *Hypothesis:* P is any point on the right bisector of AB.
Conclusion: $PA = PB$

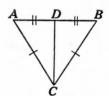

3. *Hypothesis:* $\triangle ABC$ in which $AD = BD$, $AC = BC$
Conclusion: $\angle ADC$ is a right angle.

4. *Hypothesis:* $MN = SR$,
$\quad\quad\quad\quad \angle MNR = \angle SRN$

Conclusion: $\angle M = \angle S$

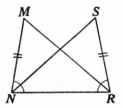

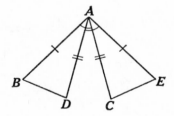

5. *Hypothesis:* $AB = AE$
$\quad\quad\quad\quad\quad AD = AC$
$\quad\quad\quad\quad \angle BAC = \angle EAD$
Conclusion: $BD = EC$

(B)

Write an analysis for each of the following deductions:

6. *Hypothesis:* $B \rightarrow \sim C$, B, $\sim C \rightarrow D$, $D \rightarrow \sim A$
Conclusion: $\sim A$

7. *Hypothesis:* $\sim A$, $B \rightarrow \sim D$, $C \rightarrow F$, $\sim A \rightarrow G$, $G \rightarrow B$, $\sim D \rightarrow C$,
$\quad\quad\quad\quad B \rightarrow \sim D$

Conclusion: F

8. If a triangle is isosceles, then the lengths of the medians drawn from the ends of the base are equal.

Write a complete analysis and proof for each of the following deductions:

9. If two triangles are congruent, then the corresponding medians have equal lengths.

10. If the median of a triangle is also an altitude, then the triangle is isosceles.

11. $\triangle PQR$ is an isosceles triangle with $PQ = PR$. QR is extended to S so that $QR = RS$, and PQ is extended to T so that $PQ = QT$. If $\angle PQR = \angle PRQ$, then $PS = TR$.

5·3 Converse statements, biconditional statements.

Consider the implications:

(i) *If a person lives in Ontario, then he lives in Canada.*

(ii) *If a person lives in Canada, then he lives in Ontario.*

The second statement is called the *converse* of the first; also, the first statement is the converse of the second.

It is important to note that the converse of a statement is not necessarily true even though the given implication is true.

DEFINITION: *When two conditional statements are so related that the hypothesis and conclusion consist of single statements which are interchanged, then each conditional statement is said to be the converse of the other.*

An implication and its converse may be represented in symbolic form as follows:

IMPLICATION	CONVERSE
If P, then Q.	If Q, then P.
$P \rightarrow Q$	$Q \rightarrow P$

The implication, *If a person lives in Ontario, then he lives in Canada,* refers to a universal set U, the set of all persons.

The statement,
   P: If a person lives in Ontario.
refers to a subset of U.

The statement,
   Q: He lives in Canada.
also refers to a subset of U.

Let A be the subset of U for which P is true, and let B be the subset of U for which Q is true.

Hence, if $P \rightarrow Q$ is true, then $A \subseteq B$.

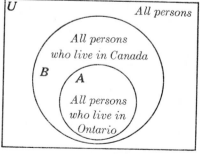

Fig. 5-7

The Venn diagram, *Fig. 5-7*, indicates that {all persons who live in Ontario} is a subset of {all persons who live in Canada}. This diagram is a representation of the relation between the sets referred to by the original implication.

The Venn diagram corresponding to the implication $P \rightarrow Q$ is shown in *Fig. 5-8*.

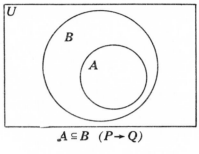

$A \subseteq B \; (P \rightarrow Q)$

Fig. 5-8

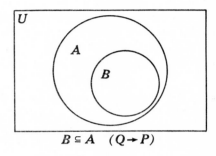

$B \subseteq A \; (Q \rightarrow P)$

Fig. 5-9

The Venn diagram corresponding to the converse of $P \rightarrow Q$, that is, $Q \rightarrow P$, is shown in *Fig. 5-9*.

A study of these Venn diagrams illustrates that the truth of an implication does not necessarily imply the truth of its converse.

In a definition one important characteristic is that the statement formed by interchanging the subject and predicate is also true. This characteristic is stated more precisely in the following manner:

The converse of a definition is true.

The implication:

If an angle is acute, then it has a degree measure less than 90.

and its converse:

If an angle has a degree measure less than 90, then it is an acute angle.

may be combined into the sentence:

An angle has a degree measure less than 90 if and only if it is an acute angle.

This statement, which makes use of the logical connective "if and only if", is called a *biconditional statement* because it contains two conditional sentences: an implication and its converse.

Example 1. Write a biconditional sentence which includes the following implication and its converse:

If two angles of a triangle are equal, then the sides opposite these angles are equal.

Solution. Two angles of a triangle are equal if and only if the sides opposite these angles are equal.

Example 2. Write the two converse implications contained in the following biconditional statement:

Two lines are parallel if and only if pairs of alternate angles formed by a transversal are equal.

Solution. 1. If two lines are parallel, then pairs of alternate angles formed by a transversal are equal.

2. If pairs of alternate angles, formed when a transversal meets two lines, are equal, then the two lines are parallel.

In general, if P and Q represent any two statements, then the implication, converse, and biconditional statements may be represented as follows:

IMPLICATION	CONVERSE	BICONDITIONAL
$P \rightarrow Q$ which is read:	$Q \rightarrow P$	$P \leftrightarrow Q$
If P then Q.	If Q then P.	P if and only if Q.
or	*or*	*or*
P implies Q.	Q implies P.	P equivalent Q.

The Venn diagram corresponding to $P \leftrightarrow Q$ consists of two circles each completely contained in the other. as in *Fig. 5-10.*

It should be noted that before a biconditional statement is accepted as true each of the conditional statements included must be proved true.

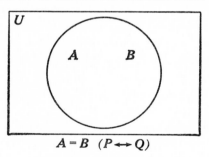

$$A = B \quad (P \leftrightarrow Q)$$

Fig. 5-10

5·4 Converse theorems; "if and only if" theorems. Since many of the theorems of geometry often involve several statements in the conclusion and several statements in the hypothesis, a converse theorem is defined as follows:

> DEFINITION: *A converse theorem is a theorem that is formed from a given theorem by interchanging any number of statements in the hypothesis of the given theorem with an equal number of statements in the conclusion.*

In geometry, it is convenient to combine a theorem and its converse theorem into a single statement by using the "if and only if" form. The combined theorem may be referred to as an *if and only if theorem.* To establish an "if and only if" theorem it is necessary to prove:

(i) the implication,

(ii) the converse of the implication.

5·5 The Isosceles Triangle Theorem.

The Isosceles Triangle Theorem

Two angles of a triangle are equal if and only if the sides opposite these angles are equal.

PART I

Hypothesis: $\triangle ABC$ in which $AB = AC$, *Fig. 5-11*

Conclusion: $\angle ACB = \angle ABC$

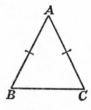 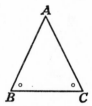

Fig. 5-11   *Fig. 5-12*

PART II

Hypothesis: $\triangle ABC$ in which $\angle ABC = \angle ACB$, *Fig. 5-12*

Conclusion: $AC = AB$

            (A proof of this theorem is given on page 448.)

Corollary: A triangle is equilateral if and only if it is equiangular.

Exercise 5-2

(A)

1. State (a) the converse statement and (b) the biconditional statement which can be formed from each of the following implications; assess the truth of the statements formed:

    (i) If two lines intersect at right angles, then the lines are perpendicular.

    (ii) If $x = 3$, then $2x + 5 = 11$.

    (iii) If two angles are the supplements of the same angle, then they are equal.

(iv) If an angle is part of a given angle, then it is less than the given angle.

(v) *Hypothesis:* $\triangle ABC$ in which $\angle A = \angle B = \angle C$
Conclusion: $BC = AC = AB$

(vi) *Hypothesis:* Lines AB and CD intersect on E.
Conclusion: $\angle AED = \angle CEB$

2. State the two conditional statements contained in each of the following biconditional statements:

(i) A geometric figure is a triangle if and only if it has three vertices.

(ii) $AB + BC = AC$ if and only if B is between A and C.

(iii) Two lines are parallel if and only if they have no point in common.

(iv) A point is on a circle if and only if it is a constant distance from a fixed point.

Give an oral analysis of each of the following deductions:

3. *Hypothesis:* In the diagram at the left below, $AD = BD = DC$.
Conclusion: $\angle BAC = \angle ABD + \angle ACD$

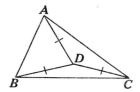 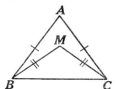

4. *Hypothesis:* In the diagram at the right above, $AB = AC$, $MB = MC$.
Conclusion: $\angle ABM = \angle ACM$

5. *Hypothesis:* In the diagram at the left below, the angles have measurements as indicated and $AB = AC$.
Conclusion: $AD = DC = BC$

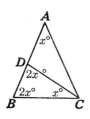 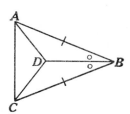

(B)

Write an analysis for each of the following deductions:

6. *Hypothesis:* In the diagram at the right above, $AB = BC$,
$\angle ABD = \angle CBD$.
Conclusion: $\angle DAC = \angle DCA$

7. In quadrilateral $PQRS$, $PQ = PS$ and $\angle PQR = \angle PSR$. Prove $RQ = RS$.

8. The median drawn to the base of an isosceles triangle is an altitude of the triangle.

Write a complete proof for each of the following deductions:

9. ABC is an isosceles triangle with $AB = AC$. BC is extended to D and CB is extended to E so that $CD = BE$. Prove that $AE = AD$.

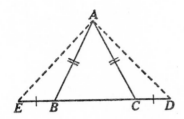 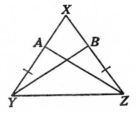

10. In $\triangle XYZ$, $XY = XZ$. A and B are points on XY and XZ, respectively, such that $AY = BZ$. Prove that $BY = AZ$.

11. MN, PR, and ST are three diameters of a circle. Prove that $\triangle MPS \cong \triangle NRT$.

12. $ABCD$ is a quadrilateral in which $AB = CD$ and $\angle ABC = \angle BCD$. Prove that $\angle DAB = \angle ADC$.

5·6 Indirect proof. The two statements:

1. $\triangle ABC$ *is an isosceles triangle.*
2. $\triangle ABC$ *is not an isosceles triangle.*

are *contradictory statements.* Each of these is the *negation* of the other. If either of these is true, the other is false; and conversely, if either is false, the other is true. This assumption is a fundamental rule of inference in logical reasoning and may be referred to as the *Law of Contradiction*.

This law may be stated as follows:

(i) If a statement is true, then its negation is false.
(ii) If a statement is false, then its negation is true.

The Law of Contradiction may be expressed using symbols as follows:

(i) If P is true, then $\sim P$ is false.
(ii) If P is false, then $\sim P$ is true.

The Law of Contradiction leads to a method of proof called *proof by contradiction* or *indirect proof.* The plan in this method of proof is to show that if the negation of a conclusion to be proved is false, then we infer by the Law of Contradiction that the conclusion is true.

The following examples illustrate the indirect method of proof.

Example 1.

Hypothesis: $\sim A \rightarrow \sim B, \sim B \rightarrow \sim C, C$

Conclusion: A

Analysis:

I CAN PROVE	IF I CAN PROVE
1. A	1. $\sim A$ is false.
2. $\sim A$ is false	2. The assumption that $\sim A$ is true leads to a contradiction of a known fact.
3. The assumption that $\sim A$ is true leads to the logical consequent $\sim B$; $\sim B$ leads to the logical consequent $\sim C$, which is a contradiction of the given premise C.	

Proof:

STATEMENTS	AUTHORITIES
1. $\sim A$ is true.	1. Assumption of the negation of the conclusion A
2. $\sim A \rightarrow \sim B$	2. Hypothesis
3. $\sim B$	3. Law of Detachment 1, 2
4. $\sim B \rightarrow \sim C$	4. Hypothesis
5. $\sim C$	5. Law of Detachment
6. $\sim A$ is false.	6. 5 contradicts the hypothesis.
7. A	7. Law of Contradiction

Example 2.

Hypothesis: $\triangle ABC$ (*Fig. 5-13*) in which $\angle B \neq \angle C$

Conclusion: $AB \neq AC$

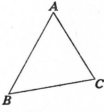

Fig. 5-13

Analysis:

I CAN PROVE	IF I CAN PROVE
1. $AB \neq AC$	1. $AB = AC$ is false.
2. $AB = AC$ is false	2. The assumption $AB = AC$ leads to a conclusion which contradicts a known fact.

I CAN PROVE	IF I CAN PROVE
3. The assumption $AB = AC$ leads to the logical consequent $\angle B = \angle C$ by the Isosceles Triangle Theorem, which is a contradiction of the premise $\angle B \neq \angle C$.	

Proof:

STATEMENTS	AUTHORITIES
1. $AB = AC$	1. Assumption of negation of conclusion $AB \neq AC$
2. $\angle B = \angle C$	2. Isosceles Triangle Theorem
3. $AB = AC$ is false.	3. 2 contradicts the hypothesis.
4. $AB \neq AC$	4. Law of Contradiction

Steps in an indirect proof.

1. Introduce the contradictory statement (negation) of the desired conclusion as a new premise.
2. From this new premise, together with the given premises, deduce a contradiction of a known fact.
3. State that the desired conclusion is true by the Law of Contradiction.

5·7 Basic triangle inequality theorems.

The Exterior Angle Theorem

An exterior angle of a triangle is greater than either remote interior angle.

Hypothesis: $\triangle ABC$ in which C is between B and D *(Fig. 5-14)*

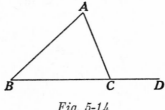

Fig. 5-14

Conclusion: $\angle ACD > \angle A$ and $\angle ACD > \angle ABC$
(A proof of the theorem is given on page 448)

Angle-Side Inequality Theorems

a. If one side of a triangle is greater than another side, then the angle opposite the greater side is greater than the angle opposite the lesser side.

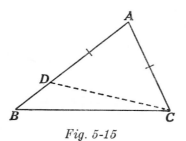

Fig. 5-15

Hypothesis: $\triangle ABC$ in which $AB > AC$

Conclusion: $\angle ACB > \angle ABC$

Proof: Copy and complete the authorities column of the proof of this theorem. Compare your solution with that on page 449.

STATEMENTS	AUTHORITIES
1. $AB > AC$	1.
2. D is the point on line segment AB such that $AD = AC$.	2.
3. $\angle ADC > \angle ABC$	3.
4. $\angle ADC = \angle ACD$	4.
5. $\angle ACD > \angle ABC$	5.
6. $\angle ACB > \angle ACD$	6.
7. $\angle ACB > \angle ABC$	7.

b. If one angle of a triangle is greater than another angle, then the side opposite the greater angle is greater than the side opposite the lesser angle.

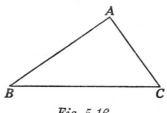

Fig. 5-16

Hypothesis: $\triangle ABC$ such that $\angle ACB > \angle ABC$

Conclusion: $AB > AC$

Analysis: One of three possibilities must be true. Either $AB > AC$, $AB = AC$, $AB < AC$ (Trichotomy Law). Write a complete analysis and proof of this theorem using the indirect method of proof and the Law of Contradiction to show that $AB = AC$ and $AB < AC$ are false statements. Compare your solution with that on page 449.

Side Inequality Theorem

The sum of the lengths of any two sides of a triangle is greater than the length of the third side.

Hypothesis: $\triangle ABC$

Conclusion: $AB + AC > BC$

Using the accompanying diagram, write a complete analysis and proof of this theorem. Compare your solution with that on page 449

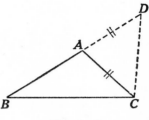

Fig. 5-17

Exercise 5-3

(A)

1. Name the sides of the triangles in increasing order of length:

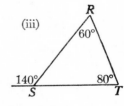

2. Name the angles of the triangles in decreasing order of size:

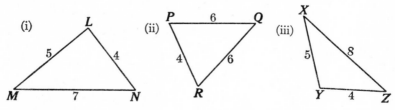

3. In $\triangle XYZ$, $XY = 5$ units, $YZ = 14$ units, $ZX = 11$ units. Without referring to a diagram, name (i) the largest angle (ii) the smallest angle.

4. In $\triangle PQR$, $\angle P = 36°$, $\angle Q = 74°$, $\angle R = 70°$. Without referring to a diagram, name (i) the longest side (ii) the shortest side.

5. State, giving reasons, which of the following sets of numbers can represent the lengths of the sides of a triangle:

(i) 2, 4, 5   (ii) 3, 6, 9   (iii) 3, 4, 5   (iv) 4, 5, 10

(B)

Write indirect proofs for deductions 6, 7, and 8:

6. In △ABC (left below), if AB ≠ AC, BD = DC, then AD is not perpendicular to BC.

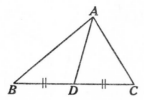 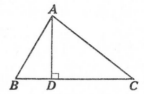

7. In △ABC (right above), if AB ≠ AC, AD ⊥ BC, then BD ≠ DC.
8. In the diagram at the left below, PQ = PR. Prove that PX > PQ.

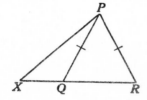 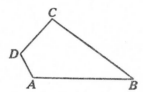

9. *Hypothesis:* In the diagram at the right above, AD is the shortest side and CB is the longest side.
   Conclusion: ∠D > ∠B

10. If a triangle contains a right angle, then the other angles are acute.

11. The shortest line segment which can be drawn to a line from a point not on the line is the line segment perpendicular to the line.

12. The sum of the lengths of the diagonals of a quadrilateral is greater than the sum of the lengths of either pair of opposite sides.

13. The sum of the lengths of the sides of a quadrilateral is greater than the sum of the lengths of the diagonals.

14. P is the intersection of the diagonals AC and BD of quadrilateral ABCD. X is any other point. Prove XA + XB + XC + XD > PA + PB + PC + PD.

15. △PQR is an isosceles triangle with PQ = PR. QP is extended to X so that PQ = PX. M is any point in the interior of △PQR and on the bisector of ∠RPQ. Prove that MQ + MR < PQ + PX.

5·8 Parallel line theorems.

Parallel Line Theorem

If a transversal meets two lines, the two lines are **parallel if and only if:**

(i) alternate angles are equal, or

(ii) corresponding angles are equal, or

(iii) interior angles on the same side of a transversal are **supplementary.**

PART I

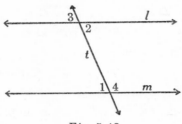

Fig. 5-18

Hypothesis: Transversal t meeting lines l and m making:

(i) $\angle 1 = \angle 2$ or (ii) $\angle 1 = \angle 3$ or (iii) $\angle 2 + \angle 4 = 180°$

Conclusion: $l \parallel m$ (in each case)

(A proof of this theorem is given on page 450.)

PART II

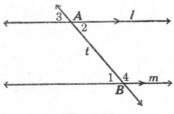

Fig. 5-19

Hypothesis: Transversal t meeting parallel lines l and m at A and B, respectively

Conclusion: (i) $\angle 1 = \angle 2$

(ii) $\angle 1 = \angle 3$

(iii) $\angle 2 + \angle 4 = 180°$

(A proof of this theorem is given on page 451.)

Corollary: If lines are perpendicular to the same line, then they are parallel to each other.

Quadrilateral-Parallelogram Theorem

If two opposite sides of a quadrilateral are equal and parallel, then the quadrilateral is a parallelogram.

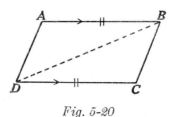

Fig. 5-20

Hypothesis: Quadrilateral $ABCD$ in which $AB = CD$ and $AB \parallel CD$

Conclusion: $ABCD$ is a parallelogram.

(A proof of this theorem is given on page 451.)

Parallelogram Theorem

In any parallelogram:

     (i) the opposite angles are equal;

     (ii) the opposite sides are equal;

     (iii) the diagonals bisect each other.

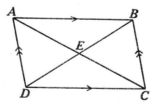

Fig. 5-21

Hypothesis: A parallelogram $ABCD$ in which AC and BD intersect on E (*Fig. 5-21*)

Conclusion: (i) $\angle ABC = \angle ADC$, $\angle DAB = \angle BCD$

           (ii) $AB = DC$, $AD = BC$

           (iii) $AE = EC$, $DE = EB$

           (A proof of this theorem is given on page 451.)

Corollary: The distance between any two parallel lines is constant.

Triangle Angle Sum Theorem

The angle sum of a triangle is 180°.
Hypothesis: $\triangle ABC$ *(Fig. 5-22)*
Conclusion: $\angle 1 + \angle 2 + \angle 3 = 180°$
(A proof is given on page 452.)

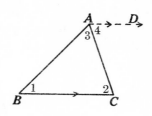

Fig. 5-22

Corollary 1: An exterior angle of a triangle is equal to the sum of the remote interior angles.

Corollary 2: If two angles of one triangle are respectively equal to two angles of another triangle, the third angles are equal.

Corollary 3: The acute angles of a right triangle are complementary.

Corollary 4: If one angle of a triangle is equal to the sum of the other two angles, then that angle is a right angle.

Corollary 5: Each angle of an equilateral triangle has a measurement of 60°.

Example 1.
Hypothesis: $AB = BE = CD$
$AB \parallel CD$ *(Fig. 5-23)*
Conclusion: $BD = EC$ and $BD \parallel EC$

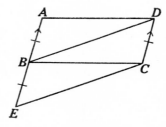

Fig. 5-23

Analysis:

I CAN PROVE	IF I CAN PROVE
1. $BD = EC$ and $BD \parallel EC$	1. Figure $BDCE$ is a parallelogram.
2. Figure $BDCE$ is a parallelogram	2. $BE = DC$ and $BE \parallel DC$.
3. $BE = DC$ and $BE \parallel DC$ by hypothesis.	

Proof:

STATEMENTS	AUTHORITIES
1. $BE \parallel CD$	1. Hypothesis
2. $BE = CD$	2. Hypothesis
3. $BDCE$ is a parallelogram.	3. Quadrilateral-Parallelogram Th.
4. $BD = EC$	4. Parallelogram Theorem
5. $BD \parallel EC$	5. Definition

Example 2.

Hypothesis: $PQRS$ is a quadrilateral having $\angle P = \angle S$, $\angle Q = \angle R$.

Conclusion: $PS \parallel QR$

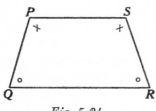

Fig. 5-24

Analysis:

I CAN PROVE	IF I CAN PROVE
1. $PS \parallel QR$	1. $\angle P + \angle Q = 180°$.
2. $\angle P + \angle Q = 180°$	2. $2(\angle P + \angle Q) = 360°$.
3. $2(\angle P + \angle Q) = 360°$	3. $\angle P + \angle S + \angle Q + \angle R = 360°$ since $\angle P = \angle S$, $\angle Q = \angle R$.
4. $\angle P + \angle S + \angle Q + \angle R = 360°$ by the Triangle Angle Sum Theorem.	

Proof: Write a proof of this deduction and compare it with that on page 452.

Example 3. Write a complete analysis and proof for the following deduction. Compare your solution with that on page 453.

X and Y are the midpoints of AD and BC, respectively, in the parallelogram $ABCD$. XC and AY intersect BD on T and S, respectively. Prove $BT = DS$.

Exercise 5-4

(A)

1. State, giving reasons, the angles which have equal measurements in the following:

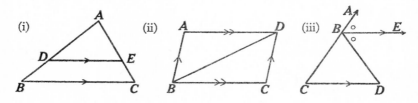

(iv)

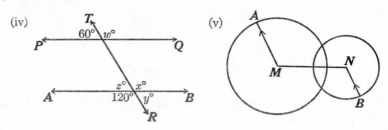

(v)

2. Find the measurements of the angles indicated in the following:

(i)

(ii)

(iii)

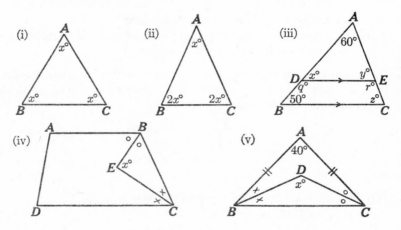

(iv)

(v)

3. In each of the parallelograms, find x, y, z, and w:

(i)

(ii)

(iii)

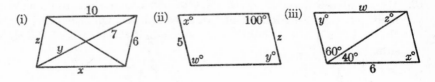

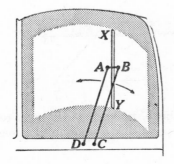

4. The windshield wiper XY on a streetcar window is fastened to the supporting arm so that $XY \perp AB$. Points A, B, C, and D of the rotating arm are the vertices of a parallelogram. If CD is horizontal, prove that XY is always vertical.

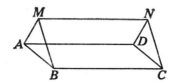

5. For the diagram above, give an oral proof that, if $ABCD$ and $MBCN$ are parallelograms, then $MADN$ is also a parallelogram.

(B)

6. Write an analysis of the following deduction:
If the bisector of an exterior angle of a triangle is parallel to the opposite side, then the triangle is isosceles.

7. Use the indirect method of proof to show that two line segments drawn from two vertices of a triangle and terminating in the opposite sides cannot bisect each other.

8. In the diagram, a chord AB of a circle sub-tends $\angle APB$ at a point P on the circle and $\angle AOB$ at the centre. Prove $\angle AOB = 2 \angle APB$.

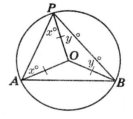

9. Write an analysis of the following deduction:
ABC is a triangle in which $AB = AC$. AB is extended to D, so that $BD = BC$. Prove that $\angle ACD = 3 \angle ADC$.

10. By using the diagram at the left below, prove that the line segment joining the midpoints of two sides of a triangle is parallel to the third side and has a length equal to one-half the length of the third side.

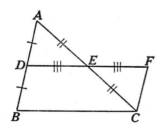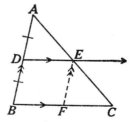

11. By using the diagram at the right above, prove that the ray from the midpoint of one side of a triangle, parallel to a second side, bisects the third side of the triangle.

5.9 Congruence theorems.

The aas *Congruence Theorem*

If two angles and a side opposite one of them in one triangle are respectively equal to two angles and the corresponding side in a second triangle, then the triangles are congruent.

Hypothesis: $\triangle ABC$ and $\triangle DEF$ such that $\angle A = \angle D$, $\angle B = \angle E$, $BC = EF$

Conclusion: $\triangle ABC \cong \triangle DEF$ (A proof of this theorem is given on page 454.)

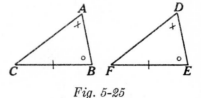

Fig. 5-25

The Right Triangle Congruence Theorem

If the hypotenuse and one side of a right triangle are respectively equal to the hypotenuse and the corresponding side of another right triangle, then the triangles are congruent.

Hypothesis: $\triangle ABC$ and $\triangle DEF$ such that $AB = DE$, $AC = DF$, and $\angle ACB = \angle DFE = 90°$

Conclusion: $\triangle ABC \cong \triangle DEF$ (A proof of this theorem is given on page 454.)

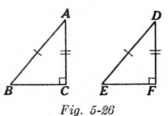

Fig. 5-26

Exercise 5-5

(A)

1. Prove triangles congruent in each of the following:

(i)   (ii)   (iii)

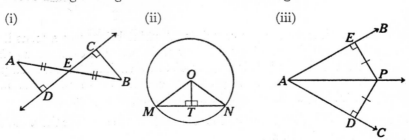

2. The distance PQ across a river was determined as follows. Stakes were set up at P and T. A third stake was placed at R, half-way between P and T. Then $\angle T$ was constructed equal to $\angle P$ and stake S located so that it was in line with R and Q. Prove that the distance PQ across the river is given by the length of ST.

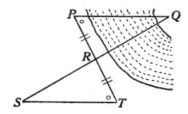 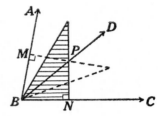

3. The diagram at the right above shows a method of bisecting a given $\angle ABC$ by using a set square. Prove that this method is correct.

(B)

4. Any point on the bisector of a given angle is equidistant from the arms of the angle.

5. The point of intersection of the right bisectors of two sides of a triangle is equidistant from the three vertices.

6. If the bisectors of $\angle B$ and $\angle C$ in $\triangle ABC$ meet on O, then the perpendiculars from O to each of the sides of the triangle have equal lengths.

7. *Hypothesis:* In the diagram, $AB = CD$; X is the centre of the circle; $XM \perp AB, XN \perp CD$.

Conclusion: $XM = XN$

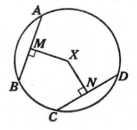

5·10 Locus. A *locus* is a set of points. A point belongs to a locus if and only if it satisfies the defining statement of the set. For example, a point is on a circle if and only if it is a given distance (radius) from a fixed point (centre). Our experience in geometry enables us to recognize many fundamental loci, as illustrated in the following examples.

Example 1. Draw the locus (point set) such that each point is a distance d units from a given line.

Solution.

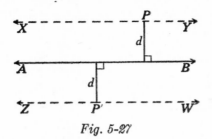

Fig. 5-27

If *AB* is the given line, then this locus is the pair of straight lines *XY* and *ZW* which are parallel to *AB* and a distance *d* units from it.

Example 2. Draw the locus (point set) such that each point is equally distant from two parallel lines.

Solution:

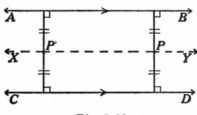

Fig. 5-28

If *AB* and *CD* are the given parallel lines, then this locus is the line *XY* which is parallel to *AB* and *CD* and is midway between them.

It is sometimes convenient to think of a locus as the set of points in the path traced out by a point which moves according to a given condition or set of conditions.

In this context, a circle is described as the path traced out by a point which moves so that its distance from a fixed point is constant.

In *Fig. 5-29*, a bicycle wheel makes one revolution on a level floor. The locus of the centre of the hub is a straight line *BA* parallel to the floor and at a distance from the floor equal to the radius.

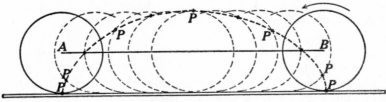

Fig. 5-29

If a chalk mark P is made on the surface of the tire, the path taken by the mark is the curve represented by the dotted line. This path or locus of P is a curved line called a *cycloid*.

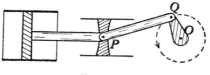

Fig. 5-30

In *Fig. 5-30*, a point P on the cross-head of a steam engine is forced to move back and forth on a straight line parallel to its guides above and below it. A point Q on the connecting rod-bearing moves in a circle, centre O, radius OQ. The locus of P is a straight line; the locus of Q is a circle. The entire mechanism converts motion in a straight line into circular motion.

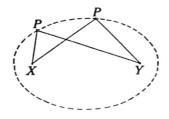

Fig. 5-31

In *Fig. 5-31*, X and Y are two fixed pegs. The ends of a cord are tied to the pegs leaving some slack. A pencil P slides inside the loop of the cord keeping it tight. The various positions of P which make up the locus of the point are determined by the fact that $PX + PY$ is a constant length. This curve, called an *ellipse*, is similar to the path of a planet in its course around the sun.

5·11 Locus theorems. Since a point belongs to a locus (point set) if and only if the point satisfies the condition(s) defining the locus, then a locus theorem involves a biconditional statement, and its proof requires the proof of two converse statements.

To prove the proposition, "The locus each point of which is equidistant from the end points of a line segment is the right bisector of the line segment", it is necessary to prove that, "A point is equidistant from the end points of a line segment if and only if it is on the right bisector of the line segment".

The Right Bisector Theorem

A point is equidistant from the end points of a line segment if and only if it is on the right bisector of the line segment.

PART I

If a point is on the right bisector of a line segment, then it is equidistant from the end points of the line segment.

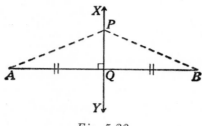

Fig. 5-32

Hypothesis: XY is the right bisector of line segment AB. P is any point on XY; Q is the intersection of XY and AB.

Conclusion: $AP = BP$

Write a proof for this theorem; compare your solution with that on page 454.

PART II (Converse)

If a point is equidistant from the end points of a line segment, then it is on the right bisector of the line segment.

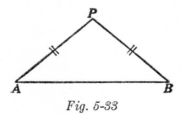

Fig. 5-33

Hypothesis: A point P and a line segment AB such that $PA = PB$

Conclusion: P is on the right bisector of AB.

Write a complete analysis and proof for this theorem. Compare your solution with that on page 455.

The Angle Bisector Theorem

A point is equidistant from the sides of an angle if and only if it is on the bisector of the angle.

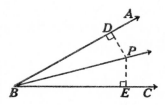

Fig. 5-34

PART I	PART II
Hypothesis: P is any point on the bisector of $\angle ABC$, $PE \perp BC$, and $PD \perp AB$.	**Hypothesis:** P is any point in the interior of $\angle ABC$ such that $PE = PD$ where $PD \perp AB$ and $PE \perp BC$.
Conclusion: $PE = PD$	**Conclusion:** P is on the bisector of $\angle ABC$.

Write a complete analysis and proof for both the implication and its converse contained in the biconditional statement of this theorem. Compare your solution with that on page 456.

Exercise 5-6

(A)

1. For each of the following, describe the locus each point of which is:
   (i) 5 inches from a given point;
   (ii) less than 5 inches from a given point;
   (iii) 3 inches from a given point;
   (iv) less than 5 inches and more than 3 inches from a given point.

2. For each of the following, describe the locus each point of which:
   (i) is a distance 4 cm. from a given point A on a line AB;
   (ii) is a distance 2 cm. from the given line AB;
   (iii) satisfies both of the conditions stated in (i) and (ii).

(B)

Using ruler and compasses only, construct the following loci:

3. Given a line segment AB, a point O not on AB, and any point P on AB. PO is extended to Q so that $OP = QO$. By locating several positions of Q, predict the locus of Q.

4. The locus such that the sum of the distances from each point to two perpendicular lines is 2 inches.

5. The locus such that each point is 2 cm. from a given line and equidistant from two points not on the line.

6. The locus such that each point is equidistant from two given intersecting lines and a given distance from a point not on the line.

7. Given $\triangle ABC$, such that $AB = 3$ cm., $BC = 4$ cm., and $AC = 5$ cm.; the locus such that each point is in the interior of the triangle, and its distance to A is less than or equal to 3 cm.

8. The *incentre* I of a triangle is the point which is equidistant from each of the sides of the triangle. Construct the incentre of a given triangle Draw the circle whose centre is the incentre and whose radius is the perpendicular distance from the incentre to one side (the inscribed circle).

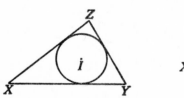 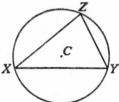

9. The *circumcentre* C of a triangle is the centre of the circle which contains the vertices of the triangle (circumscribed circle). Construct the circumscribed circle of a given triangle.

5·12 Contrapositive and inverse statements (supplementary). Previously we considered the implication:

If a person lives in Ontario, then he lives in Canada.

and discovered that a second implication, the converse, could be made from it:

If a person lives in Canada, then he lives in Ontario.

Another implication related to the original is:

If a person does not live in Canada, then he does not live in Ontario.

This statement is called the *contrapositive* of the original implication.

From the Venn diagram, it may be seen that the set of all persons who do *not* live in Canada is a subset of the set of all persons who do *not* live in Ontario. This illustrates that the implication:

If a person lives in Ontario, then he lives in Canada.

and the contrapositive statement:

If a person does not live in Canada, then he does not live in Ontario.

are logically equivalent statements: that is, if one of them is true, then the other is also true.

If P and Q represent statements, then

$$(P \rightarrow Q) \leftrightarrow (\sim Q \rightarrow \sim P) .$$

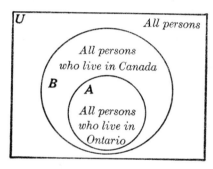

Fig. 5-35

The contrapositive of the converse of an implication is called the *inverse* of the implication. The interrelationship between the implication, converse, inverse, and contrapositive is illustrated in the following chart.

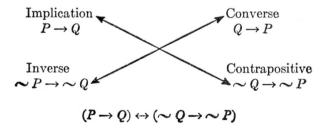

$$(P \rightarrow Q) \leftrightarrow (\sim Q \rightarrow \sim P)$$

The logical equivalence of the implication and its contrapositive leads to a third method of proof.

In addition to

(i) direct proof: *Law of Detachment*

(ii) indirect proof: *Law of Contradiction*

we may now add

(iii) contrapositive proof: *Law of the Contrapositive*

To formulate the contrapositive, $\sim Q \to \sim P$, of the implication, $P \to Q$, we negate both the premise and the conclusion and interchange them in the statement. For example:

Implication:

(A triangle is equilateral.) $\to$ (All sides of a triangle are equal.)

Contrapositive:

(All sides of a triangle are not equal.) $\to$ (The triangle is not equilateral.)

In the following example, solutions for the first four parts are given; compare your solutions for the others with those on page 456.

Example Write the contrapositive of each of the following implications:

(i) $A \to B$ (ii) $\sim R \to S$

(iii) If angles are right angles, then they are equal angles.

(iv) If $x = 5$, then $3x - \frac{1}{2} = 14\frac{1}{2}$.

(v) If a geometric figure is a square, then it is a rhombus.

(vi) $C \to \sim D$ (vii) $\sim M \to \sim N$

(viii) If a triangle has two unequal sides, then it has two unequal angles.

(ix) **Hypothesis:** Lines AB and CD intersect at E.

     Conclusion: $\angle AED = \angle CEB$

Solution:

(i) $\sim B \to \sim A$ (ii) $\sim S \to R$

(iii) If angles are unequal angles, then they are not all right angles.

(iv) If $3x - \frac{1}{2} \neq 14\frac{1}{2}$, then $x \neq 5$.

5·13 The contrapositive proof of the Parallel Line Theorem (supplementary). By examining the proof of the Parallel Line Theorem, it is seen that the second and third steps of the conclusion are derived directly from the first step; hence the initial part of the proof is to demonstrate that, "Two lines intersected by a transversal are parallel if and only if alternate angles are equal".

The two conditional statements contained in this biconditional sentence are:

(i) If a transversal meets two lines so that alternate angles are equal, then the lines are parallel.

(ii) If a transversal meets two parallel lines, then the alternate angles are equal.

The contrapositive proof of the Parallel Line Theorem consists of the proof of the contrapositive of each of these implications.

PART I

If a transversal meets two lines so that alternate angles are equal, then the lines are parallel.

. The contrapositive of this implication is:

If a transversal meets two non-parallel lines, then the alternate angles are not equal.

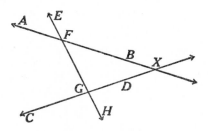

Fig. 5-36

The proof of the contrapositive theorem follows.

Hypothesis: A transversal EH meets two non-parallel lines AB and CD in F and G, respectively.

Conclusion: $\angle AFG \neq \angle FGD$, $\angle GFB \neq \angle FGC$

Proof:

STATEMENTS	AUTHORITIES
1. $AB \not\parallel CD$	1. Hypothesis
2. AB and CD meet in X.	2. Definition
3. $\angle AFG \neq \angle FGD$	3. Exterior Angle Theorem
4. $\angle GFB \neq \angle FGC$	4. 1, 2, Exterior Angle Theorem

Since the contrapositive statement has been proved, we may conclude that the original implication is true.

PART II

Write the contrapositive of the second implication.

Write a complete proof for this theorem and compare it with that on page 457.

5·14 Planes (supplementary). Although a plane is unlimited in extent in space, we usually picture it as a quadrilateral drawn obliquely. In *Fig. 5-37(a)*, quadrilateral $ABCD$ represents a plane. This plane may be referred to as plane AC or as plane p. The lines BC and CD are drawn heavier to make the plane appear horizontal. *Fig. 5-37(b)* illustrates a point M, a line, and a line segment OR in a plane AC.

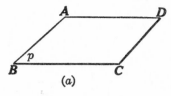

Fig. 5-37

a. *Fundamental properties of planes.*

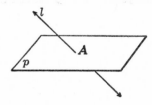

Fig. 5-38

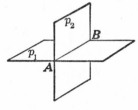

Fig. 5-39

(i) The intersection of a line and a plane is a point, *Fig. 5-38.*

(ii) The intersection of two planes is a line, *Fig. 5-39.*

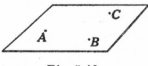

Fig. 5-40

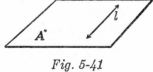

Fig. 5-41

(iii) A plane is determined by three points not in the same line, *Fig. 5-40.*

(iv) A plane is determined by a line and a point not on the line, *Fig. 5-41.*

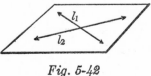

Fig. 5-42

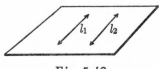

Fig. 5-43

(v) A plane is determined by two intersecting lines, *Fig. 5-42.*

(vi) A plane is determined by two parallel lines, *Fig. 5-43.*

5·15 Perpendiculars to planes (supplementary). In *Fig. 5-44*, the line *l* is perpendicular to the plane *P* because it intersects the plane *P* in the point *M* and is perpendicular to every line on *M* and in the plane. Only three of these lines, *a*, *b*, and *c*, are shown in *Fig. 5-44*.

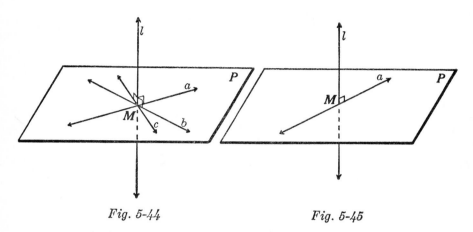

Fig. 5-44   Fig. 5-45

In *Fig. 5-45*, the line *l* intersects the plane *P* in *M*, and $l \perp a$, where line *a* is on *M* and is in plane *P*. However, *l* is not necessarily perpendicular to plane *P* because it is not known whether it is perpendicular to *all* the lines of the plane which are on *M*.

Since a plane is determined by two intersecting lines, if a line is perpendicular to two intersecting lines of the plane on the point of intersection, then the line is perpendicular to the plane

To represent a three-dimensional figure in two dimensions, certain shapes and angles are often distorted to suggest the third dimension.

In *Fig. 5-44*, line *l* is perpendicular to each of the lines *a*, *b*, and *c*, but the angles between *l* and the three lines are not drawn as right angles. The plane *P* is suggested by the quadrilateral, and the part of the line *l* which is hidden by the plane is dotted. In some diagrams this hidden part is omitted completely.

Write a solution to the following problem and compare it with that on page 457.

1. (i) Draw a diagram to illustrate the following:
   A line *AB* intersects a plane *Q* on *K*, and line *AB* is perpendicular to plane *Q*. *CK*, *DK*, and *EK* are three rays of the plane *Q*.
   (ii) Name all the right angles in this figure.

Exercise 5-7

(A)

1. If line CD is perpendicular to plane P, and R, S, T, and A are points in plane P, name the right angles in the diagram at the left below.

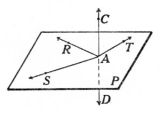 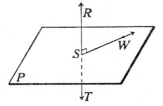

2. (i) If S and W are points in a plane P, and $\angle RSW = 90°$, explain why line RT is not necessarily perpendicular to the plane P.

  (ii) What is the least number of lines in plane P that must be perpendicular to line RT at S, so that line RT is perpendicular to plane P?

3. What is the least number of measurements a workman must make with a carpenter's square to check that a flagpole is perpendicular to the ground?

(B)

4. If $AC \perp$ plane P and B, C, D are points in plane P, and $CB = CD$, prove $\angle BAC = \angle DAC$.

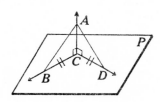 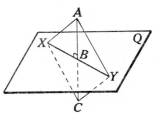

5. $AC \perp$ plane Q, and X, B, Y are collinear points in plane Q. If $AB = CB$, prove $\triangle AXY \cong \triangle CXY$.

6. A telephone pole is supported on the south side by a guy wire, which is fastened to the pole 12 ft. above the ground, and to the ground at a point 9 ft. from the base of the pole. Another guy wire on the east side is fastened to the pole 15 ft. from the ground, and to the ground at a point 20 ft. from the base. Draw and label a diagram to represent this information.

7. All surfaces of the box in the diagram are congruent squares. If $BR = BL$, prove $ER = EL$.

8. A piece of canvas 12 ft. square is stretched over a horizontal clothes-line to form a tent. The width of the tent opening at ground level is 5 ft. Draw and label a diagram to represent the tent.

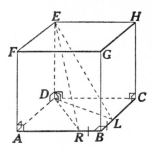

5·16 Perpendicular and parallel planes (supplementary).

a. *Perpendicular planes.* When two planes intersect, the intersection set is a line; this line separates each plane into two *half-planes.* In *Fig. 5-46,* line AB is the intersection of two planes and separates these planes into half-planes marked P_1, P_2, Q_1, and Q_2.

The set of points of a line and two non-coplanar half-planes of which the line is a common edge is a *dihedral angle.*

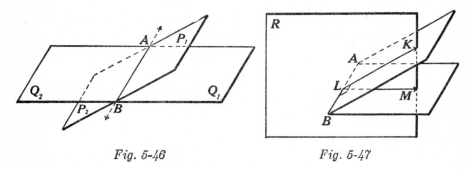

Fig. 5-46   Fig. 5-47

In *Fig. 5-46,* consider the dihedral angle formed by the line AB and the half-planes P_1 and Q_1. To find the measurement of this angle, a plane R is drawn through any point L in AB, perpendicular to AB, to cut the half-planes in rays LK and LM, respectively, as shown in *Fig. 5-47.*

The angle formed by these rays, $\angle KLM$, is called a *plane angle* of the dihedral angle.

> DEFINITION: *If a plane is drawn through any point of the edge of a dihedral angle, perpendicular to that edge and intersecting each of the half-planes in a ray, then the angle formed by these rays is called a plane angle of the dihedral angle.*

Since any two plane angles of a dihedral angle are equal, the measurement of the dihedral angle is the measurement of any of its plane angles. In order that two planes be perpendicular, they must intersect to form a dihedral angle of 90°. In *Fig. 5-48,* plane *P* is perpendicular to plane *Q,* because ∠ *KLM* = 90°.

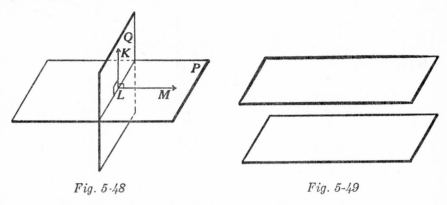

Fig. 5-48   Fig. 5-49

DEFINITION: *If two planes intersect to form a dihedral angle whose measurement is 90°, the two planes are perpendicular.*

b. *Parallel planes.* Parallel lines are defined as distinct lines lying in the same plane and having no point in common. A corresponding definition can be made for parallel planes.

DEFINITION: *If two distinct planes have no line in common, then the two planes are parallel.*

In drawing parallel planes, the quadrilaterals representing the planes are usually drawn with their corresponding sides parallel, as in *Fig. 5-49.*

c. *Parallel lines in three-dimensional space.* If two lines are selected, one in each of two parallel planes, these two lines are not necessarily parallel.

In *Fig. 5-50,* lines *l* and *m* lie in two parallel planes *P* and *Q,* respectively. Although *l* and *m* have no point in common, *l* is *not parallel* to *m* because they are not *coplanar.* *l* and *m* are called *skew lines.*

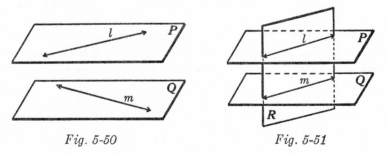

Fig. 5-50   Fig. 5-51

In *Fig. 5-51,* lines *l* and *m* are parallel because they are both contained in a plane *R.*

Parallel lines may also be contained in intersecting planes, as shown in *Fig. 5-52*.

Draw a diagram to represent the following statement and compare it with that on page 457.

1. If a plane intersects two parallel planes, then the intersections are two parallel lines.

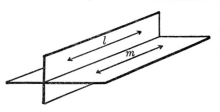

Fig. 5-52

Exercise 5-8

(A)

1. Name six dihedral angles in the figure at the right, by naming the edge of the angle. Consider point A to be above the plane containing BCD.

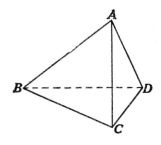

(B)

2. Draw a diagram to illustrate each of the following statements:
    (i) If a line is perpendicular to one of two parallel planes, it is also perpendicular to the other.
    (ii) Two lines parallel to the same plane may be perpendicular to each other.
    (iii) If a plane intersects a dihedral angle, the lines of intersection may be parallel.
    (iv) If a plane intersects two planes which are perpendicular to the same line, the lines of intersection are parallel.
    (v) Two planes perpendicular to the same plane are parallel to each other.
    (vi) Two lines, both parallel to the same plane, may be:
       (a) intersecting lines (b) parallel lines (c) skew lines

3. A dihedral angle whose measurement is 60° is bisected by a half-plane. From a point A on this half-plane, perpendiculars are drawn to each half-plane of the dihedral angle. What is the measurement of the angle between these perpendiculars at A?

5·17 Summary.

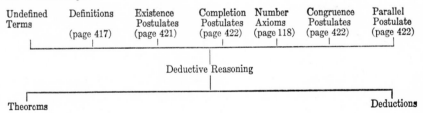

Angle $\begin{cases} \text{Complementary Angle Theorem} \\ \text{Supplementary Angle Theorem} \\ \text{Vertical Angle Theorem} \end{cases}$

Basic Biconditional $\{$ Isosceles Triangle Theorem

Inequality $\begin{cases} \text{Exterior Angle Theorem} \\ \text{Angle-Side Inequality Theorems} \\ \text{Side Inequality Theorem} \end{cases}$

Parallel $\begin{cases} \text{Parallel Line Theorem} \\ \text{Quadrilateral-Parallelogram Theorem} \\ \text{Parallelogram Theorem} \\ \text{Triangle Angle Sum Theorem} \end{cases}$

Congruence $\begin{cases} \text{aas Congruence Theorem} \\ \text{Right Triangle Congruence Theorem} \end{cases}$

Locus $\begin{cases} \text{Right Bisector Theorem} \\ \text{Angle Bisector Theorem} \end{cases}$

Exercise 5-9

(*Numerical Exercise*)

(B)

Draw a representative sketch, mark on all given data, and complete the required calculations in each of the following:

1. Calculate the measurement of each angle formed at the intersection of the bisectors of two of the angles of an equilateral triangle.

2. Calculate the measurement of each angle of a regular hexagon.

3. *ABC* is a triangle with sides $AB = 7$ cm., $BC = 8$ cm., $CA = 5$ cm. *D* is the midpoint of *BC*. If *AD* is extended to *X* so that $DX = AD$, calculate the length of *CX*.

4. In $\triangle ABC$, $AB = AC$ and $\angle A = 70°$. BK is perpendicular to AC, meeting AC on K. Find the measurement of $\angle KBC$.

5. The equal line segments OA, OB, and OC are drawn in order from O so that $\angle AOB = 100°$ and $\angle BOC = 140°$. Find the measurement of each angle of $\triangle ABC$.

6. The measurement of the exterior angle at B of $\triangle ABC$ is $108°$, and the measurement of the exterior angle at C is $112°$. Find the measurement of $\angle A$.

7. One angle of a triangle has a measurement of $58°$. Calculate the measurement of each of the other two angles if the difference of their measurements is $24°$.

8. $ABCD$ is a quadrilateral with diagonals of lengths 12 cm. and 8 cm. Calculate the lengths of the sides of the figure whose vertices are the midpoints of the consecutive sides of $ABCD$.

9. ABC is an isosceles triangle having $AB = AC$. BA is extended to D so that $AD = BA$. Find the measurement of $\angle BCD$.

10. ABC is an equilateral triangle. X, Y, Z are points on BC, CA, AB, respectively, such that $BX = CY = AZ$. Find the measurement of each angle of $\triangle XYZ$.

11. In quadrilateral $ABCD$, $\angle A = 98°$ and $\angle B = 86°$. Find the measurement of the obtuse angle formed by the bisectors of $\angle C$ and $\angle D$.

12. In $\triangle ABC$, $\angle B = 80°$, $\angle C = 20°$. AD is the bisector of $\angle A$, meeting BC on D, and AE is the altitude from A. Find the measurement of $\angle EAD$.

13. ABC is an isosceles triangle having $AB = AC$ and $\angle B = 70°$. L, M, and N are the midpoints of AB, BC, and CA, respectively. Find the measurements of $\angle ALM$ and $\angle ANM$.

14. ABC is a triangle with base BC extended in both directions. Find the sum of the measurements of the two exterior angles minus the measurement of vertical angle A.

15. The vertical angle C of isosceles $\triangle ABC$ has a measurement of $120°$. A perpendicular to AB at B meets AC extended on K. Find the measurement of $\angle K$.

16. In $\triangle ABC$, $AB = 5$ cm., $BC = 9$ cm., $CA = 7$ cm. BK bisects $\angle ABC$ meeting AC on K. A line parallel to KB through A meets CB extended on L. Calculate the length of BL.

17. In quadrilateral $ABCD$, $AB \parallel CD$. If $DK \perp AB$ meeting AB on K so that $KD = \frac{1}{2} AD$, find the measurement of $\angle ADC$.

POLYGONS
AREAS OF POLYGONS

6·1 **Polygons.** The geometric figures in *Fig. 6-1* are called *curves*.

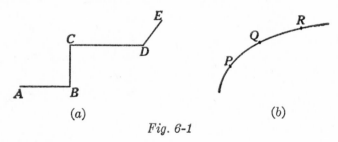

(a) (b)

Fig. 6-1

In *Fig. 6-1(a)*, the points A, B, C, D, E are points on the curve or the curve is on these points. This figure consists of all the points on the line segments AB, BC, CD, DE. Since it is made up of a succession of line segments, it is called a broken line figure or *polygonal path*. Point A is called the beginning of the path, and E is the end. The line segments are called the *sides* of the path. The points A, B, C, D, E are the vertices of the path.

The sides of a polygonal path may intersect, as in *Fig. 6-2(b)*. If they do not intersect, *Fig. 6-2(a)*, the path is called a *simple curve* or *simple polygonal path.*

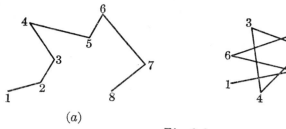

Fig. 6-2

a. *Definitions of Polygons.*

(i) *Polygon*

If the beginning and end of a polygonal path consisting of three or more line segments coincide, then the path is called a polygon.

(ii) *Simple polygon*

If the beginning and end of a polygonal path consisting of three or more line segments coincide and no two sides intersect, then the path is called a simple polygon (*Fig. 6-3*).

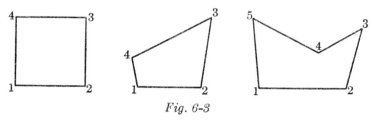

Fig. 6-3

b. *Kinds of polygons.* Polygons are named according to the number of sides, as shown in *Fig. 6-4*. It should be noted that the number of vertices of a given polygon is the same as the number of sides.

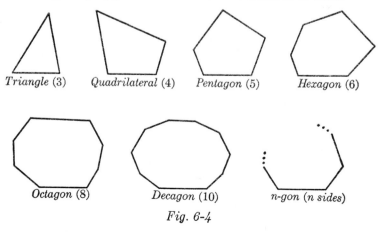

Fig. 6-4

c. *Convex polygon, concave polygon.* A *convex* polygon is a polygon in which all angles have measurements less than 180°, *Fig. 6-5(a)*.

A *concave* polygon is a polygon which has at least one reflex angle, *Fig. 6-5(b)*.

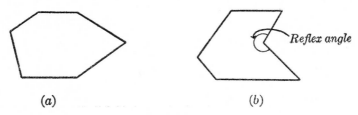

(a)   (b)

Fig. 6-5

In this text the word polygon means simple convex polygon, unless otherwise specified.

d. *Exterior angle of a polygon.* If C is between B and E, *Fig. 6-6*, then $\angle DCE$ is an exterior angle of polygon $ABCD$.

Similarly, if C is between D and F, $\angle BCF$ is an exterior angle of polygon $ABCD$. There are eight exterior angles of polygon $ABCD$, two at each vertex.

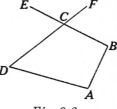

Fig. 6-6

e. *Regular Polygons.*

(i) If a polygon has all sides the same length, then the polygon is *equilateral*.

(ii) If a polygon has all angles equal, then the polygon is *equiangular*.

(iii) If a polygon is equilateral and equiangular, then it is a *regular* polygon, *Fig. 6-7*.

 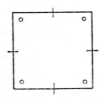 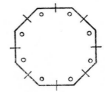

Fig. 6-7

Exercise 6-1

(B)

1. Copy and complete the following table:

POLYGON WITH DIAGONALS DRAWN FROM ONE VERTEX	NUMBER OF SIDES	NUMBER OF TRIANGLES	ANGLE SUM OF POLYGON IN STRAIGHT ANGLES	ANGLE SUM OF POLYGON IN DEGREES
Quadrilateral				
Pentagon				
Hexagon				
Septagon				
Octagon				
Decagon				
	50			
	90			
	200			
	1002			
n-gon	n			

Calculate the sum of the interior angles of each of the polygons:

2.
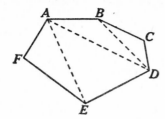

3.
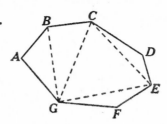

Write a complete proof for deductions 4 and 5:

4. *Hypothesis:* Pentagon *ABCDE* (diagram at the left below)
   Conclusion: $\angle 1 + \angle 2 + \angle 3 + \angle 4 + \angle 5 = 540°$

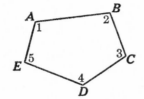
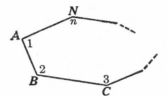

5. *Hypothesis:* n-gon *ABC ...N* (diagram at the right above)
   Conclusion: $\angle 1 + \angle 2 + \angle 3 + ... + \angle n = 180(n - 2)$ degrees

6. Since the number of degrees in the angle sum of an *n*-gon is $180(n - 2)$, calculate the number of degrees in the angle sum of a polygon of: (i) 10 sides (ii) 52 sides (iii) 3 sides

7. Using the fact that a regular polygon has all angles equal, calculate the number of degrees in the measurement of each angle of a regular polygon of: (i) 6 sides (ii) 12 sides (iii) 36 sides

Write a complete proof for the following deductions:

8. *Hypothesis:* Pentagon *ABCDE* with exterior angles $x°, y°, z°, m°, n°$, as indicated at left below.
   Conclusion: $x + y + z + m + n = 360$

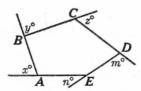
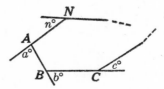

9. *Hypothesis:* n-gon *ABC ... N* with exterior angles $a°, b°, c° ...n°$, as indicated at the right above
   Conclusion: $a + b + c + ... + n = 360$

6·2 Polygonal regions. A triangular region is shown in *Fig. 6-8*.

DEFINITION: *A triangular region is the union of a triangle and its interior.*

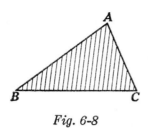

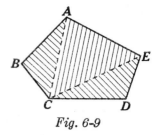

Fig. 6-8   Fig. 6-9

The simple polygonal region $ABCDE$ in *Fig. 6-9* is separated into three non-overlapping triangular regions called *component triangular regions*. The polygonal region is the union of these component regions.

With a line segment, we associate the notion of length. In a similar manner, we associate the idea of *area* with a region and make the following area postulates.

AREA POSTULATE 1. (Area Completion Postulate)

The area of a polygonal region is the sum of the areas of the component regions whose union is the polygonal region.

We use the symbols $\triangle ABC$, Fig. $DEFG$, and so on, to represent either the geometric figure or the area of the region as indicated by the context.

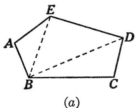

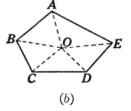

(a)   (b)

Fig. 6-10

(a) Fig. $ABCDE = \triangle ABE + \triangle EBD + \triangle DBC$
(b) Fig. $ABCDE = \triangle AOB + \triangle BOC + \triangle COD + \triangle DOE + \triangle EOA$

AREA POSTULATE 2.

If two polygonal regions are congruent, then they have the same area.

AREA POSTULATE 3. (Equal Area Postulate)

Two polygonal regions are equal in area if they can be separated into a finite number of polygons which are congruent in pairs.

6·3 Figures between the same parallel lines. A parallelogram is said to be between the pair of parallel lines determined by a pair of opposite sides.

A triangle is said to be between the pair of parallel lines determined by a side and the opposite vertex.

Example.

(i)

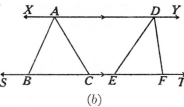

Fig. 6-11

In *Fig. 6-11 (a)*, *ABCD* and *EFGH* are ‖^gms between the same parallel lines *XY* and *ST*.

In *Fig. 6-11 (b)*, *ABC* and *DEF* are triangles between the same parallel lines *XY* and *ST*.

(ii)

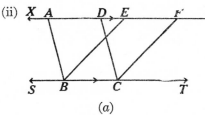 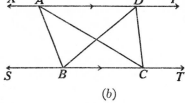

Fig. 6-12

In *Fig. 6-12 (a)*, ‖^gm *ABCD* and ‖^gm *EBCF* are on the same base *BC* and between the same parallel lines *XY* and *ST*.

In *Fig. 6-12 (b)*, △'s *ABC* and *DBC* are on the same base *BC* and between the same parallel lines *XY* and *ST*.

(iii)

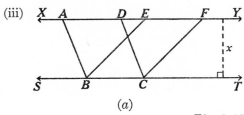 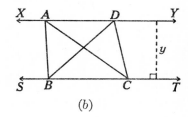

Fig. 6-13

Since the perpendicular distance between two parallel lines is constant, the phrase *between the same parallel lines* also means that the parallelograms *ABCD* and *EBCF*, *Fig. 6-13 (a)*, have the *same altitude x*, and the triangles *ABC* and *DBC*, *Fig. 6-13 (b)*, have the *same altitude y*.

6·4 Parallelogram Area Theorem.

Parallelogram Area Theorem

Parallelograms on the same base and between the same parallel lines have equal areas.

(A proof of this theorem is given on page 458.)

Corollary 1.   Parallelograms on equal bases and between the same parallel lines have equal areas.

Corollary 2.   A parallelogram and a rectangle on equal bases and between the same parallel lines have equal areas.

Example.

Hypothesis: Parallelograms $ABCD$, $AGHD$, and $GBCH$, as in *Fig. 6-14*

Conclusion: $||^{\text{gm}} ABCD = ||^{\text{gm}} AGHD + ||^{\text{gm}} GBCH$

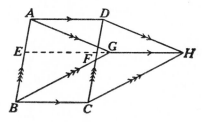

Fig. 6-14

Analysis:

I CAN PROVE	IF I CAN PROVE
1. $||^{\text{gm}} ABCD$ $= ||^{\text{gm}} AGHD + ||^{\text{gm}} GBCH$	1. $||^{\text{gm}} ABCD$ is equal to the sum of the areas of two parallelograms one equal to $||^{\text{gm}} AGHD$ and the other equal to $||^{\text{gm}} GBCH$.
2. $||^{\text{gm}} ABCD$ is equal to the sum of the areas of two parallelograms, one equal to $||^{\text{gm}} AGHD$ and the other equal to $||^{\text{gm}} GBCH$	2. By extending HG to cut DC at F and AB at E, so that $||^{\text{gm}} AGHD = ||^{\text{gm}} AEFD$ and $||^{\text{gm}} GBCH = ||^{\text{gm}} EBCF$.
3. $||^{\text{gm}} AGHD = ||^{\text{gm}} AEFD$ and $||^{\text{gm}} GBCH = ||^{\text{gm}} EBCF$ by the Parallelogram Area Theorem.	

Proof: Write a complete proof for this example and compare it with that given on page 458.

Exercise 6-2

(A)

1. In the diagram at the left below, name three parallelograms on the same base and between the same parallel lines.

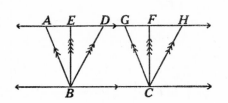 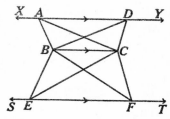

2. In the diagram at the right above, name pairs of triangles on the same base and between the same parallel lines.

3. In the diagram at the left below, name pairs of parallelograms on the same base and between the same parallel lines.

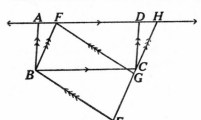 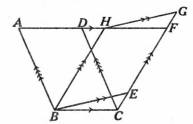

4. Give an oral analysis of the following deduction:
Hypothesis: $\|^{gms}$ *ABCD, HBEG,* and *HBCF,* as in the diagram at the right above
Conclusion: $\|^{gm}$ *ABCD* = $\|^{gm}$ *HBEG*

(B)

5. For the diagram at the right, prove $\|^{gm}$ *ABCD* = $\|^{gm}$ *EFCG.*

6. Write an analysis for the following deduction:
ABCD is a parallelogram. *X* is a point between *D* and *C*. *Y* is a point on *DC* extended such that *DX = CY*. *AX* is extended to *Z* so that *AX = XZ*. Prove that *XZYB* is a parallelogram equal in area to $\|^{gm}$ *ABCD*.

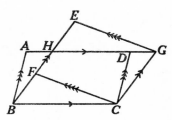

7. $PQRS$ is a parallelogram. X is the midpoint of PQ, Y is the midpoint of QR, Z is the midpoint of RS, and W is the midpoint of SP. Prove that $XYZW$ is a parallelogram and that its area is $\frac{1}{2}$ $||^{gm}$ $PQRS$.

8. E is a point on BC of $||^{gm}$ $ABCD$. F is any point on AE. Prove $\triangle AFD + \triangle BFC = \frac{1}{2}$ $||^{gm}$ $ABCD$.

9. X is any point on the diagonal DB of $||^{gm}$ $ABCD$. A line on X, parallel to AB, intersects AD on P and BC on Q. A line on X, parallel to AD, intersects AB on M and DC on N. Prove that $AMXP$ and $CNXQ$ are parallelograms and that they have equal areas.

6·5 **Parallelogram-Diagonal Theorem and Parallelogram-Triangle Area Theorem.**

Parallelogram-Diagonal Theorem

The diagonal of a parallelogram separates the parallelogram into two triangles that have equal areas.

(A proof for this theorem is given on page 458.)

Parallelogram-Triangle Area Theorem

If a triangle and a parallelogram are on equal bases and between the same parallel lines, then the area of the triangle is one-half the area of the parallelogram.

(A proof for this theorem is given on page 458.)

Corollary 1. Triangles on equal bases and between the same parallel lines have equal areas.

Corollary 2. The median of a triangle separates the triangle into two triangles that have equal areas.

Example. If in $\triangle ABC$, *Fig. 6-15*, $BD = DC$, and $AE = ED$, then $\triangle ABE = \frac{1}{4} \triangle ABC$.

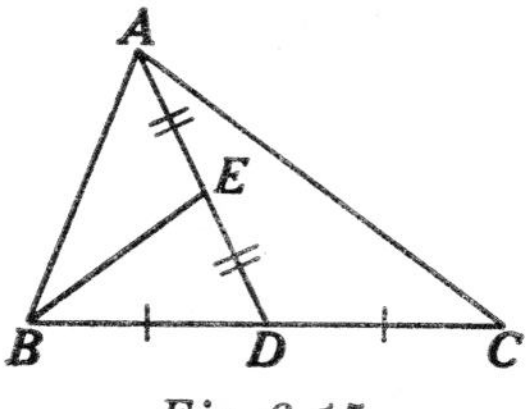

Hypothesis: $\triangle ABC$, in which $BD = DC$ and $AE = ED$

Conclusion: $\triangle ABE = \frac{1}{4} \triangle ABC$

Fig. 6-15

Analysis:

I CAN PROVE	IF I CAN PROVE
1. $\triangle ABE = \frac{1}{4} \triangle ABC$	1. $4 \triangle ABE = \triangle ABC$.
2. $4 \triangle ABE = \triangle ABC$	2. $\triangle ABE = \triangle EBD$ and $2 \triangle ABE = \triangle ADC$.

I CAN PROVE	IF I CAN PROVE
3. $\triangle ABE = \triangle EBD$ by the Parallelogram-Triangle Area Theorem.	
4. $2 \triangle ABE = \triangle ADC$	4. $\triangle ABD = \triangle ADC.$
5. $\triangle ABD = \triangle ADC$ by the Parallelogram-Triangle Area Theorem.	

Proof: Write a complete proof and compare it with that on page 459.

Exercise 6-3

(A)

1. In each of the following diagrams, name triangles whose bases have the same length and whose altitudes have the same length and, hence, have equal areas.   Give reasons.

(i)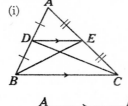

(ii)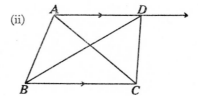

(iii)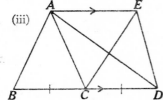

(iv)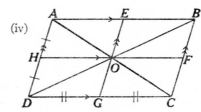

2. Into what fractional parts do the dotted lines separate each of the following triangles and parallelograms?

(i) 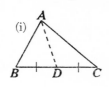 (ii) (iii) (iv)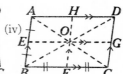

(B)

3. *ABCD* is a quadrilateral. A straight line drawn on *A* parallel to *BD* meets *CD* produced on *E*. Prove that $\triangle BCE =$ quadrilateral *ABCD*.

4. Medians BD and CE of $\triangle ABC$ intersect on F. Prove :
   (i) $\triangle DBC = \triangle EBC$ (ii) $\triangle EBF = \triangle DFC$
   (iii) quadrilateral $AEFD = \triangle FBC$

5. $ABCD$ is a parallelogram. P is any point on the diagonal AC. Prove:
   (i) $\triangle DPC = \triangle BCP$ (ii) $\triangle APD = \triangle ABP$

6. $PQRS$ is a parallelogram whose diagonals intersect on X. PR is extended to Y so that $RY = XR$. Prove $\triangle SQY = \|^{\text{gm}} PQRS$.

7. D is any point on the side AB of $\triangle ABC$. DF is parallel and equal to BC. If DF intersects AC on E, prove that $\triangle AEF = \triangle DBE$.

8. The side AB of $\|^{\text{gm}} ABCD$ is extended to E. DE intersects BC on F. Prove that $\triangle AFE = \triangle CBE$.

9. If two triangles with equal areas are on opposite sides of a common base, prove that the line segment determined by their vertices is bisected by the base or base extended.

6·6 Measurement of area. When we measure a line segment, we determine a number in terms of some unit which is called its *length*. This is done by choosing a unit length and counting the number of unit lengths in the line segment. This method is also followed in associating a real number with each angle. Similarly, by choosing a unit region, we can assign a positive real number of units to each region called the *area of the region*.

AREA POSTULATE 4.

For every polygonal region there exists a unique positive real number of units called the area of the region.

In order to find this real number of units associated with a polygonal region, it is necessary to agree on a unit area.

Since area is two-dimensional, any polygonal or curved region can be chosen to provide a unit area (*Fig. 6-16*).

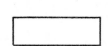

Fig. 6-16

To find the area of a polygonal region, it is necessary to separate the region into non-overlapping regions congruent to, or known fractions of, the region defined as the unit area. This is most easily performed if the unit region chosen is a square region.

Thus, the unit area is defined to be the area of a square region whose sides are each the unit length. The area of this region is called *one square unit*.

It is now possible to find the area of a rectangular region as follows.

If a point X is taken on side AD of rectangle $ABCD$ (*Fig. 6-17*) so that AX is the unit length, then rectangle $AXYB$ will contain as many unit areas as there are unit lengths in side AB. If the side AB has a length of y units ($y \in {}^+R$), then the rectangle $AXYB$ has an area of y square units.

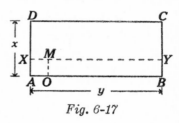

Fig. 6-17

Thus, if the length of AD is x units ($x \in {}^+R$), then
area rectangle $ABCD = x$ (area rectangle $AXYB$)
$$= xy \text{ square units.}$$

DEFINITION: *The area of a rectangular region whose sides have lengths of x units and y units is xy square units.*

Example. Rectangle $QRST$ (*Fig. 6-18*)
$$= (3.5 \times 4.5) \text{ sq. cm.}$$
$$= 15.75 \text{ sq. cm.}$$

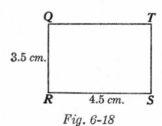

Fig. 6-18

6·7 Area of a parallelogram. If, in *Fig. 6-19*, DC and YC are b and h units, respectively, then
$$\|^{gm} ADCB = \text{rectangle } XDCY \quad \text{(Parallelogram Area Theorem)}$$
$$= bh \text{ square units.}$$

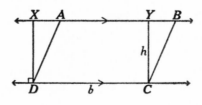

Fig. 6-19

The area of a parallelogram with a side 6.5 inches long and an altitude to that side 2 inches long is (6.5 × 2) square inches or 13 square inches.

6·8 Area of a triangle. If, in *Fig. 6-20*, DC and EM are b and h units, respectively, then by the Parallelogram-Triangle Area Theorem:

$$\triangle EDC = \tfrac{1}{2}\,\|^{\text{gm}}\,ADCB$$
$$= \tfrac{1}{2}\,bh \text{ square units}$$

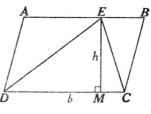

Fig. 6-20

The area of a triangle with a side 6.5 inches long and an altitude to that side 2 inches long is $\tfrac{1}{2}(6.5 \times 2)$ square inches or 6.5 square inches.

Exercise 6-4

(A)

1. For each of the diagrams below, state the area of $\|^{\text{gm}}\,ABCD$:

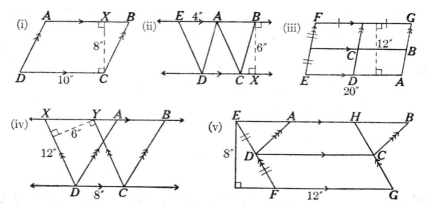

2. In diagram (iv) in question 1, what is the distance between the parallel line segments XB and DC?

3. The area of a parallelogram is 240 sq. cm. The altitude is 12 cm. Calculate the length of the base.

4. What is the effect on the area of a triangle if:
   (i) the base is doubled and the altitude is constant;
   (ii) the altitude is trebled and the base is constant;
   (iii) the base is doubled and the altitude is trebled.

5. Find the area of quadrilateral $DBCE$ in the diagram at the right above.

(B)

6. The diagonals of a rhombus have lengths 80 cm. and 60 cm., respectively. Find the area of the rhombus.

7. In $\parallel^{gm}$ *ABCD*, *AB* = 10 cm.; *AB* and *DC* are 8 cm. apart. *X* and *Y* are the midpoints of *AB* and *DC*, respectively. *XY* is extended to *E* so that *YE* = *XY*. *BC* is extended to *F* so that *CF* = *BC*. Find the area of figure *XBFE*.

8. In $\triangle ABC$, *X* and *Y* are points on *AC* and *AB*, respectively, so that *BX* $\perp$ *AC* and *CY* $\perp$ *AB*. If *AC* = 24 inches, *BX* = 15 inches, and *CY* = 18 inches, calculate the length of *AB*.

9. In $\triangle ABC$, *BC* = 20 inches, and the altitude to *BC* is 10 inches. *D* is any point on *BC*; *E* is the midpoint of *AD*. Find the sum of the areas of $\triangle AEC$ and $\triangle BDE$.

10. *AD* is a median of $\triangle ABC$. *E* is on *AD* so that *AE* = $\frac{1}{4}$ *AD*. If *BC* = 16 inches and the area of $\triangle EDC$ is 48 square inches, find the length of the altitude of $\triangle ABC$ from *A* to *BC*.

11. Using ruler and compasses only, construct a quadrilateral *ABCD* having *AB* = 2″, $\angle A$ = 60°, $\angle B$ = 90°, and *BD* = *AC*. Construct a triangle whose area is equal to the area of quadrilateral *ABCD*.

6·9 Equal Triangle-Parallel Line Theorem.

Equal Triangle-Parallel Line Theorem

If two triangles having equal areas are on the same side of a common base, then the straight line on their vertices is parallel to the common base.

(A proof of this theorem is given on page 459.)

Exercise 6-5

(B)

1. In quadrilateral *ABCD*, $\triangle ABC$ = $\triangle DBC$. Prove that the quadrilateral has one pair of opposite sides parallel.

2. *AOB* and *COD* are two intersecting line segments. If $\triangle AOD$ = $\triangle COD$, prove *AC* $\parallel$ *DB*.

3. Prove the converse of the Parallelogram-Diagonal Theorem.

4. *ABCD* is a line segment in which *AB* = *CD*. $\triangle$'s *QAB* and *RCD* have equal areas and are on the same side of *AD*. Prove *QR* $\parallel$ *AD*.

5. Prove that the straight line on the midpoints of two sides of a triangle is parallel to the third side.

6. In the diagram at the left below, $AB = BC$, $\triangle EBD = \triangle BCD$. Prove
    (i) $AE \parallel BD$ (ii) BD extended bisects CE.

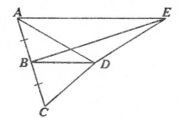 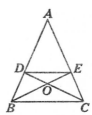

7. In the diagram at the right above, $AB = AC$ and $\triangle DBO = \triangle EOC$. Prove that the distance from D to AC is the same as that from E to AB.

6·10 Area of a trapezoid.

DEFINITION: *A trapezoid is a quadrilateral having one pair of opposite sides parallel.*

The parallel sides are called the bases of the trapezoid.

Trapezoid Area Theorem

If the lengths of the parallel sides of a trapezoid are a units and b units and the length of the perpendicular distance between these sides is h units, then the area of the trapezoid is $\frac{1}{2}(a + b) h$ square units.

Hypothesis: $ABCD$ is a trapezoid whose parallel sides AB and CD have lengths a units and b units, respectively. The perpendicular distance between AB and CD is h units (*Fig. 6-21*).

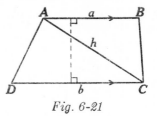

Fig. 6-21

Conclusion: Area of the trapezoid is $\frac{1}{2}(a + b)h$ square units.

Proof:

STATEMENTS	AUTHORITIES
1. Trapezoid $ABCD$ $= \triangle ABC + \triangle ADC$	1. Completion
2. Trapezoid $ABCD$ $= (\frac{1}{2}ah + \frac{1}{2}bh)$ square units	2. Triangle Area Theorem
3. Trapezoid $ABCD$ $= \frac{1}{2}(a + b)h$ square units	3. Number axioms

6·11 The Pythagorean Theorem.

The Pythagorean Theorem

In a right triangle, the area of the square on the hypotenuse is equal to the sum of the areas of the squares on the other two sides.

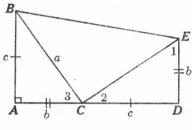

Fig. 6-22

Hypothesis: $\triangle ABC$ with $\angle A = 90°$, $AB = c$ units, $AC = b$ units, $BC = a$ units

Conclusion: $a^2 = b^2 + c^2$

Proof:

STATEMENTS	AUTHORITIES
1. D is the point on AC extended so that $CD = c$ units.	1. Existence
2. E is the point on the same side of AD as B so that $ED \perp AD$ and $ED = b$ units.	2. Existence
3. $\triangle ABC \cong \triangle DCE$	3. sas
4. $EC = a$ units.	4. Definition
5. $\angle 1 + \angle 2 = 90°$	5. Triangle Angle Sum Theorem
6. $\angle 1 = \angle 3$	6. 3, Definition
7. $\angle BCE = 90°$	7. Completion, definition
8. $BA \perp AD$, $ED \perp AD$	8. Hypothesis, 2
9. $AB \parallel ED$	9. Parallel Line Theorem
10. $ABED$ is a trapezoid .	10. Definition
11. Trapezoid $ABED$ $= \triangle ABC + \triangle BCE + \triangle CED$	11. Completion
12. $\frac{1}{2}(b + c)(b + c)$ $= \frac{1}{2}bc + \frac{1}{2}a \cdot a + \frac{1}{2}bc$	12. Trapezoid and Triangle Area Theorems
13. $b^2 + 2bc + c^2 = bc + a^2 + bc$	13. Number axioms
14. $b^2 + c^2 = a^2$	14. Subtraction

Example 1. Find the area of trapezoid *ABCD* in *Fig. 6-23*.

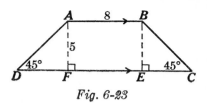

Fig. 6-23

Solution.

$$\angle DAF = 45° \qquad \text{(Triangle Angle Sum Theorem)}$$
$$\therefore\ DF = 5 \text{ inches} \qquad \text{(Isosceles Triangle Theorem)}$$
$$BE = 5 \text{ inches} \qquad \text{(Parallel Line Theorem)}$$
$$\angle EBC = 45° \qquad \text{(Triangle Angle Sum Theorem)}$$
$$EC = 5 \text{ inches} \qquad \text{(Isosceles Triangle Theorem)}$$
$$FE = 8 \text{ inches} \qquad \text{(Parallelogram Theorem)}$$
$$\therefore\ DC = (5 + 8 + 5) \text{ inches} = 18 \text{ inches}$$

Area trapezoid $ABCD = \tfrac{1}{2} \cdot 5(8 + 18)$ square inches
$$= 65 \text{ square inches}$$

Example 2.

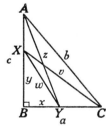

Fig. 6-24

Hypothesis: $\triangle ABC$ is right-angled at B; X and Y are points on AB and BC, respectively (*Fig. 6-24*), such that $AC = b$ units, $AB = c$ units, $BC = a$ units, $XC = v$ units, $AY = z$ units, $XY = w$ units.

Conclusion: $z^2 + v^2 = b^2 + w^2$

Analysis:

I CAN PROVE	IF I CAN PROVE
1. $z^2 + v^2 = b^2 + w^2$	1. $z^2 + v^2$ and $b^2 + w^2$ can each be expressed as the sum of the same numbers.
2. $z^2 + v^2 = c^2 + x^2 + y^2 + a^2$, and $b^2 + w^2 = c^2 + a^2 + x^2 + y^2$ by the Pythagorean Theorem and $c^2 + x^2 + y^2 + a^2 = c^2 + a^2 + x^2 + y^2$ by the number axioms.	

Proof: Write a complete proof for this deduction and compare it with that on page 460.

Exercise 6-6

(A)

1. State the area of the following trapezoids, if a units and b units represent the lengths of the parallel sides and h units represents the length of the altitude:

   (i) $a = 12$ $b = 8$ $h = 10$
   (ii) $a = 6$ $b = 9$ $h = 4$
   (iii) $a = 17$ $b = 7$ $h = 8$
   (iv) $a = x + y$ $b = x - y$ $h = 2x$

2. Find the altitude of the trapezoid whose area is 124 square inches, if the parallel sides have measurements 16 inches and 8 inches.

3. If c units is the length of the hypotenuse and a units and b units are the lengths of the sides containing the right angle in a right triangle, find:

   (i) c, if $a = 3$, $b = 4$
   (ii) c, if $a = 3$, $b = 3$
   (iii) c, if $a = 5$, $b = 12$
   (iv) a, if $c = 10$, $b = 6$
   (v) b, if $c = 8$, $a = 4\sqrt{2}$
   (vi) a, if $c = 2$, $b = \sqrt{3}$

4. State a formula for d, the number of units in the length of the diagonal of a square in terms of the length, a units, of each side.

 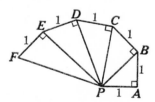

5. State the length of PB, PC, PD, PE, PF in the diagram at the right above.

(B)

6. The lengths of the parallel sides of a trapezoid are 34 inches and 41 inches. The altitude has length 24 inches. Find the length of a side of a square that has the same area as the trapezoid.

7. The lengths of the bases of a trapezoid are 25 cm. and 28 cm. Find the length of its altitude if its area is equal to that of a triangle whose base has length 26.5 cm. and whose altitude to that base has length 10 cm.

8. Calculate the area of $\triangle ABC$ in the diagram at the left below, if $BE = 4$ inches, $AF = 7$ inches, $CG = 5$ inches, $EF = 2$ inches, $FG = 4$ inches.

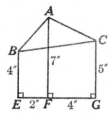 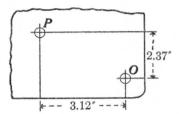

9. Find the distance between the centres of the bolt holes P and Q in the diagram at the right above.

10. Calculate the length of an altitude of an equilateral triangle whose side has length 8 mm.

11. In the diagram at the left below, find the length of AB.

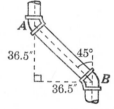 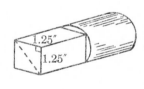

12. The end of a cylindrical shaft (diagram at the right above) is to be machined so that it is a square, each side having length 1.25 inches. What is the least diameter the shaft may have?

13. A ladder 50 feet long rests against a vertical wall with its foot 14 feet from the bottom of the wall. If the top of the ladder slides 8 feet down the wall, how far will the foot of the ladder slide from its original position?

14. In any rectangle, prove that the sum of the squares of the lengths of the diagonals is equal to the sum of the squares of the lengths of the sides.

15. Write an analysis for the following deduction:
PX is the altitude of triangle PQR. If $PQ = r$ units, $PR = q$ units, $QX = a$ units, $RX = b$ units, prove $r^2 - q^2 = a^2 - b^2$.

16. O is any point inside rectangle $PQRS$. Line segments OP, OQ, OR, OS have lengths p units, q units, r units, and s units, respectively. Prove $p^2 + r^2 = s^2 + q^2$.

6·12 The Pythagorean Converse.

Pythagorean Converse

If the area of the square on one side of a triangle is equal to the sum of the areas of the squares on the other two sides, then the triangle is a right triangle with the right angle opposite the first side.

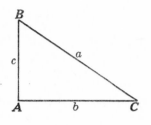

Fig. 6-25

Hypothesis: $\triangle ABC$ in which $AB = c$ units, $AC = b$ units, $BC = a$ units, and $a^2 = b^2 + c^2$

Conclusion: $\angle A = 90°$

Proof:

STATEMENTS	AUTHORITIES
1. $\triangle DEF$ is a triangle such that $\angle D = 90°$, and the lengths of DF, DE, EF are b units, c units, x units, respectively.	1. Existence
2. $x^2 = b^2 + c^2$	2. Pythagorean Theorem
3. $a^2 = b^2 + c^2$	3. Hypothesis
4. $x^2 = a^2$	4. Replacement
5. $x = a$	5. Definition
6. $\triangle ABC \cong \triangle DEF$	6. sss
7. $\angle A = \angle D = 90°$	7. Definition

Example. Write a complete analysis and proof of the following deduction; compare your solution with that on page 460.

Hypothesis: $\triangle ABC$ such that $AB = 2n$ units, $BC = (n^2 - 1)$ units, $AC = (n^2 + 1)$ units

Conclusion: $\triangle ABC$ is right-angled at B.

Exercise 6-7

(A)

1. Three positive integers, numbers a, b, c, such that $a^2 = b^2 + c^2$, are called a *Pythagorean triple*. State which of the following sets of numbers represent the measurement of the sides of a right triangle, and which of these are Pythagorean triples:

    (i) 3, 4, 5   (ii) 2, 3, 4   (iii) 1, $\sqrt{2}$, 1
    (iv) 1, 4, $\sqrt{5}$ (v) 5, 12, 13   (vi) 2, $\sqrt{3}$, 1
    (vii) 7, 24, 25   (viii) 2, 3, $\sqrt{13}$ (ix) $\sqrt{2}$, $\sqrt{3}$, $\sqrt{5}$

(B)

2. In $\triangle ABC$, D is on BC so that $AD \perp BC$. If $AD = 6$ inches, $BD = 3$ inches, $DC = 12$ inches, prove that $\angle BAC = 90°$.

3. In parallelogram $ABCD$, $AC = 16$ in., $BD = 30$ in., and $BC = 17$ in. Prove that $ABCD$ is a rhombus.

4. In quadrilateral $ABCD$, $AB = 29$ in., $BC = 21$ in., $CD = 12$ in., $AD = 16$ in., $AC \perp BC$. Prove $\angle D = 90°$.

5. $\triangle PQR$ is isosceles. Base $QR = 36$ cm. The perpendicular from P to QR is 24 cm. QR is produced to T so that $RT = 14$ cm. Prove that $\angle QPT = 90°$.

6. If m, $n \in {}^+I$ and $m > n$, prove that $m^2 + n^2$, $m^2 - n^2$, $2mn$ form a Pythagorean triple. By replacing m and n by positive integers, find five Pythagorean triples.

6·13 Construction problems.

Example 1.

Given: Quadrilateral $ABCD$

Required: To construct a triangle having AD as one side and a second side along DC such that the area of the triangle is equal to the area of quadrilateral $ABCD$

Analysis:

PRELIMINARY SKETCH

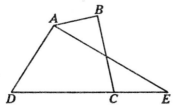 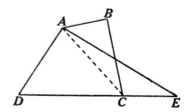

Fig. 6-26

If $\quad \triangle ADE =$ quadrilateral $ABCD$,

then $\triangle AEC + \triangle ADC = \triangle ABC + \triangle ADC$

and $\quad \triangle AEC = \triangle ABC$

$\triangle AEC$ and $\triangle ABC$ have the same base AC and hence their altitudes are equal,

and $BE \parallel AC$.

Thus, the position of E can be determined by constructing a line segment through B parallel to AC.

RULER-COMPASSES CONSTRUCTION

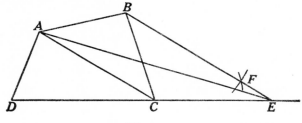

Fig. 6-27

Description of construction:

1. Draw line segment AC.
2. Construct BF parallel to AC intersecting DC on E (fundamental construction).
3. Draw line segment AE.
4. $\triangle AED$ is the required triangle.

Example 2. Construct a triangle equal in area to a given pentagon.

Given: Pentagon $ABCDE$

Required: To construct a triangle whose area is equal to the area of pentagon $ABCDE$

Analysis:

PRELIMINARY SKETCH

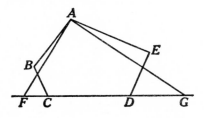 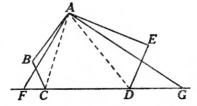

Fig. 6-28

If pentagon $ABCDE = \triangle AFG$,

then $\triangle ABC + \triangle ACD + \triangle ADE = \triangle AFC + \triangle ACD + \triangle ADG$

and $\triangle ABC = \triangle AFC$ and $\triangle AGD = \triangle AED$

and $BF \parallel AC$ and $EG \parallel AD$.

Thus, the position of F can be determined by constructing $BF \parallel AC$; the position of G can be determined by constructing $EG \parallel AD$.

Construct the required diagram and write a description of the construction. Compare your solution with that on page 460.

Example 3. Construct a square whose area is equal to the sum of the areas of two given squares.

Given: Two squares whose sides have lengths a units and b units, respectively

Required: To construct a square whose area is $(a^2 + b^2)$ square units

Analysis:

PRELIMINARY SKETCH

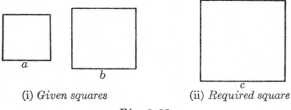

(i) *Given squares*   (ii) *Required square*

Fig. 6-29

Represent the side of the required square by c units. Then $c^2 = a^2 + b^2$. Thus, the length c units can be determined by constructing a right triangle having the sides about the right angle of lengths a units and b units.

Construct the required square and write a description of the construction. Compare your solution with that given on page 460.

Exercise 6-8

(B)

In each of the following write an analysis, make the required construction, and write a description of the construction:

1. Construct a triangle equal in area to a given triangle having one of its sides equal in length to a given line segment.

2. Construct any $\triangle ABC$. Construct a triangle having the length of its base equal to $\frac{3}{4}BC$, the measurement of one of its base angles equal to $60°$, and its area equal to the area of $\triangle ABC$.

3. In $\triangle ABC$, X is a point on AB. Find the position of a point Y on BC extended so that $\triangle YAX = \triangle CAY$.

4. Construct a triangle with a given altitude and an area equal to the area of a given triangle.

5. Construct a square whose area is the difference of the areas of two given squares.

6. Construct a square whose side has length (i) $\sqrt{8}$ inches (ii) $\sqrt{13}$ inches.

7. Divide a line segment into two parts so that the area of the square on one part is twice the area of the square on the other part.

6·14 Heron's formula. The formula used for finding the area of a triangle when the lengths of the sides are known is called *Heron's* or *Hero's formula*. It first appeared in the writing of the mathematician, Hero, who lived about 2,000 years ago in Alexandria.

The area, A square units, of a triangle is given by the formula

$$A = \sqrt{s(s-a)(s-b)(s-c)}$$

where a, b, c linear units represent the lengths of the sides and

$s = \dfrac{a+b+c}{2}$. (*s* units represents the semi-perimeter of the triangle.)

6·15 Proof of Heron's formula (supplementary).

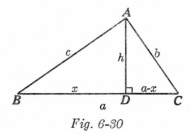

Fig. 6-30

Represent the lengths of AB, BC, CA, BD, and DA by c, a, b, x, and h units as in *Fig. 6-30*.

Then $DC = BC - BD = (a - x)$ units.

Then $\qquad\qquad (a - x)^2 + h^2 = b^2 \quad$ (1) $\qquad$ (Pythagorean Theorem)

and $\qquad\qquad\qquad x^2 + h^2 = c^2 \quad$ (2) $\qquad$ (Pythagorean Theorem)

$\therefore (a - x)^2 + h^2 - (x^2 + h^2) = b^2 - c^2$

$$a^2 - 2ax + x^2 + h^2 - x^2 - h^2 = b^2 - c^2$$
$$a^2 - 2ax = b^2 - c^2$$
$$x = \frac{a^2 - b^2 + c^2}{2a}$$

Substituting in (2) $h^2 = c^2 - \left(\dfrac{a^2 - b^2 + c^2}{2a}\right)^2$

$$
\begin{aligned}
4a^2h^2 &= 4a^2c^2 - (a^2 - b^2 + c^2)^2 \\
&= [2ac - (a^2 - b^2 + c^2)][2ac + (a^2 - b^2 + c^2)] \\
&= (2ac - a^2 + b^2 - c^2)(2ac + a^2 - b^2 + c^2) \\
&= [b^2 - (a - c)^2][(a + c)^2 - b^2] \\
&= (b - a + c)(b + a - c)(a + c - b)(a + c + b) \\
&= (a+b+c-2a)(a+b+c-2c)(a+b+c-2b)(a+b+c)
\end{aligned}
$$

$\because a + b + c = 2s$ (s units is the semi-perimeter)

$$
\begin{aligned}
\therefore 4a^2h^2 &= 2s(2s - 2a)(2s - 2b)(2s - 2c) \\
&= 16s(s - a)(s - b)(s - c) \\
\therefore \tfrac{1}{4}a^2h^2 &= s(s - a)(s - b)(s - c) \\
\therefore \tfrac{1}{2}ah &= \sqrt{s(s - a)(s - b)(s - c)}
\end{aligned}
$$

But $A = \tfrac{1}{2}ah$

$$\therefore A = \sqrt{s(s - a)(s - b)(s - c)}$$

Example. Find, to one decimal place, the area of a triangle whose sides have lengths of 4 in., 5 in., and 7 in., given $\sqrt{6} \simeq 2.449$.

Solution. $a = 4$

$b = 5$ $A = \sqrt{s(s - a)(s - b)(s - c)}$

$\underline{c = 7}$ $= \sqrt{8(4)(3)(1)}$

$\overline{2s = 16}$ $= 4\sqrt{6}$

$s = 8$ $\simeq 4(2.449)$

$s - a = 4$ $\simeq 9.80$

$s - b = 3$

$s - c = 1$

The area of the triangle is 9.8 square inches, to one decimal place.

Exercise 6-9

(B)

1. Calculate, correct to the nearest square unit, the area of the triangle whose sides have lengths: (use $\sqrt{2} = 1.4142$, $\sqrt{3} = 1.7321$)
   (i)   13, 14, 15 ft.   (ii)   20, 30, 30 cm.   (iii)   20, 28, 32 in.
   (iv)   15, 20, 25 mm.   (v)   6, 6, 6 cm.   (vi)   24, 7, 25 ft.
   (vii)   2, 3, 3 cm.   (viii)   4, 4, 4 cm.

2. Calculate the area of the quadrilateral $ABCD$, if $AB = 5$ cm., $BC = 20$ cm., $CD = 16$ cm., $DA = 13$ cm., and $DB = 12$ cm.

3. Find the lengths of the three altitudes of a triangle whose sides have lengths of $6\frac{1}{2}$, 7, and $7\frac{1}{2}$ inches.

4. Use Heron's formula to show the effect on the area of (i) doubling (ii) trebling the lengths of the sides of a triangle.

6·16 Polyhedrons. Diagrams of several three-dimensional closed geometric figures are shown in *Fig. 6-31*. These geometric figures are called *polyhedrons*.

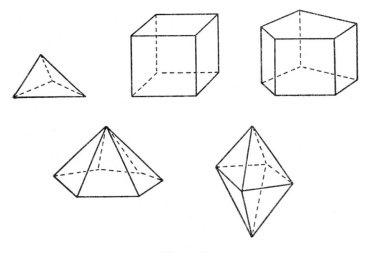

Fig. 6-31

The plane surfaces of the polyhedron are called *faces*.

The faces intersect on the *edges* of the polyhedron.

The edges intersect on the *vertices* of the polyhedron.

Regular polyhedrons are polyhedrons whose faces are congruent plane figures (*Fig. 6-32*).

Fig. 6-32

6·17 Prisms and pyramids.

DEFINITION: *Two planes are parallel if and only if they have no point in common.*

a. Prism. *A prism is a polyhedron with two faces that are congruent polygonal regions on parallel planes, and its remaining faces are parallelogram regions with two sides on these parallel planes (Fig. 6-33).*

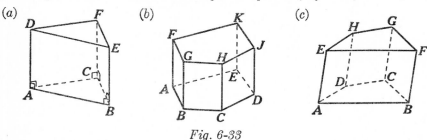

Fig. 6-33

The polygonal regions which lie on the parallel planes are called the *bases* of the prism. The faces which are parallelogram regions are called the *lateral faces.* The edges which do not lie on the parallel planes are called the *lateral edges.*

In *Fig. 6-33 (b), ABCDE* and *FGHJK* are the bases; *ABGF, BCHG, CDJH, DEKJ,* and *EAFK* are the lateral faces; *AF, BG, CH, DJ, EK* are the lateral edges.

If the lateral edges are perpendicular to the bases, *Fig. 6-33 (a),* the prism is called a *right prism.*

A *parallelepiped* is a prism whose bases are parallelogram regions, *Fig. 6-34 (a).*

A *rectangular parallelepiped* is a right prism whose base is a rectangular region, *Fig. 6-34 (b).*

A *cube* is a prism whose bases and lateral faces are square regions, *Fig. 6-34 (c).*

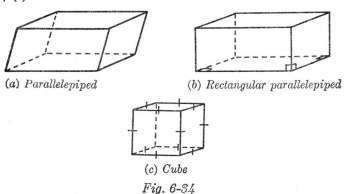

(a) *Parallelepiped*   (b) *Rectangular parallelepiped*

(c) *Cube*

Fig. 6-34

b. *Pyramid.* *A pyramid is a polyhedron with one face a polygonal region and the other faces triangular regions with a common vertex not in the plane of the polygonal region (Fig. 6-35).*

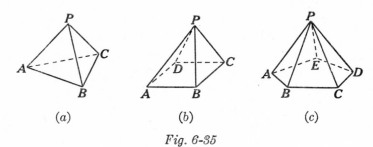

(a)   (b)   (c)

Fig. 6-35

The polygonal region is called the *base* of the pyramid. The point not in the plane of the base is called the *vertex* of the pyramid. The other faces are called the *lateral faces*. The line segments joining the vertex of the pyramid to the vertices of the base are called the *lateral edges* of the pyramid.

In *Fig. 6-35 (b)*, *P* is the vertex, *ABCD* is the base, and *PAB*, *PBC*, *PCD*, and *PDA* are the lateral faces. *PA*, *PB*, *PC*, and *PD* are the lateral edges of the pyramid. This pyramid is named *P-ABCD*.

A *regular pyramid* is a pyramid whose base is a regular polygonal region and whose lateral edges have equal lengths, *Fig. 6-36 (a)*. The *slant height* of a regular pyramid is the length of the altitude of its lateral faces, *Fig. 6-36 (b)*.

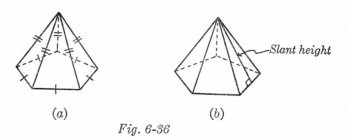

(a)   (b)

Fig. 6-36

Exercise 6-10

(B)

For each of the following prisms and pyramids:
  (*i*) *make a sketch of the figure;* (*ii*) *make ruler-compasses diagrams of the lateral faces;* (*iii*) *make a ruler-compasses diagram of the base.*

1. A triangular prism whose lateral edges are 3 inches long and whose base is an isosceles triangular region with equal angles each having a measurement of 45° and equal sides having length 2 inches.

2. A rectangular parallelepiped with lateral edges 5 cm. long and a base whose dimensions are 3 cm. and 2 cm.

3. A triangular pyramid (base is a triangular region) each of whose faces is an equilateral triangular region with sides 4 cm. long.

4. A pyramid whose base is a rectangular region with sides 4 cm. and 6 cm. and whose lateral edges are 5 cm. long.

5. A regular pyramid with five faces whose lateral edges are 3 inches long and whose base has sides each 1 inch long.

6·18 Lateral and total area of prisms and pyramids.

The lateral area of a prism or pyramid is the sum of the areas of the lateral faces of the prism or pyramid.

The total area of a prism or pyramid is the sum of the lateral area and the area of the base(s) of the prism or pyramid.

Example 1. Find (i) the lateral area (ii) the total area of a right prism whose bases are equilateral triangular regions having sides 2 inches long and whose lateral edges are 6 inches long.

Solution.

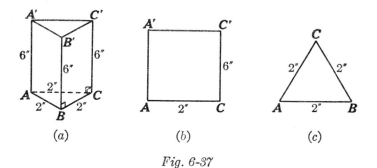

(a)   (b)   (c)

Fig. 6-37

(i) Each lateral face is a rectangular region, *Fig. 6-37* (b), with length 6 inches and width 2 inches. Since the bases are equilateral triangular regions, there are three lateral faces.

Area of one lateral face is (6 × 2) square inches
or 12 square inches.

Lateral area of the prism is (3 × 12) square inches
or 36 square inches.

(ii) The bases are equilateral triangular regions with sides of length 2 inches, *Fig. 6-37 (c)*.

The area of a base is calculated using Heron's formula:

$$s = \frac{2 + 2 + 2}{2} = 3$$

$$A = \sqrt{s(s - a)(s - b)(s - c)} = \sqrt{3(3 - 2)(3 - 2)(3 - 2)} = \sqrt{3}$$

∴ area of bases $= 2\sqrt{3}$ square inches.

Total area of the prism is $(36 + 2\sqrt{3})$ square inches.

Example 2. Find the lateral area of a regular pyramid whose slant height is 15 inches and whose base is a square region with sides 8 inches long.

Solution. Write a solution and compare it with that on page 460.

Exercise 6-11

(B)

1. Find the lateral area of a right prism whose lateral edges have a length h units and whose base is bounded by:
   (i) a triangle with sides of lengths a units, b units, c units;
   (ii) a quadrilateral with sides of lengths a, b, c, and d units.

2. Find the lateral area of a right prism whose lateral edges have a length of 16 inches and whose base has a perimeter of 18 inches.

3. Find the lateral area of a regular pyramid whose slant height is l units and whose base is bounded by:
   (i) an equilateral triangle with sides of length a units;
   (ii) a square with sides of length s units;
   (iii) a pentagon with sides of length p units.

4. Find the lateral area of a regular hexagonal pyramid whose slant height is 22 cm. and whose base perimeter is 29 cm.

5. Find the lateral area of a pyramid whose base is a square region with sides of length 10 inches, if the length of each lateral edge is 13 inches.

6. The base of a right prism is bounded by a rhombus whose diagonals have lengths 64 cm. and 48 cm. The lateral edges are 15 cm. long. Find (i) the lateral area (ii) the total area of the prism.

7. A regular pyramid *M-EHGF* whose base is a square region is cut parallel to its base, and the regular pyramid *M-ABCD* is removed. Calculate the lateral area of the remaining figure, if $MC = CG$, $FG = 2BC$, $EF = 24$ cm., and $ME = 20$ cm.

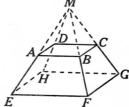

6·19 Drawing figures in three-dimensional space (supplementary). Since diagrams in geometry are aids in mathematical thinking, they do not need to be scale drawings but need only to represent the figures as a viewer would see them. This may be achieved in several ways.

(i) Right angles are distorted to show one arm either receding from, or approaching, the viewer, as shown in *Fig. 6-38.*

Fig. 6-38

(ii) Any part of a line which is hidden by a plane is either dotted or left out, as shown in *Fig. 6-39.*

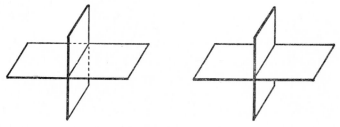

Fig. 6-39

(iii) Planes are represented as quadrilaterals. If the planes are parallel, the corresponding sides are usually drawn parallel, as in *Fig. 6-39.*

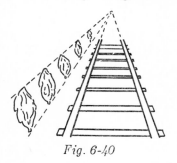

Fig. 6-40

Other techniques can be used to emphasize depth or distance in a drawing. The two parallel tracks of a long, straight railroad line appear to come together as they disappear in the distance. The railroad ties appear shorter as the distance from the viewer increases. This seeming contradiction, called *perspective,* is illustrated in *Fig. 6-40.*

Thus, in drawing parallel lines which recede from the viewer, the lines appear as concurrent rays; the point of intersection of the rays is called the vanishing point.

However, parallel lines which are perpendicular to the line of sight of the viewer are shown as parallel lines.

In *Fig. 6-41*, rays *AB*, *CD*, and *EF* are parallel; the vanishing point is *R*.

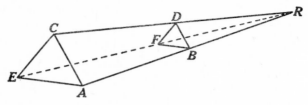

Fig. 6-41

In *Fig. 6-40*, the railroad ties are drawn shorter as the distance from the viewer increases; in *Fig. 6-41*, *BF* is drawn shorter than *AE* although *AE = BF*.

Thus, if one congruent line segment is farther from the viewer than another line segment, it is drawn shorter.

These ideas are used in drawing rectangular prisms, as shown in *Fig. 6-42* (*a*), (*b*), and (*c*).

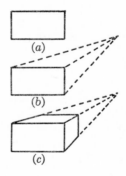

Fig. 6-42

(i) The front surface is drawn as a rectangle.

(ii) A vanishing point is selected, and segments are drawn from it to the vertices of the rectangle; line segments which cannot be seen are omitted.

(iii) The remaining edges are drawn parallel to the front surface, and the perspective lines are erased.

Fig. 6-43

A coin appears to be circular when viewed from above, and rectangular when viewed from the side. To show both aspects, the coin is represented as in *Fig. 6-43*.

In a similar way, a cone intersected by a plane not parallel to the base is represented as in *Fig. 6-44*.

Fig. 6-44

Draw diagrams to represent each of the following and compare them with those on page 461:

1. (i) a pyramid
    (ii) a plane parallel to the base to cut the pyramid
2. a cylinder cut by a plane not parallel to the base

Exercise 6-12

(A)

1. Describe six situations in the physical world in which perspective is observed.
2. Describe the techniques that have been used in the accompanying diagram to represent a three-dimensional figure.

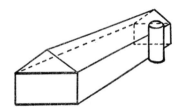

(B)

3. Draw diagrams to represent each of the following:
    (i) a cube;
    (ii) a long, straight road bordered on either side by a stone wall whose top is parallel to the ground;
    (iii) a cylindrical plastic tumbler one-third full of water;
    (iv) a conical glass funnel, two-thirds full of gasoline, inclined slightly away from the vertical;
    (v) two parallel planes intersected by a third plane;
    (vi) two perpendicular planes intersected by a third plane.

Draw a diagram to represent each of the following:

4. (i) At a football game, the linesman is standing at the 35-yard line on the sideline. He is looking at the goal-posts, which are 18′6″ apart, with the crossbar 10′ above the ground; the line joining the farther goal-post to him makes an angle whose measurement is 45° with the sideline.
    (ii) From the information in (i), calculate the width of the field, if the goal-posts are centred on the goal-line.
5. To find the height of a television tower *CD* on the other side of a river, a surveyor selects a base line *AB* on the same horizontal level as the base *D* of the tower. The surveyor then makes the following

measurements: $\angle CBD = 20°$, $\angle DAB = 60°$, $\angle ABD = 90°$

6. From a point P due south of a skyscraper KL, the angle of elevation of the point K at the top is 65°. From a point M on the same street due east of P, the angle of elevation of K is 50°. P, L, M are in the same horizontal plane.

   NOTE: "Angle of elevation" refers to any angle which has one ray in the horizontal plane and the other ray above the horizontal plane.

7. The base DE of a hill runs due east and west; the hill slopes upward to the north, making an angle of 30° with the horizontal. A ski trail DA, 1,200 feet long, runs due north up the hill. A skier leaving the top A follows a downhill course at 45° to AD.

6·20 Drawing polyhedrons (supplementary).

a. *Prism.* A prism is a polyhedron with two of its faces (bases) congruent polygonal regions on parallel planes, and its remaining faces (lateral faces) are parallelogram regions with two edges on these parallel planes. This definition is used in drawing a triangular prism, as shown in *Fig. 6-45.*

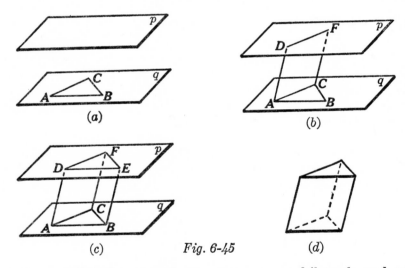

(a) (b)

(c) *Fig. 6-45* (d)

(i) Two parallel planes p and q are drawn as quadrilaterals, and a triangle ABC is drawn on plane q.

(ii) Point D on plane p is selected, and line segment DA is drawn; a parallelogram $DACF$ is drawn so that F lies on plane p.

(iii) A second parallelogram $DABE$ is drawn with E on plane p; line segment FE is drawn.

(iv) The lines representing the planes are erased, and the edges of the prism which are hidden are shown as dotted line segments.

b. *Pyramid.* A pyramid is a polyhedron with one face a polygonal region (base) and the other faces (lateral faces) triangular regions with a common vertex which is not in the plane of the polygonal region.

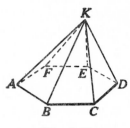

The hexagonal pyramid *K-ABCDEF* in *Fig. 6-46* has a base *ABCDEF* and a vertex *K*. The edges *AF*, *FE*, *ED*, *KF*, and *KE* are dotted to indicate that they are hidden by faces of the pyramid.

Fig. 6-46

The following problems illustrate important definitions. First read the definition; then complete the following. Compare your solutions with those on page 461.

1. A parallelepiped is a prism whose bases are parallelogram regions. Draw a parallelepiped.

2. A right prism is a prism whose lateral faces are rectangular regions. Draw a triangular right prism.

3. A rectangular parallelepiped is a right prism whose bases are rectangular regions. Draw a rectangular parallelepiped.

4. A regular prism is a right prism whose bases are regular polygonal regions. Draw a regular hexagonal prism.

5. A regular pyramid is a pyramid whose base is a regular polygonal region and whose lateral edges are equal in length. Draw a regular hexagonal pyramid.

6. The plane figure which is formed by the intersection of a plane and a polyhedron is called a section of the polyhedron. Draw a section of a rectangular pyramid which is in a plane parallel to the plane of the base.

7. A right section of a prism is a section formed by a plane which is perpendicular to each lateral edge. Draw a pentagonal oblique prism (that is, not a right prism). Draw a right section of this prism.

Exercise 6-13

(B)

1. Draw a right pentagonal prism.
2. Draw a rectangular pyramid.
3. Draw an oblique section (that is, not a right section) of a regular triangular prism.
4. Draw a section of a pentagonal prism parallel to the plane of the base.

5. Draw a diagram for each of the following theorems:

  (i) The lateral edges of a prism are perpendicular to the plane of a right section. (Use a rectangular oblique prism in your diagram.)

  (ii) Any section of a prism formed by a plane parallel to the plane of the base is congruent to the boundary of the base. (Use an oblique hexagonal prism in your diagram.)

  (iii) Two right sections of a prism are congruent. (Use an oblique triangular prism in your diagram.)

  (iv) Any section of a parallelepiped intersecting two diagonally opposite faces is a parallelogram.

6. Draw a pyramid whose base is a quadrilateral region $ABCD$.
   Draw a section $A'B'C'D'$ of this pyramid in a plane parallel to the plane of the base. The polyhedron with bases $ABCD$ and $A'B'C'D'$ is called a *frustum* of the pyramid.

6·21 **Discovery of Euler's relation for polyhedrons (supplementary).** Prisms and pyramids are special types of polyhedrons. In general, polyhedrons are classified according to the number of faces they have. The following is a list of the names of some polyhedrons.

NAME OF POLYHEDRON	NUMBER OF FACES
Tetrahedron	4
Pentahedron	5
Hexahedron	6
Heptahedron	7
Octahedron	8
Nonahedron	9
Decahedron	10
Dodecahedron	12
Icosahedron	20

Discovery Exercise 6-14

By answering the following questions, discover the relation (Euler's relation) among the number of faces, edges, and vertices of a polyhedron:

1. Copy and complete the table on page 201 by referring to the diagrams on page 200:

   F represents the number of faces of a polyhedron;
   E represents the number of edges;
   V represents the number of vertices.

(i)
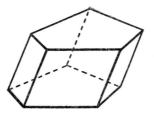

(ii)
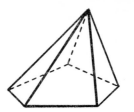

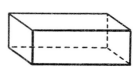

(iii)

(iv)
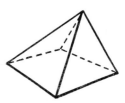

(v)
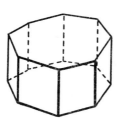

(vi)
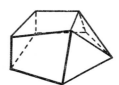

(vii)

(viii)

(ix)
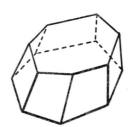

(x)
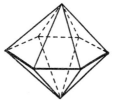

(xi)
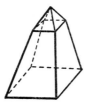

(xii)

DIAGRAM	NAME OF POLYHEDRON	F	E	V	$F + V$	$E + 2$
(i)						
(ii)						
(iii)						
(iv)						
(v)						
(vi)						
(vii)						
(viii)						
(ix)						
(x)						
(xi)						
(xii)						

2. State a probable relationship among the number of faces, edges, and vertices of any polyhedron.

This relationship was first observed by René Descartes in 1640 and later by Leonhard Euler in 1752. Euler, a Swiss mathematician, first stated the relationship in the form $F + V = E + 2$.

NOTE: If every section of a polyhedron is a convex polygon, the polyhedron is said to be *convex*. In this chapter, only convex polyhedrons are considered.

6·22 Regular polyhedrons (supplementary).

A regular polyhedron is a polyhedron whose faces are congruent regular polygonal regions, and whose polyhedral angles are congruent.

Since the faces of all pyramids are bounded by triangles, the only regular pyramid is a tetrahedron, *Fig. 6-47(a)*, whose faces are all bounded by equilateral triangles.

Since the faces of a prism are all bounded by parallelograms, a regular prism is a hexahedron whose faces are all bounded by squares. Such a regular hexahedron is called a *cube*, *Fig. 6-47(b)*.

There are only three other regular polyhedrons: a regular octahedron, a regular dodecahedron, and a regular icosahedron, *Fig. 6-47(c), (d), (e)*.

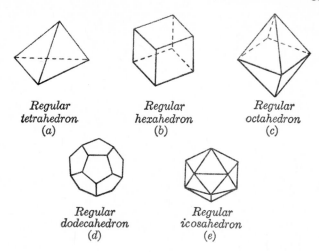

Regular
tetrahedron
(a)

Regular
hexahedron
(b)

Regular
octahedron
(c)

Regular
dodecahedron
(d)

Regular
icosahedron
(e)

Fig. 6-47

These five regular polyhedrons are often called the *Platonic solids,* because the Greek philosopher Plato associated these five solids with the four elements—fire, air, earth, and water, as well as with the universe as a whole.

Many minerals occur as regular polyhedrons. Salt crystals, for example, occur as cubes; diamonds, as regular octahedrons.

It is believed that the Greeks first discovered the dodecahedron in their study of crystals of pyrite, a sulphurous mineral.

6·23 Proof that there are only five regular polyhedrons (supplementary). Euler's relation for polyhedrons states:

$$F + V = E + 2 \qquad\qquad (1)$$

   F represents the number of faces;

   V represents the number of vertices;

   E represents the number of edges of the polyhedron.

If each of the faces of a regular polyhedron is a regular polygonal region of n edges, then

$$nF = 2E. \qquad\qquad (2)$$

(The number of edges in each face times the number of faces is twice the number of edges, since each edge is contained in two faces.)

If r edges meet at each vertex, then

$$rV = 2E. \qquad\qquad (3)$$

(The number of edges at each vertex times the number of vertices is twice the number of edges, since each edge has two vertices.)

$$\therefore F = \frac{2E}{n}, \qquad V = \frac{2E}{r}$$

Substitute in (1) $\qquad \dfrac{2E}{n} + \dfrac{2E}{r} = E + 2$

Divide by $2E$ $\qquad \dfrac{1}{n} + \dfrac{1}{r} = \dfrac{1}{2} + \dfrac{1}{E}$ (4)

Since each face of a regular polygon must have at least three edges,
$$n \geqq 3.$$
Since at least 3 edges must meet at each vertex, $r \geqq 3$.

$$\therefore \frac{1}{E} = \frac{1}{n} + \frac{1}{r} - \frac{1}{2}, \; n, r \geqq 3 \qquad (5)$$

In addition, since E is positive,
$$\therefore \frac{1}{n} + \frac{1}{r} > \frac{1}{2}.$$
$$\therefore \; n \text{ and } r \text{ cannot both be greater than 3.}$$

Consider the two cases:

(i) $n = 3, r \geqq 3$ $\qquad\qquad$ (ii) $r = 3, n \geqq 3$

(i) If $n = 3$, then $\dfrac{1}{E} = \dfrac{1}{3} + \dfrac{1}{r} - \dfrac{1}{2}$

$$= \frac{1}{r} - \frac{1}{6}.$$

For $E > 0$, $r = 3, 4$, or 5.

The following table gives the values of E, F, and V for the corresponding polyhedrons:

	$r = 3$	$r = 4$	$r = 5$
E, from (5)	6	12	30
V, from (3)	4	6	12
F, from (2)	4	8	20
NAME OF POLYHEDRON	REGULAR TETRAHEDRON	REGULAR OCTAHEDRON	REGULAR ICOSAHEDRON

(ii) If $r = 3$, then $\dfrac{1}{E} = \dfrac{1}{n} + \dfrac{1}{3} - \dfrac{1}{2}$

$$= \frac{1}{n} - \frac{1}{6}.$$

For $E > 0$, $n = 3, 4$, or 5.

The following table gives the values of E, V, and F for the corresponding polyhedrons:

	$n = 3$	$n = 4$	$n = 5$
E, from (5)	6	12	30
V, from (3)	4	8	20
F, from (2)	4	6	12
NAME OF POLYHEDRON	REGULAR TETRAHEDRON	CUBE	REGULAR DODECAHEDRON

Since these two tables represent all possible cases, there are only five regular polyhedrons.

Exercise 6-15

1. Copy and complete the following table to verify Euler's relation for the five regular polyhedrons:

	F	E	V	$E + V$	$E + 2$
Regular Tetrahedron					
Cube					
Regular Octahedron					
Regular Dodecahedron					
Regular Icosahedron					

2. Using stiff paper or cardboard, construct models of the five regular polyhedrons by means of the patterns given below. Use dimensions much larger than those used in the pattern.

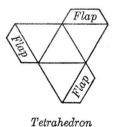

Tetrahedron

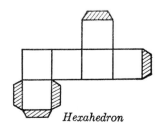

Hexahedron

Octahedron   *Dodecahedron*   *Icosahedron*

6·24 Summary.

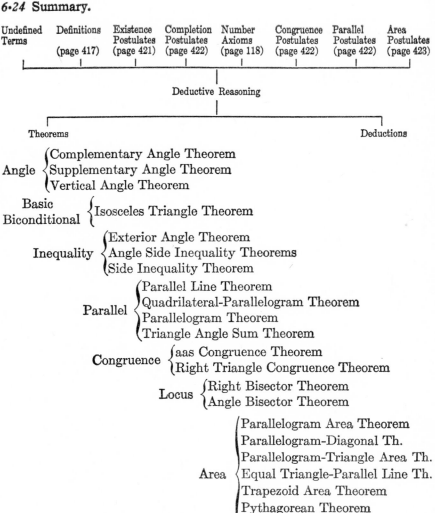

Undefined Terms	Definitions (page 417)	Existence Postulates (page 421)	Completion Postulates (page 422)	Number Axioms (page 118)	Congruence Postulates (page 422)	Parallel Postulates (page 422)	Area Postulates (page 423)

Deductive Reasoning

Theorems   Deductions

Angle {Complementary Angle Theorem
       Supplementary Angle Theorem
       Vertical Angle Theorem

Basic Biconditional {Isosceles Triangle Theorem

Inequality {Exterior Angle Theorem
            Angle Side Inequality Theorems
            Side Inequality Theorem

Parallel {Parallel Line Theorem
          Quadrilateral-Parallelogram Theorem
          Parallelogram Theorem
          Triangle Angle Sum Theorem

Congruence {aas Congruence Theorem
            Right Triangle Congruence Theorem

Locus {Right Bisector Theorem
       Angle Bisector Theorem

Area {Parallelogram Area Theorem
      Parallelogram-Diagonal Th.
      Parallelogram-Triangle Area Th.
      Equal Triangle-Parallel Line Th.
      Trapezoid Area Theorem
      Pythagorean Theorem
      Pythagorean Converse

Exercise 6-16

(*Numerical Exercise*)

(B)

Draw a representative sketch, mark on all given data, and complete the required calculations for each of the following:

1. In $\triangle ABC$, X and Y are on AC and AB, respectively, so that $BX \perp AC$, and $CY \perp AB$. If $AC = 32$ in., $BX = 12$ in., and $CY = 16$ in., find AB.

2. The lengths of the diagonals of a rhombus are 12 cm. and 10 cm. What is the area of the rhombus?

3. In trapezoid $ABCD$, $AB \parallel CD$. $AB = 5$ in., $CD = 3$ in. If the distance between AB and CD is 2 in., find the area of $ABCD$.

4. The medians BD and CE of $\triangle ABC$ intersect on F. The areas of $\triangle$'s DFC and FBC are 2 sq. in. and 4 sq. in., respectively. Find the area of (i) $\triangle EBF$ (ii) figure $AEFD$.

5. P is any point on AB of $\parallel^{\text{gm}}$ $ABCD$. The length of the altitude drawn to BC is 10 in., and $BC = 10$ in. What is the area of $\triangle PCD$?

6. In $\parallel^{\text{gm}}$ $ABCD$, base $BC = 16$ in., and the length of the altitude to BC is 12 in. P is a point on AC such that $AP = \frac{1}{3} AC$. What is the area of $\triangle PBC$?

7. In $\parallel^{\text{gm}}$ $ABCD$, the lengths of the base and the altitude drawn to this base are 8 in. and 7 in., respectively. F is the midpoint of AD, and E is the midpoint of AB. Find the area of $\triangle AEF$.

8. AD is a median of $\triangle ABC$. E is on AD so that $AE = \frac{1}{4} AD$. If $BC = 16$ in. and the area of $\triangle EDC = 48$ sq. in., find the length of the altitude of $\triangle ABC$ drawn from A to BC.

9. In $\triangle ABC$, $BC = 20$ in. and the length of the altitude to BC is 10 in. D is any point on BC; E is the midpoint of AD. Find the area of $\triangle AEC + \triangle BDE$.

10. The diagonal AC of quadrilateral $ABCD$ bisects the other diagonal DB. X is on AC so that $DX \perp AC$. $DX = 2$ in. and $AC = 4$ in. Find the area of $ABCD$.

11. The length of the hypotenuse of an isosceles right triangle is 16 millimetres. Find its area.

12. In $\parallel^{\text{gm}}$ $ABCD$, X is on DC so that $BX \perp DC$. $BX = XC$, $AB = 8.7$ in., and $BC = 6.5$ in. Find the area of $\parallel^{\text{gm}}$ $ABCD$.

13. A bracing cable on a hydro pole is fastened to the pole 30 feet from the ground and is anchored on level ground 20 feet from the foot of the pole. Find the length of the cable to the nearest foot.

14. A squared timber used on a subway is 14 inches square. Find, to one decimal place, the smallest diameter which the original log could have measured.

15. The small end of a saw log is 20 inches in diameter. Find, to one decimal place, the width of the largest square timber which can be sawn out of this log.

16. Find the lateral area of a right prism whose lateral edges have a length 10 inches and whose base has a perimeter of 14 inches.

17. Find the lateral area of a regular pyramid whose slant height is 12 cm. and whose base is a pentagonal region with perimeter 20 cm.

Review Exercise 6-17

(A)

1. In each of the following diagrams, using BC as base, state the construction required to locate another triangle equal in area to the shaded triangle:

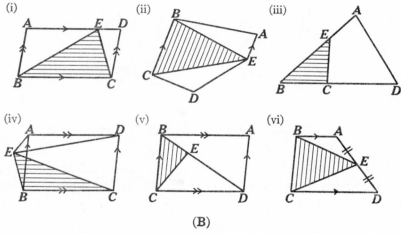

(i)   (ii)   (iii)

(iv)   (v)   (vi)

(B)

2. In the diagram below:
   (i) find the area of (a) $\triangle BDE$ (b) $||^{gm}$ $FKLG$;
   (ii) find the distance between FK and GL.

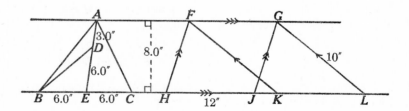

3. The length of the base of a rectangle is 45 cm. Its area is 1,260 sq. cm. Find the length of the diagonal in centimetres.

4. In the diagram at the left below, find the area of quadrilateral $ADFE$.

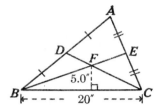 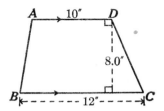

5. Find the area of the trapezoid $ABCD$ (right above).

6. In $\triangle ABC$, left below, find AC.

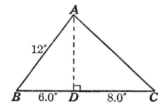 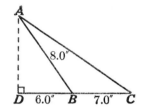

7. In $\triangle ABC$, right above, find AC.

8. Prove that the diagonals of a parallelogram separate it into four parts with equal areas.

9. In a trapezoid, the straight line on the midpoints of the parallel sides separates the trapezoid into two trapezoids with equal areas.

10. In $||^{\text{gm}} ABCD$, P is any point on BC. Prove that $\triangle APD = \triangle ABP + \triangle DPC$.

11. If the diagonals of a quadrilateral intersect at right angles, the sum of the squares on one pair of opposite sides equals the sum of the squares on the other pair.

12. In $\triangle ABC$, $\angle B = 90°$, P is any point on AB, and Q is any point on BC. Prove $CP^2 + AQ^2 = PQ^2 + AC^2$.

13. In $||^{\text{gm}} ABCD$, E is on AD and F on CD, so that $EF \parallel AC$. Prove: (i) $\triangle AEB = \triangle FBC$ (ii) BD bisects quadrilateral $DEBF$

14. Prove that a quadrilateral which is separated into two equal triangles by each of its diagonals is a parallelogram.

15. In $\triangle ABC$, D is on AB and E on AC, so that $DE \parallel AB$. DE is extended to F making $DF = BC$. Prove that $\triangle DBE = \triangle AEF$.

16. Find the lateral area of a right triangular prism whose lateral edges are 14 inches long and whose base is bounded by a right triangle with a hypotenuse of length 26 inches and one side about the right angle of length 10 inches.

17. Find the slant height of a regular pyramid whose base is a quadrilateral region, if one side of the base is 6 inches long and the lateral edges are 9 inches long. Find the lateral area of the pyramid.

Chapter VII

RATIO AND PROPORTION
SIMILAR FIGURES

7·1 Ratio and proportion. The numbers 6, 3, 2 are said to be in the ratio 6 to 3 to 2 which is written $6 : 3 : 2$.   The ratio $6 : 3 : 2$ is called a *three-term ratio.*

Since
$$24 = 6(4)$$
$$12 = 3(4)$$
$$8 = 2(4)$$

the ratio $24 : 12 : 8$ is said to be *equivalent* to the ratio $6 : 3 : 2$. That is,
$$24 : 12 : 8 = 6 : 3 : 2.$$

Also
$$60 : 30 : 20 = 6(10) : 3(10) : 2(10)$$
$$\therefore \quad 60 : 30 : 20 = 6 : 3 : 2.$$

Similarly,
$$30 : 15 : 10 = 6(5) : 3(5) : 2(5)$$
$$\therefore \quad 30 : 15 : 10 = 6 : 3 : 2$$

and
$$600 : 300 : 200 = 6(100) : 3(100) : 2(100)$$
$$\therefore \quad 600 : 300 : 200 = 6 : 3 : 2$$

Thus,
$$x : y : z = a : b : c$$
if and only if there is a real number k ($k \neq 0$) *such that*
$$x = ka$$
$$y = kb$$
$$z = kc \, .$$

The statement $x : y : z = a : b : c$ is called a *proportion*. Each of the numbers x, y, z, a, b, c is called a *proportional*, and k is the *proportionality factor*.

DEFINITION: *A proportion is the statement of equality of two ratios.*

In general,

$$a_1 : a_2 : a_3 : \ldots : a_m = b_1 : b_2 : b_3 : \ldots : b_n$$
if and only if (i) *m = n*
and (ii) *there is a real number k (k $\neq$ o) such that*
$$a_1 = kb_1 \, , \, a_2 = kb_2 \, , \, a_3 = kb_3 \, , \ldots \, .$$

Example 1. If three tanks contain 8 quarts, 7 quarts, and 3 quarts of water, respectively, and a fourth tank is empty, what is the ratio of the volume of water in the four tanks?

Solution. The required ratio is $8 : 7 : 3 : 0$.

Example 2. What is the ratio of the following lengths?
1 foot, 1 yard, 1 mile

Solution. The ratio $1 : 1 : 1$ does not give a satisfactory comparison of these lengths. It is necessary to express each of the measurements in terms of the *same unit*. Since 1 yard = 3 feet, and 1 mile = 5,280 feet, the ratio of these lengths is $1 : 3 : 5,280$.

Example 3. Are 6, 16, 20 proportional to 9, 24, 30? Justify your answer.

Solution. Since $9 = \frac{3}{2}(6)$, $24 = \frac{3}{2}(16)$, $30 = \frac{3}{2}(20)$,
$$\therefore \; 6 : 16 : 20 = 9 : 24 : 30.$$
The proportionality factor is $\frac{3}{2}$.

7·2 Two-term ratios. The two-term ratio $60 : 30$ is equivalent to the two-term ratio $2 : 1$, since $60 : 30 = 30(2) : 30(1) = 2 : 1$.

This proportion may also be written $\dfrac{60}{30} = \dfrac{1}{2}$.

In general,

if b $\neq$ 0, the ratio a : b may be expressed in the form $\dfrac{a}{b}$.

7·3. Ratios of line segments and areas.

The ratio of line segments AB and CD means the ratio of the lengths of the line segments and is expressed AB : CD or $\dfrac{AB}{CD}$.

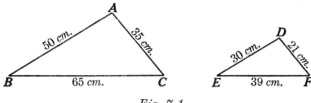

Fig. 7-1

The ratio of the sides of $\triangle ABC$ (*Fig. 7-1*) is 50 : 65 : 35 or 10 : 13 : 7.
The ratio of the sides of $\triangle DEF$ is 30 : 39 : 21 or 10 : 13 : 7.
Thus, $AB : BC : CA = DE : EF : FG$. That is, the sides of $\triangle ABC$ are
proportional to the sides of $\triangle DEF$.

The ratio of the areas of two triangles ABC and DEF is expressed

$\triangle ABC : \triangle DEF$ *or* $\dfrac{\triangle ABC}{\triangle DEF}$ *and is the ratio of the number of*

square units in the areas of the triangles.

Exercise 7-1

(A)

1. Give examples of situations where ratios are commonly used.

2. State the ratio of the following measurements: (i) 30 in. to 1 yd.
   (ii) 2 quarts to 1 gallon (iii) 3 cu. ft. to 1 cu. yd. (iv) 2 ft. 1 in. to 1 ft.
   3 in. (v) 20 ft. to 1 mi.

3. If a, $b \in R$, state ratios equivalent to each of the following:
   (i) $3a$ to $12a^2$ (ii) $a - b$ to $a^2 - b^2$ (iii) $(a + b)^2$ to $a + b$
   (iv) $4a^2b$ to $12ab^2$ (v) $(2ab)^2$ to $(3ab)^2$ (vi) $3a + 3b$ to $a^2 - b^2$

4. In the diagram below, AD is divided at B and C into segments with
   lengths as indicated.

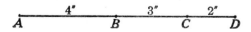

   State the ratio of:
   (i) AC to CD (ii) BD to AB (iii) AB to CD
   (iv) AC to BC to CD (v) AD to BD to AC (vi) AB to BD to AD

5. State the numbers represented by a and b in each of the following
   proportions:
   (i) $2 : 4 : 6 = 6 : a : b$ (ii) $\frac{1}{2} : \frac{1}{3} : \frac{1}{4} = a : b : 1$

(iii) $\frac{1}{2} : \frac{1}{3} : \frac{1}{4} = 1 : a : b$ (iv) $\frac{1}{2} : \frac{1}{3} : \frac{1}{4} = a : 1 : b$

(v) $x : y : z = x^2 : a : b$ (vi) $m : mn : n = mn^2 : a : b$

(B)

6. (i) List pairs of the following ratios which are equal:

    (a) $5 : -7 : 9$ (b) $12 : 18 : 24$ (c) $2 : 3 : 4$

    (d) $-\frac{10}{3} : \frac{14}{3} : -6$ (e) $\frac{8}{5} : 0 : \frac{12}{5}$ (f) $2 : 0 : 0$

    (ii) What is the proportionality factor of each of the proportions formed in (i)?

7. $\triangle XYZ$ has a base whose length is 8 feet and an altitude whose length is 6 feet. $\triangle PQR$ has a base whose length is 4 feet and an altitude whose length is 15 feet. Find the ratio of $\triangle XYZ$ to $\triangle PQR$.

8. C is a point on line segment AB such that $AC : CB = 3 : 2$. If the length of AB is 30 inches, find the lengths of AC and CB.

9. Two triangles have equal altitudes and their areas are in the ratio $5 : 3$. What is the ratio of the longer base to the shorter base?

10. Two circles have radii of lengths 8 cm. and 12 cm., respectively. Find: (i) the ratio of their circumferences

                (ii) the ratio of their areas

7·4 Properties of proportions involving two-term ratios.

In the proportion $a : b = c : d$, $a, b, c, d \in R$:

        a and d are called the *extremes;*

        b and c are called the *means;*

        d is called the *fourth proportional* to a, b, and **c**.

a. THEOREM. If $a, b, c, d \neq 0$ and $\dfrac{a}{b} = \dfrac{c}{d}$,

then   (i) $ad = bc$ (Cross multiplication)

       (ii) $\dfrac{a}{c} = \dfrac{b}{d}$ (Alternation of the means)

       (iii) $\dfrac{b}{a} = \dfrac{d}{c}$ (Inversion)

       (iv) $\dfrac{a + b}{b} = \dfrac{c + d}{d}$ (Adding unity)

       (v) $\dfrac{a - b}{b} = \dfrac{c - d}{d}$ (Subtracting unity)

Hypothesis: $a, b, c, d \neq 0$ and $\dfrac{a}{b} = \dfrac{c}{d}$

Conclusion: $ad = bc$

Proof:

STATEMENTS	AUTHORITIES
1. $\dfrac{a}{b} = \dfrac{c}{d}$	1. Hypothesis
2. $\dfrac{a}{b}(bd) = \dfrac{c}{d}(bd)$	2. Multiplication
3. $ad = bc$	3. Definition, (CM)

Write proofs of conclusions (ii), (iii), (iv), and (v) and compare your proofs with those on page 462.

b. If $\dfrac{a}{b} = \dfrac{b}{c}$, $a, b, c \neq 0$, then a, b, c are in *continued proportion; b* is the *geometric mean (mean proportional)* of a and c, and c is the *third proportional* to a and b.

c. If $\dfrac{AB}{CD} = \dfrac{PQ}{XY}$, then $AB \cdot XY = CD \cdot PQ$. Geometrically, $AB \cdot XY$ represents the number of square units in the area of a rectangle with adjacent sides equal to AB and XY. $AB \cdot XY$ is read, "the rectangle AB times XY".

Example 1. Find the fourth proportional to 3, -5, and 8.

Solution. Represent the fourth proportional by x.

$$\text{Then} \qquad \frac{3}{-5} = \frac{8}{x} \qquad \text{(Definition)}$$

$$\therefore 3x = -40 \qquad \text{(Cross multiplication)}$$

$$\therefore x = -\frac{40}{3} \qquad \text{(Division)}$$

The fourth proportional to 3, -5, and 8 is $-\dfrac{40}{3}$.

Example 2. Find the mean proportional of 9 and 16.

Solution. Represent the mean proportional by x.

$$\text{Then} \qquad \frac{9}{x} = \frac{x}{16} \qquad \text{(Definition)}$$

$$\therefore x^2 = 144 \qquad \text{(Cross multiplication)}$$

$$\therefore x = \pm 12$$

There are two mean proportionals of 9 and 16. They are $+12$ and -12.

Exercise 7-2

(A)

State the equation obtained by (i) cross multiplication (ii) alternation of the means (iii) inversion (iv) adding unity (v) subtracting unity, for each of the following proportions:

1. $\dfrac{3}{5} = \dfrac{9}{15}$ 2. $\dfrac{-4}{1} = \dfrac{12}{-3}$ 3. $\dfrac{64}{32} = \dfrac{-10}{-5}$

4. $\dfrac{x}{2} = \dfrac{y}{3}$ 5. $\dfrac{6}{x} = \dfrac{x}{150}$ 6. $\dfrac{2}{-5} = \dfrac{9}{x}$

7. $2 : 3 = 18 : 27$ 8. $5 : x = x : 125$ 9. $4 : -7 = 15 : x$

10. State the number or numbers represented by x in each of the following proportions:

   (i) $\dfrac{x}{2} = \dfrac{3}{4}$ (ii) $\dfrac{3}{x} = \dfrac{21}{-14}$ (iii) $x : 5 = 10 : 25$

   (iv) $\dfrac{5}{2} = \dfrac{25}{x}$ (v) $\dfrac{a}{3} = \dfrac{x}{5}$ (vi) $-12 : -3 = 44 : x$

   (vii) $\dfrac{1}{x} = \dfrac{x}{16}$ (viii) $\dfrac{2}{3} = \dfrac{-3}{x}$ (ix) $a : b = b : x$

11. What conclusion can be drawn from each of the following?

   (i) $\dfrac{a}{b} = \dfrac{a}{c}$ (ii) $\dfrac{a}{b} = \dfrac{ma}{c}$ (iii) $\dfrac{a}{b} = \dfrac{c}{c}$

   (iv) $\dfrac{\triangle ABC}{\triangle DEF} = \dfrac{AX}{AX}$ (v) $\dfrac{\triangle ABC}{\triangle DEF} = \dfrac{2BC}{BC}$

   (vi) $\dfrac{AB}{CD} = \dfrac{2}{1}$ and $\dfrac{CD}{PQ} = \dfrac{3}{2}$

12. If $AB \cdot XY = CD \cdot PQ$, state ratios equivalent to:

   (i) $\dfrac{AB}{CD}$ (ii) $\dfrac{XY}{CD}$ (iii) $\dfrac{PQ}{AB}$ (iv) $\dfrac{PQ}{XY}$

13. If $XY^2 = AB \cdot CD$, state ratios equivalent to: (i) $\dfrac{XY}{AB}$ (ii) $\dfrac{XY}{CD}$

(B)

14. Find the fourth proportional to:

   (i) $3, 2\frac{1}{3}, 9$ (ii) x, y, xy

   (iii) $x + y, x - y, (x + y)^2$ (iv) $a^2, a + b, a$

15. Find the third proportional to:

   (i) $3, 9$ (ii) $3, 2$ (iii) a, ar (iv) x^2, xy

16. Find the geometric mean of:

    (i) 9, 16   (ii) $9, \dfrac{1}{4}$ (iii) $\dfrac{3}{4}, \dfrac{4}{3}$ (iv) a, ar^2

17. (i) Find the ratio of x to y from each of the following:

    (a) $5x = 7y$ (b) $2x = 3y$ (c) $x + 2y = 0$ (d) $ax - by = 0$

    (ii) Evaluate $\dfrac{x + y}{y}$ for each of (a) to (d).

    (iii) Evaluate $\dfrac{x - y}{y}$ for each of (a) to (d).

18. A line segment AB is extended $\frac{2}{3}$ its own length to a point C beyond B. Find each of the following ratios:

    (i) $\dfrac{AB}{BC}$ (ii) $\dfrac{AC}{AB}$ (iii) $\dfrac{BC}{AC}$

19. A line segment PQ is extended beyond Q to R so that $\dfrac{PQ}{QR} = \dfrac{4}{3}$.   If

$PQ = 24$ cm., find the length of PR.

S is a point between R and T on the line segment RT. Find what fraction
          (i) RS is of RT   *(ii) ST is of RT*
if RS : ST equals:

20. $2 : 3$ **21.** $1 : 4$ **22.** $2m : 3s$ **23.** $a + b : a - b$

Exercise 7-3

(Practical applications of ratio and proportion)

(B)

1. Find the gear ratio of two meshed gears which have 12 and 16 teeth, respectively.

2. A plan of a house is drawn to a scale of 10 in. to 30 ft. Find the length of the line segment in the drawing which represents the height of a wall 8 ft. 6 in. high.

3. Three men own capital stock in a company. The value of the stock owned by the men is $32,000, $24,000, and $10,000, respectively. If the profit for one year is $6,600, how should they share this profit?

4. The ratio of height to width of a door should be $8 : 3$. If a door is 6 ft. 8 in. high, what should be its width?

5. The rear wheel of a tractor has a radius of 3 ft. 2 in., and the front wheel has a radius of 1 ft. 8 in. How many rotations will the front wheel make for every 50 rotations of the rear wheel?

6. For a transformer, the ratio of the number of turns on the secondary winding to the number of turns on the primary winding is called the *turns ratio* of the transformer. Find the turns ratio of a transformer with 3,600 secondary turns and 400 primary turns.

7. A company reduces the number of hours of work for its employees from 8 hours to 6 hours a day. By what per cent must the company increase the number of employees to retain the same output of work?

8. The efficiency of a transformer is the ratio of the power delivered to the load to the power taken from the line. Find, as a per cent, the efficiency of a transformer that delivers 24 watts to a load while taking 30 watts from the line.

9. In a survey, a gradient has a rise of 10 feet in every 100 yards of road. What is the rise in two miles of road if the gradient remains constant?

10. A parcel of land is subdivided into 50 lots, all 30 feet wide. How many lots 20 feet wide could be formed from the same parcel of land?

7·5 Division of a line segment in a given ratio.

a. *Internal division.* Consider a line segment AB and a point Q on the segment: that is, Q is between A and B (*Fig. 7-2*). Line segment AB is said to be divided *internally* at Q.

$$A \qquad\qquad Q \qquad\qquad\qquad B$$

Fig. 7-2

Q is called the *point of section* or the *point of division* of the line segment AB, and Q is said to divide AB in the ratio $AQ : QB$.

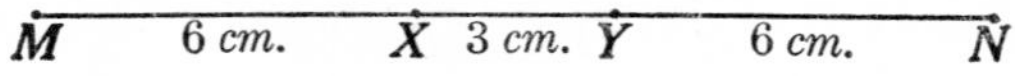

$$M \quad 6\ cm. \quad X \ \ 3\ cm.\ Y \quad 6\ cm. \quad N$$

Fig. 7-3

In *Fig. 7-3*, X and Y are points on line segment MN, such that $MX = 6$ cm., $XY = 3$ cm., $YN = 6$ cm. The point X divides MN into two segments, MX and XN, such that $MX : XN = 2 : 3$; similarly, point Y divides MN into two segments such that $NY : YM = 2 : 3$. Thus, there are two points which divide the segment MN into two segments in the ratio $2 : 3$. In order that a given ratio corresponds to a unique point of section, MN is considered to be the line segment directed *from M to N*. M is the *initial point*; N is the *terminal point* of the segment; the first term of the ratio corresponds to the segment from the initial point M to the point of division X, and the second term corresponds to the segment from the point of division X to the terminal point N.

Thus, X divides MN in the ratio $2 : 3$; Y divides MN in the ratio $3 : 2$.

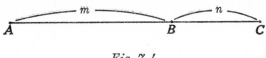

Fig. 7-4

In general (Fig. 7-4),

      (i) *B divides AC in the ratio m : n;*

      (ii) *B divides CA in the ratio n : m, where m, n ∈ ^{+}R .*

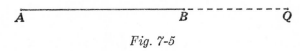

Fig. 7-5

b. *External division.* The point Q on AB extended, *Fig. 7-5*, may be considered as a point of division of the line segment AB. In this case, Q is said to divide AB *externally* into the two line segments AQ and QB or in the ratio $AQ : QB$. These particular line segments are chosen so that the convention for naming the ratio of division for internal division is extended to external division. In extending this convention, it must be noted that in going from the initial point to the point of division and then from the point of division to the terminal point, a change of direction is necessary. Thus, when a line segment is divided externally in a given ratio, one of the terms of the ratio is a negative number—in this case, the second term of the ratio.

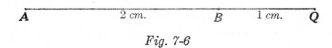

Fig. 7-6

In *Fig. 7-6*, if the direction A to B is considered to be positive, then Q divides AB in the ratio $3 : -1$.

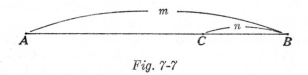

Fig. 7-7

In general (Fig. 7-7),

 (i) *the order in which the line segment is named indicates the positive sense;*

(ii) *B divides AC in the ratio m : − n;*

(iii) *B divides CA in the ratio − n : m, where m, n ∈ ^{+}R, m > n.*

LINE SEGMENT DIVISION POSTULATE

A line segment is divided at one and only one point in a given ratio.

Example. State the ratio (*Fig. 7-8*) in which:

(i)   *A* divides *XY*   (ii) *C* divides *BY*
(iii) *C* divides *AB*   (iv) *B* divides *CY*
(v)   *X* divides *AB*   (vi) *B* divides *XA*
(vii) *A* divides *XB*   (viii) *C* divides *XB*

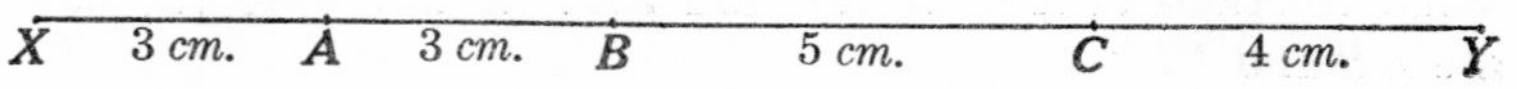

X ——— 3 cm. ——— A ——— 3 cm. ——— B ——— 5 cm. ——— C ——— 4 cm. ——— Y

Fig. 7-8

Solution.

(i)   *A* is between *X* and *Y*,   ∴ *XA* : *AY* = 1 : 4.
(ii) *C* is between *B* and *Y*,   ∴ *BC* : *CY* = 5 : 4.
(iii) *C* is not between *A* and *B*,   ∴ *AC* : *CB* = 8 : − 5.
(iv) *B* is not between *C* and *Y*,   ∴ *CB* : *BY* = − 5 : 9.
(v)   *X* is not between *A* and *B*,   ∴ *AX* : *XB* = − 1 : 2.
(vi) *B* is not between *X* and *A*,   ∴ *XB* : *BA* = 2 : − 1.
(vii) *A* is between *X* and *B*,   ∴ *XA* : *AB* = 1 : 1.
(viii) *C* is not between *X* and *B*, ∴ *XC* : *CB* = 11 : − 5.

Exercise 7-4

(A)

1. In the diagram at the left below, *B* divides *AD* in the ratio $\dfrac{AB}{BD}$.

   In a similar manner, state the ratio which indicates how:

   (i)   *AD* is divided at *C*   (ii) *DB* is divided at *A*
   (iii) *CB* is divided at *A*   (iv) *CA* is divided at *B*

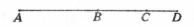 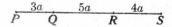

2. In the diagram at the right above, state the ratio in which:

   (i)   *RP* is divided at *Q*   (ii) *PR* is divided at *S*
   (iii) *SQ* is divided at *R*   (iv) *RS* is divided at *P*

3. In the diagram at the left below, AB is divided at P in the ratio $3 : 4$. What fractions of AB are the segments AP and PB? If $AB = 28$ ft., how long are AP and PB?

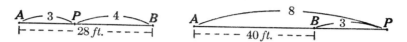

4. In the diagram at the right above, AB is divided in the ratio $8 : -3$. What fractions of AB are AP and PB? If $AB = 40$ ft., how long are AP and PB?

(B)

5. A line segment CD, 3 inches in length, is extended to E so that the length of DE is 5 inches. Find: (i) the ratio in which D divides CE (ii) the ratio in which D divides EC (iii) the ratio in which E divides CD (iv) the ratio in which C divides ED.

6. A line segment PQ is divided at A in the ratio $9 : -2$. What is the ratio of (i) PA to PQ (ii) QA to PQ?

7. A line segment ST is divided at B in the ratio $-3 : 7$. Find the ratio in which (i) S divides BT (ii) T divides BS.

8. PQ is divided at S in the ratio $m : n$, m, $n \in {}^{+}R$. What fraction is (i) PS of PQ (ii) SQ of PQ?

9. AB is divided at P in the ratio $a : -b$. Find the ratio $\dfrac{AP}{AB}$ when (i) $a > b$, $a, b \in {}^{+}R$ (ii) $a > b$, $a, b \in {}^{-}R$.

7·6 Triangle Area Ratio Theorem.

Triangle Area Ratio Theorem

If two triangles have equal altitudes, then their areas are proportional to their bases.

Hypothesis: $\triangle$'s ABC and DEF with altitudes of length h units and bases of length b_1 and b_2 units, respectively, *Fig. 7-9.*

Conclusion: $\dfrac{\triangle ABC}{\triangle DEF} = \dfrac{b_1}{b_2}$

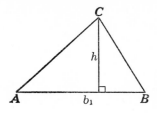

Fig. 7-9

Proof:

STATEMENTS	AUTHORITIES
1. $\triangle ABC = \frac{1}{2}b_1h$ sq. units	1. Area of a triangle
2. $\triangle DEF = \frac{1}{2}b_2h$ sq. units	2. Area of a triangle
3. $\dfrac{\triangle ABC}{\triangle DEF} = \dfrac{\frac{1}{2}b_1h}{\frac{1}{2}b_2h}$	3. Division
4. $\dfrac{\triangle ABC}{\triangle DEF} = \dfrac{b_1}{b_2}$	4. Principle of equivalent fractions

Corollary: If two triangles have equal bases, then their areas are proportional to their altitudes.

Write a proof of this corollary and compare it with that on page 462.

Exercise 7-5

(A)

1. In the diagram at the left below, find the ratio:

(i) $\triangle QTS$ to $\triangle TSR$	(ii) $\triangle QTS$ to $\triangle QPS$
(iii) $\triangle TRS$ to $\triangle PSR$	(iv) $\triangle TQR$ to $\triangle PQS$
(v) $\triangle QSP$ to $\triangle SRP$	(vi) $\triangle PQR$ to $\triangle PQS$
(vii) $\triangle PTQ$ to $\triangle TQS$	(viii) $\triangle TSR$ to $\triangle PTR$
(ix) $\triangle PRT$ to $\triangle PQT$	(x) $\triangle PTR$ to $\triangle QTS$
(xi) $\triangle TSR$ to $\triangle PQT$	(xii) $\triangle QTS$ to $\triangle PSR$

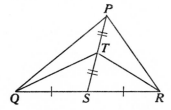
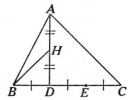

2. In the diagram at the right above, find the ratio: (i) $\triangle ABH$ to $\triangle ABD$ (ii) $\triangle ABD$ to $\triangle ABC$ (iii) $\triangle ABH$ to $\triangle ABC$

3. In the diagram at the left below, find:

   (i) $\dfrac{\triangle ABD}{\triangle ABC}$ (ii) $\dfrac{\triangle ADC}{\triangle ABE}$ (iii) $\dfrac{\triangle AGC}{\triangle ABC}$ (iv) $\dfrac{\triangle ABD}{\triangle BGC}$

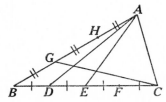 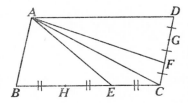

4. In the diagram at the right above, $ABCD$ is a parallelogram. What fraction is: (i) $\triangle ABE$ of $\triangle ABC$ (ii) $\triangle ABE$ of $\|^{gm} ABCD$ (iii) quadrilateral $AECF$ of $\|^{gm} ABCD$?

(B)

5. $PQRS$ is a parallelogram, and X is a point on QS such that $\dfrac{QX}{XS} = \dfrac{1}{4}$.

   Prove that $\triangle PXS = \dfrac{2}{5} \|^{gm} PQRS$.

6. $ABCD$ is a quadrilateral. The diagonals AC and BD intersect on E such that $AE = EC$. Prove that $\triangle ABD = \triangle BCD$.

7. Prove that the areas of the four triangles into which a quadrilateral is divided by its diagonals are proportional.

8. State and prove the converse of the Triangle Area Ratio Theorem.

9. $QRST$ is a parallelogram. P is a point on RT such that $TP : PR = 2 : 3$. Prove that $\triangle QPT : \triangle QST = 2 : 5$.

(C)

10. Line segments AO, BO, CO join any point O to the vertices of $\triangle ABC$.

    AO or AO extended intersects BC at D. Prove $\dfrac{\triangle AOB}{\triangle AOC} = \dfrac{BD}{DC}$.

7·7 Triangle Proportionality Theorem, Part I.

Triangle Proportionality Theorem

A line intersects two sides of a triangle in distinct points so that the segments of these sides are proportional if and only if the line is parallel to the third side of the triangle.

PART I

If a line parallel to one side of a triangle intersects the other two sides in distinct points, then the segments of these sides are proportional.

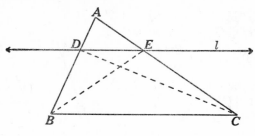

Fig. 7-10

Hypothesis: $\triangle ABC$ and a line l parallel to BC, such that l intersects AB on D and AC on E

Conclusion: $\dfrac{AD}{DB} = \dfrac{AE}{EC}$

Analysis:

I CAN PROVE	IF I CAN PROVE
1. $\dfrac{AD}{DB} = \dfrac{AE}{EC}$	1. The areas of two triangles with AD and DB as bases and with equal altitudes are proportional to the areas of two triangles with AE and EC as bases and with equal altitudes.
2. The areas of two triangles with AD and DB as bases and with equal altitudes are proportional to the areas of two triangles with AE and EC as bases and with equal altitudes	2. $\dfrac{\triangle AED}{\triangle DEB} = \dfrac{\triangle AED}{\triangle DEC}$.
3. $\dfrac{\triangle AED}{\triangle DEB} = \dfrac{\triangle AED}{\triangle DEC}$	3. $\triangle DEB = \triangle DEC$.
4. $\triangle DEB = \triangle DEC$	4. $BC \parallel DE$.
5. $BC \parallel DE$ by hypothesis.	

Write a proof of this theorem and compare it with that on page 463.

Corollary: **If a straight line parallel to one side of a triangle intersects the other two sides in distinct points, then the sides are proportional to the corresponding segments.**

Write a complete proof of this corollary and compare your proof with that on page 463. (Refer to section 7·4 a. (iv), page 213.)

Example. In $\triangle PQR$, S is on PQ and T on PR so that $ST \parallel QR$. V is on QR so that $TV \parallel PQ$. Prove that $\dfrac{PQ}{QS} = \dfrac{RQ}{RV}$.

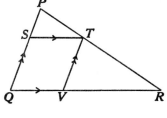

Hypothesis: In the diagram (*Fig. 7-11*), $ST \parallel QR$, $TV \parallel PQ$.

Conclusion: $\dfrac{PQ}{QS} = \dfrac{RQ}{RV}$

Fig. 7-11

Analysis:

I CAN PROVE	IF I CAN PROVE
1. $\dfrac{PQ}{QS} = \dfrac{RQ}{RV}$	1. $\dfrac{PQ}{QS} = \dfrac{PR}{RT}$ and $\dfrac{RQ}{RV} = \dfrac{RP}{RT}$.
2. $\dfrac{PQ}{QS} = \dfrac{PR}{RT}$ and $\dfrac{RQ}{RV} = \dfrac{RP}{RT}$ by the Triangle Proportionality Theorem.	

Write a proof for this example and compare it with that on page 464.

Exercise 7-6

(A)

1. For each of the following, find the numbers represented by x and y:

(i)   (ii)   (iii)

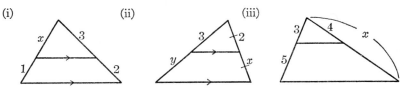

2. With reference to the diagram at the right, complete the proportions:

(i) $\dfrac{PS}{SQ} = \underline{\quad\quad}$

(ii) $\dfrac{QR}{QT} = \underline{\quad\quad}$

(iii) $\dfrac{RT}{TQ} = \underline{\quad\quad}$

(iv) $\dfrac{QP}{SP} = \underline{\quad\quad}$

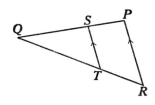

3. With reference to the diagram at the right, find the ratio:

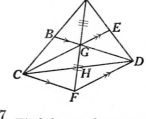

(i) *AB* to *BC*

(ii) *AE* to *ED*

(iii) *GH* to *HF*

(iv) *AG* to *GH*

(v) *CH* to *HD*

4. In each of the diagrams below, $\dfrac{AX}{XB} = \dfrac{7}{2}$. Find the number represented by *x*.

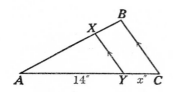

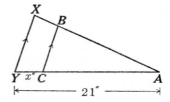

(B)

5. Copy the following proof and complete the authorities column:

Hypothesis: In the diagram, *DE* || *BC* .

Conclusion: $\triangle ADF = \triangle AEF$

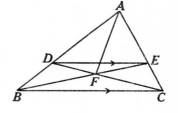

Proof:

STATEMENTS	AUTHORITIES
1. $\dfrac{\triangle ADF}{\triangle DBF} = \dfrac{AD}{DB}$	1.
2. $\dfrac{\triangle AEF}{\triangle ECF} = \dfrac{AE}{EC}$	2.
3. $DE \parallel BC$	3.
4. $\dfrac{AD}{DB} = \dfrac{AE}{EC}$	4.
5. $\dfrac{\triangle ADF}{\triangle DBF} = \dfrac{\triangle AEF}{\triangle ECF}$	5.
6. $\triangle DBC = \triangle EBC$	6.
7. $\triangle DBC - \triangle FBC = \triangle BEC - \triangle FBC$	7.
8. $\triangle DBF = \triangle ECF$	8.
9. $\dfrac{\triangle ADF}{\triangle DBF} = \dfrac{\triangle AEF}{\triangle ECF}$	9.
10. $\triangle ADF = \triangle AEF$	10.

6. Prove the Triangle Proportionality Theorem in the following cases:

   (i) The line l parallel to side BC of $\triangle ABC$ intersects CA extended on E and BA extended on D.

   (ii) The line l parallel to side BC of $\triangle ABC$ intersects AC extended on E and AB extended on D.

7. Use the Triangle Proportionality Theorem to prove that the line on the midpoint of one side of a triangle parallel to a second side bisects the third side.

8. Prove that the midpoint of the hypotenuse of a right triangle is equidistant from the three vertices.

9. In the diagram at the left below, $AB = BC = CD = DE$ and $BP \parallel CQ \parallel DR \parallel ES$. Prove $AP = PQ = QR = RS$.

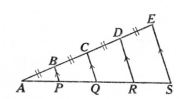 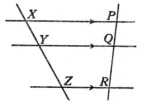

10. In the diagram at the right above, three parallel lines are intersected by two transversals at X, Y, Z and P, Q, R, respectively.
Prove $\dfrac{XY}{YZ} = \dfrac{PQ}{QR}$.

11. In $\parallel^{gm} ABCD$, X and Y are the midpoints of AD and BC, respectively. BX and DY intersect AC on M and N, respectively. Prove $AM = MN = NC$: that is, BX and DY *trisect* AC.

7·8 Triangle Proportionality Theorem, Part II.

PART II

If two sides of a triangle are divided proportionally, then the straight line on the points of section is parallel to the third side.

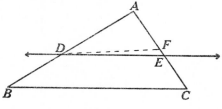

Fig. 7-12

Hypothesis: ABC is a triangle such that AB and AC are divided at D and E, respectively, so that $\dfrac{AD}{DB} = \dfrac{AE}{EC}$.

Conclusion: $DE \parallel BC$

Analysis:

I CAN PROVE	IF I CAN PROVE
1. $DE \parallel BC$	1. $DE \not\parallel BC$ is false.
2. $DE \not\parallel BC$ is false	2. The assumption $DE \not\parallel BC$ leads to a contradiction of a known fact.
3. The assumption $DE \not\parallel BC$ leads to a contradiction of a known fact	3. The assumption that $DF \parallel BC$ (*Fig. 7-12*) leads to a contradiction of a known fact.
4. The assumption $DF \parallel BC$ leads to the logical consequent $\dfrac{AD}{DB} = \dfrac{AF}{FC}$ which, by the Line Segment Division Postulate, contradicts the hypothesis that $\dfrac{AD}{DB} = \dfrac{AE}{EC}$.	

Write a proof for this theorem and compare it with that on page 464.

Example. $ABCD$ is a quadrilateral (*Fig. 7-13*). X, Y, Z are points on AB, AC, AD, respectively, such that $XY \parallel BC$, $YZ \parallel CD$. Prove $XZ \parallel BD$.

Hypothesis: $XY \parallel BC$, $YZ \parallel CD$ (*Fig. 7-13*)

Conclusion: $XZ \parallel BD$

Analysis:

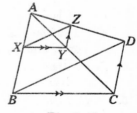

Fig. 7-13

I CAN PROVE	IF I CAN PROVE
1. $XZ \parallel BD$	1. $\dfrac{AX}{XB} = \dfrac{AZ}{ZD}$.
2. $\dfrac{AX}{XB} = \dfrac{AZ}{ZD}$	2. $\dfrac{AX}{XB} = \dfrac{AY}{YC}$ and $\dfrac{AZ}{ZD} = \dfrac{AY}{YC}$.
3. $\dfrac{AX}{XB} = \dfrac{AY}{YC}$ and $\dfrac{AZ}{ZD} = \dfrac{AY}{YC}$ by the Triangle Proportionality Th.	

Write a proof for this deduction and compare it with that on page 464.

Exercise 7-7

(A)

1. In the diagrams below, name pairs of parallel lines and state your authority:

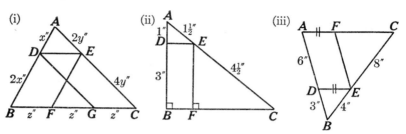

2. (a) In diagrams (ii) and (iii) above, calculate the length of EF.

(b) In diagram (iv) at the right, if CD = 8 in. and $CD \perp AB$, find the area of $\triangle EBC$.

(B)

3. Prove the Triangle Proportionality Theorem, Part II for the following cases:

(i) The line l intersects the extensions of sides AC and AB of $\triangle ABC$ on E and D, respectively.

(ii) The line l intersects the extensions of sides CA and BA of $\triangle ABC$ on E and D, respectively.

4. Prove that the line on the midpoints of two sides of a triangle is parallel to the third side.

5. PQR, SQR are two triangles on the same side of the common base QR. A is any point on QR. AB is parallel to QP, meeting RP on B; AC is parallel to QS, meeting RS on C. Prove $BC \parallel PS$.

6. $PQRS$ is a quadrilateral. E is any point within $PQRS$. A is any point on PE. AB is parallel to PQ, meeting QE on B; BC is parallel to QR, meeting RE on C; CD is parallel to RS, meeting SE on D. Prove $AD \parallel PS$.

(C)

7. $ABCD$ is a quadrilateral, and E, F, G divide AB, AC, and AD, respectively, externally in the same ratio. Prove that $\triangle$'s EFG and BCD are equiangular.

8. $ABCD$ is a trapezoid in which $AB \parallel CD$, and BC and AD are divided internally in the same ratio at P and Q, respectively. Prove $PQ \parallel AB$. (Use the Indirect Method.)

9. XO is a median of $\triangle XYZ$, and W is any point on YO. WA is parallel to YX, meeting XO on A; WB is parallel to XZ, meeting XO extended on B. Prove $AO = OB$.

7·9 Similar figures.

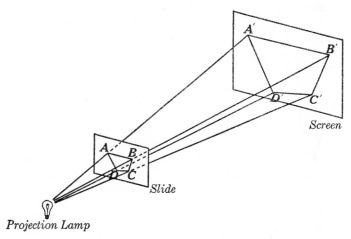

Fig. 7-14

If a picture of quadrilateral $ABCD$ (*Fig. 7-14*) is projected on a screen in a plane parallel to the plane of the slide, the image $A'B'C'D'$ will be a uniform enlargement of the original quadrilateral. Quadrilateral $ABCD$ can be considered a uniform reduction of quadrilateral $A'B'C'D'$. Two such geometric figures are said to be *similar:* that is, they have the same shape, but not the same size. This means that the angles of one figure are respectively equal to the corresponding angles of the other, and the lengths of the sides of one are proportional to the lengths of the corresponding sides of the other.

DEFINITION: *Geometric figures are similar if:*

(i) corresponding angles are equal,

and (ii) corresponding sides are proportional.

Corresponding angles of square $ABCD$ and rectangle $A'B'C'D'$ (*Fig. 7-15*) are equal, but corresponding sides are not proportional since $a : a : a : a \neq b : c : b : c$. Thus, quadrilaterals $ABCD$ and $A'B'C'D'$ are not similar.

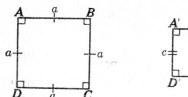

Fig. 7-15

In *Fig. 7-16*, quadrilaterals $PQRS$ and $P'Q'R'S'$ do not have corresponding angles equal, but corresponding sides are proportional, since $a : a : a : a = b : b : b : b = 1 : 1 : 1 : 1$. Thus, quadrilaterals $PQRS$ and $P'Q'R'S'$ are not similar.

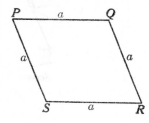
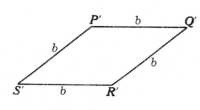

Fig. 7-16

In *Fig. 7-17*, correspending angles of quadrilaterals $WXYZ$ and $W'X'Y'Z'$ are equal, and corresponding sides are proportional, since $a : b : c : d = 2a : 2b : 2c : 2d$. Thus, quadrilateral $WXYZ$ is similar to quadrilateral $W'X'Y'Z'$. The symbol $\sim$ means *is similar to*. Thus we write, "quadrilateral $WXYZ \sim$ quadrilateral $W'X'Y'Z'$".

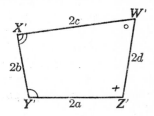

Fig. 7-17

The correspondences between the parts of the similar quadrilaterals in *Fig. 7-18* are as follows:

$\angle A = \angle Q$	$A \leftrightarrow Q$	$AB \leftrightarrow QP$
$\angle B = \angle P$	$B \leftrightarrow P$	$BC \leftrightarrow PS$
$\angle C = \angle S$	$C \leftrightarrow S$	$CD \leftrightarrow SR$
$\angle D = \angle R$	$D \leftrightarrow R$	$DA \leftrightarrow RQ$

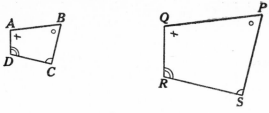

Fig. 7-18

If care is taken in listing corresponding vertices in order, all of the above correspondences are contained in the statement:

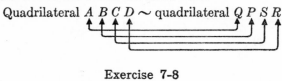

Quadrilateral $A\ B\ C\ D \sim$ quadrilateral $Q\ P\ S\ R$

Exercise 7-8

(A)

1. Name corresponding vertices and sides in each of the following:

(i)

(ii)

(iii)

(iv)

(v)

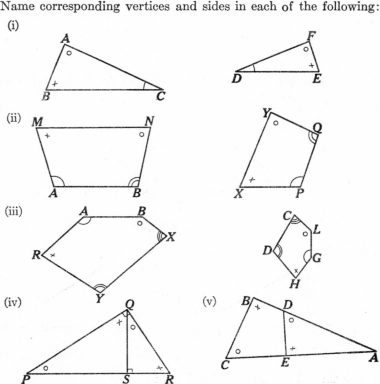

2. Quadrilateral $DGHM \sim$ quadrilateral $PRTS$. Without referring to a diagram, name: (i) corresponding sides (ii) corresponding angles

(B)

3. In each of the following, which is not similar to the other two? Give reasons.

(i)

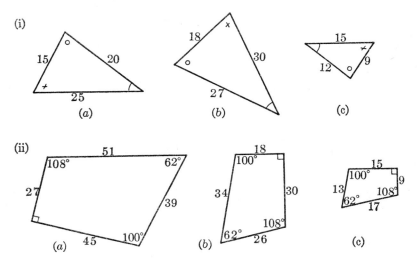

(a)   (b)   (c)

(ii)

(a)   (b)   (c)

4. In each of the following, write the proportion obtained from the lengths of corresponding sides of similar triangles:

(i)

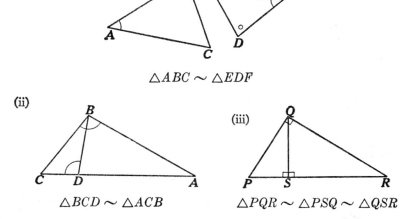

$\triangle ABC \sim \triangle EDF$

(ii)

$\triangle BCD \sim \triangle ACB$

(iii)

$\triangle PQR \sim \triangle PSQ \sim \triangle QSR$

5. Prove that all equilateral triangles are similar.

7·10 The aaa Similar Triangle Theorem. Suppose a correspondence exists between two sets of non-collinear points, $\{A, B, C,\}$ and $\{D, E, F\}$, so that $A \leftrightarrow D$, $B \leftrightarrow E$, $C \leftrightarrow F$. Under what conditions are the triangles determined by these points similar? By the definition of similar figures, it is *necessary* that corresponding angles be equal and corresponding sides be proportional.

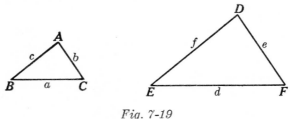

Fig. 7-19

In *Fig. 7-19*, the lengths of the sides are represented by a, b, c, d, e. f units, respectively. Then, $\triangle ABC \sim \triangle DEF$

if (i) $\angle A = \angle D$, $\angle B = \angle E$, $\angle C = \angle F$

and (ii) $\dfrac{a}{d} = \dfrac{b}{e} = \dfrac{c}{f}$.

However, we are now interested in the conditions that are *sufficient* to determine similar triangles. It has been proved that equilateral triangles are equiangular, and since corresponding sides of equilateral triangles are proportional, then all equilateral triangles are similar. This suggests that equiangular triangles are similar and leads to the aaa Similar Triangle Theorem which follows.

The aaa *Similar Triangle Theorem*

Two triangles are equiangular and hence similar if and only if the corresponding sides are proportional.

PART I

If two triangles are equiangular, then the corresponding sides are proportional and hence the triangles are similar.

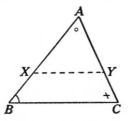

Fig. 7-20

Hypothesis: $\triangle$'s ABC and DEF such that $\angle A = \angle D$, $\angle B = \angle E$, $\angle C = \angle F$ (*Fig. 7-20*)

Conclusion: (i) $\dfrac{AB}{DE} = \dfrac{BC}{EF} = \dfrac{AC}{DF}$

(ii) $\triangle ABC \sim \triangle DEF$

Analysis: Recall that the Triangle Proportionality Theorem and its corollary are the only authorities available for proving line segments proportional.

I CAN PROVE	IF I CAN PROVE
(i) 1. $\dfrac{AB}{DE} = \dfrac{BC}{EF} = \dfrac{AC}{DF}$	1. $\dfrac{AB}{DE} = \dfrac{AC}{DF}$ and $\dfrac{AB}{DE} = \dfrac{BC}{EF}$.
2. $\dfrac{AB}{DE} = \dfrac{AC}{DF}$	2. $\dfrac{AB}{AX} = \dfrac{AC}{AY}$ where $AX = DE$
3. $\dfrac{AB}{AX} = \dfrac{AC}{AY}$	and $AY = DF$.
4. $XY \parallel BC$	3. $XY \parallel BC$.
5. $\angle AXY = \angle ABC$	4. $\angle AXY = \angle ABC$.
6. $\angle AXY = \angle DEF$	5. $\angle AXY = \angle DEF$.
7. $\triangle AXY \cong \triangle DEF$ by the sas postulate.	6. $\triangle AXY \cong \triangle DEF$.
8. $\dfrac{AB}{DE} = \dfrac{BC}{EF}$ in a similar manner.	
(ii) 9. $\triangle ABC \sim \triangle DEF$	9. $\dfrac{AB}{DE} = \dfrac{BC}{EF} = \dfrac{CA}{FD}$ and $\angle A = \angle D$, $\angle B = \angle E$, $\angle C = \angle F$.
10. $\dfrac{AB}{DE} = \dfrac{BC}{EF} = \dfrac{CA}{FD}$ by (i), $\angle A = \angle D$, $\angle B = \angle E$, $\angle C = \angle F$ by hypothesis.	

Write a complete proof of this theorem and compare it with that on page 464.

Corollary: State and prove a corollary of the aaa Similar Triangle Theorem Part I, which makes use of Corollary 3 of theTriangle Angle Sum Theorem (page 141). Compare your statement and proof with that on page 465.

PART II

If the sides of a triangle are proportional, then the triangles are equiangular and hence similar.

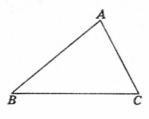
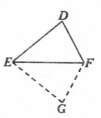

Fig. 7-21

Hypothesis: $\triangle$'s ABC and DEF in which $\dfrac{AB}{DE} = \dfrac{BC}{EF} = \dfrac{CA}{FD}$

Conclusion: (i) $\angle A = \angle D$, $\angle B = \angle E$, $\angle C = \angle F$
(ii) $\triangle ABC \sim \triangle DEF$

Analysis:

I CAN PROVE	IF I CAN PROVE
(i) 1. $\angle A = \angle D$, $\angle B = \angle E$, $\angle C = \angle F$	1. That a triangle equiangular to $\triangle ABC$ is congruent to $\triangle DEF$.
2. That there exists a triangle GEF equiangular to $\triangle ABC$ with $\angle GEF = \angle ABC$ and $\angle GFE = \angle C$, with G on the side of EF remote from D, by an existence postulate.	
3. $\triangle GEF \cong \triangle DEF$	3. $DE = GE$ and $FG = FD$.
4. $DE = GE$ and $FG = FD$, since $\dfrac{AB}{DE} = \dfrac{BC}{EF} = \dfrac{CA}{FD}$ by hypothesis, and $\dfrac{AB}{GE} = \dfrac{BC}{EF} = \dfrac{CA}{FG}$ by the Similar Triangle Theorem, Part I.	
(ii) 5. $\triangle ABC \sim \triangle DEF$ by (i) and the aaa Triangle Similarity Theorem, Part I.	

Write a proof of this theorem and compare it with that on page 465.

Example 1.

Hypothesis: In *Fig. 7-22*, $\angle MNP = \angle PQM$.

Conclusion: (i) $\triangle MNO \sim \triangle PQO$

(ii) $\dfrac{MO}{PO} = \dfrac{NO}{QO}$

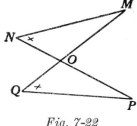

Fig. 7-22

Analysis:

I CAN PROVE	IF I CAN PROVE
(i) 1. $\triangle MNO \sim \triangle PQO$	1. Two angles of $\triangle MNO$ equal to two angles of $\triangle PQO$.
2. $\angle MNO = \angle PQO$ by hypothesis.	
3. $\angle MON = \angle QOP$ by the Vertical Angle Theorem.	
(ii) 4. $\dfrac{MO}{PO} = \dfrac{NO}{QO}$ by (i) and the Similar Triangle Theorem.	

Proof: Write a complete proof for this deduction and compare it with that on page 466.

Example 2.

Hypothesis: In *Fig. 7-23*, BX and CY are altitudes of $\triangle ABC$.

Conclusion: $AB \cdot AY = AC \cdot AX$

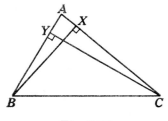

Fig. 7-23

Analysis:

I CAN PROVE	IF I CAN PROVE
1. $AB \cdot AY = AC \cdot AX$	1. (i) $\dfrac{AB}{AX} = \dfrac{AC}{AY}$ or (ii) $\dfrac{AB}{AC} = \dfrac{AX}{AY}$.
(i) 2. $\dfrac{AB}{AX} = \dfrac{AC}{AY}$	2. $\triangle ABC$ equiangular to $\triangle AXY$.
3. $\triangle ABC$ equiangular to $\triangle AXY$ (insufficient information).	

(ii) 4. $\dfrac{AB}{AC} = \dfrac{AX}{AY}$

    5. $\angle BAX = \angle CAY$ by the reflexive property, and $\angle AXB = \angle AYC$ by hypothesis.

4. $\triangle ABX$ equiangular to $\triangle ACY$.

Write a proof of this deduction and compare it with that on page 466.

Exercise 7-9

(A)

1. Name pairs of similar triangles in each of the following; give reasons in each case:

  (i)   (ii)   (iii)

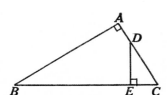 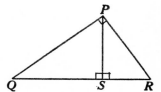

2. For each diagram in question 1, state the proportion obtained from corresponding sides of similar triangles.

3. In the following, state the authorities required to complete the proof.
   Hypothesis: In the diagram at the right,
   $$AE = BE,\ EC = ED.$$
   Conclusion: $\triangle ABE \sim \triangle DCE$
   Proof:

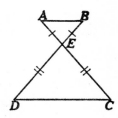

STATEMENTS	AUTHORITIES
1. In $\triangle ABE$, $AE = BE$.	1.
2. $\angle EAB = \angle EBA$	2.
3. In $\triangle EDC$, $ED = EC$.	3.
4. $\angle EDC = \angle ECD$	4.
5. $\angle AEB = \angle DEC$	5.
6. $\angle AEB + \angle EBA + \angle EAB = 180°$	6.
7. $\angle DEC + \angle ECD + \angle EDC = 180°$	7.
8. $\angle EBA + \angle EAB = \angle ECD + \angle EDC$	8.
9. $\angle EBA = \angle ECD$	9.
10. $\triangle ABE \sim \triangle EDC$	10.

(B)

Write an analysis for the following deductions:

4. $ABCD$ is a trapezoid with $AB \parallel CD$. The diagonals AC and DB meet on E. Prove that $\triangle ABE \sim \triangle CDE$.

5. D is a point on side AB in $\triangle ABC$. The line on D parallel to BC meets AC on E; the line on D parallel to AC meets BC on F.
Prove $\triangle ADE \sim \triangle DBF$.

Write a complete proof for each of the following:

6. $\triangle PQR$ is right-angled at Q. QM is the altitude from Q to PR. Prove that QM is the geometric mean of PM and MR.

7. D is the midpoint of side AB in $\triangle ABC$. The line on D parallel to BC meets AC on E. Prove: (i) $AE = EC$ (ii) $DE = \frac{1}{2} BC$

8. In the diagram at the right, $FG \parallel BC$, $GH \parallel CD$, $HK \parallel DE$, $AF = FB$. Prove $ABCDE \sim AFGHK$.

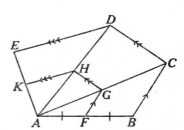

9. In similar triangles, the bisectors of corresponding angles terminated in the opposite sides are proportional to the corresponding sides.

10. In similar triangles, prove that corresponding altitudes are proportional to the corresponding sides.

11. Any three straight lines are drawn on a point P. Two parallel lines, neither of which is on P, nor is parallel to any of the lines on P, meet the lines on P at the points A, B, C, and X, Y, Z, respectively.

Prove $\dfrac{AB}{XY} = \dfrac{BC}{YZ}$.

(C)

12. AB is the shorter of two parallel line segments AB and CD. E and F divide AB and CD, respectively, in the same ratio. Prove that the lines on CA, FE, and DB are concurrent.

7·11 The sas Similar Triangle Theorem.

The sas Similar Triangle Theorem

If two triangles have an angle of one equal to an angle of the other and the sides about these angles are proportional, then the triangles are similar.

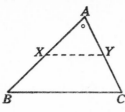

Fig. 7-24

Hypothesis: $\triangle$'s ABC and DEF such that $\angle A = \angle D$ and $\dfrac{AB}{DE} = \dfrac{AC}{DF}$

Conclusion: $\triangle ABC \sim \triangle DEF$

Proof: Copy and complete the authorities column of the following proof. Compare your proof with that on page 466.

STATEMENTS	AUTHORITIES
1. X is the point on AB or AB extended such that $AX = DE$.	1.
2. Y is the point on AC or AC extended such that $AY = DF$.	2.
3. $\triangle AXY \cong \triangle DEF$	3.
4. $\dfrac{AB}{DE} = \dfrac{AC}{DF}$	4.
5. $\dfrac{AB}{AX} = \dfrac{AC}{AY}$	5.
6. $XY \parallel BC$	6.
7. $\angle ABC = \angle AXY$	7.
8. $\angle ABC = \angle DEF$	8.
9. $\angle A = \angle D$	9.
10. $\triangle ABC \sim \triangle DEF$	10.

Example.

Hypothesis: $LP \cdot PR = PM \cdot SP$ (*Fig. 7-25*)

Conclusion: $ML \cdot PR = PM \cdot RS$

Write a complete analysis and proof of this deduction; compare them with those on page 467.

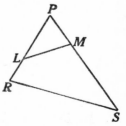

Fig. 7-25

Exercise 7-10

(A)

1. For each of the following figures, state, with reasons, the triangles which are similar, their corresponding sides, and their pairs of equal angles:

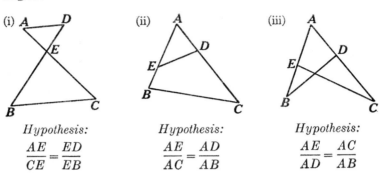

(i)

Hypothesis:
$$\frac{AE}{CE} = \frac{ED}{EB}$$

(ii)

Hypothesis:
$$\frac{AE}{AC} = \frac{AD}{AB}$$

(iii)

Hypothesis:
$$\frac{AE}{AD} = \frac{AC}{AB}$$

(B)

2. In question 1(i), prove $AD \parallel BC$.

3. In quadrilateral $ABCD$, AC and BD intersect on O. Prove that $AB \parallel CD$ if $AO : OC = BO : OD$.

4. In similar triangles, corresponding medians are proportional to corresponding sides.

5. In $\triangle PQR$, $PS \perp QR$ and $\dfrac{QS}{PS} = \dfrac{PS}{RS}$. Prove $\angle RPQ$ is a right angle.

6. In the diagram below, $\angle MAB = \angle MXY$, $\angle MBA = \angle MYX$. Prove $\triangle MXA \sim \triangle MYB$.

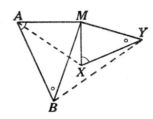

7. $\triangle ABC \sim \triangle DEF$; X and Y are points on the corresponding sides BC and EF such that $BX : XC = EY : YF$. Prove $\triangle ABX \sim \triangle DEY$.

7.12 Areas of Similar Triangles Theorem.

Areas of Similar Triangles Theorem

If two triangles are similar, then the ratio of their areas is equal to the ratio of the squares of the lengths of any two corresponding sides.

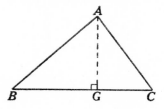

Fig. 7-26

Hypothesis: $\triangle ABC \sim \triangle DEF$

Conclusion: $\dfrac{\triangle ABC}{\triangle DEF} = \dfrac{BC^2}{EF^2} = \dfrac{AB^2}{DE^2} = \dfrac{CA^2}{FD^2}$

Proof: Copy and complete the authorities column of the following proof. Compare your proof with that on page 467.

STATEMENTS	AUTHORITIES
1. AG is the altitude from A to BC.	1.
2. DH is the altitude from D to EF.	2.
3. $\triangle ABC = \frac{1}{2} AG \cdot BC$	3.
4. $\triangle DEF = \frac{1}{2} DH \cdot EF$	4.
5. $\dfrac{\triangle ABC}{\triangle DEF} = \dfrac{\frac{1}{2} AG \cdot BC}{\frac{1}{2} DH \cdot EF}$	5.
6. $\dfrac{\triangle ABC}{\triangle DEF} = \left(\dfrac{AG}{DH}\right)\left(\dfrac{BC}{EF}\right)$	6.
7. In $\triangle$'s ABG and DEH $\left\{ \begin{array}{l} \angle B = \angle E \\ \angle AGB = \angle DHE \end{array} \right.$	7.
8.	8.
9. $\dfrac{AG}{DH} = \dfrac{AB}{DE}$	9.
10. $\dfrac{BC}{EF} = \dfrac{AB}{DE}$	10.
11. $\dfrac{AG}{DH} = \dfrac{BC}{EF}$	11.
12. $\dfrac{\triangle ABC}{\triangle DEF} = \left(\dfrac{BC}{EF}\right)\left(\dfrac{BC}{EF}\right)$	12.
13. $\dfrac{\triangle ABC}{\triangle DEF} = \dfrac{BC^2}{EF^2} = \dfrac{AB^2}{DE^2} = \dfrac{CA^2}{FD^2}$	13.

Exercise 7-11

(A)

1. In the diagram at the left below, state why $\triangle EBD \sim \triangle ABC$, and state the ratio of $\triangle EBD$ to $\triangle ABC$.

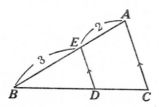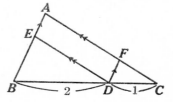

2. In the diagram at the right above, state:
   (i) why $\triangle EBD \sim \triangle ABC \sim \triangle FDC$;
   (ii) the ratio of $\triangle FDC$ to $\triangle EBD$;
   (iii) what fraction $\triangle EBD$ is of $\triangle ABC$;
   (iv) what fraction $\triangle FDC$ is of $\triangle ABC$.

3. In the diagram at the left below, $\triangle XYZ = \frac{9}{16}\triangle ABC$, and $\triangle XYZ \sim \triangle ABC$. State the ratio of XY to AB.

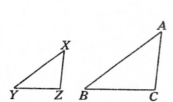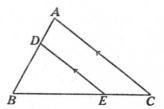

4. In the diagram at the right above, $\triangle DBE = \frac{1}{2}\triangle ABC$. Find $\dfrac{BE}{BC}$.

(B)

5. In $\triangle PQR$, medians QX and RY intersect on Z. Find the ratio of $\triangle XYZ$ to $\triangle QRZ$.

6. In $\triangle ABC$, D is on AB and E on AC so that $DE \parallel BC$. If the trapezoid $DBCE = \frac{15}{16}\triangle ABC$, find $\dfrac{AD}{DB}$.

7. In $\triangle ABC$, $\angle A = 90°$, $AB = 3$ cm., $AC = 4$ cm. X, Y, and Z are points such that $\triangle ABX \sim \triangle ACY \sim \triangle BCZ$.
   Find: (i) $\dfrac{\triangle ABX}{\triangle BCZ}$ (ii) $\dfrac{\triangle ACY}{\triangle BCZ}$

8. YZ is the hypotenuse of an isosceles right triangle XYZ. P and Q are points such that $\triangle PYX \sim \triangle QZY$. Find $\triangle PYX : \triangle QZY$.

9. Prove that the areas of similar triangles are proportional to:
   (i) the squares on corresponding altitudes;
   (ii) the squares on corresponding medians;
   (iii) the squares on the bisectors of corresponding angles.

Exercise 7-12

(*Numerical Exercise*)

(B)

Draw a representative sketch; mark on all given data; then complete the required calculations for each of the following:

1. In $\triangle ABC$, $\angle B = 40°$. BC is extended to D, and exterior $\angle ACD = 96°$. The bisectors of $\angle B$ and $\angle ACD$ meet on E. Find $\angle E$.

2. In $\triangle ABC$, $\angle C = 90°$, $AB = 13$ cm., $BC = 5$ cm. BC is extended to D so that $CD = 9$ cm. Calculate the length of AD.

3. Each angle of a regular polygon has a measurement of 165°. Find the number of sides.

4. PQR is a right triangle with PR the hypotenuse. $QS \perp PR$. If $PR = 15$ cm. and $QR = 12$ cm., calculate the length of QS.

5. ABC is an isosceles triangle with $AB = AC$. The area is 12 square inches and $BC = 8$ inches. Calculate the perimeter of the triangle.

6. A is a point within $\|^{\text{gm}}$ $PQRS$ such that AP, AQ bisect angles SPQ and PQR, respectively. Calculate $\angle PAQ$.

7. $ABCD$ is a rhombus and $AC = 10$ cm. If the area of $ABCD = 60$ sq. cm., calculate the length of BD.

8. BE, CF are altitudes of $\triangle ABC$, and H is the midpoint of BC. If $\angle A = 72°$, calculate $\angle FHE$.

9. AB is 35 cm. long and is divided at C in the ratio $7 : - 2$. Calculate the length of BC.

10. In $\triangle ABC$, Q divides BC in the ratio $3 : 2$. $QP \| CA$ meeting BA at P. If $AB = 20$ inches, calculate BP.

11. In $\triangle ABC$, $AB = 18$ cm. BC is divided at D in the ratio $5 : - 2$. CF is parallel to DA, meeting AB on F, and DE is parallel to CA, meeting BA extended on E. Calculate the lengths of AF and AE.

12. H and K divide the sides CA and BA of $\triangle ABC$ in the ratio $3 : 1$. If the area of $\triangle ABC$ is 24 square inches, calculate the area of $\triangle AKH$.

13. The area of $\triangle ABC$ is 50 sq. cm., and D divides BC in the ratio $3 : 2$. $DF \| CA$ and meets AB on F; $DE \| BA$ and meets AC on E. Calculate the area of $\|^{\text{gm}}$ $AFDE$.

14. $PBCQ$ is a trapezoid with $PQ \parallel BC$. The diagonals meet at A, and $PQ : BC = 2 : 3$. If the area of $\triangle ABC$ is 36 square inches, calculate the area of $PBCQ$.

15. $PQRS$ is a parallelogram in which $PS = 24$ inches. Y divides SQ in the ratio $1 : 5$, and $YX \parallel SP$ meeting PR on X. Find the length of XY.

7·13 Mean Proportional Theorem.

Mean Proportional Theorem

The altitude to the hypotenuse of a right triangle from the opposite vertex is a mean proportional of the segments of the hypotenuse, and each of the sides about the right angle is a mean proportional of the hypotenuse and the adjacent segment of the hypotenuse.

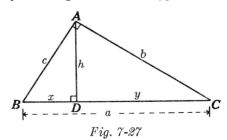

Fig. 7-27

Hypothesis: Right triangle ABC, $AD \perp BC$,
AB, BC, CA, AD, BD, and DC have lengths c, a, b, h, x, and y units, respectively (*Fig. 7-27*).

Conclusion: (i) $\dfrac{a}{c} = \dfrac{c}{x}$ (ii) $\dfrac{a}{b} = \dfrac{b}{y}$ (iii) $\dfrac{x}{h} = \dfrac{h}{y}$

Analysis:

I CAN PROVE	IF I CAN PROVE
(i) 1. $\dfrac{a}{c} = \dfrac{c}{x}$	1. $\triangle BCA \sim \triangle BAD$.
2. $\triangle BCA \sim \triangle BAD$	2. $\angle ABC = \angle DBA$ and $\angle BAC = \angle BDA$.
3. $\angle ABC = \angle DBA$ by reflexive property.	
4. $\angle BAC = \angle BDA$ by hypothesis.	

Proof: Write a complete proof for this theorem and compare it with that on page 468.

Example. In *Fig. 7-28*, *ABC* is a right triangle with $\angle BAC = 90°$, $AC = 3$ inches, $AB = 4$ inches. AD is the altitude from A to BC. Calculate the lengths of CD and DB.

Solution: $BC^2 = AC^2 + AB^2$

$$\therefore BC^2 = (9 + 16) \text{ sq. in.}$$
$$= 25 \text{ sq. in.}$$
$$\therefore BC = 5 \text{ in.}$$

Let x represent the length, in inches, of CD.

$$\frac{5}{3} = \frac{3}{x}$$
$$\therefore x = 1.8$$

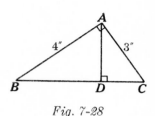

Fig. 7-28

The length of CD is 1.8 inches, and the length of DB is $(5 - 1.8)$ in. or 3.2 inches.

Exercise 7-13

(A)

1. In each of the following, name three continued proportions:

(i) 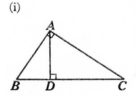 (ii) 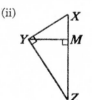 (iii)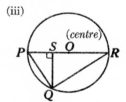

2. In the accompanying diagram, state the mean proportional of:

  (i) AD and DC
  (ii) AE and EB
  (iii) BF and FC
  (iv) AC and AD
  (v) EB and BA
  (vi) CB and CF

3. In each of the following, calculate x:

(i) 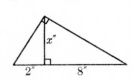 (ii) 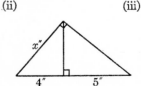 (iii)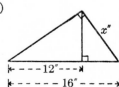

(iv)   (v) 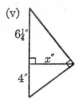   (vi)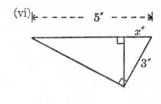

(B)

4. In $\triangle ABC$, $\angle A = 90°$ and $AD \perp BC$. If the sides about the right angle are 4.5 cm. and 6 cm., respectively, calculate the lengths of the segments of BC and the length of AD.

5. In $\triangle PQR$, $\angle P = 90°$ and $PS \perp QR$. If $QR = 13$ in. and $PS = 6$ in., calculate the lengths of the segments of QR.

6. $\triangle MNR$ is right-angled at M. MX is perpendicular to NR, meeting NR on X. MX is extended to Y so that $YN \perp MN$. Prove $NX \cdot NR = MY \cdot MX$.

7. $\triangle PQR$ is right-angled at Q. QS is perpendicular to PR, meeting PR on S. Prove that $\dfrac{PQ^2}{QR^2} = \dfrac{PS}{SR}$.

8. In the diagram at the right, $\triangle ABC$ is right-angled at A. AD is the altitude from A to BC.
   Prove: (i) $AD^2 = BD \cdot DC$
   　　　　(ii) $AB^2 = CB \cdot BD$
   　　　　(iii) $AC^2 = BC \cdot CD$

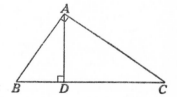

7·14 The Pythagorean Theorem: Similar Triangle Proof.

Copy the following and complete the authorities column. Compare your proof with that on page 468.

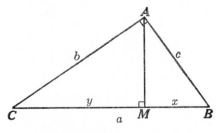

Fig. 7-29

Hypothesis: $\triangle ABC$, right-angled at A, with lengths of AB, BC, CA represented by c, a, b units, respectively

Conclusion: $b^2 + c^2 = a^2$

Proof:

STATEMENTS	AUTHORITIES
1. AM is the altitude from A to BC.	1.
2. Let x units and y units represent the lengths of BM and MC, respectively.	2.
3. $\dfrac{y}{b} = \dfrac{b}{a}$	3.
4. $b^2 = ay$	4.
5. $\dfrac{x}{c} = \dfrac{c}{a}$	5.
6. $c^2 = ax$	6.
7. $b^2 + c^2 = ay + ax$	7.
8. $b^2 + c^2 = a(y + x)$	8.
9. $b^2 + c^2 = a^2$	9.

7·15 Construction problems.

Example 1.

Given: A line segment AB and two other line segments whose lengths are x units and y units (*Fig. 7-30*)

Required: To find the points of section X and X' which divide AB in the ratio:
(i) $x : y$, $x, y \in {}^+R$
(ii) $x : - y$, $x, y \in {}^+R$, $x > y$

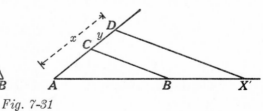

Fig. 7-30

Analysis:

PRELIMINARY SKETCH

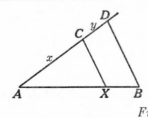

Fig. 7-31

(i) In $\triangle ABD$,

$$\frac{AX}{XB} = \frac{AC}{CD} = \frac{x}{y}$$

(ii) In $\triangle AX'D$,

$$\frac{AX'}{X'B} = \frac{AD}{DC} = \frac{x}{-y}$$

Make ruler-compasses constructions for this problem and write a complete description of the constructions. Compare your solution with that on page 469.

Example 2. Construct a line segment which is the fourth proportional to three given line segments. Discover the required construction and write a description of this construction. Compare your solution with that on page 469.

Example 3. Construct a line segment which is the mean proportional of two given line segments.

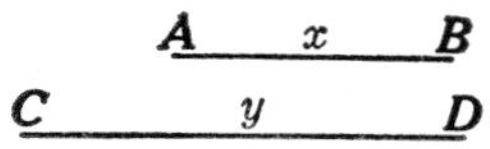

A ___ *x* ___ B

C ___ *y* ___ D

Given: Two line segments AB, CD with lengths x units and y units, respectively (*Fig. 7-32*)

Fig. 7-32

Required: To construct a line segment which is the mean proportional of AB and CD.

Analysis:

PRELIMINARY SKETCH

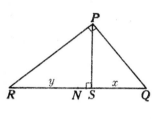

Fig. 7-33

In $\triangle RPQ$ (*Fig. 7-33*), PS is the mean proportional of RS and RQ. If $RS = y$ units, and $QS = x$ units, then PS is the required line segment. The point P may be located in the perpendicular at S by recalling that the midpoint of the hypotenuse of a right triangle is equidistant from the three vertices of the triangle (Exercise 7-6, question 8). Thus, P is the intersection of the perpendicular at S and the circle with centre N (midpoint of RQ) and radius NR.

Make the indicated ruler-compasses construction and write a description of it. Compare your solution with that on page 470.

Exercise 7-14

(B)

1. In $\triangle ABC$, divide the base BC at D in the ratio $3 : 5$. Find the ratio of $\triangle ABC$ to $\triangle ADC$.

2. Separate a triangle into two triangles whose areas are in the ratio of two given line segments.

3. Construct the fourth proportional to three line segments of lengths $2\frac{1}{2}''$, $3\frac{1}{2}''$, $1\frac{1}{4}''$.

4. Divide a given line segment in the ratio $5 : - 2$.
5. Divide a given line segment in the ratio $2 : 3 : 4$.
6. Construct a triangle of given perimeter so that its sides are in the ratio of three given line segments.
7. Construct a triangle similar to a given triangle and double its area.

(C)

8. P is a point in the interior of angle ABC. Draw on P a line segment terminated on AB and AC so that it is divided at P in the ratio of two given line segments.
9. Construct a triangle similar to a given triangle and three times its area.
10. Bisect a triangle by a line segment drawn parallel to one side.
11. Construct a square equal in area to a given rectangle.
12. Construct a square equal in area to a given triangle.
13. Construct a square equal in area to a given pentagon.

Review Exercise 7-15

(B)

1. ABC is an isosceles triangle having $CB = CA$. The right bisector of AC meets the base AB or AB extended on D. Show that AC is a mean proportional of AB and AD.
2. ABC is a triangle having $AB = 2BC$. P is a point on AB such that $PB = \frac{1}{2}BC$. Prove that $\angle BCP = \angle CAB$.
3. Similar triangles with equal vertical angles are constructed on the sides of right triangles as bases. Show that the triangle on the hypotenuse is equal in area to the sum of the other two triangles.
4. $ABCD$ is a quadrilateral having the sides AB and CD parallel. Show that the line on the midpoint of CD and on the intersection of the diagonals bisects AB.
5. In $\triangle ABC$, $\angle B = \angle C = 2\angle A$, and CD, the bisector of $\angle C$, meets AB on D. Prove: (i) $\dfrac{BC^2}{BD^2} = \dfrac{AB}{BD}$ (ii) $\dfrac{AB^2}{BC^2} = \dfrac{AB}{BD}$
6. $ABCD$ is a rectangle. Lines drawn on B and D perpendicular to any line on A meet it on X and Y, respectively. Prove that $YA \cdot AX = DY \cdot BX$.
7. In $\triangle ABC$, $AX \perp BC$, $BY \perp AC$, and AX and BY intersect on O. Prove that $\dfrac{BX}{XO} = \dfrac{AX}{XC}$.

8. Prove that the bisector of the exterior angle of a triangle divides the opposite side externally in the ratio of the other two sides.

9. Prove the converse of the deduction in question 8 above.

7·16 Summary.

Undefined Terms	Definitions (page 417)	Existence Postulates (page 421)	Completion Postulates (page 422)	Number Axioms (page 118)	Congruence Postulates (page 422)	Parallel Postulate (page 422)	Area Postulates (page 423)

Deductive Reasoning

Theorems   Deductions

Angle {
Complementary Angle Theorem
Supplementary Angle Theorem
Vertical Angle Theorem

Basic Biconditional {
Isosceles Triangle Theorem

Inequality {
Exterior Angle Theorem
Angle-Side Inequality Theorem
Side Inequality Theorems

Parallel {
Parallel Line Theorem
Quadrilateral-Parallelogram Theorem
Parallelogram Theorem
Triangle Angle Sum Theorem

Congruence {
aas Congruence Theorem
Right Triangle Congruence Theorem

Locus {
Right Bisector Theorem
Angle Bisector Theorem

Area {
Parallelogram Area Theorem
Parallelogram-Diagonal Theorem
Parallelogram-Triangle Area Theorem
Equal Triangle-Parallel Line Theorem
Trapezoid Area Theorem
Pythagorean Theorem
Pythagorean Converse

Similar Triangles {
Triangle Area Ratio Theorem
Triangle Proportionality Theorem
aaa Similar Triangle Theorem
sas Similar Triangle Theorem
Areas of Similar Triangles Theorem
Right Triangle Similarity Theorem

Chapter VIII

TRIGONOMETRY

8·1 Coordinates in a plane. It has been noted previously that there is a one-to-one correspondence between the real numbers and the points on a real number line. *Fig. 8-1* is the graph of $\{-1.5, -\frac{1}{4}, \sqrt{2}, 2\}$. These real numbers are called the *coordinates* of the corresponding points.

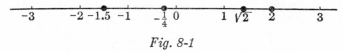

Fig. 8-1

Two real number lines drawn as illustrated in *Fig. 8-2* may be used as reference lines for indicating the position of any point in a plane. These number lines are called the *coordinate axes*.

The number line or axis drawn in the horizontal position is called the *x-axis*; the other, usually drawn vertically, is called the *y-axis*.

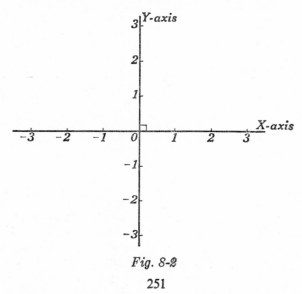

Fig. 8-2

251

If lines are drawn parallel to the x-axis through points on the y-axis whose coordinates are the integers

$$\ldots, -3, -2, -1, 1, 2, 3, \ldots,$$

and if lines are drawn parallel to the y-axis through points on the x-axis having integral coordinates, a *lattice* is formed (*Fig. 8-3*). The points of intersection of these lines are called *lattice points*, and the lines are called *lattice lines*. Each lattice point may be associated with an *ordered pair* of integers represented generally by (x, y) and called the *coordinates of the point*. The *x-coordinate* or *abscissa* is the directed distance from the y-axis to the point measured in a direction parallel to the x-axis; the *y-coordinate* or *ordinate* is the directed distance from the x-axis to the point measured in a direction parallel to the y-axis. In *Fig. 8-3*, the positions of the points $A(4, 2)$ and $B(2, 4)$ illustrate the effect of changing the order of the coordinates. Other lattice points with their coordinates are also shown in *Fig. 8-3*.

The number plane is divided into four *quadrants*, numbered as in *Fig. 8-3*.

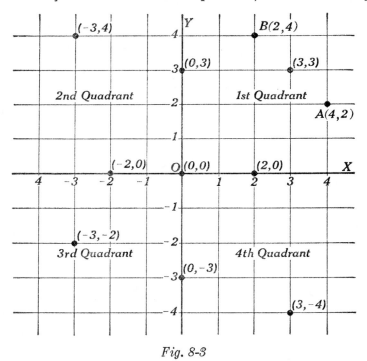

Fig. 8-3

Since the set of integers contains zero, lattice points appear on the axes as illustrated by the points whose coordinates are $(2, 0)$, $(0, 3)$, $(-2, 0)$, and $(0, -3)$. The point of intersection of the axes has coordinates $(0, 0)$ and is known as the *origin* (designated by O).

Lines parallel to the axes may be drawn through any points with co-ordinates $(x, 0)$ or $(0, y)$, $x, y \in R$, on the axes to meet in a unique point (x, y) on the plane. Thus, every point in a plane can be associated with an ordered pair of real numbers.

The French mathematician and philosopher, René Descartes (1596-1650), is credited with introducing the above method of representing the position of a point in a plane with respect to number line axes of reference. In 1637 he published the first book or treatise on coordinate geometry. The funda-mental assumption of this geometry is as follows:

There is a one-to-one correspondence between the set of all points in a plane and the set of all ordered pairs of real numbers.

Write a solution for the following problem and compare it with that on page 470.

1. Calculate the distance from the point $O(0, 0)$ to $P(6, -8)$, using the Pythagorean Theorem.

It should be noted that the length of a line segment or the distance between the end points of a line segment is a positive real number associated with the unit of the system.

For convenience, we express a length simply as a positive real number, and it is understood to be in terms of the unit of the system.

Exercise 8-1

(A)

1. In the accompanying diagram, state the coordinates of the points marked:

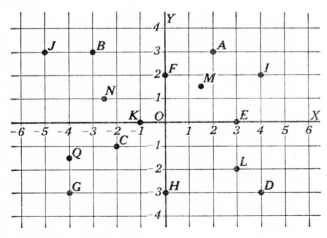

(B)

2. Write the coordinates of the points indicated in the diagram of question 1.

3. Using convenient axes and scale, plot the points $P(10, 3)$, $Q(-6, 4)$, $R(0, 10)$, $S(-2, -8)$, $T(6, 0)$, and $V(2, -9)$.

4. Plot the points $A(-3, 5)$, $B(7, 5)$, and $C(7, -3)$. Calculate:
   (i) the length of AB (ii) the length of BC

5. In the diagram for question 4, find the coordinates of the fourth point D of a rectangle $ABCD$. Find also the coordinates of the midpoints of AB and BC.

6. Plot the point $A(3, 4)$. Find the distance between A and the origin.

7. Plot the points $A(-4, 0)$ and $B(0, 3)$. Find the length of AB by using a right triangle.

8. Plot the points $P(6, 2)$ and $Q(-2, -6)$. Show that these points are equidistant from the origin.

8·2 Oriented angles. In the study of geometry, we think of an angle as a point set consisting of the union of two distinct rays having a common end point. The unit angle is called a *degree* and is defined to be $\frac{1}{180}$ of a straight angle. Thus, with every angle we associate a real number greater than zero and less than or equal to 180. This number is called the *degree measure* of the angle.

In trigonometry we think of an angle as being generated by the rotation of a ray about its end point, from an initial position to a final position. Such an angle is called an *oriented angle*. Angle AOB in *Fig. 8-4* has *initial side the ray OA* and *terminal side the ray OB*.

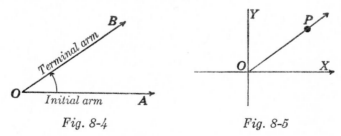

Fig. 8-4   Fig. 8-5

If an oriented angle is related to a pair of coordinate axes, *Fig. 8-5*, so that the vertex of the angle is at the origin, and the initial side lies along the positive part of the x-axis, then the angle is said to be in *standard position*.

The angle is named $\angle XOP$ which indicates the order: initial side, vertex, terminal side.

The idea of an oriented angle implies that the rotation may be *counter-clockwise*, *Fig. 8-6(a)*, or *clockwise*, *Fig. 8-6(b)*.

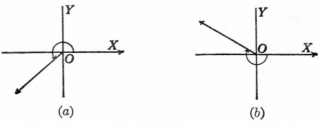

(a)   (b)

Fig. 8-6

In generating an angle, the amount of rotation may be:

　　(i) zero;

or (ii) part of a revolution, *Fig. 8-7(a)*;

or (iii) a complete revolution, *Fig. 8-7 (b)*;

or (iv) more than one revolution, *Fig. 8-7(c)*.

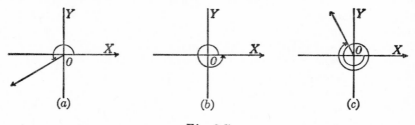

(a)   (b)   (c)

Fig. 8-7

In *Fig. 8-7*, the spiral arc and arrow indicate the *number* of revolutions and the *direction* of the rotation.

We often state the measurement of an angle (amount of rotation) in degrees rather than in revolutions.

For convenience, the following sub-units are defined:

　(i) *one minute* is $\frac{1}{60}$ of one degree;

　(ii) *one second* is $\frac{1}{60}$ of one minute,

　　　　　　or $\frac{1}{360}$ of one degree.

Thus, 1° (one degree) = 60′ (60 minutes);

　　　1′ (one minute) = 60″ (60 seconds).

By convention, if the rotation is *counter-clockwise*, the degree measure of the angle is a *positive real number*; if the rotation is *clockwise*, the degree measure of the angle is a *negative real number*. Thus, the degree measure of an angle may be any real number including zero.

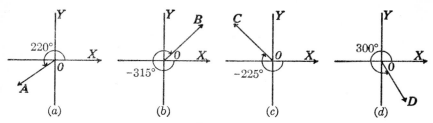

Fig. 8-8

In *Fig. 8-8 (a)*, the terminal side *AO* of ∠*XOA* lies in the third quadrant, and we say, ∠*XOA* is a third quadrant angle.

Similarly, ∠*XOB* is a first quadrant angle;

∠*XOC* is a second quadrant angle; and

∠*XOD* is a fourth quadrant angle.

If the terminal side lies on either axis, the angle is called a *quadrantal angle*.

The terminal sides of the angles with measurements 120° and − 240° coincide, as shown in *Fig. 8-9*. These angles are said to be *coterminal angles*.

Angles with measurements (360 + 120)°, (720 + 120)°, − 360° + (− 240°), and so on, are also coterminal with ∠*XOP*.

Similarly, angles with measurements $(n \times 360 + 120)°$, $n \in I$ are coterminal with ∠*XOP*.

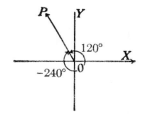

Fig. 8-9

In general, angles in standard position which have coincident terminal sides are called coterminal angles.

Write solutions for the following and compare them with those on page 470.

1. State the measurements of two positive angles and also two negative angles which are coterminal with an angle of (i) 135° (ii) − 150°.

2. Determine the measurement of the indicated angle from the information given in each of the following diagrams (*Fig. 8-10*):

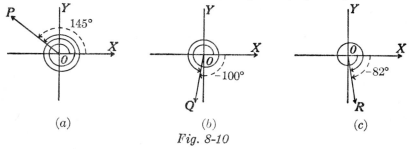

(a)   (b)   (c)

Fig. 8-10

3. (i) Write the measurements of angles coterminal with angles having the following measurements in the form $(180 \pm x)°$, where x is the degree measure of an acute angle:

    (a) 150°   (b) 255°   (c) − 135°   (d) − 190°

  (ii) Write the measurements of angles coterminal with angles having the following measurements in the form $(360 \pm x)°$, where x is the degree measure of an acute angle:

    (a) − 75°   (b) 300°   (c) 395°   (d) − 330°

4. Using a protractor, construct angles whose measurements are:

  (i) 120°   (ii) − 225°   (iii) 310°   (iv) 592°   (v) − 150°

Exercise 8-2

(A)

1. Name the initial side and the terminal side; state the sense of rotation and the number of revolutions for each of the following angles:

(i) 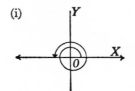   (ii) 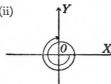   (iii)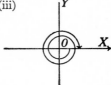

(iv) 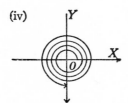   (v) 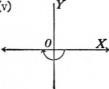   (vi)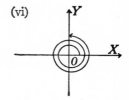

2. State the measurement, in degrees, of each of the following angles:

(i)    (ii)   (iii)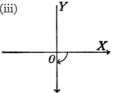

(iv) 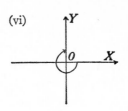   (v) 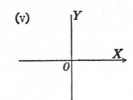   (vi)

3. State the measurements of three angles which are coterminal with the given angle:

   (i) 90°   (ii) − 360°   (iii) − 45°

   (iv) − 90°   (v) + 180°   (vi) + 450°

(B)

4. Calculate the measurement of each of the indicated angles from the information given in the diagram:

(i)   (ii)   (iii)

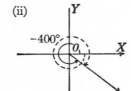

(iv)   (v)   (vi)

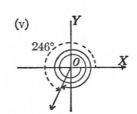 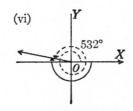

5. Each of the following diagrams indicates an angle coterminal with an angle of measurement 120°. Determine the measurement of each:

(i)   (ii)   (iii)

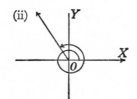 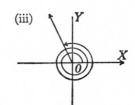

(iv) 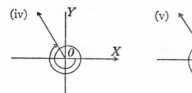 (v) 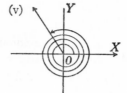 (vi)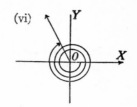

6. (i) Express each of the following measurements in one of the forms $(180 \pm x)°$, $(360 \pm x)°$, $0 < x < 90$:

    (a) 227°   (b) 110°   (c) − 70°   (d) − 132°

    (e) 305°   (f) − 205°   (g) − 338°   (h) 420°

  (ii) Using a protractor, draw the angles with measurements given in part (i).

7. (i) Determine the measurements of two positive angles and also two negative angles which are coterminal with an angle of measurement:

    (a) − 70°   (b) 342°   (c) − 162°   (d) − 550°

    (e) − 435°   (f) 485°   (g) 5°   (h) 1,500°

  (ii) Using a protractor, draw the angles with measurements given in part (i).

8. Using a protractor, draw the angles with the following measurements and state the quadrant in which the terminal side lies:

    (i) − 165°   (ii) 210°   (iii) − 62°   (iv) 705°

    (v) − 238°   (vi) − 460°   (vii) 488°   (viii) − 322°

8·3 Radian measure. Any point A on a ray OR traces out a circle with centre O and radius OA, as the ray OR rotates through one complete revolution, *Fig. 8-11*. If the ray rotates through less than one complete revolution, the locus of A is an arc of a circle.

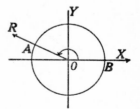

Fig. 8-11

Since $\angle BOA$ has its vertex at the centre of the circle, it is called a *central angle* or *sector angle* of the circle.

DEFINITION: *A central angle of a given circle is an angle whose vertex is the centre of the circle.*

The arc BA is said to *subtend* the central angle whose sides contain points B and A; $\angle BOA$ is said to *stand* on the arc BA.

Write a solution for each of the following problems and compare them with those on page 471.

1. Determine the ratio of the measurements of the pairs of angles indicated in each of the following diagrams:

(i) $\angle XOY : \angle XOA$ (ii) $\angle XOA : \angle XOX$ (iii) $\angle XOY : \angle XOX$

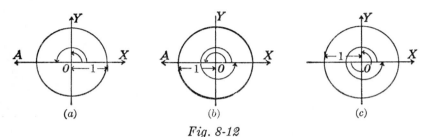

(a)   (b)   (c)

Fig. 8-12

2. Determine the ratio of the lengths of the arcs on which the angles in question 1 stand in each case. Compare the results of questions 1 and 2 for each case.

3. State a conjecture relating central angles of a circle and the arcs on which they stand.

Since the measurements of central angles are proportional to their arc lengths, the arc length may be used as the basis for a system of angle measurement. In *Fig. 8-13(a)*, $\angle XOP$ is subtended by an arc whose length is equal to the radius of the circle. The measurement of $\angle XOP$ is defined to be 1 *radian* (from 1 radius).

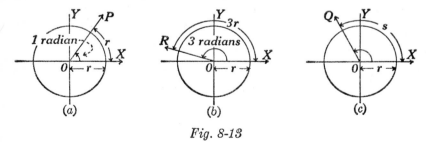

(a)   (b)   (c)

Fig. 8-13

The radian measure of $\angle XOR$, Fig. 8-13(b), is $\dfrac{3r}{r}$ or **3.**

The radian measure of $\angle XOQ$, Fig. 8-13(c), is $\dfrac{s}{r}$.

> *In general, if a central angle of a circle, radius r units, is subtended by an arc of length s units (r and s in the same unit), the radian measure of the angle is the ratio s : r.*

Thus, the statement, $\angle XOQ = \dfrac{s}{r}$, indicates that the measurement of $\angle XOQ$ is expressed in radians.

The radian measure of $\angle XOP$ (*Fig. 8-14*) can be expressed as $\dfrac{s_1}{r_1}$ or $\dfrac{s_2}{r_2}$, since $\dfrac{s_1}{r_1} = \dfrac{s_2}{r_2}$ by a theorem from plane geometry.

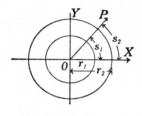 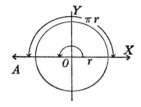

Fig. 8-14   *Fig. 8-15*

The semi-circumference of a circle of radius r units (*Fig. 8-15*) is πr units.

Thus, the radian measure of $\angle XOA$ is $\dfrac{\pi r}{r}$ or π.

The degree measure of $\angle XOA$ is 180.

The following table lists other radian measures and their corresponding degree measure.

RADIAN MEASURE (θ)	DEGREE MEASURE (m)
2π	360
$\dfrac{\pi}{2}$	90
$\dfrac{\pi}{4}$	45
$\dfrac{\pi}{6}$	30

In general, if the degree measure of an angle is represented by m, and the radian measure of the same angle is represented by θ (Greek letter Theta), then

$$\frac{m}{\theta} = \frac{180}{\pi} \quad \text{or} \quad \frac{\theta}{m} = \frac{\pi}{180}.$$

Thus, an angle of 1 radian has a measurement of

$$\left(\frac{180}{\pi}\right)^{\circ} \doteq \left(\frac{180}{3.14159}\right)^{\circ}$$

$$\doteq 57.2958^{\circ} \text{ or } 57^{\circ} \ 17' \ 44.8''.$$

Write solutions to the following and compare them with those on page 471.

4. Express each of the following angle measurements in radians:

(i) 60°   (ii) 18°

5. Express each of the following angle measurements in degrees:

(i) $\dfrac{3\pi}{4}$ radians   (ii) $1\frac{2}{3}\pi$ radians

Exercise 8-3

(B)

1. Make a table showing the equivalent radian measurement for each of the following: 30°, 45°, 60°, 90°, 120°, 135°, 150°, 180°

2. Express each of the following radian measures in degrees:

(i) $\dfrac{\pi}{20}$ (ii) $-\dfrac{3\pi}{4}$ (iii) $\dfrac{5\pi}{4}$ (iv) $10\frac{1}{6}\pi$

(v) $-2\frac{1}{2}\pi$ (vi) $1\frac{3}{8}\pi$ (vii) 0.1π (viii) $1\frac{2}{3}\pi$

3. Express each of the following angle measurements in radians:

(i) 270°   (ii) $-150°$ (iii) $-315°$ (iv) 10°

(v) $-840°$ (vi) 450°   (vii) 1°   (viii) 1,080°

4. An angle is formed by a positive rotation of $2\frac{3}{4}$ revolutions. Determine the radian measure of the angle.

8·4 Definitions of sin θ, cos θ, tan θ. In *Fig. 8-16*, $\angle XOP$ is an angle in standard position whose measurement is represented by θ units (read, "Theta units"). $P(x, y)$ is the point of intersection of the terminal side with a circle with centre O and radius r units $(r > 0)$.

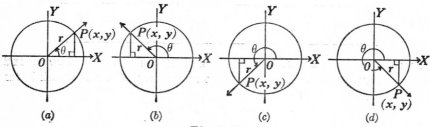

(a)   (b)   (c)   (d)

Fig. 8-16

Three fundamental ratios can be formed to relate the angle whose measurement is θ units to the coordinates of P. These ratios, called *sine* θ, *cosine* θ, and *tangent* θ, are defined as follows:

sine θ (abbreviated "sin θ") is $y : r$, which may be written $\dfrac{y}{r}$;

cosine θ (abbreviated "cos θ") is $x : r$, which may be written $\dfrac{x}{r}$;

tangent θ (abbreviated "tan θ") is $y : x$, which may be written $\dfrac{y}{x}$, $x \neq 0$.

These three ratios are often called the *primary trigonometric ratios.* Each is equivalent to a real number.

In *Fig. 8-17*, $\angle XOQ$ is in standard position, and $Q(4, 3)$ is a point on its terminal side.

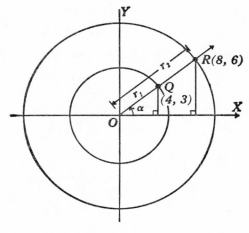

Fig. 8-17

Let us represent the measurement of $\angle XOQ$ by α radians (read, "Alpha units") and the length of OQ by r_1 units.

$$r_1{}^2 = 4^2 + 3^2 \qquad \text{(Pythagorean Theorem)}$$
$$= 16 + 9$$
$$= 25$$
$$\therefore \; r_1 = 5 \;\; \text{since} \;\; r_1 > 0$$

Thus, sin $\alpha = \dfrac{3}{5}$, cos $\alpha = \dfrac{4}{5}$, tan $\alpha = \dfrac{3}{4}$.

NOTE: θ and α are letters from the Greek alphabet and are commonly used to represent the measure of angles. If the unit of angular measure is not specified, it is understood that the measurement is in radians. Thus, sin 1 means the sine of an angle whose measurement is 1 radian; sin 1° is the sine of an angle whose measurement is 1 degree. Other letters often used are β (Beta), γ (Gamma), and ϕ (Phi).

From *Fig. 8-17*, it can be seen that the point $R(8, 6)$ also lies on the terminal side of the angle. If the length OR is represented by r_2 units,

$$r_2{}^2 = 8^2 + 6^2$$
$$= 64 + 36$$
$$= 100$$
$$\therefore \ r_2 = 10$$

$$\therefore \ \sin \alpha = \frac{6}{10} \qquad\qquad \cos \alpha = \frac{8}{10} \qquad\qquad \tan \alpha = \frac{6}{8}$$
$$= \frac{3}{5} \qquad\qquad\qquad\quad = \frac{4}{5} \qquad\qquad\qquad = \frac{3}{4}$$

These results suggest the following theorem:

For any θ, each of the ratios, sin θ, cos θ, and tan θ, is a constant.

To prove this theorem, consider a first quadrant angle, $\angle XOA = \theta$ (*Fig. 8-18*).

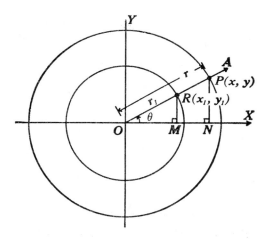

Fig. 8-18

Let $R(x_1, y_1)$ be a point on ray OA such that $OR = r_1$. Let $P(x, y)$ be any other point on OA such that $OP = r$. RM and PN are perpendicular to OX.

$$\triangle OMR \sim \triangle ONP$$
$$\therefore \ OM : MR : OR = ON : NP : OP$$

But $OM = |x_1|$ $\quad\quad\quad MR = |y_1|$ $\quad\quad\quad OR = r_1$

$\quad\quad = x_1$ $\quad\quad\quad\quad\quad = y_1$

$\quad ON = |x|$ $\quad\quad\quad\quad NP = |y|$ $\quad\quad\quad OP = r$

$\quad\quad = x$ $\quad\quad\quad\quad\quad = y$

$$\therefore x_1 : y_1 : r_1 = x : y : r$$

$$\therefore \frac{y_1}{r_1} = \frac{y}{r} = \sin \theta = \text{a constant,}$$

$$\frac{x_1}{r_1} = \frac{x}{r} = \cos \theta = \text{a constant,}$$

$$\frac{y_1}{x_1} = \frac{y}{x} = \tan \theta = \text{a constant.}$$

By a similar discussion, this result can be established for second, third, and fourth quadrant angles.

Write solutions to the following problems and compare them with those on page 472.

1. Calculate the primary trigonometric ratios of each of the following angles (*Fig. 8-19*):

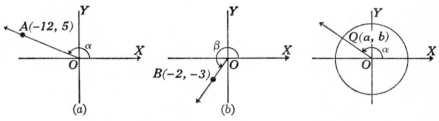

Fig. 8-19 $\quad\quad\quad\quad\quad\quad\quad\quad\quad\quad$ Fig. 8-20

2. The circle in *Fig. 8-20* has unit radius.
    (i) Determine $\sin \alpha$, $\cos \alpha$, and $\tan \alpha$.
    (ii) Determine $\sin^2 \alpha + \cos^2 \alpha$, where $\sin^2 \alpha$ means $(\sin \alpha)^2$.

8·5 Sign of $\sin \theta$, $\cos \theta$, $\tan \theta$. In *Fig. 8-21*, $\angle XOP = \theta$. $P(x, y)$ is a point on the terminal side OP, and ray OP lies in the first quadrant. The positive signs on the diagram indicate that x, y, and r are positive real numbers.

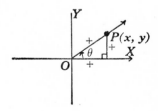

Fig. 8-21

In this quadrant:
$\sin \theta$ is a positive real number;
$\cos \theta$ is a positive real number;
$\tan \theta$ is a positive real number.

By answering the following questions, discover whether sin θ, cos θ, and tan θ are positive or negative real numbers for angles whose terminal sides lie in quadrants other than the first. Compare your answers with those on page 472.

1. Draw a second quadrant angle *XOP* in standard position, with *P(x, y)* a point on the terminal side. Indicate on the diagram the signs of *x*, *y*, and *r*. Determine which trigonometric ratios are positive and which are negative real numbers.

2. Repeat question 1 for a third quadrant angle.

3. Repeat question 1 for a fourth quadrant angle.

Exercise 8-4

(A)

1. State the three primary trigonometric ratios of each of the indicated angles:

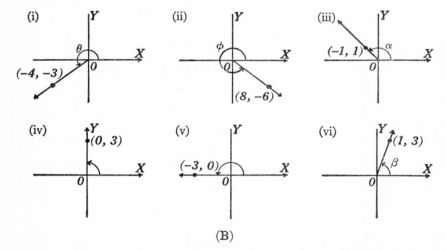

(B)

2. Draw a diagram for each of the following, showing an angle in standard position with its terminal side on the given point. State the primary trigonometric ratios of each angle:

   (i) $(-5, 12)$ (ii) $(-6, -8)$ (iii) $(2, -1)$ (iv) $(-2, 0)$

   (v) $(1, -5)$ (vi) $(4, 1)$ (vii) $(4, 0)$ (viii) $(-2, -3)$

3. From a suitable diagram, determine the sine and cosine of angles with the following measurements:

   (i) 0°   (ii) 90°   (iii) 180°   (iv) 270°

4. (i) The point $A(5, -2)$ lies on the terminal side of an angle in standard position. If the measurement of the angle is θ units, determine:

(a) $\sin^2 \theta + \cos^2 \theta$, where $\sin^2 \theta$ means $(\sin \theta)^2$

(b) $\dfrac{\sin \theta}{\cos \theta}$ (c) $\tan \theta$

(ii) Repeat part (i) for the point $B(-3, -2)$.

(iii) State a conjecture regarding:

(a) $\sin^2 \theta + \cos^2 \theta$

(b) $\dfrac{\sin \theta}{\cos \theta}$ and $\tan \theta$

(C)

5. Given that $\sin \theta = -\frac{3}{5}$, and that θ is the radian measure of an angle whose terminal side is in the third quadrant, calculate $\cos \theta$ and $\tan \theta$.

6. Given that $\tan \theta = -\frac{5}{12}$, calculate:

(i) $\sin \theta$ (2 answers)   (ii) $\cos \theta$ (2 answers)

7. Sketch all the angles such that $0° < \theta° < 360°$ for which $\cos \theta° = \dfrac{-5}{\sqrt{34}}$, and calculate the other two primary ratios of each angle.

8·6 Definitions of csc θ, sec θ, cot θ. For each of the ratios $\sin \theta$, $\cos \theta$, and $\tan \theta$, there is a ratio which is its reciprocal.

The reciprocal of $\sin \theta$, that is, $\dfrac{1}{\sin \theta}$, is called *cosecant θ (csc θ)*.

If $P(x, y)$ is a point on the terminal side of $\angle XOP$ (*Fig. 8-22*), then

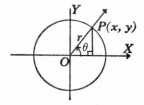

$$csc\ \theta = \frac{1}{sin\ \theta}, \quad sin\ \theta \neq 0$$

$$= \frac{r}{y}, \quad y \neq 0$$

or $sin\ \theta \cdot csc\ \theta = 1.$

Fig. 8-22

The reciprocal of $\cos \theta$ is called *secant θ (sec θ)*.

Then, $$sec\ \theta = \frac{1}{cos\ \theta}, \quad cos\ \theta \neq 0$$

$$= \frac{r}{x}, \quad x \neq 0$$

or $cos\ \theta \cdot sec\ \theta = 1.$

The reciprocal of tan θ is called *cotangent* θ *(cot θ).*

Then,
$$\cot \theta = \frac{1}{\tan \theta}, \quad \tan \theta \neq 0$$

$$= \frac{x}{y}, \quad y \neq 0$$

or $\tan \theta \cdot \cot \theta = 1$.

If $P(x, y)$ is on the x-axis, then $y = 0$. Since csc $\theta = r:y$ and cot $\theta = x:y$, these two trigonometric ratios are not equivalent to real numbers when $y = 0$.

If $P(x,y)$ is on the y-axis, then $x = 0$. Since sec $\theta = r:x$ and tan $\theta = y:x$, these two trigonometric ratios are not equivalent to real numbers when $x = 0$.

Write solutions to the following problems and compare them with those on page 473.

1. State the three pairs of reciprocal trigonometric ratios of each of the angles indicated in *Fig. 8-23*:

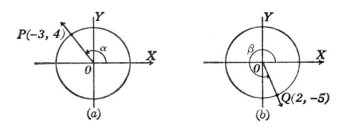

Fig. 8-23

2. In *Fig. 8-24*, a circle of radius r units meets the terminal arm of $\angle XOP$ at $P(x, y)$.
   (i) State the three pairs of reciprocal ratios of $\angle XOP$.
   (ii) If $\angle XOP = \theta$, prove that $\tan \theta = \dfrac{\sin \theta}{\cos \theta}$, and that $\cot \theta = \dfrac{\cos \theta}{\sin \theta}$.

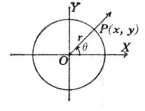

Fig. 8-24

3. Given that sin $\theta = \frac{4}{5}$ and cos $\theta = -\frac{3}{5}$, draw a diagram and determine the other four trigonometric ratios of θ.

Exercise 8-5

(A)

1. State the three pairs of reciprocal trigonometric ratios of each of the indicated angles:

(i)
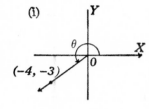

(ii)
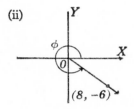

(iii)
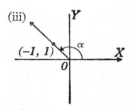

(iv)
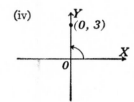

(v)
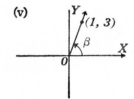

(vi)
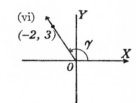

(B)

2. Draw diagrams representing angles in standard position such that the terminal side of the angle is on the point whose coordinates are given. State the six trigonometric ratios of each angle where these ratios are equivalent to real numbers:

   (i) $(-12, -5)$ (ii) $(-8, 6)$

   (iii) $(2, -1)$ (iv) $(-2, 0)$

   (v) $(0, -5)$ (vi) $(1, 4)$

   (vii) $(4, 0)$ (viii) $(-2, -3)$

3. Determine $\csc \theta°$, $\sec \theta°$, and $\cot \theta°$ where these ratios are equivalent to real numbers and $\theta°$ is:

   (i) $0°$ (ii) $90°$ (iii) $180°$ (iv) $270°$

4. (i) Draw the four angles whose terminal sides lie on the points:
   $P_1(-5, 12)$, $P_2(6, -8)$, $P_3(-2, -3)$, $P_4(5, 1)$
   For each angle find:
   (a) $\sec^2 \theta - \tan^2 \theta$
   (b) $\csc^2 \theta - \cot^2 \theta$

   (ii) Make a conjecture about (a) and (b) of part (i) for any angle.

5. If $\sin \beta = \dfrac{1}{\sqrt{10}}$ and $\cos \beta = \dfrac{-3}{\sqrt{10}}$, determine the other four trigonometric ratios of β.

6. If $\sec \alpha = -2.6$ and $\tan \alpha = 2.4$, determine the other four trigonometric ratios of α.

8·7 Discovery of the trigonometric ratios of $\dfrac{\pi}{6}, \dfrac{\pi}{4}, \dfrac{\pi}{3}, \dfrac{\pi}{2}$, and 0.

By answering the following questions, discover the trigonometric ratios of the special angles $\dfrac{\pi}{4}$ *(or 45°),* $\dfrac{\pi}{6}$ *(or 30°),* $\dfrac{\pi}{3}$ *(or 60°),* $\dfrac{\pi}{2}$ *(or 90°), and 0 (or 0°).*

In each case compare your solution with that on page 473.

1. In *Fig. 8-25*, a unit circle cuts the terminal arm of $\angle XOP$ at P. $DP \perp OX$, and $OD = DP$.

   (i) Determine the measurement of $\angle XOP$ in degrees and in radians.

   (ii) Determine the coordinates of P, and then the six trigonometric ratios of $\angle XOP$.

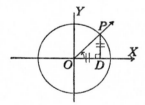 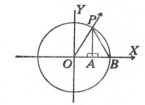

Fig. 8-25   Fig. 8-26

2. In *Fig. 8-26*, a unit circle cuts the terminal arm of $\angle XOP$ at P, such that $OP = OB = BP$. $AP \perp OB$.

   (i) Determine the measurement of $\angle XOP$ in degrees and in radians.

   (ii) Determine the length of OA and calculate the length of AP.

   (iii) State the coordinates of P and determine the six trigonometric ratios of $\angle XOP$.

3. In *Fig. 8-27*, $\angle XOP = 60°$. Q is a point on the unit circle such that ray OQ bisects $\angle XOP$. $BQ \perp OX$.

   (i) Determine the coordinates of Q by comparing $\triangle OAP$ with $\triangle OBQ$.

   (ii) Determine the six trigonometric ratios of $\angle XOQ$.

4. In *Fig. 8-28*, a unit circle cuts OX at P.

   (i) State the measurement of $\angle XOP$.

(ii) Determine the coordinates of P and the trigonometric ratios of $\angle XOP$. State which ratios are not equivalent to real numbers.

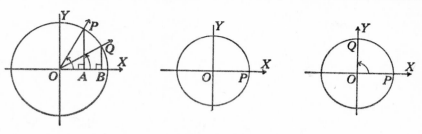

Fig. 8-27   Fig. 8-28   Fig. 8-29

5. In *Fig. 8-29*, a unit circle cuts OX at P, and OY at Q.
   (i) State the measurement of $\angle POQ$.
   (ii) Determine the coordinates of Q and the trigonometric ratios of $\angle POQ$. State which ratios are not equivalent to real numbers.

6. Copy and complete the following table. Leave blanks where the ratio is not equivalent to a real number.

θ	$\sin \theta$	$\cos \theta$	$\tan \theta$	$\csc \theta$	$\sec \theta$	$\cot \theta$
$\dfrac{\pi}{4}$						
$\dfrac{\pi}{3}$						
$\dfrac{\pi}{6}$						
$\dfrac{\pi}{2}$						
0						

Exercise 8-6

(A)

1. Which trigonometric ratios of 0 are not equivalent to a real number? Explain.

2. Which trigonometric ratios of $\dfrac{\pi}{2}$ are not equivalent to a real number? Explain.

3. For each of the following, determine $\theta°$, where $0° \leqq \theta° \leqq 90°$:

    (i) $\tan \theta° = 1$ (ii) $\sec \theta° = 2$

    (iii) $\sin \theta° = 1$ (iv) $\cot \theta° = \sqrt{3}$

    (v) $\csc \theta° = \sqrt{2}$ (vi) $\sec \theta° = \dfrac{2}{\sqrt{3}}$

(B)

4. Determine each of the following:

    (i) $\tan 30° \tan 45° \tan 60°$ (ii) $\cos^2 30° - \cos^2 45°$

    (iii) $3 \cos \dfrac{\pi}{2} - 5 \cos 0$ (iv) $\cot^2 \dfrac{\pi}{6} \tan^2 \dfrac{\pi}{4} + \sqrt{3} \csc \dfrac{\pi}{2} \cot \dfrac{\pi}{6}$

    (v) $2 \tan^2 \dfrac{\pi}{4} + \tan^2 \dfrac{\pi}{3}$ (vi) $\sin^2 30° + \sin^2 45° + \sin^2 60°$

    (vii) $\cos 0° \sin^2 45° - \cot 90° \sin 45°$

    (viii) $\cot^2 \dfrac{\pi}{6} - 2 \sin^2 \dfrac{\pi}{6} \csc^2 \dfrac{\pi}{4}$

5. Show that $\cos^2 \theta + \sin^2 \theta = 1$ for:

    (i) $\theta = \dfrac{\pi}{4}$ (ii) $\theta = \dfrac{\pi}{3}$ (iii) $\theta = \dfrac{\pi}{2}$

6. Prove each of the following:

    (i) $\cos \dfrac{\pi}{3} \cos \dfrac{\pi}{6} - \sin \dfrac{\pi}{3} \sin \dfrac{\pi}{6} = 0$ (ii) $\cos 30° = \sqrt{\dfrac{1 + \cos 60°}{2}}$

    (iii) $\sin 30° = \sqrt{\dfrac{1 - \cos 60°}{2}}$ (iv) $\sin \dfrac{\pi}{2} \neq \sin \dfrac{\pi}{4} + \sin \dfrac{\pi}{4}$

    (v) $\cos 90° \neq \cos 30° + \cos 60°$ (vi) $\cot 90° \neq \tfrac{1}{2} \cos 45°$

8·8 Trigonometric ratios of the acute angles of a right triangle; complementary angles. In *Fig. 8-30(a)*, $\triangle ABC$ is right-angled at B. There is a ray in the first quadrant, *Fig. 8-30(b)*, with its end point on O, such that $OM = CB$, $MP = BA$, and $MP \perp OX$.

      $\because OM = CB$, $MP = BA$, $\angle PMO = \angle ABC = 90°$

      $\therefore \triangle OMP \cong \triangle CBA$

      $\therefore OP = CA$, $\angle MOP = \angle BCA$

If the coordinates of P are (x, y), and the length of OP is r units, then:

$$OM = |x| \qquad\qquad MP = |y|$$
$$ = x \qquad\qquad = y$$

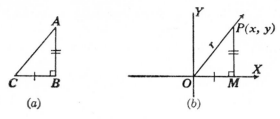

Fig. 8-30

$$\therefore \; \sin \angle C = \sin \angle MOP = \frac{y}{r} = \frac{MP}{OP} = \frac{BA}{CA}$$

$$\cos \angle C = \cos \angle MOP = \frac{x}{r} = \frac{OM}{OP} = \frac{CB}{CA}$$

$$\tan \angle C = \tan \angle MOP = \frac{y}{x} = \frac{MP}{OM} = \frac{BA}{CB}$$

We commonly refer to the interior angles of a triangle by naming only the vertex. It is common practice to use the letter naming the vertex to represent the measure of the angle. Thus, *sin A* means the sine of the interior angle of the triangle whose vertex is A; its measure is represented by A.

The sides of $\triangle ABC$ are often described with reference to $\angle ACB$ as follows:

CB is the side adjacent to $\angle ACB$
   or *the adjacent side*;

BA is the side opposite $\angle ACB$
   or *the opposite side*;

CA is *the hypotenuse* .

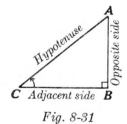

Fig. 8-31

Thus, for a right triangle ABC:

$$\sin C = \frac{\text{opposite side}}{\text{hypotenuse}}$$

$$\csc C = \frac{\text{hypotenuse}}{\text{opposite side}}$$

$$\cos C = \frac{\text{adjacent side}}{\text{hypotenuse}}$$

$$\sec C = \frac{\text{hypotenuse}}{\text{adjacent side}}$$

$$\tan C = \frac{\text{opposite side}}{\text{adjacent side}}$$

$$\cot C = \frac{\text{adjacent side}}{\text{opposite side}}$$

Write solutions for the following problems and compare them with those on page 475.

1. (i) Calculate the six trigonometric ratios of each acute angle in
   △*ABC* (*Fig. 8-32*) .

   (ii) Make a list of the pairs of equal trigonometric ratios.

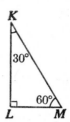

Fig. 8-32   Fig. 8-33

2. In *Fig. 8-33*, ∠*K* = 30°, ∠*L* = 90°, ∠*M* = 60° .

   (i) Determine the ratio *LM* : *KM* : *KL* .

   (ii) Determine the six trigonometric ratios of ∠*K* and ∠*M* .

   (iii) Make a list of the pairs of equal trigonometric ratios.

3. From these results, make a conjecture about the relation between the
   trigonometric ratios of complementary angles.

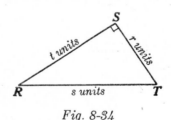

Fig. 8-34

4. Test this conjecture (question 3) for △*RST* (*Fig. 8-34*) in which
   ∠*S* = 90°, *RS* = *t* units, *ST* = *r* units, and *RT* = *s* units.

From question 4, the following results are obtained:
   If *R* and *T* are complementary angles,

sine *R* = cosine *T*	cosine *R* = sine *T*
tangent *R* = cotangent *T*	cotangent *R* = tangent *T*
secant *R* = cosecant *T*	cosecant *R* = secant *T*

   *In general, a trigonometric ratio of an acute angle is equal to
   the co-ratio of its complement.*

Exercise 8-7

(A)

1. State the trigonometric ratios of each acute angle in the given triangles:

(i)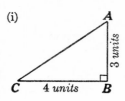

(ii)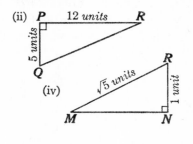

(iii)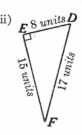

(iv)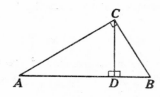

(B)

2. Given the following information about $\triangle ABC$, find the trigonometric ratios of each acute angle of $\triangle ABC$:

   (i) $\angle B = 90°$, $\quad BC = 2$ units, $\qquad AB = 3$ units

   (ii) $\angle A = 90°$, $\quad AB = 5$ units, $\qquad BC = \sqrt{29}$ units

   (iii) $\angle C = 90°$, $\quad AC = 3$ units, $\quad \tan \angle A = 1\frac{1}{3}$

   (iv) $\angle C = 90°$, $\quad BC = 2$ units, $\quad \sin \angle B = \dfrac{1}{\sqrt{2}}$

3. $\triangle PQR$ is equilateral. $PT \perp QR$. Determine the six trigonometric ratios of:

   $\qquad$ (i) $\angle PQT$ $\qquad$ (ii) $\angle QPT$

4. In the diagram at the left below, $\angle ACB = 90°$, $CD \perp AB$. State the six trigonometric ratios of $\angle A$ using:

   (i) the sides of $\triangle ABC$ $\qquad$ (ii) the sides of $\triangle ADC$

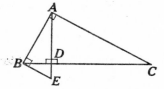

5. By referring to the diagram at the right above, determine the trigonometric ratios of:

   (i) $\angle ACB$ $\qquad$ (ii) $\angle AEB$ $\qquad$ (iii) $\angle BAE$

   Give two answers for each.

6. Express each of the following as a ratio of the complementary angle:

    (i) sec $50°$ (ii) cos $75°$ (iii) tan $48°$

    (iv) sin $57°$ (v) csc $60°$ (vi) cot $66°$

7. $ABCD$ is a square in which the sides are each 1 unit in length. Determine the six trigonometric ratios of $\angle ABD$.

8. In $\triangle ABC$, $\angle B = 90°$. From the additional information in each part below, calculate the six trigonometric ratios of $\angle A$ and of $\angle C$:

    (i) $AB = 20$ units, $\sin C = \dfrac{4}{5}$

    (ii) $AB = 1$ unit, $\tan C = .5$

    (iii) $\tan \angle A = \dfrac{8}{15}$, $\sin C = \dfrac{15}{17}$

    (iv) $AC : AB = 29 : 20$

8·9 Trigonometric tables. In section 8·7, the trigonometric ratios of $0, \dfrac{\pi}{2}, \dfrac{\pi}{3}, \dfrac{\pi}{4}$, and $\dfrac{\pi}{6}$ are calculated. It is not convenient to determine the trigonometric ratios for all angles between 0 and $\dfrac{\pi}{2}$ by geometric methods. Instead, we refer to Tables of Trigonometric Ratios which are prepared from formulas.

The trigonometric ratios of angles whose degree measures are integers from 0 to 90 are given in a table on page 433. These ratios are expressed as decimals, correct to four decimal places. The corresponding radian measures of the angles are also shown.

By answering the following questions discover how to use the Table of Trigonometric Ratios on page 433. Compare your solutions with those on page 476.

1. Write each of the following trigonometric ratios from the table on page 433:

    (i) sin $37°$ (ii) sec $80°$ (iii) tan $2°$ (iv) csc $29°$

2. For each of the following, determine the measurement of the angle to the nearest degree:

    (i) tan $\theta° = 2.0000$ (ii) cos $\alpha° = 0.8018$

3. As θ increases from 0 to $\dfrac{\pi}{2}$:

    (i) which trigonometric ratios of θ increase?

    (ii) which trigonometric ratios of θ decrease?

Exercise 8-8

(A)

Find from the tables:

1. sin 0°   **2.** sin 30°   **3.** sin 50°

4. sin 65°   **5.** sin 75°   **6.** sin 90°

7. As an angle increases in measurement from 0° to 90°, how does the sine of the angle change?

Find from the tables:

8. cos 0°   **9.** cos 30°   **10.** cos 50°

11. cos 65°   **12.** cos 75°   **13.** cos 90°

14. As an angle increases in measurement from 0° to 90°, how does the cosine of the angle change?

15. By an examination of the tangent table state how the tangent of an angle changes as the angle increases in measurement from 0° to 90°.

(B)

From the tables on page 433, find:

16. cos 29°   **17.** tan 75°   **18.** sin 58°

19. csc 21°   **20.** cot 63°   **21.** $\sin \dfrac{\pi}{36}$

22. sec 39°   **23.** tan 42°   **24.** cos 80°

25. csc 52°   **26.** sec 1.5359   **27.** $\cot \dfrac{\pi}{4}$

From the tables on page 433, find the measurement of the indicated angles to the nearest degree and state the corresponding radian measurement:

28. tan $\alpha°$ = 1.150   **29.** sin $\beta°$ = .9075

30. cos $\theta°$ = .8935   **31.** cot $\gamma°$ = .40

32. sin $\theta°$ = .5770   **33.** sec $\beta°$ = 9.20

34. cot $\gamma°$ = .750   **35.** csc $\alpha°$ = 2.816

36. tan $\theta°$ = .091   **37.** cos $\beta°$ = .202

8·10 Solution of right triangles. The Pythagorean Theorem relates the measurements of the sides of a right triangle.

In *Fig. 8-35*, the length of *BC*, the side opposite vertex *A*, is *a* units; the length of *AC*, the side opposite vertex *B*, is *b* units; the length of *AB*, the side opposite vertex *C*, is *c* units.

$$\because \ \angle C = 90°, \quad \therefore \ c^2 = a^2 + b^2$$
$$\text{or } a^2 = c^2 - b^2$$
$$\text{or } b^2 = c^2 - a^2.$$

In this Chapter, *a*, *b*, and *c* represent the number of units in the measurements of the sides opposite $\angle A$, $\angle B$, and $\angle C$, respectively. It is understood that each is expressed in the same unit.

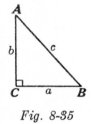

Fig. 8-35

The trigonometric ratios relate the sides of a right triangle to the angles of the triangle:

$$\sin B = \frac{b}{c} \qquad \sin A = \frac{a}{c}$$

$$\cos B = \frac{a}{c} \qquad \cos A = \frac{b}{c}$$

$$\tan B = \frac{b}{a} \qquad \tan A = \frac{a}{b}$$

These relationships can be used to *solve a triangle:* that is, to determine the measurements of certain parts of a triangle when the measurements of the other parts are given. In order to solve a *right triangle*, we must be given the measurements of

(i) two sides of the triangle or (ii) one side and one acute angle.

Write solutions to the following problems to discover how to solve right triangles for each of these cases; compare them with those given on page 476.

1. In $\triangle ABC$, $\angle B = 90°$, $a = 2.6$, $b = 4.2$.

(i) Draw a diagram to represent $\triangle ABC$.

(ii) Using the Pythagorean Theorem, calculate *c* to one decimal place.

(iii) Calculate sin *A* to four decimal places.

(iv) Using the table on page 433, find $\angle A$ to the nearest degree.

(v) Calculate the measurement of $\angle C$ to the nearest degree.

As an alternative method of determining $\angle C$:

(vi) Find tan *C* to four decimal places (from the table on page 433).

(vii) Using the relation $\dfrac{c}{a} = \tan C$ or $c = a \tan C$, find *c* to one decimal place.

(viii) How can tan *A* be used to calculate *c* ?

2. In $\triangle PQR$, $\angle Q = 90°$, $\angle P = 32°$, $r = 7.4$.

   (i) Draw a diagram to represent $\triangle PQR$.

   (ii) From the table on page 433, find tan P to four decimal places.

   (iii) From the relation tan $P = \dfrac{p}{r}$ or $p = r$ tan P, calculate p to one decimal place.

   (iv) Use the relation sec $P = \dfrac{q}{r}$ or $q = r$ sec P to calculate q to one decimal place.

   (v) State the measurement of $\angle R$.

Exercise 8-9

(A)

1. Give a relationship from which $\angle A$ can be determined for each of the following triangles:

  (i)   (ii)   (iii)

2. For each of the following triangles, state a trigonometric ratio which could be used to determine b:

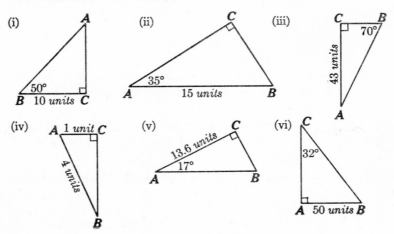

(B)

3. From the given information, solve each of the following triangles. State all angle measurements to the nearest degree and all lengths to one decimal place:

    (i) $\angle A = 90°$, $b = 12$, $a = 13$

    (ii) $\angle B = 90°$, $a = 2.5$, $c = 1.5$

    (iii) $\angle B = 90°$, $\angle A = 58°$, $c = 10$

    (iv) $\angle C = 90°$, $\angle B = 29°$, $b = 5.6$

    (v) $\angle B = 90°$, $c = 31$, $b = 76$

    (vi) $\angle C = 90°$, $\angle A = 23°$, $a = 5$

    (vii) $\angle A = 90°$, $\angle C = 40°$, $a = 8$

    (viii) $\angle B = 90°$, $a = 23$, $c = 24$

    (ix) $\angle C = 90°$, $\angle B = 72°$, $c = 8.4$

    (x) $\angle A = 90°$, $\angle C = 15°$, $b = 20$

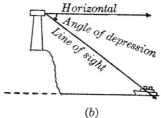

4. From the information in the diagram at the right above, calculate the length of QR.

8·11 Problems involving the solution of right triangles. In referring to angles in a vertical plane, the two terms following are frequently used.

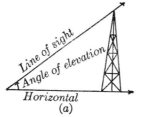 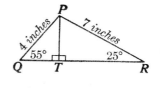

Fig. 8-36

(i) If the object observed is above the horizontal, *Fig. 8-36(a)*, the angle determined by the horizontal and the line of sight is called the *angle of elevation.*

(ii) If the object observed is below the horizontal, *Fig. 8-36(b)*, the angle determined by the horizontal and the line of sight is called the *angle of depression.*

In referring to angles in a horizontal plane, the direction of an object from an observer is obtained by measuring the angle determined by the line of sight and one of the compass directions: north, south, east, or west. This angle is called the *bearing* of the object with respect to the *compass direction.* In *Fig. 8-37 (a)*, the object has a bearing 15° *east of north*, which is usually expressed N 15° E.

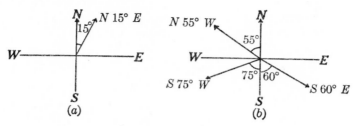

Fig. 8-37

Other compass bearings are shown in *Fig. 8-37(b)*.

Many problems in surveying, navigation, and engineering involve the calculation of heights, distances, and angles.

Discover how to solve problems involving heights, distances, and angles by answering the following questions. Compare your solutions with those on page 477.

1. The angle of elevation of the top of a flagpole from a point 108 feet from its base is 48°. Find the height of the flagpole.
   (i) Make a diagram to represent the data.
   (ii) What measurement are we asked to find? Represent this measurement by h feet.
   (iii) State a value for tan 48° in terms of h.
   (iv) Using the Trigonometric Tables on page 433, solve this equation for h.
   (v) Write a conclusion to the problem, giving your answer to the nearest foot.

2. From the top of a lighthouse which is 250 feet above sea level, the angle of depression of a small ship is observed to be 32°. Calculate the distance of the ship from the base of the lighthouse.
   (i) Make a diagram to represent the data.
   (ii) Make a statement in which the required measurement in the problem is represented by x feet.
   (iii) Name the right triangle in the diagram and name an angle of this triangle which has a measurement of 32°.
   (iv) State a value for cot 32° in terms of x.
   (v) Using the Trigonometric Tables on page 433, solve this equation for x.
   (vi) Write a conclusion to the problem, giving your answer to one decimal place.

3. A ship travels N 32° E for 2 hours at 14 knots (1 nautical mile per hour). The ship then changes course to S 58° E and travels in this direction for 3 hours. Find the distance in nautical miles of the ship from the starting point.

  (i) Make a diagram to represent the data.

  (ii) Show that the triangle in the diagram is a right triangle.

  (iii) Calculate the length of the third side using the Pythagorean Theorem.

  (iv) Write a conclusion to the problem giving your answer to the nearest nautical mile.

Exercise 8-10

(B)

In each of the following, state angle measurements to the nearest degree and lengths to the nearest whole number of units:

1. The angle of elevation of the top of a building from a point 1,000 ft. from its foot is 35°. Find the height of the building.

2. The string of a kite is 500 ft. long. Find the height of the kite when its angle of elevation is 40°.

3. A tree casts a shadow 30 ft. long when the angle of elevation of the sun is 62°. Find the height of the tree.

4. From the top of a 300-ft. tower, the angle of depression of an object is 32°. How far is the object from the tower?

5. The combined height of a flagpole and the building on which it stands is 160 ft. At a point 115 ft. from the foot of the building, the angle of elevation of the top of the building is 42°. Find the length of the flagpole.

6. Three towns A, B, and C are located so that B is due north of C, A is 31 miles due west of C, and the bearing of B from A is N 56° E. Find the distance from town A to town B.

7. Two ships A and B start from the same harbour jetty. A sails S 45° E at 16 knots, and B sails N 45° E at 17 knots. Find their distance apart after 7 hours.

8. The angle of inclination of a road is 8°. Find the rise for 500 feet measured along the road.

9. At a distance of 14,000 ft. from the foot of the Empire State Building, the angle of elevation of its top is 5°. Find the height of the building.

10. From the top of a perpendicular cliff 325 ft. above water level, the angle of depression of a ship at sea is 32°. Find the distance of the ship from the foot of the cliff.

11. The bridge over the railroad track, shown in the diagram at the left below, is 33 ft. high. If the approach to the bridge must have an angular elevation of 10°, find the length of the approach measured along the road surface.

12. To find the distance from *A* to *B* across a pond, a surveyor makes the measurements shown in the diagram at the right above. Find *AB*.

13. To find the distance from *X* to *Y* across a river, a surveyor makes the measurements shown in the diagram at the left below. Find *XY*.

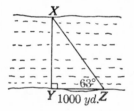 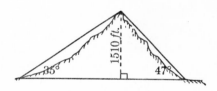

14. The angles of elevation of the top of a mountain from points on opposite sides of it, on the same level, are 35° and 47°. The top of the mountain is 1,510 ft. above the level of the two points. Find the length of a tunnel through the mountain between the two points.

8·12 Fundamental trigonometric relations. Certain relations among the trigonometric ratios have been established. These may be classified as follows.

a. *Reciprocal relations.* ***For any angle*** θ:

(i) $\sin \theta \cdot \csc \theta = 1$

Thus, $\sin \theta = \dfrac{1}{\csc \theta}$, $\csc \theta \neq 0$, and $\csc \theta = \dfrac{1}{\sin \theta}$, $\sin \theta \neq 0$.

(ii) $\cos \theta \cdot \sec \theta = 1$

Thus, $\cos \theta = \dfrac{1}{\sec \theta}$, $\sec \theta \neq 0$, and $\sec \theta = \dfrac{1}{\cos \theta}$, $\cos \theta \neq 0$.

(iii) $\tan \theta \cdot \cot \theta = 1$

Thus, $\tan \theta = \dfrac{1}{\cot \theta}$, $\cot \theta \neq 0$, and $\cot \theta = \dfrac{1}{\tan \theta}$, $\tan \theta \neq 0$.

b. *Quotient relations.* **For any angle** θ**:**

(i) $\tan \theta = \dfrac{\sin \theta}{\cos \theta}$, $\cos \theta \neq 0$

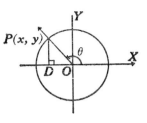

Fig. 8-38

(ii) $\cot \theta = \dfrac{\cos \theta}{\sin \theta}$, $\sin \theta \neq 0$

c. *Pythagorean relations.*

By answering the following questions, develop the Pythagorean relations. Compare your solutions with those on page 478.

In *Fig. 8-38*, a unit circle cuts the terminal arm of $\angle XOP$ at $P(x, y)$.

$$\angle XOP = \theta, \quad DP \perp OX$$

1. Express the Pythagorean relation for $\triangle POD$ in terms of x and y.

2. Determine $\sin \theta$ and $\cos \theta$.

3. State the Pythagorean relation in terms of $\sin \theta$ and $\cos \theta$.

4. Divide each term of the relation obtained in question 3 by $\cos^2 \theta$ ($\cos \theta \neq 0$) to obtain a second relation.

5. Divide each term of the relation obtained in question 3 by $\sin^2 \theta$ ($\sin \theta \neq 0$) to obtain a third relation.

These three relations are referred to as the *Pythagorean relations.*

For any angle θ**:**

(i) $\sin^2 \theta + \cos^2 \theta = 1$

(ii) $1 + \tan^2 \theta = \sec^2 \theta$ ($\cos \theta \neq 0$)

(iii) $1 + \cot^2 \theta = \csc^2 \theta$ ($\sin \theta \neq 0$)

These relations can be written in different forms, as follows:

$\sin^2 \theta = 1 - \cos^2 \theta$ or $\cos^2 \theta = 1 - \sin^2 \theta$ or $|\sin \theta| = \sqrt{1 - \cos^2 \theta}$

$\tan^2 \theta = \sec^2 \theta - 1$ or $\sec^2 \theta - \tan^2 \theta = 1$ or $|\tan \theta| = \sqrt{\sec^2 \theta - 1}$

$\cot^2 \theta = \csc^2 \theta - 1$ or $\csc^2 \theta - \cot^2 \theta = 1$ or $|\cot \theta| = \sqrt{\csc^2 \theta - 1}$

Exercise 8-11

(A)

1. Using a Pythagorean relation, state an equivalent expression for:

(i) $\sin^2 \theta$ (ii) $\cos^2 \theta$ (iii) $\tan^2 \theta$

(iv) $\csc^2 \theta$ (v) $\sec^2 \theta$ (vi) $\cot^2 \theta$

2. Using a quotient relation, state an equivalent expression for:

(i) $\tan \alpha$ (ii) $\tan^2 \alpha$ (iii) $\cot \alpha$ (iv) $\cot^2 \alpha$

3. Repeat question 2 using a reciprocal relation.

(B)

Write an expression equivalent to each of the following:

4. $\dfrac{\sin A}{\cos A}$ **5.** $1 + \tan^2 B$ **6.** $1 - \cos^2 \theta$

7. $\cot \beta \, \tan \beta$ **8.** $\tan C \, \cos C$ **9.** $\cot C \, \sin C$

10. $\dfrac{1}{\sec X}$ **11.** $\cos^2 M + \sin^2 M$ **12.** $1 - \sin^2 P - \cos^2 P$

Write equivalent expressions for each of the following in terms of sin A:

13. $\cos^2 A$ **14.** $\sec A \, \tan A$ **15.** $\csc A$

16. $\tan^2 A$ **17.** $\cot^2 A$ **18.** $\dfrac{\sin^2 A - 1}{\cos^2 A}$

Write equivalent expressions for each of the following in terms of cos A:

19. $\sec A$ **20.** $\tan^2 A$ **21.** $\tan A \, \sin A$

22. $\sin^2 A$ **23.** $\csc A \, \cot A$

24. $(\sin^2 A - \cos^2 A)(\sin^2 A + \cos^2 A)$

Write an equivalent expression in lowest terms for each of the following in terms of either sin A, cos A, or both:

25. $\tan \theta + \cot \theta$ **26.** $\dfrac{\tan \theta}{\cot \theta}$ **27.** $\dfrac{1 + \tan \theta}{1 + \cot \theta}$

28. $\dfrac{2 \tan \theta}{1 - \tan^2 \theta}$ **29.** $\tan A - \sec A$ **30.** $\dfrac{1 - \tan^2 B}{1 + \tan^2 B}$

31. $\dfrac{\sin P}{1 + \cos P} + \cot P$ **32.** $\dfrac{\tan A + \cot B}{\tan B + \cot A}$

33. Since $\cos^2 \alpha = 1 - \sin^2 \alpha$, what expression is $\cos \alpha$ equivalent to when α is an angle of:

    (i) the first quadrant   (ii) the second quadrant

    (iii) the third quadrant   (iv) the fourth quadrant

8·13 Trigonometric identities. In algebra, the equation

$$(x + 2)^2 = x^2 + 4x + 4, \; x \in R$$

is called an *identity* because it is a true statement for all real values of x.

Since each of the reciprocal, quotient, and Pythagorean relations is true for all θ for which the ratios are equivalent to real numbers, these relations are called *trigonometric identities.*

In each of the following examples, the relations involved are valid for all angles for which the fundamental identities are valid. Although this will not be pointed out explicitly in each case, it is only in this sense that the equations are identities.

Two trigonometric expressions may be proved to be equivalent if each can be shown to be equivalent to the same expression by use of relations already known.

For example, to prove
$$\cos \alpha \sin \alpha \tan \alpha = 1 - \cos^2 \alpha:$$

(i) Find an equivalent expression for $\cos \alpha \sin \alpha \tan \alpha$.

L.S. $= \cos \alpha \sin \alpha \tan \alpha$

$\qquad = \cos \alpha \sin \alpha \dfrac{\sin \alpha}{\cos \alpha}$ \qquad\qquad (Quotient relation)

$\qquad = \sin^2 \alpha$

(ii) Find an equivalent expression for $1 - \cos^2 \alpha$.

R.S. $= 1 - \cos^2 \alpha$

$\qquad = \sin^2 \alpha$ \qquad\qquad\qquad (Pythagorean relation)

Thus, since each expression is equivalent to $\sin^2 \alpha$

$$\therefore \cos \alpha \sin \alpha \tan \alpha = 1 - \cos^2 \alpha.$$

Prove the following identity and compare your solution with that on page 478.

1. $1 + \tan^2 \beta = \dfrac{1}{1 - \sin^2 \beta}$

Exercise 8-12

(B)

Prove each of the following identities:

1. $\sin \theta \cot \theta = \cos \theta$
\qquad **2.** $\sin \theta \sec \theta \cot \theta = 1$

3. $\cos^2 \theta - \sin^2 \theta = 1 - 2 \sin^2 \theta$
\qquad **4.** $\sec \theta \csc \theta \cot \theta = \dfrac{1}{\sin^2 \theta}$

5. $\dfrac{\tan \theta}{\cos \theta} = \sin \theta \sec^2 \theta$
\qquad **6.** $\sec^2 \theta - 1 = \sin^2 \theta \sec^2 \theta$

7. $(1 - \sin^2 \theta)(1 - \cos^2 \theta) = \dfrac{1}{\sec^2 \theta \csc^2 \theta}$

8. $\dfrac{1 - \sin^2 \theta}{\csc^2 \theta - 1} = \sin^2 \theta$
\qquad **9.** $\dfrac{1 + \tan^2 \theta}{1 + \cot^2 \theta} = \dfrac{1 - \cos^2 \theta}{\cos^2 \theta}$

10. $\csc \theta \cot \theta \cos \theta + 1 = \csc^2 \theta$

(C)

Prove each of the following identities:

11. $\dfrac{\cos \theta + \sin \theta}{1 + \tan \theta} = \cos \theta$

12. $\cos^2 \theta + \cos^2 \theta \tan^2 \theta = 1$

13. $\tan^2 \theta - \sin^2 \theta = \sin^2 \theta \tan^2 \theta$

8·14 Sine Law for acute triangles (supplementary). In section 8·10, right triangles are solved using the six trigonometric ratios and the Pythagorean Theorem. The solution of an *oblique triangle* (a triangle which does not contain a right angle) requires additional trigonometric relations.

Discover one of these relations by answering the following questions. Compare your solutions with those on page 478.

In *Fig. 8-39*, $\triangle ABC$ is an acute oblique triangle. $CD \perp AB$, and $CD = h$ units.

1. From triangle ACD, determine $\sin A$; from triangle CDB, determine $\sin B$.

2. Combine these two statements by eliminating h to obtain:

$$\frac{a}{\sin A} = \frac{b}{\sin B}$$

3. By a similar argument, prove that:

$$\frac{b}{\sin B} = \frac{c}{\sin C}$$

Combining these two results:

$$\frac{a}{\sin A} = \frac{b}{\sin B} = \frac{c}{\sin C}$$

This statement is called the *Sine Law*.

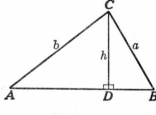

Fig. 8-39

By answering the following question, discover how the Sine Law may be used to solve certain oblique triangles. Compare your solution with that on page 478. State all angle measurements to the nearest degree, and lengths to one decimal place.

4. Solve $\triangle ABC$ in which $a = 3.2$, $\angle A = 34°$, $\angle B = 75°$.

    (i) Determine $\angle C$.

    (ii) Use the Sine Law to obtain an equation involving b; calculate b.

    (iii) In a similar manner, calculate c.

Exercise 8-13

(A)

1. For each of the given triangles, state an expression for a in terms of the given parts:

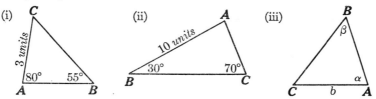

(i) (ii) (iii)

2. For each of the given triangles, state an expression for the ratio indicated:

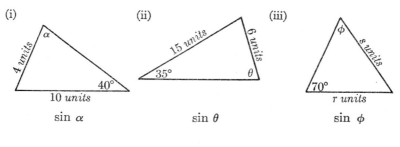

(i) (ii) (iii)

sin α sin θ sin ϕ

(B)

Solve each of the following triangles stating angle measurements to the nearest degree and lengths to one decimal place:

3. $a = 8.4$, $\angle A = 78°$, $\angle B = 34°$

4. $b = 7.9$, $\angle A = 63°$, $\angle C = 41°$

5. $c = 3$, $\angle A = 54°$, $\angle C = 48°$

6. $b = 10$, $\angle A = 85°$, $\angle C = 27°$

7. Two adjacent sides of a parallelogram make angles of 42° and 68°, respectively, with the diagonal. If the length of the diagonal is 8 units, find the lengths of the sides of the parallelogram.

8. A ship is sailing a course from A to B past a lighthouse C. The captain finds the measurements of $\angle A$ and $\angle B$ to be 55° and 42°, respectively. If $AB = 6.5$ miles, find AC and BC, the distances from the lighthouse to A and B.

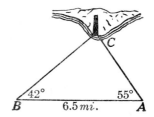

9. A greenhouse is 24 feet wide. One side of the roof makes an angle of 25° with the horizontal, while the other side makes an angle of 70°. Find the rafter lengths, *AB* and *AC*.

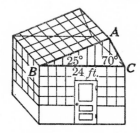 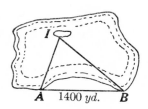

10. Two docks *A* and *B* are 1,400 yards apart. How far is an island dock *I* from *A* and *B*, if ∠*IBA* = 40° and ∠*IAB* = 65°? State the distance to the nearest yard.

8·15 Ratios of supplementary angles (supplementary). Supplementary angles are two angles such that the sum of their measurements is 180°.

By answering the following question, discover the relation between the trigonometric ratios of supplementary angles. Compare your solution with that on page 479.

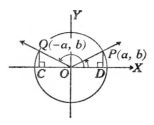

Fig. 8-40

1. A circle with centre *O* and radius *r* cuts the terminal side of ∠*XOP* at *P* (*a*, *b*) and the terminal side of ∠*XOQ* at *Q* (− *a*, *b*), where *a*, *b* ∈ ^{+}R (*Fig. 8-40*).

   (i) Show that ∠*XOQ* is the supplement of ∠*XOP*.

   (ii) Compare the trigonometric ratios of these two angles. List (a) those ratios which are equal and (b) those ratios which are equal in magnitude but opposite in sign.

8·16 Sine Law for obtuse triangles (supplementary). In *Fig. 8-14*, △*ABC* is an obtuse triangle because ∠*ABC* is an obtuse angle.

Show that the Sine Law holds for obtuse triangles by answering the following questions. Compare your solutions with those on page 479.

In *Fig. 8-41*, $CD \perp AB$, $CD = h$ units.

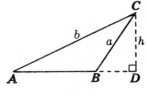

Fig. 8-41

1. From $\triangle ADC$, determine sin A.
2. From $\triangle CBD$, determine sin $\angle CBD$.
3. Determine sin B. ($\angle CBD$ is the supplement of $\angle B$).
4. Combine the statements obtained in questions 1 and 3 by eliminating h to obtain

$$\frac{a}{\sin A} = \frac{b}{\sin B}.$$

5. In a similar manner, by drawing a perpendicular from A to CB extended, prove that

$$\frac{b}{\sin B} = \frac{c}{\sin C}.$$

Exercise 8-14

(B)

1. Using the table on page 433, determine:
   (i) cos 125° (ii) cot 160° (iii) sin 95°
   (iv) tan 148° (v) sec 170° (vi) csc 132°

Solve each of the following triangles stating angle measurements to the nearest degree and lengths to one decimal place:

2. $a = 12$, $\angle B = 22°$, $\angle C = 146°$
3. $c = 5.2$, $\angle A = 41°$, $\angle C = 101°$
4. $b = 10$, $\angle A = 32°$, $\angle B = 128°$
5. In an isosceles triangle, the length of each of the equal sides is 5.8 inches, and each of the equal angles has a measurement of 68°. Calculate the length of the third side.
6. To find the width TM of a river, a man sights a small tree T on the opposite bank from two points A and B which are 390 feet apart. If $\angle TAB = 72°$ and $\angle TBA = 39°$, find AT and TM to the nearest foot.

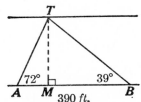

8·17 The Cosine Law (supplementary). Another relation useful in solving triangles involves the three sides of a triangle and the cosine of one of the interior angles.

Discover this relationship by answering the following questions. Compare your solutions with those on page 480.

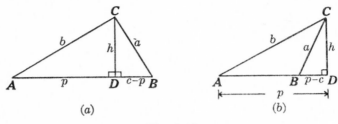

Fig. 8-42

In *Fig. 8-42* (*a*), $\triangle ABC$ is an acute triangle. $CD \perp AB$, and $CD = h$ units.

1. Using the Pythagorean Theorem, write two different expressions, each equal to h^2; equate the two expressions and simplify the result.

2. State a value for p in terms of b and A; substitute this value for p in the equation obtained in 1.

3. Prove that this result is true for the obtuse triangle ABC in *Fig. 8-42* (*b*).

Similar results can be obtained for the other two sides. These results are usually called the *Cosine Law* and are stated as follows:

$$a^2 = b^2 + c^2 - 2bc \cos A \quad \text{or} \quad \cos A = \frac{b^2 + c^2 - a^2}{2bc}$$

$$b^2 = c^2 + a^2 - 2ca \cos B \quad \text{or} \quad \cos B = \frac{c^2 + a^2 - b^2}{2ca}$$

$$c^2 = a^2 + b^2 - 2ab \cos C \quad \text{or} \quad \cos C = \frac{a^2 + b^2 - c^2}{2ab}$$

8·18 Solving oblique triangles (supplementary). In section 8.14, the Sine Law is used to solve a triangle, given the measurements of two angles and one side of the triangle. It is now possible to solve a triangle given

(i) the measurements of two sides and the contained angle of the triangle or (ii) the measurements of the three sides of the triangle.

Write solutions to the following questions. Compare your solutions with those on page 480. State angle measurements to the nearest degree and lengths to one decimal place:

1. Solve $\triangle ABC$, given $a = 4$, $b = 5$, $c = 6$, using the Cosine Law.

2. Solve $\triangle ABC$, given $a = 4.9$, $b = 8.2$, and $\angle C = 52°$, as follows:

    (i) Use the Cosine Law to calculate c .

    (ii) Use the Sine Law to calculate $\angle A$.

    (iii) Calculate $\angle B$.

Exercise 8-15

(A)

1. For each of the given triangles, state an expression for a in terms of the given parts:

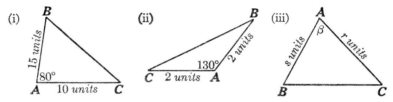

2. For each of the given triangles, state an expression for $\cos B$:

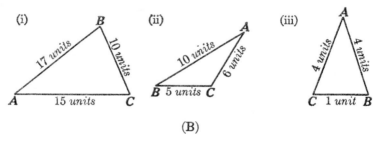

(B)

Solve each of the following triangles, stating angle measurements to the nearest degree and lengths to one decimal place:

3. $a = 3.0$, $b = 2.0$, $c = 2.5$

4. $b = 6.4$, $c = 4.8$, $\angle A = 62°$

5. $a = 32$, $c = 40$, $\angle B = 72°$

6. $a = 24$, $b = 22$, $c = 25$

7. Two ships sail from the same port; one sails NE for 60 miles; the other sails S 70° E for 42 miles. What is the bearing of the second ship from the first ship in these new positions?

8. The goal posts in a hockey rink are 6 feet apart. A boy scores a goal by shooting the puck along the ice from a point 30 feet from one post and 35 feet from the other. Within what angle does he make his shot?

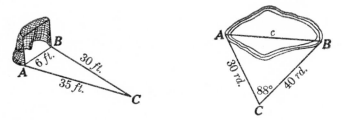

9. To find the length of a pond, the following measurements are made: $AC = 30$ rods, $BC = 40$ rods, and $\angle C = 88°$. Find the length of the pond to the nearest rod.

10. A parallelogram has sides 4 inches and 5 inches. The longer diagonal is 7 inches. Find the angles of the parallelogram.

8.19 Perpendicular projection (supplementary). In the following discussion, the word "projection" means *perpendicular projection*.

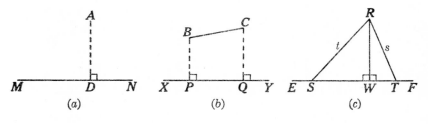

Fig. 8-43

In *Fig. 8-43 (a)*, D is the projection of A into MN.

In *Fig. 8-43 (b)*, PQ is the projection of BC into XY.

In *Fig. 8-43 (c)*, SW is the projection of SR into EF, and $SW = t \cos S$. WT is the projection of RT into EF, and $WT = s \cos T$.

8.20 Geometric interpretation of the Cosine Law (supplementary).

A relation among the sides of a right triangle is given by the Pythagorean Theorem, *Fig. 8-44 (a)*, while a relation among the sides of an oblique triangle is given by the Cosine Law, *Fig. 8-44 (b) (c)*.

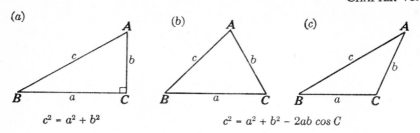

(a)   (b)   (c)

$c^2 = a^2 + b^2$ $c^2 = a^2 + b^2 - 2ab \cos C$

Fig. 8-44

It is seen that the Pythagorean Theorem is a special case of the Cosine Law.

In *Fig. 8-45*, AD is perpendicular to BC in $\triangle ABC$, and the length of CD is p units.

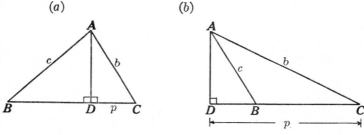

(a)   (b)

Fig. 8-45

∵ DC is the projection of AC into the line on BC,

∴ $p = b \cos C$.

Thus, $c^2 = a^2 + b^2 - 2ap$ (Cosine Law).

This relation is stated as follows:

In any triangle, the area of the square on the side opposite an acute angle is equal to the sum of the areas of the squares on the other two sides decreased by twice the area of the rectangle contained by one of these sides and the projection of the other side into the line on it.

A similar theorem can be stated for an obtuse triangle with the required side opposite the obtuse angle.

In *Fig. 8-46*, $AD \perp BC$, $CD = p$ units.

∵ CD is the projection of CA into the line on BC

∴ $p = b \cos \angle ACD$
   $= b \cos (\pi - C)$
   $= -b \cos C$.

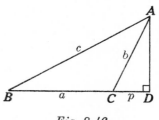

Fig. 8-46

Thus, $c^2 = a^2 + b^2 + 2ap$ (Cosine Law).

This relation is stated as follows:

In an obtuse triangle, the area of the square on the side opposite the obtuse angle is equal to the sum of the areas of the squares on the other two sides increased by twice the area of the rectangle contained by one of these sides and the projection of the other side into the line on it.

Write solutions to the following problems; compare them with those on page 480.

(a)   (b)

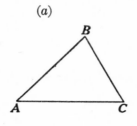

Fig. 8-47

1. (i) In *Fig. 8-47*, $\triangle ABC$ is an acute triangle, and $\triangle PQR$ is an obtuse triangle with $\angle P > 90°$. Describe the construction necessary to show:

      (a) the projection of AC into AB ;

      (b) the projection of PR into the line on QP .

   (ii) Using a projection relation, state:

      (a) an expression for b^2 in $\triangle ABC$;

      (b) an expression for p^2 in $\triangle PQR$.

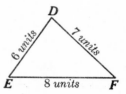

2. Find the length of the projection of EF into DF in acute triangle DEF (*Fig. 8-48*).

Fig. 8-48

Exercise 8-16

(A)

1. In the diagram at the right, what is the projection of:

   (i) AB into BC

  (ii) AB into BY

 (iii) BC into BA

 (iv) AB into AC

  (v) CO into CB

 (vi) CO into CA

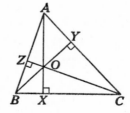

2. In each of the following diagrams, $\angle ACB$ is obtuse. Determine:
(i) AC^2 (ii) AB^2

(i)   (ii)

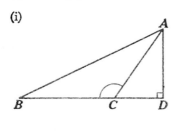

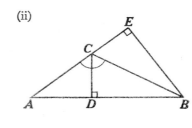

(B)

3. In each of the following diagrams, find AC to one decimal place:

(i)   (ii)   (iii)

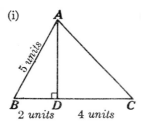

2 units   4 units

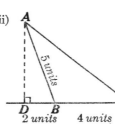

2 units   4 units

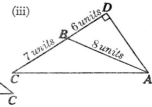

4. If the rafter of a spire makes an angle of 60° with the floor of the spire, prove that the projection of the rafter into the floor is half the rafter length.

5. In the equilateral $\triangle ABC$, $AD \perp BC$.
     Prove: (i) $AB = 2BD$
                    (ii) $AD = \sqrt{3}BD$
                    (iii) $AC^2 = 2BC \cdot DC$

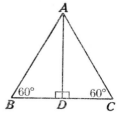

6. In $\triangle ABC$, $\angle B = 60°$, $c = 10$, $a = 8$. Find b.

7. In $\triangle ABC$, $\angle B = 120°$, $c = 16$, $a = 8$. Find b.

8. In $\triangle ABC$, $\angle B$ is acute, and X is on BC so that $AX \perp BC$. $AB = 16$ in., $BX = 10$ in., and $XC = 12$ in. Find AC to one decimal place.

9. AB, BC, CA of acute $\triangle ABC$ are 13 in., 21 in., 20 in., respectively. X is on BC so that $AX \perp BC$. Find XC and AX.

8·21 Problems in three dimensions (supplementary). The problems considered up to this point have all presented two-dimensional situations. The following problems involve three dimensions.

Discover how to solve problems in three dimensions by doing the following problems; compare your solutions with those on page 481.

1. In order to find the height of a hydro tower situated on the opposite side of a river, surveyors made measurements, as shown in *Fig. 8-50*. The plane ABD is horizontal, and the plane BDC is vertical. Calculate the height of the tower DC to the nearest foot.

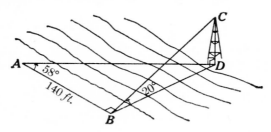

Fig. 8-50

  (i) By considering $\triangle ABD$ and using a relation involving tan 58°, calculate the length of BD.

  (ii) By considering $\triangle CBD$ and using the measurement of BD obtained in (i), calculate CD.

  (iii) Express the height of the tower to the nearest foot.

2. From a point P, due south of a skyscraper TR, the angle of elevation of the top T is 64°. From a point Q on the same street, due east of P, the angle of elevation of T is 50°. If PQ is on the same level as R, and $PQ = 500$ feet, find the height of the skyscraper.

  (i) Draw a diagram to represent the given information.

  (ii) Let x represent the height of the skyscraper in feet, $x \in {}^{+}R$. By considering $\triangle PRT$, write an expression for PR in terms of x.

  (iii) By considering $\triangle QRT$, write an expression for QR in terms of x.

  (iv) By considering $\triangle PRQ$, write the Pythagorean relation involving PR and QR.

  (v) Rewrite this relation in terms of x and solve the resulting equation.

  (vi) Express the height of the skyscraper to the nearest foot.

Exercise 8-17

(B)

In each of the following questions express lengths to the nearest foot and angle measurements to the nearest degree:

1. When an aircraft is directly above a control tower T, its angle of elevation from a point A due south of T is 64°. From another point B, which is 150 ft. due west of T, the angle of elevation of the aircraft at the same time is 61°. Find:
   (i) the height of the aircraft   (ii) the distance AT

2. A smokestack AB is 510 ft. high. From two points P and Q on the same level as its base B, the angles of elevation of A are 45° and 36°, respectively. If P is due south of B, and Q is due east of B, find PQ.

3. The angular elevation of a hill AB from a point C due south of the hill is 30°, and from a point D due west of the hill it is 20°. If $B, C,$ and D are on the same level and CD is 2,000 feet, find AB, the height of the hill.

4. A forest-ranger tower T is due north of P, a point at one end of a lake. Q, the other end of the lake, is due east of P. The angle of elevation of T is 25° at P and 15° at Q. T is 300 feet above the level of PQ. Find PQ.

5. To find the height DF of a hill, a surveyor makes the following measurements: from a point A, he finds the angle of elevation of the top of the hill to be 36°; he measures from A a horizontal distance AB so that $AB \perp AD$, and AB is 100 feet. He then finds the angle ABD is 71°. Find the height of the hill.

6. From a point W, due west of a transmitting tower BT, a surveyor finds the angle of elevation of the top of the tower T is 35°. From a second point S, 86 feet due south of W, he finds $\angle WSB$ is 48°. If W, S, and B are in the same horizontal plane, find the height of the tower.

7. A point K is 720 feet due east of a point L. A third point M, on the same horizontal level as K and L, bears N 54° W from K and N 36° E from L. A point D, vertically above M, has an angle of elevation of 14° at K. Find its angle of elevation at L.

(C)

8. On a rugby field the goal posts are 18′ 6″ apart. The horizontal cross-bar CD is 10′ from the ground. On the 5-yard line a point P is chosen centrally in front. Find $\angle CPD$.

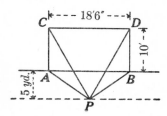
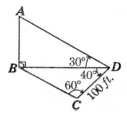

9. In the diagram at the lower right, page 298, B, C, D are on the same horizontal plane. AB is vertical. Find AB.

Review Exercise 8-18

(A)

1. State the six trigonometric ratios of each of the following angles:

(i)   (ii)

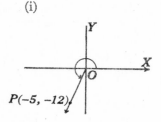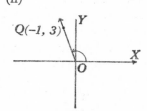

2. State the measurement of one positive angle and one negative angle which is coterminal with an angle of measurement:

   (i) $-150°$ (ii) $580°$ (iii) $-860°$ (iv) $5\frac{1}{2}\pi$

3. State one value of A which satisfies each of the following:

   (i) $\tan A° = 1$ (ii) $\sin A° = \dfrac{1}{\sqrt{2}}$ (iii) $\cos A° = \dfrac{\sqrt{3}}{2}$

   (iv) $\tan A° = \sqrt{3}$ (v) $\sin A° = 0$ (vi) $\cos A° = 0$

(B)

Determine each of the following:

4. $3 \sec 0° + 2 \tan 45° + 3 \cot 60°$

5. $\cot^2 30° \tan^2 45° + \sqrt{3} \csc 90° \cot 30°$

6. $\cos 0° \sin^2 45° - \cot 90° \sin 45°$ **7.** $2 \csc 90° - 3 \sin 0° - 1$

8. $\dfrac{\sin^2 60° \tan^2 0° + \cot^2 60°}{\frac{1}{3} + \sin 30° \sin 90°}$

9. Given that $\cos \alpha = -\frac{2}{3}$, find   (i) $\tan \alpha$ (ii) $\csc \alpha$.

Prove the following identities:

10. $(\csc^2 \theta - 1)(1 - \cos^2 \theta) = \cos^2 \theta$

11. $\dfrac{\sin^2 \alpha}{\cot^2 \alpha} = \tan^2 \alpha - \sin^2 \alpha$ **12.** $1 - 2 \sin^2 x = \cos^2 x - \sin^2 x$

13. $(1 + \tan^2 \theta) \cos^2 \theta = 1$ **14.** $\sec^2 \beta + \csc^2 \beta = \sec^2 \beta \csc^2 \beta$

In each of the following, state angle measurements to the nearest degree and lengths to the nearest whole number of units:

15. From the top of a tower 215 ft. high, a forest ranger sighted a fire. If the angle of depression of the fire was 17°, how far was the fire from the tower?

16. The navigator on a ship finds that the angle of elevation of the top of a lighthouse is 35°. The ship navigation chart shows that the lighthouse is 157 ft. above water level. If the measurement of the angle of elevation is made at a point 20 ft. above water level, how far is the ship from the lighthouse?

17. An overpass must clear a through highway by 40 feet. If the approaches to the overpass must have an elevation of 15°, find the length of the approach.

18. A pendulum 4.2 feet long swings through an angle of 18° on each side of the vertical. How high does the end of the pendulum rise above its lowest point? (Express your answer to one decimal place.)

Chapter IX

RELATIONS

9.1 A binary relation. In mathematics, the relations "is greater than", "is the square of", and "is the additive inverse of" apply between two numbers. For this reason they are called *binary relations*. Each relation determines a set of *ordered pairs* of numbers when applied on a given set of numbers. For example, three of the ordered pairs determined by the relation "is greater than" applied on the set of real numbers are:

$(2, 3)$,	$(9.2, 10.5)$,	$(-10.7, -3.5)$
since $3 > 2$,	$10.5 > 9.2$,	$-3.5 > -10.7$

Note that the number which is greater than the other is placed second in each ordered pair.

Example. Given $A = \{-2, -1, 0, 1, 2\}$, list the ordered pairs determined by each of the following relations applied on A:

(i) R_1: "is greater than"

(ii) R_2: "is the square of"

(iii) R_3: "is the additive inverse of"

(iv) R_4: "is equal to"

Solution. (i) $R_1 = \{(-2, -1), (-2, 0), (-2, 1), (-2, 2), (-1, 0)$
$(-1, 1), (-1, 2), (0, 1), (0, 2), (1, 2)\}$

(ii) $R_2 = \{(-1, 1), (0, 0), (1, 1)\}$

(iii) $R_3 = \{(-2, 2), (2, -2), (-1, 1), (1, -1), (0, 0)\}$

(iv) $R_4 = \{(-2, -2), (-1, -1), (0, 0), (1, 1), (2, 2)\}$

9.2 Ordered pairs in cross-products. A set of ordered pairs may be determined from any two sets or even a single set. For example, the two sets

$$A = \{2, 5\} \text{ and } B = \{-1, 1, 3\}$$

give rise to the set of ordered pairs with first elements taken from A and second elements from B, as follows:

The set of ordered pairs is $\{(2, -1), (2, 1), (2, 3), (5, -1), (5, 1), (5, 3)\}$. It is referred to as the *cross-product* of the two sets A and B and is designated $A \times B$, read, "A cross B", and consists of 2×3 or 6 ordered pairs.

$$A \times B = \{(x, y) \mid x \in A, y \in B\}$$
$$= \{(2, -1), (2, 1), (2, 3), (5, -1), (5, 1), (5, 3)\}$$
$$B \times A = \{(x, y) \mid x \in B, y \in A\}$$
$$= \{(-1, 2), (-1, 5), (1, 2), (1, 5), (3, 2), (3, 5)\}$$

may also be formed from the two sets. It also contains 3×2 or 6 ordered pairs.

The cross-product $A \times A$ may be formed from a single set A. For example:

$$A \times A = \{(x, y) \mid x \in A, y \in A\}$$
$$= \{(2, 2), (2, 5), (5, 2), (5, 5)\}$$

In this case, $A \times A$ consists of 2×2 or 2^2 ordered pairs.

9.3 Graphs of ordered pairs and cross-products. Since the fundamental assumption of coordinate (Cartesian) geometry is "there is a one-to-one correspondence between the set of all points in a plane and the ordered pairs of real numbers", the ordered pairs of relations and cross-products may be pictured as points in a plane. The method is indicated in the following examples. It is interesting to note that cross-products are often referred to as *Cartesian products* in deference to the French mathematician René Descartes (1596-1650) who established the foundation for coordinate geometry.

Example 1. If $A = \{-3, 2, 4\}$, determine $A \times A$ and draw its graph.

Solution. $A \times A = \{(-3, -3), (-3, 2), (-3, 4), (2, -3), (2, 2),$
$$(2, 4), (4, -3), (4, 2), (4, 4)\}$$

The graph is shown in *Fig. 9-1.*

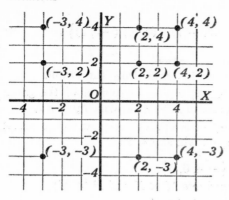

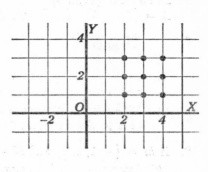

Fig. 9-1   Fig. 9-2

Example 2. If $A = \{2, 3, 4\}$ and $B = \{1, 2, 3\}$, determine $A \times B$ and draw its graph.

Solution. $A \times B = \{(2, 1), (2, 2), (2, 3), (3, 1), (3, 2), (3, 3), (4, 1), (4, 2), (4, 3)\}$

The graph is shown in *Fig. 9-2*.

Exercise 9-1

(B)

1. Given the set $A = \{-2, 0, 2, 4, 6, 8\}$, list the set of ordered pairs determined by each of the following relations on A:

   (i) R_1: "is three times"   (ii) R_2: "is equal to"

   (iii) R_3: "is the square of"   (iv) R_4: "is two more than"

   (v) R_5 "is greater than"   (vi) R_6: "is the square root of"

2. Given the set $B = \left\{\frac{1}{1}, \frac{1}{2}, \frac{1}{3}, \frac{3}{5}, \frac{7}{8}, \frac{5}{3}, \frac{3}{1}\right\}$, list the ordered pairs determined by each of the following relations on B:

   (i) B_1: "is less than"   (ii) B_2: "is greater than"

   (iii) B_3: "is the reciprocal of"   (iv) B_4: "is more than twice as great as"

3. $A = \{0, 2, 4, 6, 8\}$, $B = \{1, 3, 5, 9\}$

   (i) How many ordered pairs are there in $A \times B$? in $B \times A$? in $A \times A$?

   (ii) List the first elements in the ordered pairs of $A \times B$; of $B \times A$.

   (iii) How many ordered pairs of $A \times B$ have 6 as the first element?

4. List $\{(m, n) \mid m, n \in P\}$ where $P = \{-2, 0, 2\}$.

5. Draw the graph of

$A = \{(-3, 2),\ (4, 6),\ (0, 1),\ (5, -7),\ (3, 0),\ (-6, 2)\}$.

6. $A = \{1, 2, 3, 4\}$

  (i) List the ordered pairs of $A \times A$ and draw the graph.

  (ii) If $A \times A = \{(x, y) \,|\, x, y \in A\}$, circle the points of the graph which correspond to the subset of $A \times A$ for which $y = x$.

  (iii) Where in the graph are the points which correspond to the subset of $A \times A$ for which $y > x$; for which $y < x$?

7. If $M = \{-1, 1, 3\}$ and $N = \{-4, 0, 5\}$,

  (i) determine the Cartesian products $M \times N$ and $N \times M$;

  (ii) draw the graphs of $M \times N$ and $N \times M$.

8. If $D = \{-2, 0, 2, 4\}$,

  (i) list the ordered pairs of $D \times D = \{(x, y) \,|\, x, y \in D\}$;

  (ii) select the subset $D_1 = \{(x, y) \,|\, y = x\}$ and draw its graph;

  (iii) select the subset $D_2 = \{(x, y) \,|\, y > x\}$ and draw its graph;

  (iv) select the subset $D_3 = \{(x, y) \,|\, y < x\}$ and draw its graph.

9·4 Relations in $U \times U$. If with each element of set A there is associated an element of set B, then this association is called a *relation* from A to B in $A \times B$. Since the association determines a set of ordered pairs, a relation in $A \times B$ determines a subset of $A \times B$. Also, a relation in $A \times A$ determines a subset of $A \times A$.

A relation P in $U \times U$ involves:

(i) a universal set U on which the relation is applied;

(ii) a defining sentence (rule of correspondence or association);

(iii) a set of ordered pairs determined by the defining sentence.

The relation P "is less than" applied on set U is conveniently expressed

$$P = \{(x, y) \,|\, y < x, x, y \in U\}$$

which indicates that the relation P:

(i) is applied on U;

(ii) has the defining sentence $y < x$, $x, y \in U$;

(iii) determines a set of ordered pairs (x, y) which is a subset of $U \times U$.

The *domain of a relation* is the set of all *first* members of the ordered pairs of the relation.

The *range of a relation* is the set of all *second* members of the ordered pairs of the relation.

Example. Determine the ordered pairs of the following relation and state its domain and range:

$R = \{(x, y) | y = 2x, x, y \in U\}$, where $U = \{-2, -1, 0, 1, 2, 4\}$

Solution. The *defining sentence* of this relation is $y = 2x$, x, $y \in U$. The relation is an equality relation defined on U and determines a subset of $U \times U$. Both x and y must be elements of U.

Thus, $R = \{(-1, -2), (0, 0), (1, 2), (2, 4)\}$.

The domain of R is $\{-1, 0, 1, 2\}$.

The range of R is $\{-2, 0, 2, 4\}$.

9·5 Relations and their graphs.

Example 1. Draw the graph of the relation

$$P_1 = \{(x, y) | y = x + 2, x, y \in I\} .$$

Solution. $P_1 = \{(x, y) | y = x + 2, x, y \in I\}$

For P_1 :

x	-3	-2	-1	0	1	2
y	-1	0	$+1$	$+2$	$+3$	$+4$

The partial graph of P_1 is shown in *Fig. 9-3*.

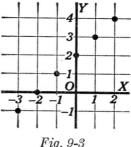

Domain is $\{x | x \in I\}$.

Range is $\{y | y \in I\}$.

Fig. 9-3

DISCUSSION. This is an equality relation defined in $I \times I$. Both x and y must be selected from I. Since I is an infinite set, the relation determines an infinite set of ordered pairs. The graph consists of an infinite number of points. To obtain the *partial graph* of P_1, we arbitrarily select a convenient number of replacements for x from the set I, construct the corresponding table of values, and plot the corresponding points; these points are a partial graph of P_1. The complete graph cannot be drawn. The partial graph implies that the complete graph is an extension of this graph in the directions indicated by the plotted points.

The table does not state the domain and range, nor does it list all the ordered pairs. The domain and range are inferred from the nature of the graph or by the following argument.

Since $y = x + 2$, y is an integer for all replacements of x from I; $\therefore$ the domain is $\{x | x \in I\}$. Since $x = y - 2$, x is an integer for all replacements of y from I; $\therefore$ the range is $\{y | y \in I\}$.

Example 2. Draw the graph of the relation
$$P_2 = \{(x, y)|y = x + 2, x, y \in R\} .$$

Solution. $P_2 = \{(x, y)|y = x + 2, x, y \in R\}$

For P_2:

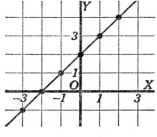

x	-3	-2	-1	0	1	2
y	-1	0	1	2	3	4

Domain is $\{x \mid x \in R\}$.

Range is $\{y \mid y \in R\}$.

Fig. 9-4

DISCUSSION. Since the replacement set for x and y is an infinite set, the relation determines an infinite number of ordered pairs, and the graph is an infinite number of points. To obtain the graph, arbitrarily select a convenient number of replacements for x from R and construct the corresponding table of values. Plot the corresponding points. Since all real replacements for x determine a corresponding real number for y, it is a reasonable assumption that the graph is the continuous line or smooth curve drawn through the plotted points. Since these lie in a straight line, we say the graph is the straight line determined by these points.

Exercise 9-2

(B)

In each of the following, list the ordered pairs determined by the relation and state its domain and range. $U = \{-1, 0, 1, 2, 3, 4\}$ *and* (x, y) *belongs to* $U \times U$.

1. $A = \{(x, y)|y = x\}$ **2.** $B = \{(x, y)|y = 2x\}$

3. $C = \{(x, y)|x < 2y\}$ **4.** $D = \{(x, y)|y = 4\}$

5. $E = \{(x, y)|y = x + 1\}$ **6.** $F = \{(x, y)|x = -1\}$

In each of the following, list four ordered pairs determined by the relation and state its domain and range, if $x, y \in I$:

7. $M = \{(x, y)|x = -3\}$ **8.** $N = \{(x, y)|y = 2\}$

9. $P = \{(x, y)|y = x - 1, 0 < x < 10\}$ **10.** $V = \{(x, y)|x = y^2\}$

11. $Q = \{(x, y)|y = 2|x|, -4 < x < 3\}$

12. $R = \{(x, y)|3x + 2y = 6\}$

13. $S = \{(x, y)|y = 0\}$ **14.** $T = \{(x, y)|x = 0\}$

Draw the graph of each of the following relations; state the domain and range:

15. $A = \{(x, y)|x = 4, x, y \in I\}$ **16.** $B = \{(x, y)|y = 3, x, y \in R\}$

17. $C = \{(x, y)|y = x, x, y \in I\}$ **18.** $D = \{(x, y)|y = x + 1, x, y \in R\}$

19. $E = \{(x, y)|x + y = 2, x, y \in I\}$

20. $F = \{(x, y)|x + 2y = 3, x, y \in R\}$

21. $G = \{(x, y)|x = 3y - 2, 0 \leq x \leq 8, x \in R\}$

22. $H = \{(x, y)|3x - 2y = 6, x, y \in R\}$

23. $J = \{(x, y)|2x + 5y = 10, x, y \in R\}$

9·6 Linear relations. It has been observed that relations whose defining sentences are equations of the first degree in two variables, for example $2x - 3y = 6$, $x, y \in R$, appear to have graphs which are straight lines. We assume that this is true. Such relations are referred to as *linear relations*. Other relations, defined by inequations of the first degree in two variables, are also referred to as linear relations; the inequation is referred to as a *linear inequation*. Examples of inequality relations are discussed in section 9·8.

9·7 The x- and y-intercepts of a graph. The graph of the linear relation, $F = \{(x, y)|2x - 3y = 6, x, y \in R\}$, is illustrated in *Fig. 9-5*.

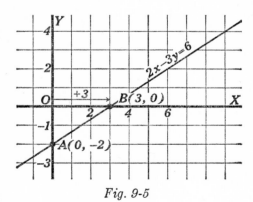

Fig. 9-5

The graph crosses the x-axis at the point B (3, 0). This point is a directed distance, $+ 3$, from the origin. The graph crosses the y-axis at the point $A(0, - 2)$. This point is a directed distance, $- 2$, from the origin. These directed distances are called the *x-intercept* and the *y-intercept*, respectively, of the graph. The points $B(3, 0)$ and $A(0,- 2)$ are the points of intersection of the graph with the x- and y- axis, respectively.

To determine the x-intercept, let $y = 0$ in the defining sentence of the relation.

Thus, in this example, if $y = 0$, then $2x = 6$
$$\therefore x = 3$$
$$\therefore \text{ the } x\text{-intercept is } 3.$$
Similarly, if $x = 0$, then $-3y = 6$
$$\therefore y = -2$$
$$\therefore \text{ the } y\text{-intercept is } -2.$$

The position of a straight line graph may be determined by finding its x- and y-intercepts, provided the line does not pass through the origin.

9.8 Relations defined by inequations and their graphs. The graph of the linear relation $A = \{(x, y)|y = x, x, y \in R\}$ is shown in *Fig. 9-6*. All the points with abscissa 2 lie on the line parallel to the y-axis and through the point with coordinates $(2, 0)$. For the point with coordinates $(2, 2), y = x$. For all other points vertically above this point, $y > x$, and for all points vertically below this point, $y < x$.

Thus:

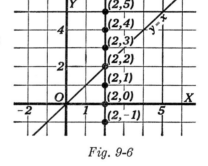

(i) for any point *on* the line, $y = x$;

(ii) for any point *above* the line, $y > x$;

(iii) for any point *below* the line, $y < x$.

The set of points of the line is the graph of the relation,
$$A = \{(x, y)|y = x, x, y \in R\}.$$

The set of points of the half-plane above the line is the graph of the relation,

Fig. 9-6

$$B = \{(x, y)|y > x, x, y \in R\}.$$

The set of points of the half-plane below the line is the graph of the relation,
$$C = \{(x, y)|y < x, x, y \in R\}.$$

Example 1. Draw the graph of the relation
$$A = \{(x, y)|3x + y \leqq 3, x, y \in R\}.$$

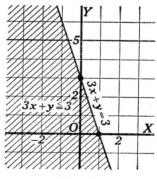

Solution. The graph of the relation defined by $3x + y = 3$ has x-intercept 1 and y-intercept 3. The graph of A consists of:

(i) all the points on the line defined by the equation $3x + y = 3$, and

(ii) all the points below this line.

The graph of A is shown in *Fig. 9-7*.

Fig. 9-7

Example 2. Draw the graph of the relation
$$B = \{(x, y)|x - 2y < 4, x, y \in I\},$$
and state its domain and range.

Solution. Since $x, y \in I$, the graph of B is the set of *lattice points* in the region above the line whose equation is $x - 2y = 4$, $x, y \in R$.

The x-intercept of the line is 4; the y-intercept of the line is -2. The graph of B is shown in *Fig. 9-8*.

The domain is $\{x \,|\, x \in I\}$; the range is $\{y \,|\, y \in I\}$.

The line is indicated by a broken line since the points on it are not included in the graph.

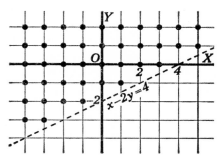

Fig. 9-8

Exercise 9-3

(Unless otherwise stated, the variables represent real numbers.)

(B)

Draw the graphs of each of the following relations:

1. $A = \{(x, y)|y > x\}$ 2. $B = \{(x, y)|y < 2x, x, y \in I\}$
3. $C = \{(p, q)|p + q > 1\}$ 4. $D = \{(a, b)|b \leqq 2a - 1, a, b \in I\}$
5. $E = \{(r, s)|3r + 2s \geqq 6\}$ 6. $F = \{(x, y)|x - 3y \leqq 5\}$
7. $G = \{(x, y)|y \leqq 2x + 1, -2 \leqq x \leqq +3\}$
8. $H = \{(z, y)|z + 3y < 7, z < 3\}$
9. $K = \{(x, y)|x \leqq 3 \text{ and } y \geqq 1\}$

(C)

10.   (i) Draw the graph of the relation
$$P_1 = \{(x, y)|y = x^2, x, y \in I, -3 \leqq x \leqq +3\}.$$
    (ii) From this graph, obtain the graph of
$$P = \{(x, y)|y = x^2, x, y \in R\}.$$
    (iii) Shade, in horizontal lines, the graph of
$$P_2 = \{(x, y)|y > x^2, x, y \in R\}.$$
    (iv) Shade, in vertical lines, the graph of
$$P_3 = \{(x, y)|y < x^2, x, y \in R\}.$$
The graph of P is called a *parabola*.

9·9 Discovery of the concept of a function (supplementary).

Write solutions for the following problems and compare your solutions with those on page 481.

1. For the relation
$$R_1 = \{(x, y) \mid y = 2x - 1, -1 \leq x \leq 2, x, y \in I\}:$$
   (i) List the ordered pairs determined by R_1.
   (ii) State the domain and range of R_1.
   (iii) How many elements of the range correspond to each element of the domain?
   (iv) Draw the graph of the relation.
   (v) If a line drawn parallel to the y-axis intersects the graph, in how many points does it do so?

2. For the relation
$$R_2 = \{(x, y) \mid y^2 = 4x, x \leq 4, x, y \in I\}:$$
   (i) List the ordered pairs determined by the relation.
   (ii) State the domain and range of R_2.
   (iii) What elements of the range correspond to the number 1 of the domain?
   (iv) How many elements of the range correspond to each element of the domain?
   (v) Draw the graph of R_2.
   (vi) If a line drawn parallel to the y-axis intersects the graph, in how many points does it do so?

3. For the relation
$$R_3 = \{(x, y) \mid y = x^2 - 2, |x| \leq 3, x, y \in R\}:$$
   (i) List six ordered pairs determined by the relation.
   (ii) Determine the intercepts of the graph.
   (iii) Plot the points corresponding to the ordered pairs and the intercepts.
   (iv) Draw a smooth curve through the points.
   (v) From the graph, state the domain and range of the relation.
   (vi) From the graph, determine whether there is a unique element of the range for each element of the domain.
   (vii) If a line drawn parallel to the y-axis intersects the graph, in how many points does it do so?

4. For the relation
$$R_4 = \{(x, y) \mid x = 2, |y| \leq 4, x, y \in I\}:$$
   (i) List the ordered pairs determined by the relation.
   (ii) State the domain and range of the relation.
   (iii) How many elements of the range correspond to the element 2 of the domain?

(iv) If a line drawn parallel to the *y*-axis intersects the graph, in how many points does it do so?

5. A relation in which each element of the domain is associated with one and only one element of the range is called a *function*.

(i) Which of the relations R_1, R_2, R_3, and R_4 in problems 1 to 4 are functions?

(ii) If a line drawn parallel to the *y*-axis intersects the graph of a function, in how many points does it do so?

DEFINITION: *A function on a set A is a relation on A such that for every element of the domain there corresponds a unique element of the range.*

Exercise 9-4

(A)

State which of the following are graphs of functions:

1.
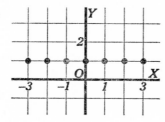

2.
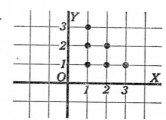

3.
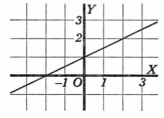

4.
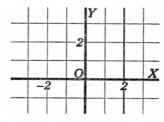

5.
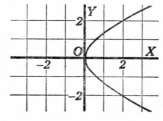

6.
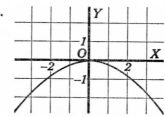

7.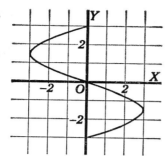

8.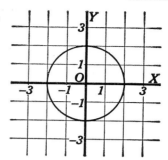

State which of the following relations are functions:

9. $S = \{(p, q) \mid q = 5p - 7, p, q \in R\}$

10. $M = \{(x, y) \mid x^2 = -5y, x, y \in I\}$

11. $K = \{(x, y) \mid y^2 = -5x, x, y \in R\}$

12. $R = \{(x, y) \mid y = 4, x, y \in R\}$

13. $U = \{(m, n) \mid m > n, m, n \in I\}$

14. $N = \{(t, s) \mid s = 10t + 15t^2, t \geqq 0, t, s \in R\}$

15. $C = \{(x, y) \mid x^2 + y^2 = 9, x, y \in I\}$

16. $H = \{(x, y) \mid x^2 - y^2 = 16, x, y \in R\}$

17. $Q = \{(1, 1), (2, 2), (3, 3), (4, 4)\}$

18. $G = \{(-8, 4), (-4, 1), (0, 0), (4, 1), (8, 4)\}$

(B)

19. Draw the graph of the function
$$F = \{(x, y) \mid 2y = 5x - 3, \quad -1 \leqq x \leqq 1, x, y \in I\}.$$

20. List the elements of $F = \{(x, y) \mid y = x^2 + 1, \quad |x| \leqq 2, x, y \in I\}$ and draw its graph.

21. Write an algebraic sentence in x and y which defines the function
$$\{(-2, -1), (-1, 0), (0, 1), (1, 2)\}.$$

22. For the function
$$\{(-3, 9), (-2, 4), (-1, 1), (0, 0), (1, 1), (2, 4), (3, 9)\}:$$
   (i) State the domain and range.
   (ii) Write a defining sentence.

23. A set of rectangles is such that each has a width of 5 units. The lengths vary and are represented by x units, where $x \in R$. The largest rectangle has a length of 25 units.
   (i) Define the relation between the area of the rectangles (y) and the given units.
   (ii) Determine whether the relation is a function.
   (iii) State the domain and range of the relation.

24.   (i) Define the relation between the area of a circle A and its radius r.

     (ii) State the domain and range of this relation.

     (iii) Determine whether the relation is a function.

25. A jet-plane has an average speed of 600 miles per hour. It can carry sufficient fuel for a 6-hour run.

     (i) Define the relation between distance (in miles) and time (in hours) for this plane.

     (ii) State the domain and range of the relation.

     (iii) Is this relation a function?

26. A boy takes a job for eight weeks during the summer. He opens an account in the bank and deposits $25 a week.

     (i) Define the relation between his total deposit d in dollars and the numbers of weeks worked n.

     (ii) State the domain and range of the relation.

     (iii) Is the relation a function?

9·10 Relations involving the intersection and union of sets.

Example 1. Draw the graph of the relation
$$M = \{(x, y) | y = 2x \text{ and } y = x + 1, x, y \in R\} .$$

Solution. The defining sentence $y = 2x$ and $y = x + 1$, $x, y \in R$ is a compound sentence which determines the ordered pairs which belong to both the relations

$$M_1 = \{(x, y) | y = 2x, x, y \in R\} \text{ and } M_2 = \{(x, y) | y = x + 1, x, y \in R\} .$$

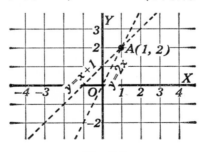

Fig. 9-9

Hence, $M = M_1 \cap M_2$, the intersection set of M_1 and M_2. Thus, M may be determined by drawing the graphs of M_1 and M_2 (in broken lines, *Fig. 9-9*). These two lines determine the point A with coordinates $(1, 2)$.
$\therefore M = \{(1, 2)\}$, and its graph is the corresponding point A. The domain of M is $\{1\}$, and the range is $\{2\}$.

Example 2. Draw the graph of the relation
$$P = \{(x, y)|y = 2x \text{ or } y = x + 1, x, y \in R\} .$$

Solution. The defining sentence $y = 2x$ or $y = x + 1$, $x, y \in R$ is a compound sentence which determines the ordered pairs which belong to at least one of the relations

$M_1 = \{(x, y)|y = 2x, x, y \in R\}$ and
$M_2 = \{(x, y)|y = x + 1, x, y \in R\}$.

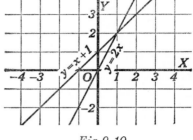

Fig 9-10

Hence $P = M_1 \cup M_2$, the union set of M_1 and M_2. Thus, P is the set of all points on the two lines in *Fig. 9-10*. The domain of P is $\{x|x \in R\}$, and the range is $\{y|y \in R\}$.

Exercise 9-5

(A)

Classify each of the following as an intersection or a union of two relations and state these two relations:

1. $A = \{(x, y)|x + y = 8 \text{ and } x - y = 2\}$
2. $B = \{(x, y)|x = 2y \text{ or } 2x = y\}$
3. $C = \{(a, b)|2a + 3b = 6 \text{ and } a - 3b = 3\}$
4. $D = \{(p, q)|5p + 2q = 11 \text{ or } 3p + 4q = 1\}$

(B)

5. Determine graphically the ordered pairs of the relations in questions 1 to 4. Where possible, list the ordered pairs of the relations. State the domain and range in each case.

Find graphically:

6. $\{(x, y)|2x + y = 8 \text{ and } x + y = 5\}$
7. $\{(x, y)|2x + 3y = 13\} \cup \{(x, y)|2x + y = 7\}$
8. $\{(x, y)|2x + 3y = 7\} \cap \{(x, y)|x + 2y = 4\}$
9. $\{(x, y)|x + 2y = 6 \text{ or } x = 2\}$

9·11 **Linear relations in Physics (supplementary).** Many laws in Physics express a relation between two or more variables. For example, the relation among potential difference, current strength, and resistance in an electrical circuit is expressed by the equation,

$$V = IR$$

>where the potential difference is V volts,
>the current strength is I amperes,
>and the resistance is R ohms.

Example 1. (i) Draw a graph relating potential difference and current strength for an electrical circuit with a resistance of 25 ohms, if the current strength varies from 0 to 6 amperes.

(ii) From the graph, find (a) the potential difference for a current strength of 3.4 amperes (b) the current strength for a potential difference of 130 volts.

Solution. (i) Since the resistance is 25 ohms, the relation involving potential difference and current strength is

$$P = \{(I, V) \mid V = 25I, 0 \leq I \leq 6, I, V \in R\}.$$

The defining sentence of the relation contains a first degree equation in the variables I and V, $(V = 25I)$, and therefore the graph is a line segment.

For this relation:

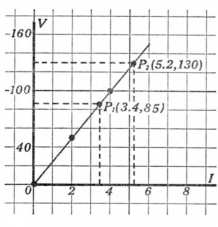

I	0	2	4
V	0	50	100

The graph, shown in *Fig. 9-11*, lies in the first quadrant, since I and V are always positive or zero.

(ii) From the graph:

(a) The potential difference for a current strength of 3.4 amperes is 85 volts (ordinate of P_1).

(b) The current strength for a potential difference of 130 volts is 5.2 amperes (abscissa of P_2).

Fig. 9-11

The process of estimating a value of the range of a relation for a given value of the domain, or vice-versa, by a procedure other than using the defining sentence (using a graph, for example) is called *interpolation*. The result obtained is approximate.

If d represents the distance in miles, v the average speed in miles per hour, and t the time in hours, then the relation among distance, speed, and time for a moving object is expressed by the equation,

$$d = vt.$$

It should be noted that this relation holds for any units of distance and time, provided the speed is expressed in a consistent unit.

Example 2. Two cars A and B start at the same time, on the same road, in the same direction. Car B starts 30 miles ahead of car A. Car A travels at 60 m.p.h., and car B travels at 50 m.p.h.

With reference to the same set of axes, draw a graph relating time and distance for each car. From the graph find (i) the time taken for car A to overtake car B (ii) the distance between the cars after 2 hours (iii) the distance between the cars after 5 hours.

Solution. The relation between time and distance for car A is

$$g_1 = \{(t, d) \mid d = 60t, t, d \geq 0, t, d \in R\}.$$

Since car B starts 30 miles ahead of car A, the distance-time relation for car B is

$$g_2 = \{(t, d) \mid d = 30 + 50t, t, d \geq 0, t, d \in R\}.$$

For car A:

t	0	2	4
d	0	120	240

For car B:

t	0	2	4
d	30	130	230

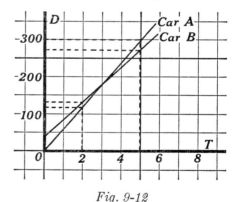

Fig. 9-12

The graph, shown in *Fig. 9-12*, is often referred to as a *distance-time graph.*

(i) Since the coordinates of the point of intersection are (3, 180), car A will overtake car B in 3 hours.

(ii) From the graph, by interpolation, car A has travelled 120 miles in 2 hours, and car B has travelled 130 miles in the same time. Thus, the distance between the cars at the end of two hours is (130 − 120) miles, or 10 miles.

(iii) From the graph, car A has travelled 300 miles in 5 hours, while car B has travelled 280 miles in the same time. Thus, the distance between the cars after 5 hours is (300 − 280) miles, or 20 miles.

In this case, each of the ordinates obtained (300 and 280) is greater than those used in obtaining the table of values. However, the graph can be extended indefinitely in the first quadrant, because the domain and range of the relation have no upper bound. The procedure for finding coordinates of points on this extended part is called *extrapolation*.

Example 3. The following graphs, *Fig. 9-13* (a) and (b), represent the distance-time relations of two racing cars. Using set-builder notation, write a sentence which defines the relation in each case.

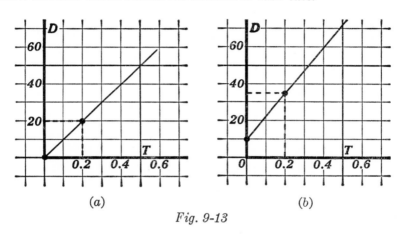

(a)   (b)

Fig. 9-13

Solution. (i) Because the origin lies on the graph, *Fig. 9-13* (a), and the graph is a straight line segment, the defining sentence contains an equation of the form $d = vt$.

Because the point with coordinates (.20, 20) lies on the graph:
$$20 = v(.20)$$
$$\therefore \ 100 = v$$
$\therefore$ the defining sentence is $d = 100t,\ t, d \geqq 0,\ t, d \in R$.

The graph is the graph of the relation
$$H = \{(t, d) | d = 100t,\ t, d \geqq 0,\ t, d \in R\}\ .$$

(ii) Because the point with coordinates (0, 10) lies on the graph, *Fig. 9-13* (b), and the graph is a line segment, the defining sentence contains an equation of the form $d = vt + 10$.

Because the point with coordinates (.20, 35) lies on the graph:
$$35 = v(.20) + 10$$
$$\therefore \ \ 25 = .20v$$
$$\therefore \ 125 = v$$

∴ the defining sentence is $d = 125t + 10$, $t, d \geqq 0$, $t, d \in R$.

The graph is the graph of the relation

$$F = \{(t, d) | d = 125t + 10,\ t, d \geqq 0,\ t, d \in R\} .$$

Example 4. From a standing start, a car can attain a speed of 60 m.p.h. in 20 seconds.

(i) Calculate the acceleration, assuming it to be uniform.

(ii) Draw a speed-time graph and define the relation using set-builder notation. Consider only the first 20 seconds.

Solution. (i) Because the car attains a speed of 60 m.p.h. in 20 seconds, then the car would attain a speed of 3 m.p.h. in 1 second. Thus, the acceleration is 3 m.p.h. each second.

(ii) For this relation:

t	0	1	2	3	5	10	20
d	0	3	6	9	15	30	60

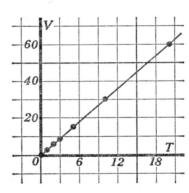

Fig. 9-14

Because the graph is a line segment on the origin, the defining sentence contains the equation

$$v = at$$

where the acceleration is a m.p.h. each second,

the speed is v m.p.h.,

and the time is t sec.

In part (i), the acceleration was found to be 3 m.p.h. each second. Thus, the relation can be written

$$G = \{(t, v) | v = 3t,\ 0 \leqq t \leqq 20,\ t, v \in R\} .$$

Exercise 9-6

(B)

1. Using the equation $V = IR$, draw a graph relating potential difference and resistance for a circuit in which the current strength is always 8.2 amperes, and the resistance varies from 1 ohm to 10 ohms.

2. (i) Draw a graph relating the variables T and V, where $V = 1089 + 2T$. The speed of sound in air is V feet per second, the air temperature is T degrees centigrade, and the air temperature varies from 0°C to 60°C.

   (ii) From the graph, find:
   (a) the speed of sound in air for an air temperature of 26°C;
   (b) the air temperature necessary for the speed of sound to be 1,100 feet per second.

3. (i) Draw a graph relating temperature readings in degrees Fahrenheit (F) with the corresponding readings in degrees centigrade (C), where $C = \frac{5}{9}(F - 32)$ and F varies from -50 to $+100$.

   (ii) From the graph, find:
   (a) the temperature in degrees Fahrenheit equivalent to $+15°C$;
   (b) the temperature in degrees centigrade equivalent to $10°F$;
   (c) the temperature at which the centigrade and Fahrenheit readings are the same.

4. For a sound wave, $V = n\lambda$, where the velocity of the sound wave is V cm. per second, the frequency in vibrations per second is n, and the wave-length is λ cm. Draw a graph relating wave-length and velocity for a sound wave of frequency 256 vibrations per second, wave-lengths varying from 100 cm. to 150 cm.

5. The following graphs represent the speed-time relations of two moving objects. Using set-builder notation, write a sentence which defines the relation in each case.

(i)
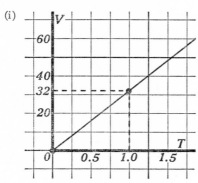

(ii)
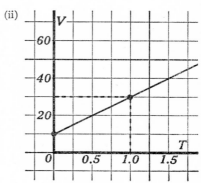

6. Two cars A and B pass the same point at the same time travelling in the same direction. Car A is travelling at a constant rate of 40 m.p.h.; car B is travelling at 10 m.p.h. as it passes the point and accelerates 5 m.p.h. each second thereafter.

    (i) From a speed-time graph, find how much time it takes for car B to overtake car A.

    (ii) Using set-builder notation, write sentences defining the speed-time relation for each car.

9.12 Relations involving the intersection and union of sets defined by inequations.

Example 1. Graph the relations and state the domain and range of each:

(i) $A = \{(x, y) \mid y > 3 - x \text{ and } y > 2x + 2\}$

(ii) $B = \{(x, y) \mid y > 3 - x \text{ or } y > 2x + 2\}$

Solution. (i) Let $A_1 = \{(x, y) \mid y > 3 - x\}$ and $A_2 = \{(x, y) \mid y > 2x + 2\}$.

For A_1 consider $y = 3 - x$. The x-intercept of the graph is 3; the y-intercept of the graph is 3.

For A_2 consider $y = 2x + 2$. The x-intercept of the graph is -1; the y-intercept of the graph is 2.

The graph of A_1 is the set of all the points in the region above the line defined by $y = 3 - x$ in *Fig. 9-15*.

The graph of A_2 is the set of all the points in the region above the line defined by $y = 2x + 2$ in *Fig. 9-15*.

Since $A = A_1 \cap A_2$, the graph of A is the set of points common to the two regions, *Fig. 9-15*.

The intersection point of the graphs of $y = 3 - x$ and $y = 2x + 2$ has coordinates $(\frac{1}{3}, 2\frac{2}{3})$. This point is not on the graph of A.

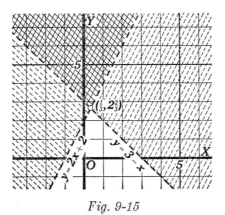

Fig. 9-15   *Fig. 9-16*

The domain of A is $\{x \,|\, x \in R\}$; the range of A is $\{y \,|\, y > 2\frac{2}{3},\, y \in R\}$.
(ii) Since $B = A_1 \cup A_2$, the union of A_1 and A_2, therefore the graph of B is the set of all the points in the region marked with solid lines in *Fig. 9-16.* Note again that the point with coordinates $(\frac{1}{3}, 2\frac{2}{3})$ is not an element of B. The domain of B is $\{x \,|\, x \in R\}$; the range of B is $\{y \,|\, y \in R\}$.

Example 2. Using intersection or union of sets, define the relations for which the following are the graphs:

(i)   (ii)

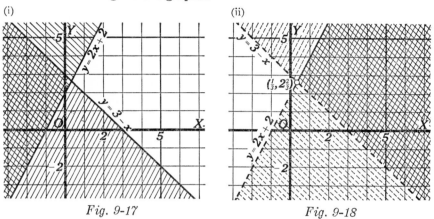

Fig. 9-17   Fig. 9-18

Solution. (i) The graph includes all the points in the region above the line whose equation is $y = 2x + 2$, together with all the points on the line. These points are the graph of the relation
$$C_1 = \{(x, y) \,|\, y \geq 2x + 2\}.$$
The graph also includes all the points in the region below the line whose equation is $y = 3 - x$, together with all the points on the line. These points are the graph of the relation
$$C_2 = \{(x, y) \,|\, y \leq 3 - x\}.$$
Therefore, the complete graph is the graph of the relation $C = C_1 \cup C_2$, or
$$C = \{(x, y) \,|\, y \geq 2x + 2 \text{ or } y \leq 3 - x\}.$$
The domain of C is $\{x \,|\, x \in R\}$; the range is $\{y \,|\, y \in R\}$.

(ii) The graph includes only those points on the line whose equation is $y = 2x + 2$ and in the region below this line which are also in the region above the line whose equation is $y = 3 - x$.

Thus, the required relation D is the intersection of the two relations D_1 and D_2, where
$$D_1 = \{(x, y) \,|\, y \leq 2x + 2\},\ D_2 = \{(x, y) \,|\, y > 3 - x\}.$$
Thus, $D = \{(x, y) \,|\, y \leq 2x + 2 \text{ and } y > 3 - x\}$.
The point whose coordinates are $(\frac{1}{3}, 2\frac{2}{3})$ is not included in the graph.
The domain of D is $\{x \,|\, x > \frac{1}{3},\, x \in R\}$; the range of D is $\{y \,|\, y \in R\}$.

Exercise 9-7

(B)

Graph the following relations; state the domain and range of each:

1. $A = \{(x, y)|2x - y \geq 0 \text{ or } x + 2y \geq 5\}$
2. $B = \{(x, y)|2x - y < 0 \text{ and } x + 2y \geq 5\}$
3. $C = \{(x, y)|2x + y = 0 \text{ and } x + 2y \leq 5\}$
4. $D = \{(x, y)|2x + y \geq 0 \text{ and } x + 2y \geq 5\}$ or
   $\{(x, y)|2x + y \leq 0 \text{ and } x + 2y = 5\}$,
5. If $A = \{(x, y)|y \geq -3\}$, $B = \{(x, y)|x \leq 5\}$,
   $C = \{x, y)|y \leq x + 1\}$,
   graph $A \cap B \cap C$ (the intersection of A, B, and C).
6. Graph $\{(x, y)|y > 3\} \cup \{(x, y)|x < -2\}$.
7. Graph $\{(x, y)|2x + y \geq 3\} \cap \{(x, y)|2x + y \leq 5\}$.
8. If $M = \{(x, y)|y < 4\}$, $N = \{(x, y)|y > 1\}$,
   $P = \{(x, y)|x < 3\}$, $Q = \{(x, y)|x > -2\}$,
   graph $M \cap N \cap P \cap Q$.
9. If $D = \{(x, y)|y < 2x - 2\}$, $E = \{(x, y)|y < -x + 5\}$,
   $F = \{(x, y)|y > -1\}$,
   graph: (i) $D \cap E \cap F$ (ii) $D \cup E \cup F$
10. Graph $\{(x, y)|y = x^2 \text{ and } x = 2\}$.
11. Graph $\{(x, y)|y > x^2 \text{ and } x < 2\}$.
12. Graph $\{(x, y)|y \leq x^2 \text{ and } y \leq 3\}$.
13. Graph $\{(x, y)|y \geq x^2 \text{ and } x \geq -1 \text{ and } x \leq 2\}$.

Using intersection of sets, define the relations for which the following are the graphs:

14.

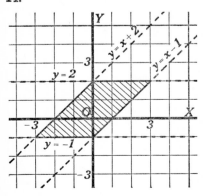

15.

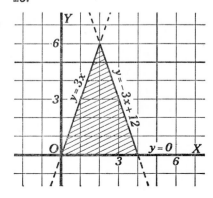

16.

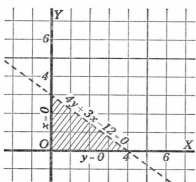

17.

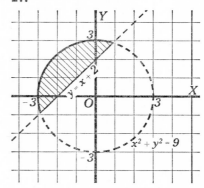

18.

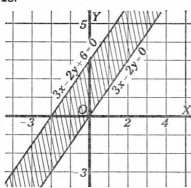

19.

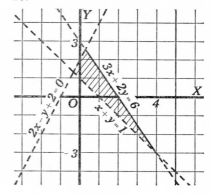

9·13 Linear programming (supplementary). If x, y, $\in R$, each of the following defining sentences defines a relation, the graph of which is a straight line (*Fig. 9-19*). The lines are parallel lines.

(i) $x + y = 1$
(ii) $x + y = 3$
(iii) $x + y = 5$
(iv) $x + y = 8$

These equations differ from each other only in the *absolute term*, and the farther to the right the graph of the equation is, the greater the absolute term.

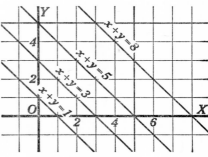

Fig. 9-19

In *Fig. 9-20*, the graphs of the following inequalities are shown:

(i) $x \geqq 0$

(ii) $y \geqq 0$

(iii) $2x + y \leqq 6$

(iv) $x + 2y \leqq 6$

The points within and on the polygon $AOBC$ are points whose coordinates satisfy *all* the conditions or *constraints* on x and y given by the above inequations. These points are the graph of the intersection set of the sets defined by the inequalities.

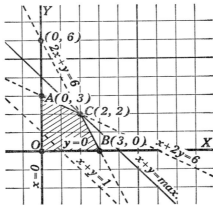

Fig. 9-20

To discover what values of x and y make $x + y$ a maximum under the four constraints above, we must find the coordinates of the point, or points, in the interior of, or on, the quadrilateral, whose sum is a maximum.

Consider the line whose equation is $x + y = 1$, *Fig. 9-20*. The coordinates of all points on the line segment cut off by the axes satisfy all the conditions or constraints defined by the inequations and also make the sum $x + y$ equal to 1. In a similar manner, lines drawn parallel to this line and intersecting the quadrilateral determine points whose coordinates satisfy all the constraints and make $x + y$ equal to sums other than 1. Of these lines, the line on C (2, 2), being farthest to the right, has the equation with the maximum absolute term. For this line, $x + y$ is 4. Thus, the values of x and y, which maximize $x + y$ under the four constraints above, are $x = 2, y = 2$.

Similarly, $x = 0$, $y = 0$ minimize $x + y$.

The coordinates of any other point within or on the quadrilateral make the sum $x + y$ a number between 0 and 4.

The preceding discussion outlines a graphical approach to what is called *linear programming*. The following example illustrates the application of this method.

Example 1. An automobile and truck manufacturer produces vehicles under the following production constraints:

(i) Metal stamping of frames for either truck or auto takes the same amount of time, and the manufacturer can make a total of 8,000 in all during a month.

(ii) The manufacturer can assemble two automobile engines in the time it takes to assemble one truck engine. Further, if he makes automobile engines only, he can assemble 10,000 in one month; however, if he makes truck engines only, he can assemble just 5,000 in one month.

(iii) The maximum number of truck body-engine assemblies he can make in one month is 4,000; the maximum number of auto body-engine assemblies is 7,000 per month.

(iv) The manufacturer makes a total profit after all deductions of $400 on each truck and $300 on each auto.

If the manufacturer wishes to make the largest profit possible, how many autos and how many trucks should he produce each month?

Solution. Let the number of trucks be represented by x.

Let the number of autos be represented by y.

The constraints are expressed in the following inequations:

$$\text{(i)} \quad x + y \leq 8,000$$
$$\text{(ii)} \quad 2x + y \leq 10,000$$
$$\text{(iii)} \quad x \leq 4,000$$
$$\text{(iv)} \quad y \leq 7,000$$
$$\text{(v)} \quad x \geq 0, \ y \geq 0$$

x and y must represent integers, but this need be considered only in stating the conclusion.

The profit is given by the expression

$$400x + 300y,$$

which is referred to as the *objective function* or *profit function* in this case. The problem is to maximize this function in integers, subject to the linear constraints (i) to (v).

From *Fig. 9-21*, it may be seen that any point within or on the polygon *EOABCD*, which has integral coordinates, satisfies the conditions of the problem. The broken line is a typical profit line. It has equation $400x + 300y = 1,200,000$. It is seen that the parallel line intersecting the polygon and farthest to the right passes through C (2,000, 6,000). Since the coordinates of C are positive integers, the solution of the problem is:

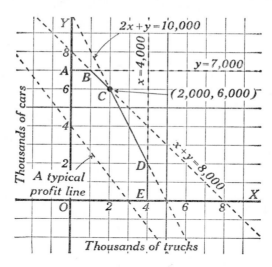

Fig. 9-21

For maximum profit he should manufacture 2,000 trucks and 6,000 autos.

DISCUSSION. (i) If the point C had not had integral coordinates, then the maximum profit line would pass through a point within the polygon having integral coordinates. It is possible that such a line might pass through more than one such point. In this case, several solutions provide the same profit, and the manufacturer could choose the number of autos and trucks in several ways to realize maximum profit. He could manufacture the least number possible of those for which the profit is least. In this way he could exert some market control by increasing the demand for the vehicle which provides the lesser margin of profit.

(ii) If a profit line were parallel to BC, for example, then all points on BC satisfying the conditions would provide solutions to the problem.

(iii) The point O (0, 0) corresponds to a minimum profit.

Exercise 9-8

(B)

1. Given the constraints:

    (i) $x \geqq 0$ (ii) $y \geqq 0$ (iii) $x \leqq 6$

    (iv) $y \leqq 3$ (v) $x + 2y \leqq 8$

    find x and y to maximize $C = x + y$, and find the maximum value of C.

2. Find x and y to maximize $K = x + 4y$, subject to the same constraints as in question 1.

3. Find x and y so as to minimize $Q = x + y$ and find the minimum value of Q, subject to the constraints:

   (i) $x \geq 0$ (ii) $y \geq 0$ (iii) $2x + y \geq 4$ (iv) $x + 3y \geq 7$

4. Find x and y so as to minimize $C = 2x + 3y$ and find the minimum value of C subject to the constraints:

   (i) $x \geq 0$ (ii) $y \geq 0$ (iii) $2x + y \geq 6$ (iv) $x + 3y \geq 8$

5. An electronics firm produces two models of transistor radios. Model I provides a profit of \$3 for each radio, and Model II a profit of \$6 for each radio. Two machines are used in manufacturing these models. Radio Model I requires 3 hours of work by machine A and 1 hour of work by machine B, while radio Model II requires 1 hour of work by machine A and 3 hours of work by machine B. The machines are limited to 12 hours of work each per day. How many radios of each type should be manufactured to produce maximum profit for a day's operation?

6. A plant makes use of three machines, I, II, and III. These machines are used to manufacture two models of TV sets. The standard model yields a profit of \$20 per set, and the deluxe model yields a profit of \$30 per set.

   The standard model requires:

   > 39 hours of work on machine I;
   >
   > $\frac{20}{3}$ hours of work on machine II;
   >
   > 1 hour of work on machine III.

   The deluxe model requires:

   > 1 hour of work on machine I;
   >
   > $\frac{20}{3}$ hours of work on machine II;
   >
   > $\frac{19}{2}$ hours of work on machine III.

   No machine may work more than 40 hours per week. How many sets of each model should be manufactured per week to produce a maximum profit?

7. An animal feed is to be a mixture of two foods, A and B, each ounce of which contains protein, fat, and carbohydrate. One ounce of food A contains 10 grams of protein, 0.1 grams of fat, and 15 grams of carbohydrate. One ounce of food B contains 5 grams of protein, 0.9 grams of fat, and 20 grams of carbohydrate. The cost of food A and B is 4 cents and 3 cents per ounce, respectively. Each bag of the feed mixture is to contain at least 50 grams of protein, 1.8 grams of fat, and 150 grams of carbohydrate. Find the number of ounces of A and B which will produce a mixture satisfying these requirements **at a minimum** cost.

8. A refinery produces standard gasoline at a profit of 15¢ per barrel, and premium gasoline at a profit of 20¢ per barrel. The refinery has a contract to provide 2,000 barrels of standard gasoline per day and another contract for a daily supply of 1,000 barrels of premium gasoline. Both customers will accept more than the amount of gasoline mentioned in their contract, if it is available. The standard gasoline must be delivered to a town 10 miles from the refinery, and the premium gasoline to a city 20 miles distant. Trucks are the only means of transport, and there are only enough trucks available to deliver 180,000 barrels 1 mile, or 18,000 barrels 10 miles, or 9,000 barrels 20 miles (i.e. 180,000 barrel-miles). Only 13,000 barrels of gasoline can be produced in one day. Find the number of barrels of each type of gasoline which should be produced daily to give a maximum profit.

9. A drug manufacturer uses a mixture of two compounds as a vitamin supplement. Each mixture should contain 920,000 units of vitamin A and 920,000 units of vitamin D. The first compound (called alpha) contains 184,000 units of vitamin A and 40,000 units of vitamin D per ounce, while the second compound (called beta) contains 92,000 units of vitamin A and 200,000 units of vitamin D per ounce. Alpha costs $.20 per ounce, and beta costs $.40 per ounce. How many ounces of alpha and beta should be used to provide the desired units of vitamin A and vitamin D, while keeping the cost at a minimum?

10. A man who has just bought a home in a small town discovers that the lawn is in poor condition. He sends a sample of the soil to the Department of Agriculture. They recommend an application of 30 lbs. of nitrogen, phosphorus, and potash, by weight: 5-8 4 fertilizer, per 1,000 square feet. He has 2,000 square feet to fertilize. The local hardware, however, does not have this formula but does sell "Tops-N-Turf" formula 10-6-4 costing $10.00 per 100 lbs., and "Lush-S-Lawn" formula 4-12-4 costing $6.00 per 100 lbs. What amount of these fertilizers will give at least the required lawn feeding at minimum cost?

Review Exercise 9-9

(B)

1. $A = \{-2, 0, 2, 4\}$ and $B = \{-3, -1, 0, 1, 3, 5\}$
   (i) How many ordered pairs are there in $A \times B$? in $B \times A$? in $A \times A$?
   (ii) List the ordered pairs in $A \times B$ whose first elements are 2.
   (iii) List the ordered pairs in $B \times B$ whose first elements are -1.

Draw the graphs of the following relations:

2. $A = \{(x, y)| x = 3, x, y \in I\}$

3. $B = \{(x, y)| 2x - y = 4, x, y \in R\}$

4. $C = \{(x, y)| 3x + 2y = 3, -3 \le x \le +3, x, y \in R\}$

5. $D = \{(x, y)| x \ge 2 \text{ and } y \ge -4, x, y \in I\}$

6. $E = \{(x, y)| x \ge 0, y \ge 0, x + y = 3, x, y \in I\}$

7. $F = \{(x, y)| y > |x| \text{ or } 2y = x + 4, x, y \in R\}$

Draw the graphs of the following relations. State the domain and range of each. Consider that $(x, y) \in R \times R$.

8. $G = \{(x, y)| y - 2x = 2 \text{ and } y + x = 8\}$

9. $H = \{(x, y)| y - 2x = 5 \text{ and } |x| = 3\}$

10. $L = \{(x, y)| y > |x| \text{ and } 2y = x + 4\}$

11. $M = \{(x, y)| y \ge |x| \text{ and } 2y \le x + 4\}$

12. $N = \{(x, y)| y - 2x \le 5 \text{ and } x \le 3\}$

(C)

13. $P = \{(x, y)| x^2 + y^2 = 25 \text{ and } 3x - 4y = 0\}$

14. $R = \{(x, y)| x^2 + y^2 = 25 \text{ and } 3x - 4y \le 0\}$

15. Find graphically the ordered pair which has the greatest value for the range of the relation:

$$S = \{(x, y)| x > 0, y > 0, y \le 5x + 3, 4x + y - 6 \le 0\}$$

Chapter X

SYSTEMS OF LINEAR EQUATIONS

10·1 Solving a system. The defining equations of the relation
$A = \{(x, y)|2x - y = -1 \text{ and } 3x - 5y = 9, x, y \in R\}$ are:

$$\begin{cases} 2x - y = -1 & (1) \\ 3x - 5y = 9 & (2) \end{cases}$$

Each equation defines a set of ordered pairs, the graph of which is a straight line (*Fig. 10-1*), and the relation A determines the one ordered pair $(-2, -3)$ which is common to the two sets and whose graph is the point of intersection of the two lines (*Fig. 10-1*).

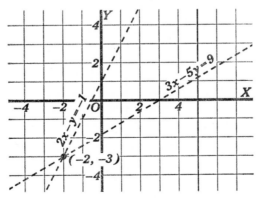

Fig. 10-1

The pair of equations

$$\begin{cases} 2x - y = -1 \\ 3x - 5y = 9 \end{cases}$$

is called a *system of two linear equations*.
$\{(-2, -3)\}$ is called the *solution set* of the system.

330

The solution set of a system of equations in two variables x and y is the set of all ordered pairs (x, y) which are common to the solution sets defined by each of the given equations.

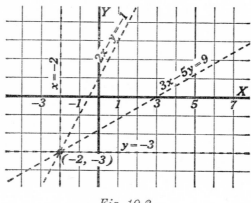

Fig. 10-2

It is seen from *Fig. 10-2* that the systems

$$\text{(i)} \begin{cases} 2x - y = -1 \\ 3x - 5y = 9 \end{cases}$$

$$\text{(ii)} \begin{cases} x = -2 \\ 2x - y = -1 \end{cases} \qquad \text{(iii)} \begin{cases} x = -2 \\ 3x - 5y = 9 \end{cases}$$

$$\text{(iv)} \begin{cases} y = -3 \\ 2x - y = -1 \end{cases} \qquad \text{(v)} \begin{cases} y = -3 \\ 3x - 5y = 9 \end{cases}$$

$$\text{(vi)} \begin{cases} x = -2 \\ y = -3 \end{cases}$$

have the same solution set $\{(-2, -3)\}$.

To find the solution set of the given system algebraically, it is necessary to find a way to obtain system (vi) from system (i).

The relation A consists of the intersection set of the two relations

$$A_1 = \{(x, y) \mid 2x - y = -1, x, y \in R\} \text{ and}$$
$$A_2 = \{(x, y) \mid 3x - 5y = 9, x, y \in R\}$$

which may be expressed as

$$A_1 = \{(x, 2x + 1) \mid x, y \in R\} \text{ and}$$
$$A_2 = \left\{\left(x, \frac{3x - 9}{5}\right) \middle| x, y \in R\right\} .$$

Since $x \in R$, then $(2x + 1)$ and $\dfrac{3x - 9}{5} \in R$ by the Law of Closure.

Comparing the ordered pairs of A_1 and A_2, it is seen that the ordered pairs which belong to both A_1 and A_2 must be such that:

$$2x + 1 = \frac{3x - 9}{5}, \, x \in R$$

or $10x + 5 = 3x - 9$ (Multiplication property)
or $\quad\quad 7x = -14$ (Addition property)
or $\quad\quad\; x = -2$ (Division property)

Thus, to obtain the solution set, we solve either of the two simpler systems:

(ii) $\begin{cases} \quad x = -2 \\ 2x - y = -1 \end{cases}$ or   (iii) $\begin{cases} \quad x = -2 \\ 3x - 5y = 9 \end{cases}$

This may be done simply by substitution:

$\quad\quad -4 - y = -1$ or $-6 - 5y = 9$
$\quad\quad\;\; \therefore -y = 3$ $\quad\quad\; \therefore -5y = 15$
$\quad\quad\;\; \therefore y = -3$ $\quad\quad\; \therefore y = -3$

The system $\begin{cases} x = -2 \\ y = -3 \end{cases}$ is obtained.

It is readily seen that the steps of the argument are reversible; therefore the systems are *equivalent*, and the solution set is $\{(-2, -3)\}$.

The pattern of algebraic solution and the reason for each step is shown in the following:

$$\begin{cases} 2x - y = -1 \quad\quad (1) \\ 3x - 5y = 9 \quad\quad (2) \end{cases}$$

From (1) $\quad\quad\quad y = 2x + 1$ (3)   (Addition property)

From (2) $\quad\quad\quad y = \dfrac{3x - 9}{5}$ (4)   (Addition, Division property)

From (3) and (4)

$$2x + 1 = \frac{3x - 9}{5}$$ (5)   (Replacement property)

$\therefore 10x + 5 = 3x - 9$ (Multiplication property)
$\quad\;\; \therefore 7x = -14$ (Addition property)
$\quad\;\;\; \therefore x = -2$ (Division property)

$\because y = 2x + 1$ or $\because y = \dfrac{3x - 9}{5}$

$\therefore y = 2(-2) + 1$ $\quad\quad \therefore y = \dfrac{3(-2) - 9}{5}$

$\therefore y = -3$ $\quad\quad\quad\quad \therefore y = -3$

The solution set is $\{(-2, -3)\}$.

Verification.

L.S. (1) $= (-4) - (-3)$ L.S. (2) $= (-6) - (-15)$

$\qquad = -1$ $= 9$

R.S. (1) $= -1$ R.S. (2) $= 9$

The algebraic process of determining the solution set of a system of equations is called *solving the system*. The essential feature of the procedure in the preceding example is that by *comparison* of equations (3) and (4), equation (5) which does not contain the variable y is formed. By eliminating y in this way, an equation in one variable is obtained, and this can be solved easily. This method of solving is referred to as the method of *elimination by comparison*.

Elimination by comparison in the preceding example can also be carried out as follows:

The system
$$\begin{cases} 2x - y = -1 & (1) \\ 3x - 5y = 9 & (2) \end{cases}$$

is equivalent to
$$\begin{cases} x = \dfrac{y-1}{2} & (3) \\[2mm] x = \dfrac{5y+9}{3} & (4) \end{cases}$$

and, by *comparison:*

$$\frac{y-1}{2} = \frac{5y+9}{3}$$

$$\therefore \ 3(y-1) = 2(5y+9)$$

$$\therefore \ 3y - 3 = 10y + 18$$

$$\therefore \ -7y = 21$$

$$\therefore \ y = -3$$

Then, to obtain the solution set we solve either of the two simpler systems:

(iv) $\begin{cases} y = -3 \\ 2x - y = -1 \end{cases}$ or   (v) $\begin{cases} y = -3 \\ 3x - 5y = 9 \end{cases}$

This may be done by substitution to obtain:

$$\begin{cases} x = -2 \\ y = -3 \end{cases}$$

In the worked examples of the text the authorities which are most significant in the development are given in brackets. When writing a solution you should think the authorities, but it is not necessary to include them in your solution.

Unless otherwise stated, the variables are real numbers.

Write solutions for the following problems and compare them with those on page 483.

1. Find the solution set defined by the following system of equations; verify:

$$\begin{cases} x + 2y = 5 \\ 2x + 3y = 7 \end{cases}$$

2. Find $\left\{ (x, y) \mid \dfrac{1}{2}x - \dfrac{1}{3}y = 2 \text{ and } \dfrac{1}{3}x + \dfrac{1}{2}y = \dfrac{-5}{6} \right\}.$

Exercise 10-1

(A)

1. From each of the following graphs state equivalent systems of equations; state the solution set:

(i)   (ii)

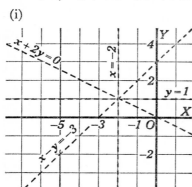   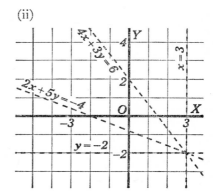

2. Express each of the following in terms of x:

    (i) $\{ (x, y) \mid 2y - x = 0 \}$ (ii) $\{ (x, y) \mid 2x + y = 3 \}$

    (iii) $\{ (x, y) \mid x + \frac{1}{2}y = 3 \}$ (iv) $\{ (x, y) \mid y - 2x = 7 \}$

By expressing y in terms of x, state a system of equations equivalent to the given system for each of the following:

3. $\begin{cases} x - y = 0 \\ x + y = 5 \end{cases}$ **4.** $\begin{cases} 2x + y = 1 \\ x + y = 4 \end{cases}$ **5.** $\begin{cases} 2x + y = 2 \\ 3x + 2y = 5 \end{cases}$

Use the method of comparison to obtain a system of two equations equivalent to the given system in each of the following:

6. $\begin{cases} y = x + 1 \\ y = 2x - 3 \end{cases}$ **7.** $\begin{cases} x = 4y + 2 \\ x = 2y - 3 \end{cases}$ **8.** $\begin{cases} y = \dfrac{x - 2}{3} \\ x - y = 0 \end{cases}$

(B)

Use the method of comparison to determine the ordered pairs (x, y) defined by the following systems of equations; verify:

9. $\begin{cases} -3x = y + 6 \\ 5x = -3y - 2 \end{cases}$
10. $\begin{cases} \frac{1}{5}x - \frac{1}{3}y = -2 \\ \frac{3}{5}x + \frac{2}{3}y = 9 \end{cases}$
11. $\begin{cases} \frac{1}{2}x - 3y = 4 \\ x + 2y = -1 \end{cases}$

Find, using the method of comparison:

12. $\{(x, y) \mid 2x + y = -4 \text{ and } x - 3y = 5\}$

13. $\{(a, b) \mid 2a + 3b = 10 \text{ and } a + 4b = 10\}$

14. $\left\{(x, y) \middle| x = \dfrac{7 - y}{3} \text{ and } y = \dfrac{3x - 2}{4}\right\}$

15. $\{(m, n) \mid 3m - n = 1 \text{ and } m + 5n = 15\}$

Solve each of the following systems:

16. $3x - 4y = 5x + y = 23$

17. $\begin{cases} \dfrac{x - 2}{3} = \dfrac{y + 5}{2} \\ \dfrac{13 - y}{6} = \dfrac{2x - 7}{3} \end{cases}$
18. $\begin{cases} \frac{1}{3}x + \frac{1}{4}y = 6 \\ y - \frac{1}{4}(x - y) = 7 \end{cases}$

10·2 Elimination of a variable by substitution. The following example illustrates a method of eliminating a variable from a system of equations by *substitution*.

The relation $B = \{(x, y) \mid x + y = 2 \text{ and } x - 2y = 5\}$ involves the intersection set of $B_1 = \{(x, y) \mid x + y = 2\}$ and $B_2 = \{(x, y) \mid x - 2y = 5\}$.

The graphical solution in *Fig. 10-3* indicates that the solution set is $\{(3, -1)\}$ and that the following systems have the same solution set:

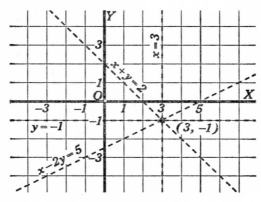

Fig. 10-3

$$\text{(i)} \quad \begin{cases} x + y = 2 \\ x - 2y = 5 \end{cases}$$

$$\text{(ii)} \quad \begin{cases} x = 3 \\ x + y = 2 \end{cases} \qquad\qquad \text{(iii)} \quad \begin{cases} x = 3 \\ x - 2y = 5 \end{cases}$$

$$\text{(iv)} \quad \begin{cases} y = -1 \\ x + y = 2 \end{cases} \qquad\qquad \text{(v)} \quad \begin{cases} y = -1 \\ x - 2y = 5 \end{cases}$$

$$\text{(vi)} \quad \begin{cases} x = 3 \\ y = -1 \end{cases}$$

To obtain system (vi) from system (i) algebraically, we note that the set B_1 may be described as

$$B_1 = \{ (x,\, 2 - x) | x \in R \} \, .$$

From the set of ordered pairs $(x,\, 2 - x)$ we are required to select those ordered pairs that belong to B_2: that is, those which satisfy the equation $x - 2y = 5$.

These may be found by *substituting* $(x,\, 2 - x)$ in the equation and solving to find the replacements for x which permit this.

On substitution: $x - 2(2 - x) = 5$
$$\therefore \; x - 4 + 2x = 5 \qquad (D)$$
$$\therefore \; 3x = 9 \qquad (D, \text{ Addition property})$$
$$\therefore \; x = 3 \qquad (\text{Division property})$$

Thus, to obtain the solution set, we must solve either of the two simpler systems:

$$\text{(ii)} \quad \begin{cases} x = 3 \\ x + y = 2 \end{cases} \qquad \text{or} \qquad \text{(iii)} \quad \begin{cases} x = 3 \\ x - 2y = 5 \end{cases}$$

This may be done simply by substitution:

$$3 + y = 2 \qquad\qquad \text{or} \qquad\qquad 3 - 2y = 5$$
$$\therefore \; y = -1 \qquad\qquad\qquad\qquad \therefore \; -2y = 2$$
$$\therefore \; y = -1$$

The system $\begin{cases} x = 3 \\ y = -1 \end{cases}$ is obtained.

It is readily seen that the steps of the argument are reversible; therefore, the systems are equivalent, and the solution set is $\{ (3,\, -1) \} \, .$

The pattern of algebraic solution and the reason for each step is shown as follows:

$$\begin{cases} x + y = 2 & (1) \\ x - 2y = 5 & (2) \end{cases}$$

From (1) $\qquad\qquad\qquad y = 2 - x \quad (3) \quad (\text{Addition property})$
Substitute in (2) $\quad x - 2(2 - x) = 5 \qquad\qquad (\text{Replacement})$

$$\therefore x - 4 + 2x = 5 \qquad (D)$$
$$\therefore 3x = 9 \qquad (D, \text{ Addition property})$$
$$\therefore x = 3 \qquad (4) \quad (\text{Division property})$$

Substitute in (3)
$$y = 2 - 3$$
$$\therefore y = -1 \qquad (5)$$

The solution set is $\{(3, -1)\}$.

Verification.

L.S. (1) $= 3 + (-1)$ L.S. (2) $= 3 - 2(-1)$
$= 2$ $= 5$
R.S. (1) $= 2$ R.S. (2) $= 5$

It should be noted that the above solution could have been obtained in several ways. For example:

From (1) $x = 2 - y$

From (2) $x = 5 + 2y$ and $y = \dfrac{x - 5}{2}$

Substitution in the other equation would have provided one or other of the systems illustrated in *Fig. 10-3.*

Exercise 10-2

(A)

Use the method of substitution to obtain a system of equations equivalent to the given system for each of the following:

1. $\begin{cases} y = 1 - x \\ 2x + y = 3 \end{cases}$ 2. $\begin{cases} x = 3 + y \\ 3x - 2y = 11 \end{cases}$ 3. $\begin{cases} a + b = 2 \\ 2b + 3a = 3 \end{cases}$

(B)

Solve each of the following systems using the method of substitution; verify:

4. $\begin{cases} 3x + 7y = 17 \\ 2x - y = 0 \end{cases}$ 5. $\begin{cases} \dfrac{x - y}{5} = 1 \\ 2x + \dfrac{y}{3} = 17 \end{cases}$

6. $\begin{cases} \frac{1}{2}x + 2 = \frac{2}{3}y \\ \frac{3}{2}x - y = 0 \end{cases}$ 7. $\begin{cases} .3x + .5y = .23 \\ 6x - 2.6 = -5y \end{cases}$

8. $\begin{cases} 4x - 3 = \dfrac{y + 10}{3} \\ 7(y - 5) = x - 2 \end{cases}$ 9. $\begin{cases} x - \frac{1}{2}(y - 3) = -4 \\ y - \frac{1}{5}(3 - x) = 6 \end{cases}$

Find, using the method of substitution:

10. $\{(x, y) \mid 3x - 2y = 1 \text{ and } 3y + 5x + 11 = 0\}$

11. $\left\{(x, y) \left| \dfrac{x}{2} - \dfrac{y}{3} = 0 \text{ and } y - \dfrac{5x}{12} = 13\right.\right\}$

12. (i) Find the solution set defined by the system
$2x + 3y = 1, \quad 3x + 4y = 2 .$

    (ii) Show that the elements of the solution set for part (i) satisfy each of the following equations:

        (a) $2(2x + 3y - 1) - (3x + 4y - 2) = 0$

        (b) $4(2x + 3y - 1) + 3(3x + 4y - 2) = 0$

        (c) $2x + 3y - 1 + k(3x + 4y - 2) = 0$ where $k \in R$

Find the solution set defined by each of the following systems of equations:

13.
$$\begin{cases} \dfrac{x + 5}{3} + \dfrac{y + 3}{2} = 7 \\ \dfrac{y + 4}{3} - 2 = \dfrac{2x - 3}{5} \end{cases}$$

14.
$$\begin{cases} \dfrac{2x - 5}{5} = \dfrac{-(2y - 11)}{7} \\ \tfrac{1}{3}(x - 2) - \tfrac{1}{4}(y + 2) = 0 \end{cases}$$

15. $3x - 8 - \dfrac{y + 7}{11} = 2y - 10 + \dfrac{x + 11}{7} = 0$

16. $\dfrac{4x - 3y - 5}{4} = x - \dfrac{9}{2}y = 7x - \dfrac{12y + 23}{6}$

10·3 Elimination of a variable by addition or subtraction. The following example illustrates a third method of solving a system of equations. The systems developed in the procedure are equivalent systems, as is illustrated graphically.

The graph of $A = \{(x, y) \mid 3x + 2y = 19 \text{ and } 3x - 5y = 5\}$ is shown in *Fig. 10-4.* The solution set is $\{(5, 2)\}$.

From the graph in *Fig. 10-4,* it can be seen that the systems of equations

$$\text{(i)} \quad \begin{cases} 3x + 2y = 19 & (1) \\ 3x - 5y = 5 & (2) \end{cases}$$

$$\text{(ii)} \quad \begin{cases} x = 5 \\ 3x + 2y = 19 \end{cases} \qquad \text{(iii)} \quad \begin{cases} x = 5 \\ 3x - 5y = 5 \end{cases}$$

$$\text{(iv)} \quad \begin{cases} y = 2 \\ 3x + 2y = 19 \end{cases} \qquad \text{(v)} \quad \begin{cases} y = 2 \\ 3x - 5y = 5 \end{cases}$$

$$\text{(vi)} \quad \begin{cases} x = 5 \\ y = 2 \end{cases}$$

have the same solution set $\{(5, 2)\}$.

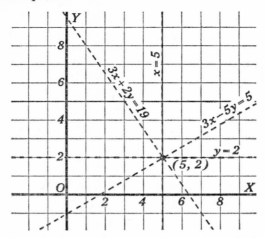

Fig. 10-4

The equation $x = 5$ may be obtained by eliminating y from the given equations. The multiplication property of equality is used to write equivalent equations in which the coefficients of y are equal in absolute value.

$$5 \times (1) \quad \begin{cases} 15x + 10y = 95 & (3) \\ 6x - 10y = 10 & (4) \end{cases}$$
$$2 \times (2)$$
$$(3)+(4) \qquad\qquad 21x = 105 \quad (5)$$
$$\therefore\ x = 5 \qquad (6)$$

The equation $y = 2$ may be obtained by eliminating x from the given equations by subtraction.

$$\begin{cases} 3x + 2y = 19 & (1) \\ 3x - 5y = 5 & (2) \end{cases}$$
$$(1) - (2) \qquad\quad 7y = 14 \quad (3)$$
$$\therefore\ y = 2 \quad (4)$$

If the original system is now replaced by one of the simpler systems, for example:

or

$$\begin{cases} x = 5 \\ 3x + 2y = 19 \end{cases} \qquad\qquad \begin{cases} y = 2 \\ 3x - 5y = 5 \end{cases}$$

Then by substitution:

$$15 + 2y = 19$$
$$\therefore\ 2y = 4$$
$$\therefore\ y = 2$$

Then by substitution:

$$3x - 10 = 5$$
$$\therefore\ 3x = 15$$
$$\therefore\ x = 5$$

The system in each case is equivalent to the system $\begin{cases} x = 5 \\ y = 2 \end{cases}$

from which the solution set $\{(5, 2)\}$ is obtained.

The solution is usually arranged as follows:

$$\begin{cases} 3x + 2y = 19 & (1) \\ 3x - 5y = 5 & (2) \end{cases}$$

$$(1) - (2) \qquad 7y = 14$$
$$\therefore \ y = 2 \qquad (3)$$

Substitute in (2) $\quad 3x - 10 = 5$
$$\therefore \ 3x = 15$$
$$\therefore \ x = 5 \qquad (4)$$

The solution set is $\{(5, 2)\}$.

Verification.

L.S. (1) $= 15 + 4 \qquad$ L.S. (2) $= 15 - 10$
$\qquad\qquad = 19 \qquad\qquad\qquad\qquad = 5$
R.S. (1) $= 19 \qquad\qquad$ R.S. (2) $= 5$

Write solutions for the following problems and compare them with those on page 483.

1. Solve the following system; verify:
$$\begin{cases} 4x + 3y = 24 \\ 3x + 2y = -17 \end{cases}$$

2. Find $\left\{ (x, y) \mid \frac{2}{5}x + \frac{3}{8}y = \frac{7}{2} \text{ and } \frac{1}{5}x - \frac{1}{8}y = \frac{1}{2} \right\}$.

Exercise 10-3

(A)

Eliminating a variable by addition or subtraction, find the solution set for each of the following systems of equations:

1. $\begin{cases} 6x + 3y = -9 \\ 2x + 3y = -1 \end{cases}$
   2. $\begin{cases} 2x + 4y = 32 \\ 2x - 5y = 5 \end{cases}$
   3. $\begin{cases} 3x + 2y = 20 \\ x + 2y = 12 \end{cases}$

4. $\begin{cases} \frac{1}{2}x + \frac{3}{4}y = 9 \\ \frac{1}{2}x - \frac{1}{4}y = 1 \end{cases}$
   5. $\begin{cases} -2x + 3y = -17 \\ 2x - 5y = 23 \end{cases}$
   6. $\begin{cases} \dfrac{x}{2} + \dfrac{y}{3} = 1 \\ \dfrac{x}{2} - \dfrac{2y}{3} = 4 \end{cases}$

(B)

Find the solution set defined by each of the following systems:

7. $\begin{cases} \frac{1}{3}x + 2y = 1 \\ \frac{2}{3}x - 3y = -5 \end{cases}$
   8. $\begin{cases} x = 3y \\ \frac{1}{2}x - y = 1 \end{cases}$

9. $\begin{cases} 7y = 5x + 21 \\ 20x - 9y = 68 \end{cases}$
   10. $\begin{cases} 3 = 2m + b \\ -1 = 5m + b \end{cases}$

Find:

11. $\{(x, y) \mid 7x + 8y = 9 \text{ and } x + 5y = 9\}$

12. $\left\{(x, y) \mid \dfrac{y}{6} = 3 - \dfrac{x}{5} \text{ and } \dfrac{y}{3} = 1 + \dfrac{x}{10}\right\}$

13. $\left\{(a, b) \mid \dfrac{a - 3}{5} + \dfrac{b + 3}{6} = 8 \text{ and } \dfrac{a}{2} = \dfrac{b}{3}\right\}$

14. $\{(x, y) \mid 1.5x = 17 + 2.8y \text{ and } y = 0.5x + 4\}$

15. $\left\{(x, y) \mid \dfrac{3x}{2} = \dfrac{y}{8} + 10 \text{ and } \dfrac{3y}{2} = \dfrac{2x}{3} - 16\right\}$

16. $\left\{(x, y) \mid \dfrac{x - y}{2} = 6 \text{ and } \tfrac{1}{4}(x + y) = \tfrac{1}{2}\right\}$

17. $\left\{(x, y) \mid \dfrac{3x - 7}{4} = 0 \text{ and } \dfrac{2y + 3}{6} = 0\right\}$

18. $\{(x, y) \mid 3(x + 2) - 2(y - 3) = -6 \text{ and } 2(x - 3) - 3(y + 2) = -29\}$

19. $\left\{(x, y) \mid \dfrac{x - 1}{2} + \dfrac{y + 1}{4} = -5 \text{ and } \dfrac{x + 1}{3} - \dfrac{y - 1}{2} = 1\right\}$

20. $\left\{(p, q) \mid 3(p + 1) - 2(q - 5) = -7 \text{ and } \dfrac{p + 5}{3} + \dfrac{q - 3}{2} = 3\right\}$

10·4 Solving systems of equations in more than two variables. We learned in Chapter IX that one equation in two variables has an unlimited number of solutions or defines an unlimited number of ordered pairs. Two equations of the first degree in two variables usually define a *single ordered pair*.

To solve systems of equations the general method is:

(i) *eliminate variables to obtain equations with fewer variables;*

(ii) *obtain at each step a system of equations equivalent to the previously obtained system.*

This method is a general one and may be applied to solving a system of any number of equations. For example, consider the following system.

$$\begin{cases} x + y - z = 0 & (1) \\ x + 2y + z = 11 & (2) \\ x - y + z = 2 & (3) \end{cases}$$

One method of solving the system is as follows:

$$\begin{array}{ll} x + y - z = 0 & (1) \\ x - y + z = 2 & (3) \\ \hline \end{array}$$

$(1) + (3)$
$$\begin{array}{ll} 2x \phantom{{}+ y + z} = 2 & \\ \therefore \ x = 1 & (4) \end{array}$$

$$x + y - z = 0 \qquad (1)$$
$$x + 2y + z = 11 \qquad (2)$$

(1) + (2) $\qquad 2x + 3y \quad = 11 \qquad (5)$

From (4) $\qquad\quad 2 + 3y \quad = 11$

$$\therefore 3y \quad = 9$$

$$\therefore \; y \quad = 3 \qquad (6)$$

Substitute in (1) $\qquad 1 + 3 - z = 0$

$$\therefore \; z = 4 \qquad (7)$$

The solution set is $\{(1, 3, 4)\}$.

The equivalent systems of equations in the solution are:

$$\begin{cases} x + y - z = 0 \\ x + 2y + z = 11 \\ x - y + z = 2 \end{cases} \begin{cases} x = 1 \\ x + y - z = 0 \\ x - y + z = 2 \end{cases} \begin{cases} x = 1 \\ y = 3 \\ x + y - z = 0 \end{cases} \begin{cases} x = 1 \\ y = 3 \\ z = 4 \end{cases}$$

We see that this system of three first degree equations in three variables defines only one set of three numbers (ordered triple).

The method of solution used to solve the following system suggests that the particular pattern of elimination used in the preceding example does not always need to be followed.

$$\begin{cases} x + y = 14 & (1) \\ y + z = 9 & (2) \\ z + x = 11 & (3) \end{cases}$$

Adding the three equations:

(1) + (2) + (3) $\qquad 2x + 2y + 2z = 34$

$$x + y + z = 17 \qquad (4)$$
$$x + y \qquad\;\; = 14 \qquad (1)$$

(4) − (1) $\qquad\qquad\qquad\qquad z = 3 \qquad (5)$

$$x + y + z = 17 \qquad (4)$$
$$y + z = 9 \qquad (2)$$

(4) − (2) $\qquad\quad x \qquad\qquad\; = 8 \qquad (6)$

$$x + y + z = 17 \qquad (4)$$
$$x \qquad + z = 11 \qquad (3)$$

(4) − (3) $\qquad\qquad y \qquad = 6 \qquad (7)$

The solution set is $\{(8, 6, 3)\}$.

One should always study the equations carefully before proceeding to solve them in order to take advantage of any pattern observed which will simplify or reduce the work required.

Write solutions for the following problems and compare them with those on page 484.

1. Solve the following system; verify:

$$\begin{cases} 4a + 5b + c = 0 & (1) \\ 8a - b + c = 24 & (2) \\ 3a + 2b + 2c = 1 & (3) \end{cases}$$

2. Solve the following system:

$$\begin{cases} m + n = 5 & (1) \\ n + p = 3 & (2) \\ p + q = 7 & (3) \\ m + 5q = 9 & (4) \end{cases}$$

10·5 Graphical interpretation of a linear equation in three variables (supplementary).

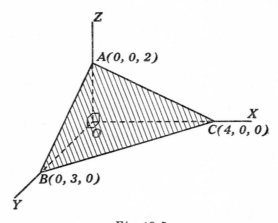

Fig. 10-5

The graphical interpretation of an equation in three variables is a set of points in three-dimensional space. Three coordinates are required to determine a point in space with reference to three axes. The equation

$$3x + 4y + 6z = 12$$

defines the set of points of the plane containing $\triangle ABC$, shown in *Fig. 10-5*.

Such graphs do not provide a convenient method for determining the solution of three equations in three variables.

Exercise 10-4

(B)

Solve and verify:

1. $\begin{cases} 2x + 3y + 7z = 0 \\ x - 2y - 3z = 3 \\ 3x - y + z = 4 \end{cases}$

2. $\begin{cases} a - 2b + 3c = 6 \\ 2a + b - 2c = -1 \\ 3a - 3b - c = 5 \end{cases}$

3. $\begin{cases} 4p + 7q - 2r = -4 \\ -3q + 5r = 11 \\ p - 3r = 0 \end{cases}$

4. $\begin{cases} 2a + b = 1 \\ 3a - c = 7 \\ 5b + 4c = -19 \end{cases}$

Solve:

5. $\begin{cases} x + 2y + 3z = 4 \\ x + y + z = 1 \\ x + 3y + 7z = 13 \end{cases}$

6. $\begin{cases} 3m - 2n - 3p = -1 \\ 6m + n + 2p = 7 \\ 9m + 3n + 4p = 9 \end{cases}$

7. $\begin{cases} 2a - 4b + c = 0 \\ a + 2b - c = 5 \\ 3a + 2b + 2c = 3 \end{cases}$

8. $\begin{cases} r + 2s - t = 0 \\ 2r - s + t = 5 \\ 4r + 2s + 5t = 6 \end{cases}$

9. $\begin{cases} 2a + 3b - 4c = 12 \\ 3a - b + 2c = 15 \\ 4a + b - 3c = 19 \end{cases}$

10. $\begin{cases} p + q = 25 \\ q + r = 75 \\ r + p = 70 \end{cases}$

11. $\begin{cases} x + y + z = 3 \\ y + z + p = 5 \\ z + p + x = 7 \\ p + x + 4y = 9 \end{cases}$

12. $\begin{cases} x + 2y - z + m = 4 \\ 2x - y - z - m = 7 \\ 3x + 4y + z + 2m = 1 \\ 4x - 2y + 3z - 3m = -2 \end{cases}$

10·6 Solving problems by means of a system of equations. Problems involving two or more quantities to be determined may be expressed in terms of two or more letter symbols. To solve the problem, the facts of the problem may be expressed in a system of equations with as many equations as there are representative symbols. If the number of symbols involved is two, the analysis of the problem requires the development of two equations. The following examples illustrate this.

Example 1. Fifty coins, consisting of quarters and dimes, have a value of $9.80. How many coins of each kind are there?

Solution. Represent the number of quarters by x,
 and the number of dimes by y.

$\therefore$ the total number of coins is $x + y$.

But this is 50.

$\therefore x + y = 50 \qquad (1)$

The value of x quarters is $25x$ cents,
and the value of y dimes is $10y$ cents.
∴ the value of the coins is $(25x + 10y)$ cents.
But this is $9.80.
∴ $25x + 10y = 980$ (2)

$$\begin{cases} x + y = 50 & (1) \\ 25x + 10y = 980 & (2) \end{cases}$$

From (1) $y = 50 - x$ (3)

Substitute in (2) $25x + 500 - 10x = 980$

∴ $15x = 480$

∴ $x = 32$

From (3) $y = 18$

The number of quarters is 32, and the number of dimes is **18**.

Verification. Number of coins is $32 + 18$ or 50

Value of 32 quarters is $8.00

Value of 18 dimes is $1.80

Total value $9.80

Example 2. A dealer has crushed corn and soybean meal which he mixes for feed. Corn contains about 9% protein by weight, and soybean meal about 16%. How many pounds of each should the dealer use in a 1,000-pound mixture that is to contain 12% protein?

Solution: Represent the number of pounds of corn by x,
and the number of pounds of soybeans by y.
∴ the total number of pounds is $(x + y)$.
But this is 1,000.
∴ $x + y = 1,000$ (1)
Weight of protein in x pounds of corn is $.09x$ pounds.
Weight of protein in y pounds of soybeans is $.16y$ pounds.
Total weight of protein is $(.09x + .16y)$ pounds.
But this is $.12(1,000)$ pounds or 120 pounds.
∴ $.09x + .16y = 120$ (2)

$$\begin{cases} x + y = 1,000 & (1) \\ .09x + .16y = 120 & (2) \end{cases}$$

From (1) $x = 1,000 - y$ (3)

Substitute in (2) $.09(1000 - y) + .16y = 120$

∴ $90 - .09y + .16y = 120$

∴ $.07y = 30$

∴ $7y = 3,000$

∴ $y = 428\tfrac{4}{7}$

From (3) $x = 1,000 - 428\tfrac{4}{7}$

∴ $x = 571\tfrac{3}{7}$

The number of pounds of corn is $571\frac{3}{7}$, and the number of pounds of soybean meal is $428\frac{4}{7}$.

Verification. Number of pounds of mixture $\quad= 571\frac{3}{7} + 428\frac{4}{7}$
$\qquad\qquad\qquad\qquad\qquad\qquad\qquad\qquad\quad = 1000$
Number of pounds of protein in $571\frac{3}{7}$ lb. of corn $= .09(571\frac{3}{7})$
$\qquad\qquad\qquad\qquad\qquad\qquad\qquad\qquad\qquad\quad = 51\frac{3}{7}$
Number of pounds of protein in $428\frac{4}{7}$ lb. of soybean $= .16(428\frac{4}{7})$
$\qquad\qquad\qquad\qquad\qquad\qquad\qquad\qquad\qquad\quad = 68\frac{4}{7}$
$\qquad\qquad\qquad\qquad\qquad$ Total weight of protein $= 120$ lb.

Example 3. A man travelled 2,440 miles, part by train at an average speed of 80 m.p.h., and the remainder by plane at an average speed of 450 m.p.h. If his total time of travel was 12 hours, find the time he spent travelling (i) by train (ii) by plane.

Solution. The relation between distance (d miles), speed (v m.p.h.), and time (t hours) is given by the equation

$$d = vt.$$

Represent the time travelled by train by x hours, and the time travelled by plane by y hours.

	TIME IN HOURS	SPEED IN m.p.h.	DISTANCE IN MILES
Train	x	80	$80x$
Plane	y	450	$450y$

But it is given that the total time is 12 hours, and the total distance is 2,440 miles.

$$\therefore \begin{cases} x + \quad y = 12 & (1) \\ 80x + 450y = 2{,}440 & (2) \end{cases}$$

$8 \times (1) \qquad\qquad 8x + 8y = 96 \qquad\qquad (3)$
$(2) \div 10 \qquad\qquad 8x + 45y = 244 \qquad\quad (4)$
$(4) - (3) \qquad\qquad\qquad 37y = 148$
$\qquad\qquad\qquad \therefore \quad y = 4 \qquad\qquad\quad (5)$
Substitute in (1) $\qquad x + 4 = 12$
$\qquad\qquad\qquad \therefore \quad x = 8 \qquad\qquad\quad (6)$

The time travelled by train is 8 hours, and the time by plane is 4 hours.

Verification. Total travelling time $\qquad = (4 + 8)$ hours $= \quad$ 12 hours
$\qquad\qquad$ Distance travelled by train $= (8 \times 80)$ miles $= \quad$ 640 miles
$\qquad\qquad$ Distance travelled by plane $= (4 \times 450)$ miles $= \underline{1{,}800 \text{ miles}}$
$\qquad\qquad$ Total distance travelled $\qquad\qquad\qquad = 2{,}440$ miles

Example 4. A number has three digits whose sum is 12. If 396 is added to the number, the digits are reversed. The sum of the number and the number formed by reversing the digits is 1,050. Find the number.

Solution. Represent the hundreds digit by x,
the tens digit by y,
and the units digit by z.

Then the sum of the digits is $x + y + z$.
But it is given that this sum is 12.
$\therefore$ $x + y + z = 12$ (1)

The number is represented by $100x + 10y + z$, and the number formed by reversing the digits is $100z + 10y + x$.

But it is given that when 396 is added to the number, the digits are reversed.

$\therefore$ $100x + 10y + z + 396 = 100z + 10y + x$
or $99x - 99z = -396$
or $x - z = -4$ (2)

The sum of the number and the number formed by reversing the digits is $100x + 10y + z + 100z + 10y + x$ or $101x + 20y + 101z$.

But it is given that this sum is 1,050.

$\therefore$ $101x + 20y + 101z = 1,050$ (3)

$$\begin{cases} x + y + z = 12 & (1) \\ x \quad\quad - z = -4 & (2) \\ 101x + 20y + 101z = 1,050 & (3) \end{cases}$$

$(1) - (2)$ $y + 2z = 16$
                      $\therefore y = 16 - 2z$ (4)
                       $x - z = -4$ (2)
                       $\therefore x = z - 4$ (5)

Substitute in (3)

       $101(z - 4) + 20(16 - 2z) + 101z = 1,050$
$\therefore$ $101z - 404 + 320 - 40z + 101z = 1,050$
                $\therefore 162z - 84 = 1,050$
                   $\therefore 162z = 1,134$
                      $\therefore z = 7$
                       $y = 16 - 2z$ (4)
                    $\therefore y = 16 - 14$
                      $\therefore y = 2$
                       $x = z - 4$ (5)
                    $\therefore x = 7 - 4$
                      $\therefore x = 3$

The number is 327.

Verification. Sum of the digits $= 3 + 2 + 7 = 12$

Number plus 396 $= 327 + 396 = 723$

Number reversed $= 723$

Number plus number reversed $= 327 + 723 = 1,050$

Exercise 10-5

(B)

1. The length of a rectangle is 40% greater than its width. If the perimeter is 24 cm., find the dimensions.

2. Find two numbers such that one-third of their sum is 9 and three times their difference is 15.

3. A man invests $10,000, part of it at 5% and the remainder at 6%. How much did he invest at each rate if his total income from the investments is $540?

4. One train travels from station A to station B in 2 hr. 24 min. A second train travelling 10 m.p.h. faster makes the trip in 2 hr. What is the average speed of the faster train?

5. A boy is three years older than his sister. Six years ago he was twice as old as his sister. What is his present age?

6. A number consisting of two digits is three less than five times the sum of its digits. If the digits are reversed, the number is increased by 18. Find the number.

7. The sum of three numbers is 59. The sum of one-half of the first, one-seventh of the second, and one-third of the third is 20. The sum of the first two exceeds the third by 5. Find the numbers.

8. The cost of admission to a basketball game was 60¢ for adults and 15¢ for students. If the gate receipts from 724 paid admissions amounted to $339.45, how many adults and how many students attended the game?

9. The units digit exceeds the tens digit of a two-digit number by 7. The number with the digits interchanged is 9 times the sum of the digits. Find the number.

10. An advertising agency sent 4,000 letters to 4,000 different businessmen. If some letters required 4¢ postage and the rest required 5¢ postage, how many of each were sent, if the total postage bill was $95?

11. The money for a $440 scholarship is obtained from the interest on a $20,000 investment which is divided between a savings bond paying 4% interest and a bank deposit paying 3% interest. What amount of money is invested at each rate?

12. An airliner travelled with the wind 1,040 miles in 2 hr. and returned against the wind in 2 hr. 10 min. Find the airspeed of the airliner in still air and determine the wind velocity.

13. Find a fraction such that, if 5 is added to the numerator the fraction is reduced to $\frac{3}{4}$, but if 11 is subtracted from the denominator the fraction becomes unity.

14. The hypotenuse of a right triangle is 18 inches longer than the shortest side. If the sum of the two shorter sides is 31 inches, and the perimeter is 56 inches, find the lengths of the sides.

15. If 6 pens and 4 pencils cost $13.26, and 4 pens and 6 pencils cost $10.14, find the cost of each.

16. How much water must be added to 500 cc. of a 12% solution of salt to change it to a 10% solution?

17. A marksman's score in an archery contest is 46 for 10 shots. If a bull's eye counts 5 and an inner counts 4, find how many there were of each if he scored on every shot.

18. Two persons 26 miles apart meet in 4 hours if they walk in opposite directions, and in 17 hours 20 minutes if they walk in the same direction. Find their rates of walking.

19. In cashing a cheque for $400, a man received 50 bills, consisting of five- and ten-dollar bills. How many five-dollar bills did he receive?

20. If A gave B $100, A would have one-half as much as B; if B gave A $100, B would have one-third as much as A. How much does each have?

21. The sum of the three digits of a number is 15. The hundreds digit is 3 less than the sum of the other two. If the hundreds digit is interchanged with the tens digit, the number is decreased by 360. Find the number.

22. Separate 96 into 3 parts, such that the first divided by the second gives 2 with a remainder of 3, and the second divided by the third gives 4 with a remainder of 5.

10·7 Classification of systems of two linear equations.

a. *Consistent systems.* A system is *consistent* if the equations have a unique common solution.
$$\{(x, y) \mid 2x - 3y = 8 \text{ and } 3x + y = 1\} = \{(1, -2)\}$$
is defined by the system of equations
$$\begin{cases} 2x - 3y = 8 & (1) \\ 3x + y = 1 & (2) \end{cases}$$
which have the ordered pair $(1, -2)$ as a unique common solution. The graphical solution, *Fig. 10-6*, indicates the point common to the two lines

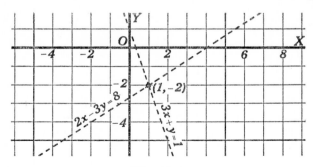

Fig. 10-6

which are defined by the individual equations. This system of equations is said to be *consistent*. It is also referred to as *independent*.

b. *Dependent systems.* A system is *dependent* if each equation has the same solution set.

$$\{(x, y) \mid 2x - 3y = 8 \text{ and } 6x - 9y = 24\}$$

is defined by the system of equations:

$$\begin{cases} 2x - 3y = 8 & (1) \\ 6x - 9y = 24 & (2) \end{cases}$$

It is seen that equation (2) is equivalent to equation (1): that is, (2) is obtained from (1) by multiplying by 3. Thus, any ordered pair which satisfies equation (1) will satisfy equation (2).

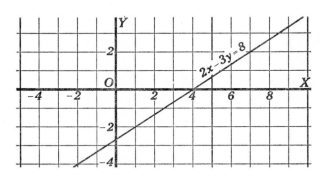

Fig. 10-7

The graph of the solution set of each equation is the same straight line, *Fig. 10-7*.

This system of equations has an unlimited number of solutions. Each equation is said to be *dependent* on the other, and the system is referred to as a *dependent system*.

c. *Inconsistent systems.* A system is *inconsistent* if the two equations have no solution in common.

$$\{(x, y) \mid 2x - 3y = 8 \text{ and } 4x - 6y = 12\} = \emptyset$$

is defined by the system of equations

$$\begin{cases} 2x - 3y = 8 & (1) \\ 4x - 6y = 12 & (2) \end{cases}$$

$$2 \times (1) \qquad 4x - 6y = 16 \qquad (3)$$
$$(2) - (3) \qquad 0x + 0y = -4 \qquad (4)$$

There are no ordered pairs (x, y) which satisfy this equation. Thus the solution set is $\emptyset$.

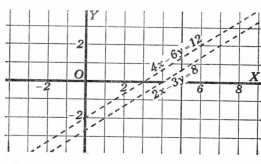

Fig. 10-8

The graph of the solution set of each equation indicates that the lines are parallel and have no point in common, *Fig. 10-8*. This system is said to be *inconsistent*.

Exercise 10-6

(B)

Draw the graph of each of the following systems of equations and then classify each as consistent, inconsistent, or dependent:

1. $\begin{cases} x + y = 3 \\ 2x + y = 4 \end{cases}$ 　　　 **2.** $\begin{cases} 2x + 3y = 6 \\ 4x + 6y = 7 \end{cases}$ 　　　 **3.** $\begin{cases} x - y = 3 \\ 3x - 3y = 9 \end{cases}$

10·8 Solution of systems of two linear equations with literal coefficients.

Example 1. If $x, y \in R$, and b, c represent real constants, find the solution set of the following system of equations and verify:

$$\begin{cases} bx + y = b^2 + c \\ x + cy = b + c^2 \end{cases}$$

While any one of the three methods of eliminating a variable may be used, it is often simplest to use the method of elimination by addition or subtraction.

Solution.

$$\begin{cases} bx + y = b^2 + c & (1) \\ x + cy = b + c^2 & (2) \end{cases}$$

$b \times (2)$ $\qquad\qquad bx + lcy = b^2 + bc^2 \qquad\qquad (3)$

$\qquad\qquad\qquad\quad \underline{lx + y = b^2 + c} \qquad\qquad\qquad (1)$

$(1) - (3)$ $\qquad\qquad y - lcy = c - bc^2$

$\qquad\qquad \therefore\ y(1 - bc) = c(1 - bc)$

$\qquad\qquad\qquad\qquad \therefore\ y = c,\ 1 - bc \neq 0 \qquad (4)$

Substitute in (2) $\qquad x + c^2 = b + c^2$

$\qquad\qquad\qquad\qquad \therefore\ x = b \qquad\qquad\qquad\qquad (5)$

The solution set is $\{(b,\, c)\}$.

Example 2. If $x,\, y \in R$, and $a,\, b,\, c,\, d$ represent real constants, solve the following system for x and y:

$$\begin{cases} ax + by = cd \\ cx - dy = ab \end{cases}$$

Solution.

$$\begin{cases} ax + by = cd & (1) \\ cx - dy = ab & (2) \end{cases}$$

$c \times (1)$ $\qquad\qquad acx + bcy = c^2d \qquad\qquad (3)$

$a \times (2)$ $\qquad\qquad acx - ady = a^2b \qquad\qquad (4)$

$(3) - (4)$ $\qquad\qquad bcy + ady = c^2d - a^2b$

$\qquad\qquad \therefore\ y(bc + ad) = c^2d - a^2b$

$\qquad\qquad \therefore\ y = \dfrac{c^2d - a^2b}{bc + ad},\ bc + ad \neq 0 \qquad (5)$

Since the substitution of $\dfrac{c^2d - a^2b}{lc + ad}$ for y in either equation (1) or (2) is cumbersome, x may best be determined by eliminating y from the two given equations.

$d \times (1)$ $\qquad\qquad adx + bdy = cd^2 \qquad\qquad (6)$

$b \times (2)$ $\qquad\qquad \underline{bcx - bdy = ab^2} \qquad\qquad (7)$

$(5) + (6)$ $\qquad\qquad adx + bcx = cd^2 + ab^2$

$\qquad\qquad \therefore\ x(ad + bc) = cd^2 + ab^2$

$\qquad\qquad \therefore\ x = \dfrac{cd^2 + ab^2}{ad + bc},\ ad + bc \neq 0 \qquad (8)$

The solution is $\qquad \left(\dfrac{cd^2 + ab^2}{ad + bc},\ \dfrac{c^2d - a^2b}{bc + ad} \right).$

Exercise 10-7

(B)

Solve for x and y:

1. $\begin{cases} rx - sy = r^2 - s^2 \\ x + y = r + s \end{cases}$

2. $\begin{cases} 2x - ay = c \\ x + by = c \end{cases}$

3. $\begin{cases} mx + ny = 4mn \\ mx - ny = 0 \end{cases}$

4. $\begin{cases} ax - by = a^2 + b^2 \\ x + y = 2a \end{cases}$

5. $\begin{cases} hx = ky \\ 3hx - 2ky = hk \end{cases}$

6. $\begin{cases} ax + by = c \\ - bx + ay = c \end{cases}$

7. $\begin{cases} x + y = 1 \\ a_1x + b_1y = c_1 \end{cases}$

8. $\begin{cases} ax + by = 2 \\ a^2x - b^2y = a - b \end{cases}$

9. $\begin{cases} ax + by = 2ab \\ bx - ay = b^2 - a^2 \end{cases}$

10. $\begin{cases} \dfrac{x}{a} + \dfrac{y}{b} = 2 \\ ax - by = a^2 - b^2 \end{cases}$

10·9 The solution and classification of the general system of equations of the first degree in two variables (supplementary). The general system of two equations of the first degree in two variables, x and y, may be represented by the system of equations

$$\begin{cases} a_1x + b_1y = c_1 \quad (1) \\ a_2x + b_2y = c_2 \quad (2) \end{cases}$$

where $x, y \in R$ and $a_1, b_1, c_1, a_2, b_2, c_2$ also represent real numbers and stand for the coefficients of the variables x and y and the constant terms.

To solve these equations, first eliminate x by subtraction.

$a_2 \times (1)$ $a_1a_2x + b_1a_2y = c_1a_2$ (3)

$a_1 \times (2)$ $a_1a_2x + a_1b_2y = a_1c_2$ (4)

$(4) - (3)$ $(a_1b_2 - b_1a_2)y = a_1c_2 - c_1a_2$ (5)

$$\therefore \; y = \frac{a_1c_2 - c_1a_2}{a_1b_2 - b_1a_2}, \quad a_1b_2 - b_1a_2 \neq 0$$

Similarly, eliminate y to find the corresponding value of x.

$b_2 \times (1)$ $a_1b_2x + b_1b_2y = b_2c_1$ (6)

$b_1 \times (2)$ $b_1a_2x + b_1b_2y = b_1c_2$ (7)

$(6) - (7)$ $(a_1b_2 - b_1a_2)x = b_2c_1 - b_1c_2$ (8)

$$\therefore \; x = \frac{b_2c_1 - b_1c_2}{a_1b_2 - b_1a_2}, \quad a_1b_2 - b_1a_2 \neq 0$$

Thus the solution is the ordered pair:

$$\left(\frac{b_2c_1 - b_1c_2}{a_1b_2 - b_1a_2}, \frac{a_1c_2 - c_1a_2}{a_1b_2 - b_1a_2} \right)$$

The denominator of each fraction is the same, $a_1b_2 - b_1a_2$ and is formed from the coefficients of x and y in a manner easily remembered, as follows:

Write the coefficients

$$\begin{vmatrix} a_1 & b_1 \\ a_2 & b_2 \end{vmatrix}$$

and subtract the upward product (a_2b_1 or b_1a_2) from the downward product (a_1b_2 or b_2a_1).

The numerator for x may be determined in a similar manner, if the coefficients of x, a_1 and a_2, are replaced by c_1 and c_2, respectively.

Thus $\qquad \begin{vmatrix} c_1 & b_1 \\ c_2 & b_2 \end{vmatrix}$ gives rise to $b_2c_1 - b_1c_2$.

Similarly $\qquad \begin{vmatrix} a_1 & c_1 \\ a_2 & c_2 \end{vmatrix}$ gives rise to $a_1c_2 - c_1a_2$, the numerator

of the fraction corresponding to y.

Thus $\qquad x = \dfrac{\begin{vmatrix} c_1 & b_1 \\ c_2 & b_2 \end{vmatrix}}{\begin{vmatrix} a_1 & b_1 \\ a_2 & b_2 \end{vmatrix}}$ and $y = \dfrac{\begin{vmatrix} a_1 & c_1 \\ a_2 & c_2 \end{vmatrix}}{\begin{vmatrix} a_1 & b_1 \\ a_2 & b_2 \end{vmatrix}}$

where the arrays are evaluated as indicated. The values of these arrays or the corresponding expressions are called *determinants*.

Thus, the solution to the system $\begin{cases} 2x - 3y = 8 \\ 3x + y = 1 \end{cases}$ is:

$$x = \frac{\begin{vmatrix} 8 & -3 \\ 1 & 1 \end{vmatrix}}{\begin{vmatrix} 2 & -3 \\ 3 & 1 \end{vmatrix}} \qquad\qquad y = \frac{\begin{vmatrix} 2 & 8 \\ 3 & 1 \end{vmatrix}}{\begin{vmatrix} 2 & -3 \\ 3 & 1 \end{vmatrix}}$$

$$x = \frac{8+3}{2+9} \qquad\qquad y = \frac{2-24}{2+9}$$

$$x = 1 \qquad\qquad y = -2$$

This solution is illustrated in *Fig. 10-6* (page 350) by the point with coordinates $(1, -2)$ at which the lines defined by the equations intersect.

a. *A consistent system.* A system is consistent if the equations have a unique common solution. This can occur if and only if

$$a_1b_2 - b_1a_2 \text{ or } \begin{vmatrix} a_1 & b_1 \\ a_2 & b_2 \end{vmatrix} \text{ is not zero.}$$

If $\qquad\qquad a_1b_2 - b_1a_2 \neq 0$

then $\qquad\qquad a_1b_2 \neq b_1a_2$

or
$$\frac{a_1}{a_2} \neq \frac{b_1}{b_2}, \ a_2, b_2 \neq 0$$

or
$$a_1 : b_1 \neq a_2 : b_2.$$

Thus the system $\begin{cases} 2x - 3y = 8 \\ 3x + y = 1 \end{cases}$

is consistent because $\dfrac{2}{3} \neq \dfrac{-3}{1}$ or $2 : (-3) \neq 3 : 1$.

This situation is illustrated in *Fig. 10-6* in which the graphs defined by the two equations intersect in the unique point with coordinates $(1, -2)$.

b. *A dependent system.* A system is dependent if each equation has the same solution set. This can occur only if the system is equivalent to the system

$$\begin{cases} 0x = 0 \\ 0y = 0 \end{cases}$$

which is satisfied by every real value of x and y. This can occur only when:

(i) $a_1 b_2 - b_1 a_2 = 0$: that is, $a_1 : b_1 = a_2 : b_2$ or $\dfrac{a_1}{a_2} = \dfrac{b_1}{b_2}, \ a_2, b_2 \neq 0$

and (ii) $b_2 c_1 - b_1 c_2 = 0$: that is, $b_1 : c_1 = b_2 : c_2$ or $\dfrac{b_1}{b_2} = \dfrac{c_1}{c_2}, \ b_2, c_2 \neq 0$

and (iii) $a_1 c_2 - c_1 a_2 = 0$: that is, $a_1 : c_1 = a_2 : c_2$ or $\dfrac{a_1}{a_2} = \dfrac{c_1}{c_2}, \ a_2, c_2 \neq 0$

These three equations are equivalent to the statement

$$\frac{a_1}{a_2} = \frac{b_1}{b_2} = \frac{c_1}{c_2}, \ a_2, b_2, c_2 \neq 0$$

or $a_1 : b_1 : c_1 = a_2 : b_2 : c_2$.

Thus the system $\begin{cases} 2x - 3y = 8 \\ 6x - 9y = 24 \end{cases}$

is dependent because $\dfrac{2}{6} = \dfrac{-3}{-9} = \dfrac{8}{24}$.

This situation is illustrated in *Fig. 10-7* (page 350) in which the graphs defined by the two equations are coincident, and thus any ordered pair which satisfies the one equation also satisfies the other. Such a system has an unlimited number of solutions.

c. *An inconsistent system.* A system is inconsistent if the equations have no solution in common. This can only occur if the system is equivalent to any one of the following:

(i) $\begin{cases} 0x = k, \ k \neq 0 \\ 0y = l, \ l \neq 0 \end{cases}$ or   (ii) $\begin{cases} 0x = k, \ k \neq 0 \\ 0y = 0 \end{cases}$ or   (iii) $\begin{cases} 0x = 0 \\ 0y = l, l \neq 0 \end{cases}$

That is, either x or y, or both, must be undefined.

These situations occur respectively when:

(i) $a_1b_2 - b_1a_2 = 0$ or   (ii) $a_1b_2 - b_1a_2 = 0$ or   (iii) $a_1b_2 - b_1a_2 = 0$
$\quad c_1b_2 - c_2b_1 \neq 0$ $\quad c_1b_2 - c_2b_1 \neq 0$ $\quad c_1b_2 - c_2b_1 = 0$
$\quad a_1c_2 - c_1a_2 \neq 0$ $\quad a_1c_2 - a_2c_1 = 0$ $\quad a_1c_2 - a_2c_1 \neq 0$

These three situations are equivalent to the statement:

$$\frac{a_1}{a_2} = \frac{b_1}{b_2} \neq \frac{c_1}{c_2}, \; a_2, \, b_2, \, c_2 \neq 0$$

or $a_1 : b_1 = a_2 : b_2$ and $b_1 : c_1 \neq b_2 : c_2$

Thus the system $\begin{cases} 2x - 3y = 8 \\ 4x - 6y = 12 \end{cases}$

is inconsistent because

$$\frac{2}{4} = \frac{-3}{-6} \neq \frac{8}{12}.$$

This situation is illustrated in *Fig. 10-8* (page 351) in which the graphs defined by the two equations are parallel lines and have no point in common.

Example 1. Classify the following systems of equations. Describe the graph of the solution set.

(i) $\begin{cases} 3x + 2y = 6 \\ 2x - 4y = 7 \end{cases}$ (ii) $\begin{cases} 3x + 2y = 6 \\ 12x + 8y = 24 \end{cases}$ (iii) $\begin{cases} 3x + 2y = 6 \\ 6x + 4y = 7 \end{cases}$

Solution. (i) $\dfrac{a_1}{a_2} = \dfrac{3}{2}, \quad \dfrac{b_1}{b_2} = \dfrac{2}{-4}, \quad \dfrac{c_1}{c_2} = \dfrac{6}{7} \qquad \therefore \; \dfrac{a_1}{a_2} \neq \dfrac{b_1}{b_2}$

The system has a unique solution and is consistent. The graph of the solution set is a single point.

(ii) $\dfrac{a_1}{a_2} = \dfrac{1}{4}, \quad \dfrac{b_1}{b_2} = \dfrac{1}{4}, \quad \dfrac{c_1}{c_2} = \dfrac{1}{4} \qquad \therefore \; \dfrac{a_1}{a_2} = \dfrac{b_1}{b_2} = \dfrac{c_1}{c_2}$

The system has an unlimited number of solutions and is dependent. The graph of the solution set is the straight line defined by either equation.

(iii) $\dfrac{a_1}{a_2} = \dfrac{1}{2}, \quad \dfrac{b_1}{b_2} = \dfrac{1}{2}, \quad \dfrac{c_1}{c_2} = \dfrac{6}{7} \qquad \therefore \; \dfrac{a_1}{a_2} = \dfrac{b_1}{b_2} \neq \dfrac{c_1}{c_2}$

The system has no solution and is inconsistent. The solution set $\emptyset$ has no graph.

Example 2. State the number of ordered pairs in the following relation and define its graph:

$$A = \{(x,y) \mid 2x - y = 6 \text{ and } 4x - 2y = 9, \, x, \, y \in R\}$$

Solution. For the system $\begin{cases} 2x - y = 6 \\ 4x - 2y = 9 \end{cases}$

$$\frac{a_1}{a_2} = \frac{1}{2}, \quad \frac{b_1}{b_2} = \frac{1}{2}, \quad \frac{c_1}{c_2} = \frac{2}{3} \qquad \therefore \; \frac{a_1}{a_2} = \frac{b_1}{b_2} \neq \frac{c_1}{c_2}$$

The relation has no ordered pairs; the solution set is ∅. There is no graph.

Example 3. Determine the solution set of the system:

$$\begin{cases} 4x + 9y = -1 \\ x - 3y = 4 \end{cases}$$

Solution.

$$x = \frac{\begin{vmatrix} -1 & 9 \\ 4 & -3 \end{vmatrix}}{\begin{vmatrix} 4 & 9 \\ 1 & -3 \end{vmatrix}} \qquad\qquad y = \frac{\begin{vmatrix} 4 & -1 \\ 1 & 4 \end{vmatrix}}{\begin{vmatrix} 4 & 9 \\ 1 & -3 \end{vmatrix}}$$

$$\therefore \; x = \frac{3 - 36}{-12 - 9} \qquad\qquad \therefore \; y = \frac{16 + 1}{-12 - 9}$$

$$\therefore \; x = \frac{11}{7} \qquad\qquad \therefore \; y = -\frac{17}{21}$$

The solution set is $\left\{ \left(\dfrac{11}{7}, \dfrac{-17}{21} \right) \right\}$.

Example 4. Find $\left\{ (x, y) \mid x + 4 = \dfrac{y - 3}{2} \text{ and } \dfrac{x - 3}{5} = 6 - y \right\}$; verify.

Solution.

$$\begin{cases} x + 4 = \dfrac{y - 3}{2} & \qquad (1) \\ \dfrac{x - 3}{5} = 6 - y & \qquad (2) \end{cases}$$

$2 \times (1)$ $\qquad\qquad 2x + 8 = y - 3$

$\qquad\qquad \therefore \; 2x - y = -11 \qquad (3)$

$5 \times (2)$ $\qquad\qquad x - 3 = 30 - 5y$

$\qquad\qquad \therefore \; x + 5y = 33 \qquad (4)$

From (3) and (4)

$$x = \frac{\begin{vmatrix} -11 & -1 \\ 33 & 5 \end{vmatrix}}{\begin{vmatrix} 2 & -1 \\ 1 & 5 \end{vmatrix}} \qquad\qquad y = \frac{\begin{vmatrix} 2 & -11 \\ 1 & 33 \end{vmatrix}}{\begin{vmatrix} 2 & -1 \\ 1 & 5 \end{vmatrix}}$$

$$\therefore \; x = \frac{-55 + 33}{10 + 1} \qquad\qquad \therefore \; y = \frac{66 + 11}{11}$$

$$\therefore \; x = -2 \qquad\qquad \therefore \; y = 7$$

The solution set is $\{(-2, 7)\}$.

Verification.

L.S. (1) $= -2 + 4$ L.S. (2) $= \dfrac{-2-3}{5}$

$\qquad\qquad = 2$ $\qquad\qquad = -1$

R.S. (1) $= \dfrac{7-3}{2}$ R.S. (2) $= 6 - 7$

$\qquad\qquad = 2$ $\qquad\qquad = -1$

Exercise 10-8

(A)

Classify each of the following systems of equations, giving the reason. State the kind of graph obtained in each case:

1. $\begin{cases} 4x + 2y = 6 \\ 3x - 4y = 7 \end{cases}$
2. $\begin{cases} 3x - 4y = 7 \\ 6x - 4y = 14 \end{cases}$
3. $\begin{cases} 2a - 4b + 6 = 0 \\ 6a - 12b + 7 = 0 \end{cases}$

4. $\begin{cases} 8m - 7n = 3 \\ 4m - \dfrac{7}{2}n = 10 \end{cases}$
5. $\begin{cases} 7x - 2y = 8 \\ 14x - 4y = 16 \end{cases}$
6. $\begin{cases} 5x - 4y = 10 \\ 3x + 7y = 11 \end{cases}$

Evaluate the following arrays:

7. $\begin{vmatrix} 4 & -2 \\ 3 & -1 \end{vmatrix}$
8. $\begin{vmatrix} -3 & 1 \\ 2 & -3 \end{vmatrix}$
9. $\begin{vmatrix} -4 & 4 \\ -1 & 1 \end{vmatrix}$

10. $\begin{vmatrix} 10 & 3 \\ -5 & 2 \end{vmatrix}$
11. $\begin{vmatrix} a & y \\ b & x \end{vmatrix}$
12. $\begin{vmatrix} p_1 & -q_1 \\ -p_2 & -q_2 \end{vmatrix}$

(B)

For each of the systems of equations defining the following relations, calculate the ratios $\dfrac{a_1}{a_2}, \dfrac{b_1}{b_2}, \dfrac{c_1}{c_2}$ *and classify the system stating the number of ordered pairs in the relation. Describe the graph of each relation and draw the graphs for questions 22, 23, 24:*

13. $A = \{(x, y) \mid 3x - y = 5 \text{ and } x - \tfrac{1}{3}y = 1\}$
14. $B = \{(x, y) \mid 3x - y = 5 \text{ and } 2x + y = 4\}$
15. $C = \{(x, y) \mid x = 2 - \tfrac{y}{2} \text{ and } 2x + y = 4\}$
16. $D = \{(x, y) \mid y = 4 - 2x \text{ and } x + \tfrac{y}{2} = 1\}$
17. $E = \{(x, y) \mid y = 2x - 6 \text{ and } 4x - 2y = 12\}$
18. $F = \{(x, y) \mid 2x + y = 5 \text{ and } 3x - 2y = 4\}$

19. $G = \{(x, y)\,|\, 2x - 3y = 1 \text{ and } 4x + 6y = 2\}$

20. $H = \{(x, y)\,|\, 3x - y = -1\} \cap \{(x, y)\,|\, 6x - 2y = -5\}$

21. $J = \{(x, y)\,|\, y = \dfrac{x}{3} + 7\} \cap \{(x, y)\,|\, \dfrac{x - 3y}{7} = -3\}$

22. $K = \{(x, y)\,|\, 45x - 27y = 21 \text{ and } 9y = 15x - 7\}$

23. $L = \{(x, y)\,|\, \dfrac{x}{3} = \dfrac{y}{4} \text{ and } \dfrac{x - 4}{4} - \dfrac{y - 13}{3} = 1\}$

24. $M = \{(x, y)\,|\, \dfrac{2x}{3} - 7y = 1\} \cap \{(x, y)\,|\, \dfrac{21}{2} y = x - 6\}$

Solve the following systems using determinants; verify:

25. $\begin{cases} 5x + y = 15 \\ 2x - 3y = 6 \end{cases}$
   26. $\begin{cases} 2x + 3y = 7 \\ x + 2y = 4 \end{cases}$
   27. $\begin{cases} \dfrac{x}{6} + y = 3 \\ x + \dfrac{y}{2} = 7 \end{cases}$

28. $\begin{cases} 10x + 8y = -7 \\ 4x - 12y = 1 \end{cases}$
   29. $\begin{cases} \dfrac{x}{2} - y = -6 \\ \dfrac{2}{3}x - \dfrac{1}{8}y = \dfrac{10}{3} \end{cases}$
   30. $\begin{cases} 6x + 5y = 2.6 \\ 0.3x + 0.5y = 0.23 \end{cases}$

Use determinants to find:

31. $\{(x, y)\,|\, 2x + 6y = 13 - 2x \text{ and } 9y + 6 = 8x + 15\}$

32. $\{(x, y)\,|\, 5(3x - y) = x + 3 \text{ and } 3(x + y) = 7(y - x)\}$

33. $\{(x, y)\,|\, y = 3x + 1\} \cap \{(x, y)\,|\, 6x - 2y = -2\}$

34. $\{(x, y)\,|\, x + \dfrac{y}{3} = y\} \cap \{(x, y)\,|\, y + \tfrac{1}{4}x = x + 3\}$

10·10 Linear Diophantine equations (supplementary). The graph of the linear relation

$$F = \{(x, y)\,|\, x + 2y = 4, \, x, y \in R\}$$

is shown in *Fig. 10-9.*

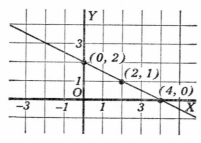

Fig. 10-9

The graph has x-intercept 4 and y-intercept 2.

All the ordered pairs which are the coordinates of points on the graph satisfy the defining equation $x + 2y = 4$, x, $y \in R$.

Thus, there are an unlimited number of solutions for this equation. Such an equation is called an *indeterminate* equation.

If we impose the additional restriction that both x and y must represent integers, there may be a limited number of solutions. Such an equation is referred to as a *Diophantine equation*.

From the graph of *Fig. 10-9* the positive integral solutions of $x + 2y = 4$ are:

$$\begin{array}{ccc} x = 0 & x = 2 & x = 4 \\ y = 2 & y = 1 & y = 0 \end{array}$$

It is interesting to note that many of the early studies of algebra concentrated on indeterminate equations. The writings of the Greek algebraist, Diophantus of Alexandria (*ca.* 350 A.D.), are devoted mainly to finding integral solutions of indeterminate equations. Diophantus did not develop algebraic methods for finding the integral solutions. He was content with finding a single solution by trial. It was at a later date that the study of algebraic methods for determining the integral solutions of indeterminate equations was begun by the Hindus.

Write solutions for the following problems and compare them with those on page 485.

1. Find graphically the positive integral solutions of $3x + 4y = 24$.

2. Show graphically and algebraically that the equation $2x + 3y = -6$ has no positive integral solutions.

An algebraic method of finding the positive integral solutions of an indeterminate equation is illustrated in the following examples.

Example 1. Solve $3x + 5y = 36$, x, $y \in {}^{+}I$.

Solution. $3x + 5y = 36$

$$\therefore \ 3x = 36 - 5y$$

$$\therefore \ x = 12 - y - \frac{2y}{3}$$

Since $x \in {}^{+}I$, then $\frac{2y}{3} \in I$.

We can now find positive integral values of y so that $\frac{2y}{3}$ is an integer:

that is, so that $2y$ is divisible by 3; then corresponding values of x may be obtained by substitution. The table at the right gives the first four possible values for y and the corresponding values for x.

y	x
0	12
3	7
6	2
9	-3

Examination of the pattern in the table and the original equation indicates that any other possible value for y produces a negative integral value for x. Thus, the positive integral solutions of $3x + 5y = 36$ are:

$$x = 7 \qquad \text{and} \qquad x = 2$$
$$y = 3 \qquad\qquad\qquad y = 6$$

Example 2. Solve $7x + 12y = 152$, $x, y \in {}^+I$.

Solution. $\qquad 7x + 12y = 152$

$$\therefore \ 7x = 152 - 12y$$

$$\therefore \ x = 21 + \frac{5}{7} - y - \frac{5y}{7}$$

$$\therefore \ x = 21 - y + \frac{5 - 5y}{7}$$

Since $x \in {}^+I$, then $\dfrac{5 - 5y}{7} \in I$.

We could now find positive integral values of y for which $5 - 5y$ is divisible by 7 and then find x by substitution. However, these values may be more readily determined by simplifying further. Thus, let

$$\frac{5 - 5y}{7} = m, \ m \in I.$$

$$\therefore \ 5y = 5 - 7m$$

$$y = 1 - m - \frac{2m}{5}$$

Since y is an integer, then $\dfrac{2m}{5}$ is an integer.

We can now find y by giving m integral values, such that $2m$ is divisible by 5, and then find x by substitution; the table at the right provides representative values which make it possible to predict all positive integral solutions.

m	y	x
0	1	20
5	-6	32
-5	8	8
10	-13	44
-10	15	-4

The positive integral solutions of $7x + 12y = 152$ are:

$$x = 20 \qquad\qquad x = 8$$
$$y = 1 \qquad \text{and} \qquad y = 8$$

Example 3. Betty bought knives at 29¢ each and forks at 19¢ each. If she spent \$4.03 in all, how many knives and how many forks did she buy?

Solution. Represent the number of knives by x, $x \in {}^+I$.

Represent the number of forks by y, $y \in {}^+I$.

The cost of the knives is $29x$ ¢.

The cost of the forks is $19y$ ¢.

Total cost of knives and forks is $(29x + 19y)$ ¢.

But the total cost is \$4.03.

$$\therefore \ 29x + 19y = 403$$

$$\therefore \ 19y = 403 - 29x$$

$$\therefore \ y = 21 + \frac{4}{19} - x - \frac{10x}{19}$$

$$\therefore \ y = 21 - x + \frac{4 - 10x}{19}$$

Since y is an integer, then $\dfrac{4 - 10x}{19}$ is an integer.

$$\text{Let } \frac{4 - 10x}{19} = m, \ m \in I.$$

$$\therefore \ 10x = 4 - 19m$$

$$x = \frac{4 - 19m}{10}$$

$$= \frac{4 - 9m}{10} - m$$

Since x is an integer, then $\dfrac{4 - 9m}{10}$ is an integer.

$$\text{Let } \frac{4 - 9m}{10} = k, \ k \in I.$$

$$\therefore \ 9m = 4 - 10k$$

$$m = \frac{4 - k}{9} - k$$

We now can give values to k so that $4 - k$ is divisible by 9 and thus find m; then by substitution find x and y as in the table at the right.

k	m	x	y
4	− 4	8	9
− 5	6	− 11	38
13	− 14	27	− 20
− 14	16	− 30	67

The only positive integral solution of $29x + 19y = 403$ is $x = 8$, $y = 9$. Thus, Betty purchased 8 knives and 9 forks.

10·11 General solution of linear Diophantine equations (supplementary).

Given one solution in positive integers of the equation $ax + by = c$, a, b, c, x, $y \in I$, *find all integral solutions.*

Let (h, k) be a solution of $ax + by = c$.   (1)

Then, $ah + bk = c$ (2)

(1) $-$ (2) $a(x - h) = -b(y - k)$

$$\therefore \frac{x - h}{+b} = \frac{y - k}{-a} = t, \; t \in I$$

$$\therefore \quad x = h + bt, \quad y = k - at$$

which is the general solution in integers.

Example 1. Solve $14x - 11y = 29$, x, $y \in {}^{+}I$.

Solution. By the method of section $10 \cdot 10$, or simply by inspection, one solution is $x = 6$, $y = 5$.

The general solution is $\quad x = h + bt$, $\quad y = k - at$.

That is, $x = 6 - 11t$, $\quad y = 5 - 14t$.

Positive integral solutions are:

$t = 0$	$x = 6$	$y = 5$
$t = -1$	$x = 17$	$y = 19$
$t = -2$	$x = 28$	$y = 33$
$t = -3$	$x = 39$	$y = 47$

and so on; the number of integral solutions is unlimited in this case.

It is important to note that if the solution of a problem gives rise to a system of two equations in three variables, it is often possible to obtain a solution in positive integers. Such a system is called a *Diophantine system* and is illustrated by the problem of Example 2.

Example 2. If \$100 can be divided among a group of 100 people so that the men receive \$10 each, the women 50¢ each, and the children 12½¢ each, find the number of men, the number of women, and the number of children in the group.

Solution. Represent the number of men by x ,

         the number of women by y ,

         the number of children by z .

         Then the men receive $10x$ dollars,

         the women receive $\frac{1}{2}y$ dollars,

         the children receive $\frac{1}{8}z$ dollars.

         But the total amount divided is 100 dollars.

$$\therefore \quad 10x + \tfrac{1}{2}y + \tfrac{1}{8}z = 100$$

or $80x + 4y + z = 800$ (1)

Also the total number present is 100.

$\therefore \ x + y + z = 100$ (2)

Solving, $80x + 4y + z = 800$ (1)

$x + y + z = 100$ (2)

$(1)-(2)$ $79x + 3y = 700$ (3)

Since the number of men, women, and children must be positive integers, it is now necessary to solve equation (3) in positive integers.

Complete the solution and compare it with that on page 485.

Exercise 10-9

(B)

Solve for all positive integral solutions:

1. $4x + 5y = 36$ **2.** $3x + 5y = 130$

3. $3x + 5y = 12$ **4.** $5x + 2y = 53$

5. $35x + 15y = 210$ **6.** $35x + 19y = 372$

7. A man spent $36 buying two varieties of apples, the first costing $3 per bushel and the second $5 per bushel. How many bushels of each did he buy?

8. Separate 81 into two parts, so that one part is a multiple of 8 and the other is a multiple of 5.

9. Separate 37 into two parts, one of which is divisible by 5 and the other by 11.

10. How many selections of coins can be made to pay a debt of $5 using only dimes and quarters?

11. Show that the equation $2x + 8y = 9$ has no integral solutions.

Solve for all positive integral solutions:

12. $\begin{cases} x + 2y + z = 8 \\ 10x + 6y + z = 25 \end{cases}$ **13.** $\begin{cases} 10x + 5y + 2z = 229 \\ x + y + z = 43 \end{cases}$

14. A group of fifty men, women, and children pay $50 for entrance to a baseball game. The men pay $2 each, the women $1 each, and the children 20¢ each. Find the number of men, the number of women, and the number of children in the group.

15. Find a positive integer which when divided by 39 gives a remainder of 16 and when divided by 56, a remainder of 27.

16. Find the smallest positive integer which when divided by 3, 5, 7 has remainders 2, 3, 2, respectively.

Chapter **XI**

COORDINATE GEOMETRY
OF THE STRAIGHT LINE

***11·1** Introduction.* Coordinate geometry links algebra and geometry. It enables us to solve geometric problems by using algebraic methods. Conversely, the methods of coordinate geometry are used to study algebraic problems, as in the study of relations.

In coordinate geometry, by selecting coordinate axes and a unit length, we assign to each point in a plane an ordered pair of real numbers. The length of a line segment, or the distance between the end points of a line segment, is a positive real number associated with the unit of the system.

In coordinate geometry, for convenience, we express a length simply as a positive real number, and it is understood to be in terms of the unit of the system. Similarly, when we express an area as a positive real number, it is understood to be in terms of the unit square of the coordinate system.

***11·2** Discovery of the method of calculating lengths of line segments parallel to the axes.*

Discovery Exercise 11-1

(B)

Write solutions for the following problems and compare them with those on page 486.

1. In *Fig. 11-1*, points *P* and *Q* have the same ordinate 2.

　(i) How is line segment *PQ* related to the *x*-axis? Why?

(ii) Find the length of PQ from the graph in *Fig. 11-1*.

(iii) Recalling that distance or length is a positive real number, show how PQ may be calculated from the abscissas of P and Q.

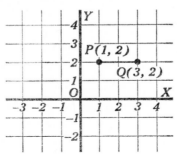

Fig. 11-1

2. In *Fig. 11-2*, points A and B have the same ordinate 1.

(i) How is line segment AB related to the x-axis?

(ii) Find the length of AB from the graph in *Fig. 11-2*.

(iii) Calculate AB from the abscissas of A and B.

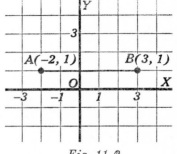

Fig. 11-2

3. In *Fig. 11-3*, R and S have the same abscissa 2.

(i) How is line segment RS related to the y-axis?

(ii) From the graph (*Fig. 11-3*), find the length of RS.

(iii) Calculate RS from the ordinates of points R and S.

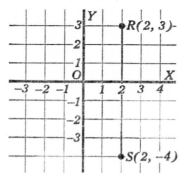

Fig. 11-3

4. In *Fig. 11-4*, P_1 and P_2 have the same ordinate.

(i) How is line segment P_1P_2 related to the *x*-axis?

(ii) Write two expressions for the length of P_1P_2.

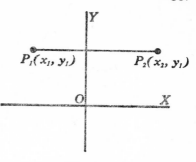

Fig. 11-4

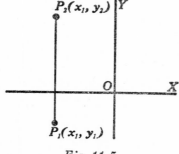

Fig. 11-5

5. In *Fig. 11-5*, P_1P_2 is parallel to the *y*-axis. Write two expressions for the length of P_1P_2.

11·3 General expressions for lengths of line segments parallel to the axes.

(i) **Length of a line segment parallel to the *x*-axis and with end points** $P_1(x_1, y_1)$ **and** $P_2(x_2, y_1)$ **is**

$$|x_2 - x_1|.$$

(ii) **Length of a line segment parallel to the *y*-axis and with end points** $P_1(x_1, y_1)$ **and** $P_2(x_1, y_2)$ **is**

$$|y_2 - y_1|.$$

Write a solution for the following problem and compare it with that on page 486.

1. Determine the lengths of the line segments joining the following pairs of points:

(i) $A(-2, 0)$, $B(-8, 0)$ (ii) $P(4, -2)$, $Q(4, 0)$

(iii) $C(0, 0)$, $A(0, -5)$ (iv) $R(-2, -3)$, $S(0, -3)$

(v) $M(a, -1)$, $N(a, -4)$ (vi) $W(p, q)$, $Z(r, q)$

(vii) $A(a_1, b_1)$, $B(a_1, b_2)$ (viii) $C(0, y_1)$, $D(0, y_2)$

11·4 Discovery of the method of calculating the length of the line segment determined by any two points (distance between any two points).

Discovery Exercise 11-2

(B)

Write solutions for the following problems and compare them with those on page 486.

1. In *Fig. 11-6*, *PR* and *QR* are parallel to the axes.
    (i) Calculate *PR* and *RQ*.
    (ii) Using the Pythagorean Theorem, calculate *PQ*.

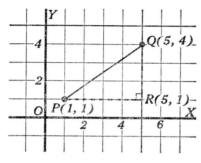

Fig. 11-6

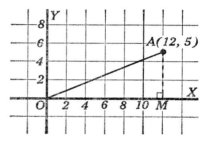

Fig. 11-7

2. With reference to *Fig. 11-7*:
    (i) determine the coordinates of *M*;
    (ii) calculate *OM*, *AM*, and *OA*.

3. In *Fig. 11-8*, *AC* and *BC* are drawn parallel to the axes.
    (i) Find the coordinates of *C*.
    (ii) Calculate *CB*, *AC*, and *AB*.

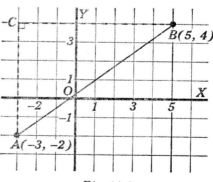

Fig. 11-8

4. Calculate the lengths of the line segments joining the following pairs of points:

(i) $P(-2, 3)$, $Q(3, -9)$ (ii) $A(1, 1)$, $B(5, 3)$

(iii) $P_1(-3, -4)$, $P_2(3, 4)$ (iv) $R(7, -1)$, $S(-8, 7)$

(v) $M(a, b)$, $N(c, d)$ (vi) $P_1(x_1, y_1)$, $P_2(x_2, y_2)$

11·5 General expression for the distance between any two points.

Hypothesis: A line segment joining any two points $P_1(x_1, y_1)$ and $P_2(x_2, y_2)$

Required: To find the length of P_1P_2

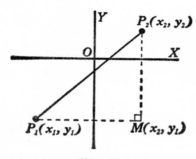

Fig. 11-9

Line segments P_1M and P_2M parallel to the axes meet on M (*Fig. 11-9*).

Since the coordinates of M are (x_2, y_1),

$$\therefore \quad P_1 M = |x_2 - x_1|$$
$$\text{and } M P_2 = |y_2 - y_1|.$$

By the Pythagorean Theorem:

$$P_1P_2{}^2 = P_1M^2 + M^2P_2$$
$$\therefore \ P_1P_2{}^2 = |x_2 - x_1|^2 + |y_2 - y_1|^2$$

Since P_1P_2 is a positive real number,

$$\therefore \ P_1P_2 = \sqrt{|x_2 - x_1|^2 + |y_2 - y_1|^2}$$
$$\therefore \ P_1P_2 = \sqrt{(x_2 - x_1)^2 + (y_2 - y_1)^2}.$$

Corollary: If $P_2(x_2, y_2)$ is the origin, then $x_2 = 0$, $y_2 = 0$, and

$$P_1O = \sqrt{x_1{}^2 + y_1{}^2}.$$

The completion postulate states that B is between A and C if and only if $AB + BC = AC$. Thus, A, B, and C are collinear if $AB + BC = AC$.

Example. Show that $A(0, 3)$, $B(-2, 6)$, $C(4, -3)$ are collinear.

Solution.

$$BA = \sqrt{(-2-0)^2 + (6-3)^2} = \sqrt{4+9} = \sqrt{13}$$
$$BC = \sqrt{(4-(-2))^2 + (-3-6)^2} = \sqrt{36+81} = \sqrt{117} = 3\sqrt{13}$$
$$AC = \sqrt{(4-0)^2 + (-3-3)^2} = \sqrt{16+36} = \sqrt{52} = 2\sqrt{13}$$

Since $BA + AC = BC$, $\therefore$ B, A, C are collinear.

Exercise 11-3

(A)

1. State expressions for the distance between each of the following pairs of points:

    (i) $(0, 0)$, $(-3, 4)$ (ii) $(9, -12)$, $(0, 0)$ (iii) $(2, 4)$, $(10, 10)$

    (iv) $(-3, -5)$, $(2, 7)$ (v) $(-5, 4)$, $(4, 16)$ (vi) $(1, -4)$, $(9, 14)$

(B)

2. Calculate the lengths of line segments whose end points have co-ordinates as follows:

    (i) $(-4, 3)$, $(0, 0)$ (ii) $(-4, 7)$, $(3, -2)$ (iii) $(-1, -4)$, $(4, 6)$

    (iv) $(3, 3)$, $(-1, -1)$ (v) $(2, 4)$, $(-6, 4)$ (vi) $(1, -4)$, $(1, -6)$

3. Find x so that the length of the segment joining the origin to $A(x, 8)$ is 10.

4. Find the perimeters of the figures determined by:

    (i) $A(4, 0)$, $B(0, 3)$, $C(-4, 0)$

    (ii) $P(2, -4)$, $Q(2, 6)$, $R(-2, 6)$, $S(-2, -4)$

5. Determine the type of triangle having vertices:

    (i) $A(-4, 2)$, $B(7, 2)$, $C(-4, 6)$

    (ii) $P(-2, -2)$, $Q(-2, 8)$, $R(7, 3)$

6. Prove that the points $A(3, 4)$, $B(-4, 3)$, $C(-3, 4)$, $D(5, 0)$, and $E(0, -5)$ lie on the circle with centre $O(0, 0)$, the origin.

7. Find the real number y so that the point $M(-2, y)$ is equidistant from $P(-3, 2)$ and $Q(5, -4)$.

8. Find the coordinates of a point (i) on the x-axis (ii) on the y-axis, which is equidistant from $A(-1, 2)$ and $B(3, -2)$.

9. Show that $M(1, 0)$ is the centre of the circle circumscribing the triangle with vertices $A(6, 0)$, $B(4, 4)$, and $C(-3, 3)$.

10. Show that $B(-3, 1)$ is the midpoint of the line segment whose end points are $A(-8, 7)$ and $C(2,-5)$.

11. The distance from the point $P(x, y)$ to $Q(-2, 4)$ is 5. Write and simplify the algebraic equation corresponding to this statement.

12. Find the ratio in which the point $C(4, 2)$ divides the line segment with end points $A(-4, 8)$ and $B(8, -1)$.

13. Prove that $A(-2, 3)$, $B(2, -1)$, and $C(4, -3)$ are collinear.

14. Determine whether the points $P(3, -2)$, $Q(-4, 3)$, and $R(-10, 8)$ are collinear.

15. Find the real number x so that $A(-3, 2)$, $B(3, -4)$, and $C(x, -8)$ are collinear.

11·6 Discovery of the method of calculating the coordinates of the midpoint of a line segment.

Discovery Exercise 11-4

(B)

Write solutions for the following problems and compare them with those on page 487.

1. In *Fig. 11-10*, M is the midpoint of P_1P_2.

  (i) Find, by inspection, the coordinates of M.

  (ii) Verify your conclusion by proving that $P_1M = MP_2 = \frac{1}{2}P_1P_2$.

  (iii) How may the abscissa of M be obtained from the abscissas of P_1 and P_2?

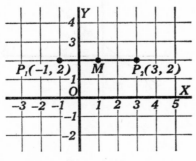

Fig. 11-10

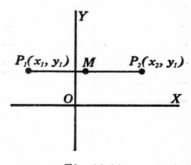

Fig. 11-11

2. In *Fig. 11-11*, M is the midpoint of P_1P_2.

  (i) Predict the coordinates of M.

  (ii) Verify your conclusion by proving that $P_1M = MP_2 = \frac{1}{2}P_1P_2$.

3. In *Fig. 11-12*, M is the midpoint of P_1P_2.

    (i) Find, by inspection, the coordinates of M.

    (ii) Verify your conclusion by proving that $P_1M = MP_2 = \frac{1}{2}P_1P_2$.

    (iii) How may the ordinate of M be obtained from the ordinates of P_1 and P_2?

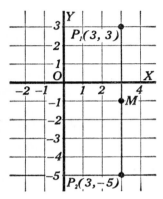

Fig. 11-12

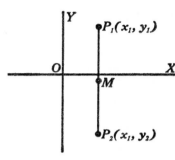

Fig. 11-13

4. In *Fig. 11-13*, M is the midpoint of P_1P_2.

    (i) Predict the coordinates of M.

    (ii) Verify your conclusion by proving that $P_1M = MP_2 = \frac{1}{2}P_1P_2$.

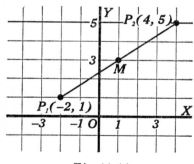

Fig. 11-14

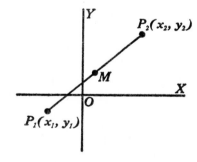

Fig. 11-15

5. In *Fig. 11-14*, M is the midpoint of P_1P_2.

    (i) Find, by inspection, the coordinates of M.

    (ii) Verify your conclusion by proving that $P_1M = MP_2 = \frac{1}{2}P_1P_2$.

    (iii) How may the coordinates of M be found from the coordinates of P_1 and P_2?

6. In *Fig. 11-15*, M is the midpoint of P_1P_2.

    (i) Predict the coordinates of M.

    (ii) Verify your conclusion by proving that $P_1M = MP_2 = \frac{1}{2}P_1P_2$.

    (iii) How may the coordinates of M be found from the coordinates of P_1 and P_2?

11·7 General expression for the coordinates of the midpoint of the line segment joining any two points.

Hypothesis: M is the midpoint of the line segment joining $P_1(x_1, y_1)$ and $P_2(x_2, y_2)$.

Conclusion: The coordinates of M are $\left(\dfrac{x_2 + x_1}{2}, \dfrac{y_2 + y_1}{2}\right)$.

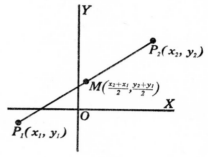

Fig. 11-16

Proof:

$$P_1M = \sqrt{\left(\frac{x_2 + x_1}{2} - x_1\right)^2 + \left(\frac{y_2 + y_1}{2} - y_1\right)^2}$$

$$= \sqrt{\left(\frac{x_2 + x_1 - 2x_1}{2}\right)^2 + \left(\frac{y_2 + y_1 - 2y_1}{2}\right)^2}$$

$$= \sqrt{\left(\frac{x_2 - x_1}{2}\right)^2 + \left(\frac{y_2 - y_1}{2}\right)^2}$$

$$= \frac{1}{2}\sqrt{(x_2 - x_1)^2 + (y_2 - y_1)^2}$$

$$MP_2 = \sqrt{\left(x_2 - \frac{x_2 + x_1}{2}\right)^2 + \left(y_2 - \frac{y_2 + y_1}{2}\right)^2}$$

$$= \sqrt{\left(\frac{2x_2 - x_2 - x_1}{2}\right)^2 + \left(\frac{2y_2 - y_2 - y_1}{2}\right)^2}$$

$$= \sqrt{\left(\frac{x_2 - x_1}{2}\right)^2 + \left(\frac{y_2 - y_1}{2}\right)^2}$$

$$= \frac{1}{2}\sqrt{(x_2 - x_1)^2 + (y_2 - y_1)^2}$$

$\because\ P_1P_2 = \sqrt{(x_2 - x_1)^2 + (y_2 - y_1)^2}$

$\therefore\ P_1M = MP_2 = \frac{1}{2}P_1P_2$

$\therefore\ M\left(\dfrac{x_2 + x_1}{2}, \dfrac{y_2 + y_1}{2}\right)$ or $M\left(\dfrac{x_1 + x_2}{2}, \dfrac{y_1 + y_2}{2}\right)$ is the midpoint of P_1P_2.

Write a solution for the following problem and compare it with that on page 489.

1. Find the coordinates of the midpoints of line segments joining the following points:

   (i) $A(-2, -3)$, $B(4, 2)$ (ii) $P(2, -5)$, $Q(-3, -1)$

   (iii) $W(-4, -5)$, $Z(-6, -7)$ (iv) $C(0, -1)$, $D(1, 1)$

   (v) $R(-3, -2)$, $S(3, 2)$ (vi) $M\left(\dfrac{a}{2}, \dfrac{b}{2}\right)$, $N\left(\dfrac{c}{2}, \dfrac{d}{2}\right)$

Exercise 11-5

(A)

1. Find the coordinates of the midpoints of the line segments having the following end points:

   (i) $(2, 3)$ and $(-2, -3)$ (ii) $(-6, 5)$ and $(3, -4)$

   (iii) $(-4, -7)$ and $(-4, 3)$ (iv) $(-2, 3)$ and $(6, 3)$

   (v) $(0, 0)$ and $(-3, 2)$ (vi) $(-1, -2)$ and $(-5, -6)$

(B)

2. For the triangle $A(-7, 4)$, $B(3, -2)$, $C(1, 2)$, find the lengths of the three medians.

3. $C(1, 0)$ is a point of trisection of the line segment joining $A(-1, -2)$ to $B(5, 4)$. Find the coordinates of the other point of trisection.

4. For the triangle with vertices $A(1, 5)$, $B(-1, -1)$, $C(2, -2)$, prove that the midpoint of AC is equidistant from the three vertices.

5. Show that the y-axis bisects the line segment joining $P(-5, 7)$ and $Q(5, 2)$.

6. Find the coordinates of the centre of the circle for which the ends of a diameter are $R(-3, 2)$ and $S(6, -7)$.

7. Determine whether the diagonals of the figure with vertices $A(-5, 3)$, $B(-4, -2)$, $C(7, -1)$, and $D(6, 4)$ bisect each other.

8. For the triangle with vertices $A(-2, -3)$, $B(6, -3)$, and $C(4, 5)$, prove that the length of the line segment joining the midpoints of the sides AC and BC is one-half the length of AB.

9. If M is the midpoint of the side AB in question 8, prove that
   $AC^2 + BC^2 = 2\ AM^2 + 2\ CM^2$.

10. A quadrilateral has vertices $A(3,\ 2)$, $B(-2,\ 1)$, $C(-3,\ -5)$, and
    $D(5,\ -3)$. E, F, G, and H are the midpoints of AB, BC, CD, and
    DA, respectively. Prove that $FE = GH$.

11·8 Internal division of a directed line segment.

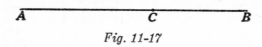

Fig. 11-17

If C is a point on a directed line segment AB (*Fig. 11-17*), where A is
the initial point and B is the terminal point of the line segment, then AB
is said to be divided *internally* at C in the ratio $AC : CB$. Also, C is said
to divide the directed segment BA in the ratio $BC : CA$.

We shall agree that in naming a directed line segment, the first named
point is the *initial* point. Also, we shall agree that the direction from the
initial to the terminal point is the *positive* sense of the directed line segment.

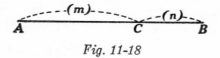

Fig. 11-18

In general, if C divides AB internally at C (*Fig. 11-18*), then the ratio
of the lengths of the segments is $m : n$, where m, $n \in {}^+R$. Also, C divides
BA in the ratio $n : m$.

It should be noted that the lengths of AC and CB are multiples of the
corresponding terms of the ratio.

11·9 Discovery of the method of calculating the coordinates of the point dividing the line segment joining any two points internally in a given ratio.

Discovery Exercise 11-6

(B)

*Write solutions for the following problems and compare them with those on
page* 489.

1. In *Fig. 11-19*, $P(x,\ y)$ divides the line segment joining $A(-3,\ -1)$
   and $B(5,\ 3)$ in the ratio $3:1$. Line segments parallel to the axes
   meet at M and N, as shown.

(i) Find AM.

(ii) Find PN.

(iii) Since $\dfrac{AP}{PB} = \dfrac{3}{1}$, evaluate the ratio $\dfrac{AM}{PN}$. Justify your conclusion.

(iv) Using (i), (ii), and (iii), find x.

(v) Find MP.

(vi) Find NB.

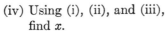

Fig. 11-19

(vii) Evaluate the ratio $\dfrac{MP}{NB}$ and justify your conclusion.

(viii) Using (v), (vi), and (vii) find y.

(ix) State the coordinates of P.

2. In *Fig. 11-20*, $R(x, y)$ divides the line segment joining $P_1(-3, 2)$ and $P_2(4, -3)$ in the ratio $4:3$. Line segments parallel to the axes meet at M and N, as shown.

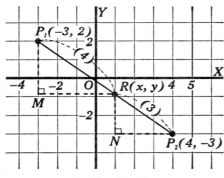

Fig. 11-20

(i) Find MR.

(ii) Find NP_2.

(iii) Evaluate the ratio $\dfrac{MR}{NP_2}$ and justify your conclusion.

(iv) Using (i), (ii), and (iii), find x.

(v) Find MP_1.

(vi) Find NR.

(vii) Evaluate the ratio $\dfrac{MP_1}{NR}$ and justify your conclusion.

(viii) Using (v), (vi), and (vii), find y.

(ix) State the coordinates of R.

3. In *Fig. 11-21*, $R(x, y)$ divides the line segment joining $P_1(x_1, y_1)$ and $P_2(x_2, y_2)$ in the ratio $m : n$, $m, n \in {}^+R$. Line segments parallel to the axes meet at S and T, as shown.

(i) Find P_1S.

(ii) Find RT.

(iii) Evaluate the ratio $\dfrac{P_1S}{RT}$ in terms of m and n; justify your conclusion.

(iv) Using (i), (ii), and (iii), find x.

(v) Find SR.

(vi) Find TP_2.

(vii) Evaluate the ratio $\dfrac{SR}{TP_2}$ in terms of m and n and justify your conclusion.

(viii) Using (v), (vi), and (vii), find y.

(ix) State the coordinates of R.

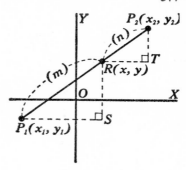

Fig. 11-21

These examples suggest the following conclusion:

The line segment joining $P_1(x_1, y_1)$ and $P_2(x_2, y_2)$ is divided in the ratio $m : n$, m, $n \in {}^+R$ at $R\left(\dfrac{mx_2 + nx_1}{m + n}, \dfrac{my_2 + ny_1}{m + n}\right)$.

The following array showing the coordinates of P_1 and P_2 and the ratio $m : n$ may facilitate computation:

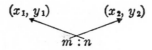

It may be observed that if $m : n = 1 : 1$, R is the midpoint of P_1P_2.

If $m : n = 1 : 1$, the coordinates

$$\left(\frac{mx_2 + nx_1}{m + n}, \frac{my_2 + ny_1}{m + n}\right)$$

become

$$\left(\frac{x_2 + x_1}{2}, \frac{y_2 + y_1}{2}\right)$$

which are the coordinates of the midpoint of P_1P_2.

This expression for the midpoint agrees with that obtained in section 11·7.

Example. Find the coordinates of the point dividing the line segment with initial point $A(4, -2)$ and terminal point $B(-1, 3)$ in the ratio $1 : 4$.

Solution. Let R be the point of division. For this problem, P_1 is $A(4, -2)$, P_2 is $B(-1, 3)$, and $m : n = 1 : 4$. Using the general expression for the coordinates of the point of division, R has coordinates

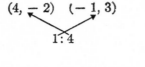

$$\left(\frac{1(-1) + 4(4)}{1 + 4}, \frac{1(3) + 4(-2)}{1 + 4}\right)$$

or $(3, -1)$.

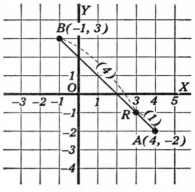

Fig. 11-22

Write solutions for the following problems and compare them with those on page 490.

1. Find the coordinates of the point which divides the line segment joining $A(-2, 3)$ to $B(5, 4)$ in the ratio 5 : 3 .

2. Find the coordinates of the centroid of the triangle with vertices $A(5, 4)$, $B(-2, 3)$, and $C(3, -1)$.

Exercise 11-7

(A)

1. State an expression for the coordinates of the point dividing the line segment joining $P(4, -1)$ to $Q(-6, -3)$ in the ratio 1 : 3 .

2. State the coordinates of the end points of the line segment and the ratio in which it is divided if the coordinates of the point of division are:

    (i) $\left(\dfrac{rc + a}{r + 1}, \dfrac{rd + b}{r + 1}\right)$ (ii) $\left(\dfrac{p + r}{2}, \dfrac{q + s}{2}\right)$

    (iii) $\left(\dfrac{2x_2 + x_1}{3}, \dfrac{2y_2 + y_1}{3}\right)$ (iv) $\left(\dfrac{lx + mx}{l + m}, \dfrac{ly + my}{l + m}\right)$

    (v) $\left(\dfrac{a \cdot 2 + b \cdot 3}{a + b}, \dfrac{a \cdot 4 + b \cdot 5}{a + b}\right)$ (vi) $\left(\dfrac{3 \cdot 4 + 2 \cdot 6}{3 + 2}, \dfrac{3 \cdot 5 + 2 \cdot 7}{3 + 2}\right)$

(B)

3. For the given ratios, determine the coordinates of the point of section for line segments having initial and terminal points as follows:

    (i) $A(2, -1)$, $B(-6, 5)$;   4 : 3

    (ii) $P(-6, 2)$, $Q(7, -4)$;   2 : 7

(iii) $M(-3,0)$, $N(-1, -2)$; $2:1$

(iv) $O(0, 0)$, $A(5, -1)$; $2:5$

4. Find the coordinates of the points of trisection of the line segment with end points $A(-1, -3)$ and $B(2, -6)$.

5. Find the coordinates of the centroid of the triangle with vertices $A(5, 4)$, $B(-3, -1)$, and $C(4, -3)$.

6. Find the coordinates of the three points dividing the line segment joining $A(-4, -8)$ and $B(4, 0)$ into four equal parts.

7. Find x so that the line segment with initial point $A(x, 4)$ and terminal point $B(3, 0)$ is divided at $C(2, 1)$ in the ratio $3:1$.

(C)

8. The point $P(2, -3)$ divides the line segment with initial point $A(2, 4)$ and terminal point B in the ratio $1:2$. Find the coordinates of B.

9. Find the coordinates of the centroid of the triangle with vertices $P_1(x_1, y_1)$, $P_2(x_2, y_2)$, and $P_3(x_3, y_3)$.

11·10 External division of a directed line segment (supplementary).

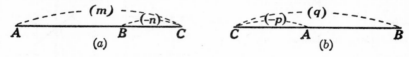

Fig. 11-23

If C is a point on the extension of directed line segment AB, as in *Fig. 11-23 (a), (b)*, then AB is divided *externally* at C in the ratio $AC:CB$.

Since it was agreed (section $11\cdot8$) that the direction from the initial to the terminal point is the positive sense of the directed line segment, it follows that:

In *Fig. 11-23 (a)*

$$\frac{AC}{CB} = \frac{m}{-n}, \quad m, n \in {}^{+}R, \; m > n.$$

Also, $\quad \dfrac{AC}{BC} = \dfrac{m}{n}$ and

$$\frac{AC - BC}{BC} = \frac{m - n}{n}$$

$$\therefore \quad \frac{AB}{BC} = \frac{m - n}{n}$$

In *Fig. 11-23 (b)*

$$\frac{AC}{CB} = \frac{-p}{q}, \quad p, q \in {}^{+}R, \; p < q.$$

Also, $\quad \dfrac{BC}{AC} = \dfrac{q}{p}$ and

$$\frac{BC - AC}{AC} = \frac{q - p}{p}$$

$$\therefore \quad \frac{BA}{AC} = \frac{q - p}{p}$$

11·11 Discovery of the method of calculating the coordinates of the
point dividing the line segment joining any two points externally in
a given ratio (supplementary).

Discovery Exercise 11-8

(B)

Write solutions for the following problems and compare them with those on
page 491.

1. In *Fig. 11-24*, $B(2, 2)$ divides the line segment joining $A(-3, -2)$ to
   $P(x, y)$ in the ratio $3 : 2$.
   (i) Express the abscissa of B in terms of the abscissas of A and P.
   (ii) Find x by equating the expression to its known value 2.
   (iii) Express the ordinate of B in terms of the ordinates of A and P.

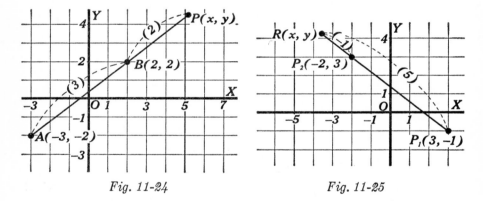

Fig. 11-24   Fig. 11-25

   (iv) Find y by equating the expression to its known value 2.
   (v) State the ratio in which P divides the line segment AB.

2. In *Fig. 11-25*, $R(x, y)$ divides the line segment joining $P_1(3, -1)$ to
   $P_2(-2, 3)$ in the ratio $5 : -1$.
   (i) State the ratio in which P_2 divides the line segment P_1R .
   (ii) Express the abscissa of P_2 in terms of the abscissas of P_1 and R.
   (iii) Find x by equating the expression to its known value -2 .
   (iv) Express the ordinate of P_2 in terms of the ordinates of P_1 and R .
   (v) Find y by equating the expression to its known value 3 .
   (vi) State the coordinates of the point R which divides the line
        segment P_1P_2 in the ratio $5 : -1$.

3. In *Fig. 11-26*, $R(x, y)$ divides the line segment joining $P_1(x_1, y_1)$ and $P_2(x_2, y_2)$ in the ratio $m : - n$, $m, n \in {}^{+}R$, $m > n$.

  (i) State the ratio in which P_2 divides the line segment P_1R .

  (ii) Express the abscissa of P_2 in terms of the abscissas of P_1 and R .

  (iii) Find x by equating the expression to its known value x_2 .

  (iv) State the value of y by employing a similar pattern.

  (v) State the coordinates of the point R which divides the line segment P_1P_2 in the ratio $m : - n$, $m, n \in {}^{+}R$, $m > n$.

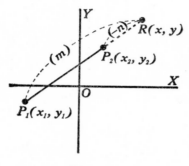

Fig. 11-26

These examples suggest the following conclusion:

The line segment joining $P_1(x_1, y_1)$ and $P_2(x_2, y_2)$ is divided in the ratio $m : -n$, $m, n \in {}^{+}R$, $m > n$, at the point

$$R\left(\frac{mx_2 - nx_1}{m - n}, \frac{my_2 - ny_1}{m - n}\right).$$

Similarly it may be shown that if the ratio in which R divides P_1P_2 is $- m : n$, $m, n \in {}^{+}R$, $m < n$, then the point of section is

$$R\left(\frac{- mx_2 + nx_1}{- m + n}, \frac{- my_2 + ny_1}{- m + n}\right).$$

It may be observed that the two forms are equivalent, since multiplying the numerator and denominator by $- 1$ in either expression produces the other expression.

The following arrays, showing the coordinates of P_1 and P_2 and the ratio of division, may facilitate computation.

Example. Find the coordinates of the point which divides the line segment with initial point $M(-1, 2)$ and terminal point $N(3, 5)$ in the ratio $-2 : 5$.

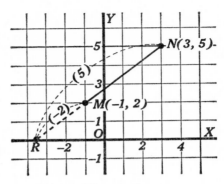

Fig. 11-27

Solution 1.   From the array
      it may be seen that the point of section is

$(-1, 2)$ $(3, 5)$

$-2 : 5$

$$R\left(\frac{(-2)(3)+(5)(-1)}{-2+5}, \frac{(-2)(5)+(5)(2)}{-2+5}\right)$$

or $R\left(-\dfrac{11}{3}, \dfrac{0}{3}\right)$

or $R(-3\tfrac{2}{3}, 0)$.

Solution 2. $\because M(-1, 2)$ divides RN in the ratio $2 : 3$, then, if R has coordinates (x, y):

$$\frac{(2)(3)+(3)(x)}{2+3} = -1 \qquad\qquad \frac{(2)(5)+(3)(y)}{2+3} = 2$$

$$\therefore\ 6+3x = -5 \qquad\qquad\qquad \therefore\ 10+3y = 10$$

$$\therefore\ x = -\frac{11}{3} \qquad\qquad\qquad\qquad \therefore\ y = 0$$

Hence the point of section is $R(-3\tfrac{2}{3}, 0)$.

Write solutions for the following problems and compare them with those on page 491.

1. Find the coordinates of the point dividing the line segment joining $A(-1, -2)$ and $B(1, 0)$ in the ratio $-2 : 5$.

2. $A(-4, 3)$, $B(-2, -2)$, and $C(4, -1)$ are three vertices of a parallelogram, and the fourth vertex D is in the first quadrant. Find the coordinates of D .

Exercise 11-9

(A)

1. State an expression for the coordinates of the point dividing the directed line segments having the following initial and terminal points in the ratios indicated:

   (i) $R(3, -2)$, $P(4, 3)$; $5 : -1$

   (ii) $A(-1, 4)$, $B(2, -1)$; $-1 : 4$

   (iii) $M(2, 0)$, $N(0, -3)$; $4 : -3$

   (iv) $O(0, 0)$, $B(4, -3)$; $5 : -2$

2. Find the coordinates of the point dividing the line segment with initial point $O(0, 0)$ and terminal point $A(3, 0)$ in the ratio $-2 : 5$.

3. State the initial and terminal points of the line segment and the ratio in which it is divided at the point with coordinates:

   (i) $\left(\dfrac{pr - ql}{p - q}, \dfrac{ps - qm}{p - q}\right)$

   (ii) $\left(\dfrac{a \cdot 3 - b \cdot 2}{a - b}, \dfrac{a \cdot 4 - b \cdot 3}{a - b}\right)$

   (iii) $\left(\dfrac{rc - a}{r - 1}, \dfrac{rd - b}{r - 1}\right)$

   (iv) $\left(\dfrac{3 \cdot 4 - 2 \cdot 6}{3 - 2}, \dfrac{3 \cdot 5 - 2 \cdot 7}{3 - 2}\right)$

(B)

4. Find the coordinates of the points dividing the line segments having the following initial and terminal points in the ratios indicated:

   (i) $A(2, -3)$, $B(5, 1)$; $3 : -2$

   (ii) $X(-1, 0)$, $Y(2, -3)$; $-1 : 4$

   (iii) $P(2, 7)$, $Q(-1, -2)$; $-3 : 4$

   (iv) $R(-3, 5)$, $S(0, 0)$; $5 : -3$

5. The line segment with initial point $A(3, -1)$ and terminal point $B(x, 2)$ is divided at $C(-18, 8)$ in the ratio $3 : -2$, where x is a real number. Find x.

6. The line segment with initial point $A(4, -3)$ and terminal point B is divided in the ratio $3 : -1$ at $C(-5, -3)$. Find the coordinates of B.

7. The line segment with initial point $P(-1, 0)$ and terminal point $Q(3, -2)$ is extended to R so that $QR = 2\,PQ$. Find the coordinates of R.

8. The line segment with initial point $A(0, -3)$ and terminal point $B(4, 0)$ is extended 2 units to C. Find the coordinates of C.

(C)

9. Find the ratio in which the point $C(4, 2)$ divides the line segment
   with initial point $A(8, -2)$ and terminal point $B(5, 1)$.

10. $A(2, 3)$ and $B(-4, -1)$ are two vertices of a triangle, the centroid
    of which is $G(3, -2)$. Find the third vertex.

11·12 Slope of a line. In *Fig. 11-28*, $P(x_1, y_1)$ and $Q(x_2, y_2)$ are any two
points on line l. If a right-angled triangle PMQ has sides parallel to the
axes, as shown, then:

  (i) the change in x from P to Q is $x_2 - x_1$ and is represented by
      $\triangle x$ (read, "Delta x");

  (ii) the change in y from P to Q is $y_2 - y_1$ and is represented by $\triangle y$.

Thus $\triangle x = x_2 - x_1$
and $\triangle y = y_2 - y_1$.

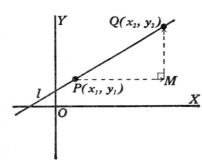

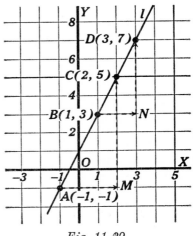

Fig. 11-28   Fig. 11-29

In *Fig. 11-29*, the points $A(-1, -1)$, $B(1, 3)$, $C(2, 5)$, and $D(3, 7)$ lie
on line l.

For the directed segment AC:

$$\triangle x = 2 - (-1) = 3$$
$$\triangle y = 5 - (-1) = 6$$
$$\therefore \frac{\triangle y}{\triangle x} = \frac{6}{3} = \frac{2}{1}$$

For the directed segment BD:

$$\triangle x = 3 - 1 = 2$$
$$\triangle y = 7 - 3 = 4$$
$$\therefore \frac{\triangle y}{\triangle x} = \frac{4}{2} = \frac{2}{1}$$

Thus, for the segments AC and BD of line l, $\dfrac{\triangle y}{\triangle x}$ is constant.

This result might have been anticipated, since $\triangle AMC \sim \triangle BND$, and
hence $\dfrac{MC}{AM} = \dfrac{ND}{BN}$.

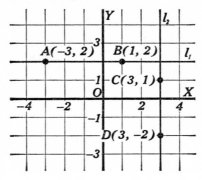

Fig. 11-30

In *Fig. 11-30*, l_1 is parallel to the x-axis, and l_2 is parallel to the y-axis.

For directed segment AB of l_1:

$$\triangle x = 1 - (-3) = 4$$
$$\triangle y = 2 - 2 = 0$$
$$\therefore \frac{\triangle y}{\triangle x} = 0$$

For directed segment CD of l_2:

$$\triangle x = 3 - 3 = 0$$
$$\triangle y = -2 - 1 = -3$$
$$\therefore \frac{\triangle y}{\triangle x} \text{ is undefined.}$$

Thus, $\dfrac{\triangle y}{\triangle x}$ or $\dfrac{y_2 - y_1}{x_2 - x_1}$ is constant for any line segment not parallel to the y-axis. $\dfrac{\triangle y}{\triangle x}$ is equal to zero for line segments parallel to the x-axis, and it is undefined for line segments parallel to the y-axis.

The number $\dfrac{\triangle y}{\triangle x}$ or $\dfrac{y_2 - y_1}{x_2 - x_1}$ is called the *slope* of the line of which the segment is a part.

Thus, the slope m of a line not parallel to the y-axis is given by:

$$m = \frac{\triangle y}{\triangle x}$$
$$= \frac{y_2 - y_1}{x_2 - x_1}$$
$$= \frac{y_1 - y_2}{x_1 - x_2}$$

The number $\dfrac{\triangle y}{\triangle x}$ (i.e. slope) may be thought of as a measure of the "steepness" of the line or line segment. As the absolute value of $\dfrac{\triangle y}{\triangle x}$ increases, the steepness increases also.

Write solutions for the following problems and compare them with those on page 492.

1.   (i) Find the slope of the line segment joining $P_1(-2, 1)$ and $P_2(5, 4)$.

      (ii) What sign has the slope of a line segment which rises toward the right?

2.   (i) For the line segment having $R(-1, 2)$ and $S(4, -2)$ as end points, calculate:

         (a) the slope of RS (b) the slope of SR

         Compare the slopes and draw a conclusion.

      (ii) What sign has the slope of a line segment which rises to the left?

3.   (i) Find the slope of the line segment joining $A(-2, 3)$ and $B(3, 3)$.

      (ii) What is the slope of a line parallel to the x-axis?

4.   (i) Find the slope of the line segment having end points $M(3, -2)$ and $N(3, 4)$.

      (ii) What is the slope of a line segment parallel to the y-axis?

5.   (i) When calculating the slope of a line segment, is the order in which the points are named of any significance?

      (ii) State the sign of the slope of a line segment which rises to the right.

     (iii) State the sign of the slope of a line segment which rises to the left.

     (iv) State the slope of a line segment parallel to the x-axis.

     (v) What may be said of the slope of a line segment parallel to the y-axis?

Exercise 11-10

(A)

In each of the following, find $\triangle x$ and $\triangle y$ from A to B:

1.

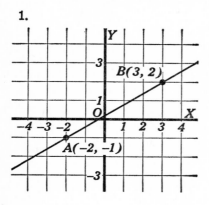

2.

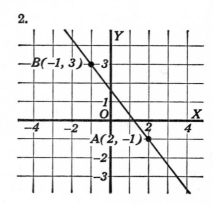

3.

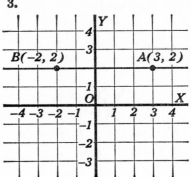

4.

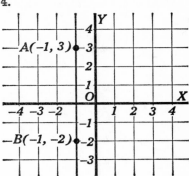

State the slope of the line in each of the following graphs:

5.

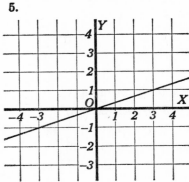

6.

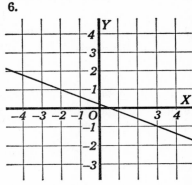

7.

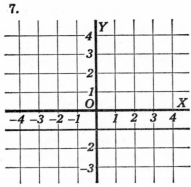

8.

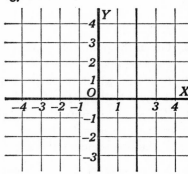

Find the slopes of the line segments joining pairs of points having coordinates as follows:

9. (7, 0) and (− 2, 0)

10. (3, 6) and (3, − 2)

11. (− 2, 7) and (− 2, 2)

State the slope of the line in each of the following graphs:

12.   **13.**

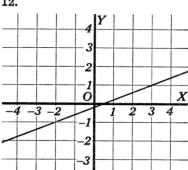   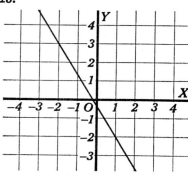

14. State a characteristic of the slope when a line segment rises upward:
    (i) to the right   (ii) to the left

15. What is the slope of a line segment parallel:
    (i) to the x-axis   (ii) to the y-axis

(B)

Find the slopes of line segments joining points having coordinates:

16. $(5, -2)$ and $(3, -4)$ **17.** $(-5, 4)$ and $(2, -3)$

18. $(-4, 2)$ and $(3, 2)$ **19.** $(-1, 0)$ and $(-1, -4)$

20. $(2a, 3a)$ and $(6a, 5a)$ **21.** $(0, -1)$ and $(0, -3)$

22. $(-5, -1)$ and $(-3, -4)$ **23.** $(-p, -2p)$ and $(6p, -2p)$

24. (a, b) and $(-2a, -2b)$

25. What real number does a represent, if the line segment joining $A(a, 0)$ to $B(0, 3)$ has the same slope as the line segment joining $C(-5, 4)$ to $D(3, -2)$?

26. Given the points $A(-3, -4)$, $O(0, 0)$, and $B(3, 4)$, find the slopes of the two line segments AO and OB.

27. Find b for which the slope of the line segment joining $L(0, b)$ to $M(3, 2)$ is equal to the slope of the line segment joining M to $N(5, 7)$.

28. Write and simplify the algebraic sentence which states that the slope of the line segment joining $P(x, y)$ to $Q(-3, 7)$ is equal to the slope of the line segment joining Q to $R(4, -3)$.

11·13 Discovery of a second test for collinearity of three points.

Discovery Exercise 11-11

(B)

Write solutions for the following and compare them with those on page 493.

1. (i) In *Fig. 11-31*, find AB, BC, and AC; determine whether A, B, and C are collinear.

   (ii) In *Fig. 11-31*, prove that the slope of the line segment joining $A(0, -2)$ and $B(1, 0)$ is equal to the slope of the line segment joining $B(1, 0)$ and $C(3, 4)$.

   (iii) Suggest a second test for determining whether three points are collinear.

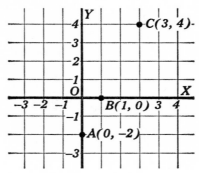

Fig. 11-31

2. Using the slope test discovered in problem 1, determine whether the points $A(2, -3)$, $B(-1, -1)$, and $C(-4, 1)$ are collinear.

3. Find the real number x, such that the points $P(x, 2)$, $Q(-1, 3)$, and $R(3, -2)$ are collinear.

   These examples suggest the following property:

   If three points P_1, P_2, and P_3 are such that the slope of the line segment P_1P_2 is equal to the slope of the line segment P_2P_3, or is equal to the slope of the line segment P_1P_3, then P_1, P_2, and P_3 are collinear.

Exercise 11-12

(A)

1. Describe two tests for collinearity of three points.

   Determine if the points with coordinates as follows are collinear:

2. $(-2, -3)$, $(0, 0)$, $(2, 3)$ 3. $(-2, 3)$, $(1, 3)$, $(6, 4)$
4. $(3, 5)$, $(3, 0)$, $(3, -4)$ 5. $(3, -1)$, $(0, 0)$, $(-3, 2)$
6. $(6, 1)$, $(3, -1)$, $(0, 1)$ 7. $(-4, 3)$, $(-1, -1)$, $(-7, 7)$

(B)

   Determine if the points with coordinates as follows are collinear:

8. $(3, -7)$, $(1, -1)$, $(0, 2)$ 9. $(5, 7)$, $(3, -4)$, $(-5, -7)$

10. $(3, 7)$, $(3, 1)$, $(- 3, 1)$ **11.** $(- 5, 4)$, $(- 1, 1)$, $(3, - 2)$

12. $(2, 5)$, $(2, - 3)$, $(- 2, 4)$ **13.** $(3, 7)$, $(3, 0)$, $(3, - 7)$

14. $(- 3, - 2)$, $(0, - 2)$, $(5, - 2)$ **15.** $(- 8, 0)$, $(0, 6)$, $(- 4, 9)$

16. Find y such that $P(- 2, 1)$, $Q(3, - 4)$, and $R(-3, y)$ are collinear.

17. Determine if points having coordinates $(a, 3b)$, $(2a, 6b)$, and $(- 3a, - 9b)$ are collinear.

18. Find the condition that $A(x, y)$, $B(2, - 3)$, and $C(- 5, 3)$ are collinear. (A *condition* is an algebraic statement (equation or inequation) expressing a relationship between the elements involved in a situation: in this case, the coordinates of the three given points.)

19. Find x such that $P(x, - 2)$, $Q(0, - 4)$, and $R(3, 0)$ are collinear.

11·14 The inclination of a line. In *Fig. 11-32*, $P_1(x_1, y_1)$ and $P_2(x_2, y_2)$ are any two points on the line l. The line intersects the x-axis at N. The angle XNP_2 (θ units) is called the *angle of inclination* or the *inclination* of the line l.

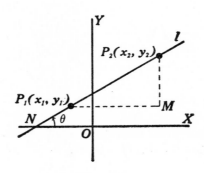

Fig. 11-32

By geometry: $\angle MP_1P_2 = \angle XNP_2 = \theta$ units

By trigonometry: $\tan \theta = \dfrac{\triangle y}{\triangle x} = \dfrac{y_2 - y_1}{x_2 - x_1}$

But $\dfrac{\triangle y}{\triangle x}$ is the slope m of line l. Thus, for any line l, not parallel to the y-axis,

$$m = \tan \theta$$

where θ is the inclination of l and $0 < \theta < \pi$.

This is illustrated in *Fig. 11-33.*

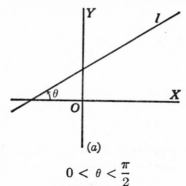

$$0 < \theta < \frac{\pi}{2}$$

m or tan θ is positive.
l rises to the right.

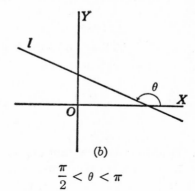

$$\frac{\pi}{2} < \theta < \pi$$

m or tan θ is negative.
l rises to the left.

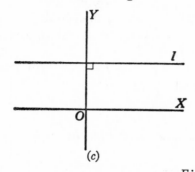

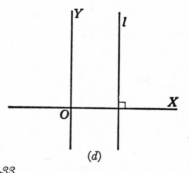

Fig. 11-33

l is parallel to the *x*-axis.   *l* is parallel to the *y*-axis.

$$m = 0$$

$$\theta = \frac{\pi}{2}$$

m or tan $\frac{\pi}{2}$ is undefined.

A table of tangents may be found on page 433. For convenience, the tangents of commonly used angles are listed in the following table.

$\theta°$	30°	45°	60°	120°	135°	150°
tan $\theta°$	$\dfrac{1}{\sqrt{3}}$ $\div 0.5774$	1	$\sqrt{3}$ $\div 1.7321$	$-\sqrt{3}$	-1	$-\dfrac{1}{\sqrt{3}}$

It should be recalled that the tangent of an obtuse angle is the negative of the tangent of its supplement.

Write solutions for the following problems and compare them with those on page 494.

1. Find the slope of the line with inclination 75°.
2. Find the inclination of the line having slope $-\sqrt{3}$.
3. Find the slope of the line with inclination 140°.

Exercise 11-13

(A)

1. Referring to the table of natural tangents if necessary, state the inclination, to the nearest degree, of the line with slope:

    (i) 1   (ii) 0.466   (iii) -2.747

    (iv) $-\sqrt{3}$ (v) 0.839   (vi) $\dfrac{1}{\sqrt{3}}$

    (vii) 57.290   (viii) -11.430 (ix) undefined

2. State the slope of the line with inclination (use tables where necessary):

    (i) 73°   (ii) 90°   (iii) 60°   (iv) 150°   (v) 130°
    (vi) 30°   (vii) 91°   (viii) 135°   (ix) 179°

(B)

3. Find, to the nearest degree, the inclination of the line determined by each of the following pairs of points:

    (i) $(3, 2), (1, -4)$ (ii) $(-2, -3), (3, 2)$
    (iii) $(-5, \sqrt{3}), (-4, 2\sqrt{3})$ (iv) $(4, 2), (4, -5)$
    (v) $(-3, 2), (5, -1)$ (vi) $(1, 11), (-2, -7)$

4. Find the slope, correct to two decimal places, of the line with inclination:

    (i) 30°   (ii) 135°   (iii) $67\frac{1}{2}$°
    (iv) 155°   (v) 120°   (vi) 91°

5. Find the angle between the line determined by the points $A(1, -1)$ and $B(7, 5)$ and the line determined by the points $C(6, 0)$ and $D(0, 6)$.

6. Find the lesser of the two angles between two lines whose slopes are as follows:

    (i) $\sqrt{3}$ and $-\sqrt{3}$ (ii) $-\dfrac{1}{\sqrt{3}}$ and 1

    (iii) $\dfrac{1}{\sqrt{3}}$ and $-\sqrt{3}$ (iv) 0.70 and 1.43

    (v) -1.00 and 1.73   (vi) -5.67 and -0.84

7. Find x so that the line determined by $A(x, 6)$ and $B(10, -9)$ has an inclination of $135°$.

8. Find, to the nearest degree, the lesser angle between the line determined by $A(4, 7)$ and $B(-1, 2)$ and the line determined by $C(-3, 2)$ and $D(1, 5)$.

11·15 The equation of a line. The following properties of a line have been observed:

(i) The constant slope property of a line: the slopes of all segments of a line are equal.

(ii) A line may be regarded as the set of points (locus) such that the slopes of the line segments determined by all pairs of points in the set are equal.

In *Fig. 11-34*, the line:

(i) is on the point $A(3, 1)$;

(ii) has slope $m = \dfrac{5}{2}$;

(iii) has $P(x, y)$ representing any other point on the line.

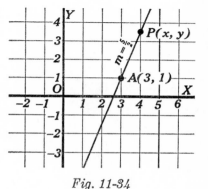

Thus, by the constant slope property:

$$\text{slope of } PA = \frac{5}{2}$$

$$\therefore \frac{y-1}{x-3} = \frac{5}{2}$$

Fig. 11-34

$$\text{or} \quad 5x - 15 = 2y - 2$$
$$\text{or} \quad 5x - 2y - 13 = 0$$

$5x - 2y - 13 = 0$ is the algebraic statement of the *condition* which is satisfied by the coordinates of every point on the line.

Conversely, it may be proved that any point $Q(a, b)$, whose coordinates satisfy the equation, lies on the line.

Since the coordinates of Q satisfy the equation $5x - 2y - 13 = 0$,

$$\therefore \ 5a - 2b - 13 = 0$$
$$\therefore \ 5a - 15 = 2b - 2$$
$$\therefore \ 5(a - 3) = 2(b - 1)$$
$$\therefore \ \frac{b-1}{a-3} = \frac{5}{2}$$
$$\therefore \ \text{the slope of } QA = \frac{5}{2}.$$

$\therefore \ Q$ lies on the line, since there is only one line on A having slope $\frac{5}{2}$.

11·16   The slope-point form of the equation of a line.

Hypothesis: *A* line l passing through $P_1(x_1, y_1)$ and having slope m
($m \in R$: that is, l is not parallel to the y-axis)

Required: To find the equation of line l

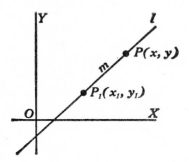

Fig. 11-35

Solution: Let $P(x, y)$ be any other point on the line.
   Then the slope of $P_1P = m$ (constant slope property of a line).

$$\therefore \ \frac{y - y_1}{x - x_1} = m$$

$$\therefore \ y - y_1 = m\,(x - x_1)$$

Since this equation is satisfied by the coordinates of P, it is satisfied
by the coordinates of every point on the line l.

   Since the steps in the proof are reversible, it follows that every point
whose coordinates satisfy the equation lies on the line.

**Corollary 1: The equation of the line parallel to the x-axis and passing
      through $P_1(x_1, y_1)$ is $y = y_1$.**

Proof: If $l \parallel x$-axis, then $m = 0$.

$$\therefore \ \frac{y - y_1}{x - x_1} = 0$$

$$\therefore \ y - y_1 = 0$$

$$\therefore \ y = y_1$$

**Corollary 2: The equation of the line parallel to the y-axis and passing
      through $P_1(x_1, y_1)$ is $x = x_1$.**

Proof: If $l \parallel y$-axis, then m is undefined.

$$\therefore \ \text{the denominator of } \frac{y - y_1}{x - x_1} \text{ is zero.}$$

$$\therefore \ x - x_1 = 0$$

$$\therefore \ x = x_1$$

Corollary 3: The equation of a line passing through the origin is $y = mx$.
Proof: If $P_1(x_1, y_1)$ is the origin, then $x_1 = 0$, $y_1 = 0$.
$$\therefore \text{ the equation is } y - 0 = m(x - 0)$$
$$\text{or } y = mx .$$

Write solutions for the following problems and compare them with those on page 494.

1. Find the equation of the line on the point $A(4, -3)$ and (i) parallel to the x-axis (ii) parallel to the y-axis.
2. Find the equation of the line on the points $A(-2, 3)$ and $B(4, -1)$.
3. Find the equation of the line on $A(2, -1)$ and having inclination $120°$.

Exercise 11-14

(A)

State, in simplified form, the slope of the line determined by each pair of points having coordinates as follows:

1. $(2, 3), (4, 7)$
2. $(-3, 5), (2, -7)$
3. $(-4, -6), (-1, -2)$
4. $(0, 0), (-3, 5)$
5. $(0, -3), (4, 0)$
6. $(-2, -2), (2, 2)$
7. $(2, 3), (-1, 3)$
8. $(-3, 4), (-5, -6)$
9. $(-3, 3), (3, -3)$

In each of the following, the slope of a line and the coordinates of a point on it are given. State the equation of the line in unsimplified form:

10. $\frac{2}{3}$; $(-4, 1)$
11. $-\frac{4}{3}$; $(3, -2)$
12. 1; $(3, 4)$
13. -1; $(2, -2)$
14. $-\frac{5}{6}$; $(-1, 0)$
15. $\frac{7}{2}$; $(0, -5)$
16. 0; $(1, 4)$
17. 0; $(0, 0)$
18. $-\frac{1}{4}$; $(-3, 2)$

(B)

19. Using the information below, find, in simplified form, the equation of each of the following lines and show each line on a diagram:
    (i) on $A(-2, 7)$ and having slope $\frac{4}{5}$
    (ii) on $A(0, 0)$ and $B(3, 3)$
    (iii) on $Q(-5, 4)$ and $R(1, 4)$

19. Using the information below, find, in simplified form, the equation of each of the following lines and show each line on a diagram:

  (iv) having slope -1 and on $(-3, 7)$

  (v) on $M(4, -3)$ and having an inclination of $135°$

  (vi) having slope 0 and on $A(2, -4)$

  (vii) on $A(1, -3)$ and $B(1, 7)$

  (viii) having slope $-\frac{3}{2}$ and on $A(-\frac{2}{3}, \frac{3}{4})$

  (ix) on $A(\frac{3}{2}, 0)$ and $B(0, -\frac{4}{3})$

  (x) having slope $-\frac{2}{3}$ and on $A(\frac{1}{2}, -\frac{1}{2})$

20. What is the equation of a straight line parallel to the x-axis and on $A(5, -4)$?

21. Find the equation of the x-axis.

22. A straight line is on the point $A(3, 4)$ and is parallel to the y-axis. Find its equation.

23. Find the equation of the y-axis.

24. Find the equation of the straight line on $P_1\ (a, b)$ and $O(0, 0)$. Does this equation have any special feature? Is this characteristic of the equations of all lines passing through the origin?

11·17 Discovery of other forms of the equation of a line.

Discovery Exercise 11-15

(B)

Using the two given conditions in each of the following, find the equation of the line and compare your solution with that on page 495.

1. Write the equation of line l in *Fig. 11-36*.

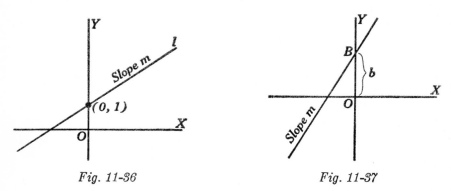

Fig. 11-36   Fig. 11-37

2. The line in *Fig. 11-37* has slope m and y-intercept b. Find its equation.

3. In *Fig. 11-38*, the line has slope m and x-intercept a. Find its equation.

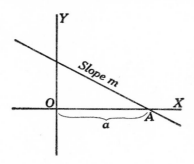

Fig. 11-38

Summary. Forms of the equation of a line.

GIVEN CONDITIONS	EQUATION OF THE LINE
Slope m Point $P_1(x_1, y_1)$	$y - y_1 = m(x - x_1)$
Slope m y-intercept b	$y = mx + b$
Slope m x-intercept a	$y = m(x - a)$

Write solutions for the following problems and compare them with those on page 495.

1. Find the equation of the line determined by each of the following:
   (i) angle of inclination $60°$ and y-intercept -2;
   (ii) x-intercept 3 and slope $-\frac{3}{4}$.

2. By transforming the equation $2x - 3y + 6 = 0$ to the form $y = mx + b$, find the slope and y-intercept and draw the graph of the line defined by the equation.

3. Find the slope of the line with equation $Ax + By + C = 0$, $B \neq 0$.

4. Find the equation of a line having x-intercept 3 and y-intercept 4.

5. Find the equation of a line having x-intercept a and y-intercept b.

Exercise 11-16

(A)

1. State in unsimplified form the equation of the line determined by each of the following:
   (i) x-intercept 3, slope $-\frac{1}{2}$ (ii) slope $-\frac{1}{2}$, y-intercept $3\frac{1}{2}$
   (iii) $A(3, 0)$ and $B(0, -2)$
   (iv) angle of inclination 135°, y-intercept -2
   (v) $A(0, 5)$, angle of inclination 120°

(B)

2. Find the equation of the line with angle of inclination 30° and x-intercept $3\frac{1}{2}$.
3. A line has x-intercept -2 and slope $\frac{3}{4}$. Find its equation.
4. Find the equations of lines, segments of which form the sides of the rectangle of which three vertices are $A(-3, 2)$, $B(-3, -1)$, and $C(4, -1)$.
5. (i) Find the y-intercept of the line with equation $2x - y + 4 = 0$.
   (ii) Find the equation of the line having the same y-intercept as the line in (i) and having an angle of inclination 150°.
6. By transforming the equation $x + 2y - 5 = 0$ to the form $y = mx + b$, find the slope and y-intercept of the line defined by the equation.
7. For the triangle with vertices $A(-1, 5)$, $B(-6, -3)$, and $C(4, 1)$, find the equation of the line of which the median from A is a segment.

(C)

8. (i) Determine the slope of the set (or family) of lines defined by the equation $y = 3x + b$.
   (ii) Determine the value of the *parameter* b for the particular member of the set on $A(1, -2)$.
9. (i) Determine the coordinates of the point common to the set (or family) of lines defined by the equation $y - 3 = m(x + 4)$.
   (ii) Determine the value of the parameter m for the particular member of the set with angle of inclination 60° and find its equation.
10. (i) Write the equation of the family of lines with slope -2.
    (ii) Determine the value of the parameter for the member of the family having x-intercept 3 and find the equation of the line.

11·18 Conditions for parallelism and perpendicularity.

a. *Parallelism.*

Given: Lines l_1 and l_2 such that $l_1 \parallel l_2$

Required: To find the relation between the slopes of l_1 and l_2

Proof: Let θ_1 and θ_2 be the inclinations, and m_1 and m_2 the slopes of l_1 and l_2, respectively.

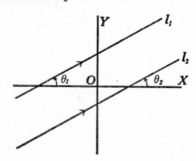

Then, $m_1 = \tan\theta_1$, and $m_2 = \tan\theta_2$.

Since $l_1 \parallel l_2$, $\theta_1 = \theta_2$

$\therefore \ \tan\theta_1 = \tan\theta_2$

Fig. 11-39

$\therefore \ m_1 = m_2$.

Conversely it may be proved that if $m_1 = m_2$, then $l_1 \parallel l_2$.

b. *Perpendicularity.*

Given: Lines l_1 and l_2 intersecting at P such that $l_1 \perp l_2$

Required: To find the relation between the slopes of l_1 and l_2

Proof: θ_1 and θ_2 are the inclinations, and m_1 and m_2 are the slopes of l_1 and l_2, respectively.

PS is the perpendicular from P to the x-axis, and h, a, and b are the lengths of PS, QS, and SR, respectively, h, a, $b \in {}^+R$.

Then, $m_1 = \dfrac{h}{a}$ and $m_2 = \dfrac{h}{-b}$.

Since $\triangle PQS \sim \triangle RPS$

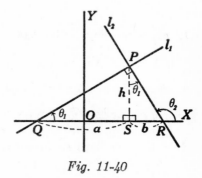

$\therefore \ \dfrac{h}{a} = \dfrac{b}{h}$

$\therefore \ m_1 = \dfrac{b}{h}$ and $m_2 = \dfrac{h}{-b}$

$\therefore \ m_1 m_2 = \dfrac{b}{h} \times \dfrac{h}{-b} = -1$

$\therefore \ m_1 = -\dfrac{1}{m_2}$.

Fig. 11-40

Conversely, by reversing the steps, it may be proved that if $m_1 = -\dfrac{1}{m_2}$, the lines are perpendicular.

Thus, the condition for perpendicularity of two lines is:

$$m_1 = -\frac{1}{m_2} \qquad \text{or} \qquad m_1 m_2 = -1$$

m_2 is the *negative reciprocal* of m_1, and m_1 is the *negative reciprocal* of m_2.

Alternate Proof: Let θ_1 and θ_2 be the inclinations of l_1 and l_2, respectively.

$$\text{Then, } \theta_2 = \frac{\pi}{2} + \theta_1$$

$$\therefore \ \tan \theta_2 = \tan \left(\frac{\pi}{2} + \theta_1 \right)$$

$$\therefore \ \tan \theta_2 = - \cot \theta_1$$

$$\therefore \ \tan \theta_2 = - \frac{1}{\tan \theta_1}$$

$$\therefore \ m_2 = - \frac{1}{m_1}$$

Write solutions for the following examples and compare them with those on page 496.

1. Prove that the quadrilateral with vertices $A(-3, 3)$, $B(-4, -3)$, $C(4, -2)$, and $D(5, 4)$ is a parallelogram.
2. Prove that the line on $A(-5, 3)$ and $B(7, 1)$ is perpendicular to the line on $C(4, 6)$ and $D(3, 0)$.
3. Prove that the triangle with vertices $A(-1, 6)$, $B(-3, 3)$, and $C(5, 2)$ is right-angled at A.

Exercise 11-17

(A)

1. State the slope of lines perpendicular to lines with slope:

   (i) -2 (ii) $\frac{3}{5}$ (iii) $\frac{p}{q}$ (iv) a (v) 0

2. State the inclination of lines parallel to the lines with slope:

   (i) 1 (ii) $-\sqrt{3}$ (iii) 0 (iv) $\frac{1}{\sqrt{3}}$ (v) -1

3. State the slope of lines perpendicular to lines with inclination:

   (i) $30°$ (ii) $90°$ (iii) $135°$ (iv) $120°$ (v) $45°$

(B)

4. Find the coordinates of a point P on the y-axis such that the line joining P to $A(-7, -3)$ is parallel to the line on $C(-4, 3)$ and $D(4, 7)$.
5. Determine whether the triangle with vertices $A(2, 4)$, $B(0, -4)$, and $C(5, -1)$ is right-angled.

6. Find the equation of the line on $A(2, -3)$ and parallel to the line on $C(-4, 0)$ and $D(2, 5)$.

7. Find the equation of the line on $A(-3, 2)$ which is perpendicular to the line segment joining A to $B(1, 5)$.

8. Find the abscissa of the point A with ordinate 2, such that the line segment joining A to the origin is perpendicular to the line segment joining the origin to $B(2, -6)$.

9. $A(1, -4)$, $B(-3, 0)$, and $C(1, -5)$ are three vertices of parallelogram $ABCD$. If D is in the fourth quadrant, find the equations of the lines of which AD and CD are segments.

10. Find the slope of a line which is parallel to the line with equation $3x - 4y + 7 = 0$.

(C)

11. Find the slope of lines perpendicular to the line with equation $Ax + By + C = 0$.

12. Two sides of a parallelogram are segments of lines with equations $4x + 3y - 12 = 0$ and $x - 3y = 0$. One of the vertices is $(2, 7)$. Find the equations of the lines of which the remaining two sides are segments.

13. A line which is perpendicular to the line with equation $5x - 2y - 3 = 0$ intersects the line segment joining $A(-1, 4)$ to $B(3, 0)$ at a point which divides AB internally in the ratio $3 : 1$. Find the equation of the line.

14. Find the coordinates of the point of intersection of the diagonals of a quadrilateral having vertices $A(-1, 3)$, $B(-3, -2)$, $C(1, -1)$, and $D(4, 2)$.

11·19 **Discovery of a general expression for the area of a triangle in terms of the coordinates of the vertices (supplementary).**

Discovery Exercise 11-18

(B)

Write solutions for the following problems and compare them with those on page 497.

1. In *Fig. 11-41*, AR, BS, and CT are perpendicular to the x-axis.
    (i) State the coordinates of R, S, and T.
    (ii) Calculate the areas of trapezoids $ABSR$, $ARTC$, and $BSTC$.
    (iii) Using the information in (ii), calculate the area of $\triangle ABC$.

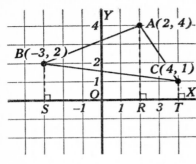

Fig. 11-41

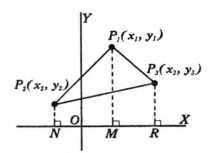

Fig. 11-42

2. In *Fig. 11-42*, P_1M, P_2N, and P_3R are perpendicular to the x-axis.

    (i) State the coordinates of M, N, and R.

    (ii) Write expressions for the areas of trapezoids P_1P_2NM, P_1MRP_3, and P_2NRP_3.

    (iii) Using the information in (ii), find an expression for the area of $\triangle ABC$.

The solution to problem 2 above provides the following expression for the area of a triangle:

$$\triangle P_1P_2P_3 = \tfrac{1}{2}[x_1(y_2 - y_3) + x_2(y_3 - y_1) + x_3(y_1 - y_2)]$$

If the vertices P_1, P_2, and P_3 are in clockwise order instead of in counter-clockwise order, as in *Fig. 11-42*, the expression for the area of $\triangle P_1P_2P_3$ becomes the negative of that obtained in problem 2.

Since area is a positive real number of units, the absolute value of the expression is used in calculating the area. Thus, the area of $\triangle P_1P_2P_3$ is given by:

$$\tfrac{1}{2}\,|\,x_1(y_2 - y_3) + x_2(y_3 - y_1) + x_3(y_1 - y_2)\,|$$
$$= \tfrac{1}{2}\,|\,x_1y_2 + x_2y_3 + x_3y_1 - x_1y_3 - x_3y_2 - x_2y_1\,|$$

The array at the right may be used to facilitate computation:

If P_3 has coordinates $(0, 0)$, the area of the triangle is $\tfrac{1}{2}\,|\,x_1y_2 - x_2y_1\,|$.

Example 1. Calculate the area of the triangle, *Fig. 11-43*, with vertices $A(-4, 3)$, $B(5, 1)$, and $C(-1, -2)$.

Solution: Using the array:

$$\begin{vmatrix} -4, & 3 \\ 5, & 1 \\ -1, & -2 \\ -4, & 3 \end{vmatrix}$$

Area $\triangle ABC$
$= \frac{1}{2} \mid -4 - 10 - 3 - 8 + 1 - 15 \mid$
$= \frac{1}{2} \mid -39 \mid$
$= 19.5$

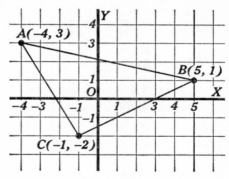

Example 2. The triangle
$A(x, -3), B(4, 2), C(3, -1)$
has area 7. Calculate x.

Solution. Using the array:

$$\begin{vmatrix} x, & -3 \\ 4, & 2 \\ 3, & -1 \\ x, & -3 \end{vmatrix}$$

Fig. 11-43

The area of $\triangle ABC = \frac{1}{2} \mid 2x - 4 - 9 + x - 6 + 12 \mid$
$= \frac{1}{2} \mid 3x - 7 \mid$.

But the area is 7.

$$\therefore \tfrac{1}{2} \mid 3x - 7 \mid = 7$$
$$\therefore \mid 3x - 7 \mid = 14$$

$$\therefore 3x - 7 = 14 \quad \text{or} \quad 3x - 7 = -14$$
$$\therefore x = 7 \quad \mid \quad \therefore x = -2\tfrac{1}{3}$$

Hence, A may have two positions: namely, $A_1(7, -3)$ and $A_2(-2\tfrac{1}{3}, -3)$.

11·20 Collinearity of points (supplementary). The following tests for collinearity of points have been developed.

P_1, P_2, and P_3 are collinear:

  (i) if $P_1P_2 + P_2P_3 = P_1P_3$ (length test);

  (ii) if slope P_1P_2 = slope P_2P_3 (slope test).

    The expression for the area of a triangle may be used, also, to test collinearity of three points.

P_1, P_2, and P_3 are collinear:

  (iii) if area $\triangle P_1P_2P_3 = 0$ (area test).

Example. Prove that the points $A(-7, -1)$, $B(1, 3)$, and $C(5, 5)$ are collinear, using (i) the length test (ii) the slope test (iii) the area test.

Solution.
  (i) $AB = \sqrt{64 + 16} = \sqrt{80} = 4\sqrt{5}$
     $BC = \sqrt{16 + 4} = \sqrt{20} = 2\sqrt{5}$
     $AC = \sqrt{144 + 36} = \sqrt{180} = 6\sqrt{5}$
     $\because AB + BC = AC$
     $\therefore A, B,$ and C are collinear.

(ii) Slope $AB = \dfrac{3 - (-1)}{1 - (-7)} = \dfrac{4}{8} = \dfrac{1}{2}$

Slope $BC = \dfrac{5 - 3}{5 - 1} = \dfrac{2}{4} = \dfrac{1}{2}$

$\because$ slope AB = slope BC

$\therefore$ A, B, and C are collinear.

(iii) Area $\triangle ABC = \frac{1}{2} | -21 + 5 - 5 + 35 - 15 + 1 |$ $\qquad \begin{vmatrix} -7, & -1 \\ 1, & 3 \\ 5, & 5 \\ -7, & -1 \end{vmatrix}$

$\qquad\qquad\quad = \frac{1}{2} | 0 |$

$\qquad\qquad\quad = 0$

$\because$ the area of $\triangle ABC$ is 0.

$\therefore$ the points A, B, and C are collinear.

Exercise 11-19

(A)

1. State the sign of the number between the absolute value bars in the expression for the area of a triangle if the coordinates of the vertices are listed in (i) clockwise order (ii) counter-clockwise order.

2. Describe three methods of testing whether or not three points are collinear.

(B)

3. Find the area of the triangle with vertices $A(3, -4)$, $B(-2, 1)$, and $C(1, 6)$ by listing the coordinates of the points in (i) counter-clockwise order (ii) clockwise order.

4. Calculate the area of a triangle for which the coordinates of the vertices are:

    (i) $(7, -3), (3, 5), (-3, 2)$ (ii) $(9, 4), (4, -3), (-3, -2)$
    (iii) $(2, -2), (-3, -1), (-1, 3)$
    (iv) $(4, 7), (1, 1), (-3, -1)$ (v) $(-6, 4), (0, 0), (3, -2)$

5. Test for collinearity the points $A(3, -1)$, $B(0, 1)$, and $C(-6, 5)$.

6. Find x for which the points $A(x, 4)$, $B(-1, 0)$, and $C(2, -2)$ are collinear.

7. For the triangle with vertices $A(4, 0)$, $B(-1, 3)$, and $C(-4, -1)$, calculate (i) the area (ii) the altitude from A.

8. State algebraically that the triangle with vertices $P(x, y)$, $Q(-5, 2)$, and $R(2, 0)$ has area 5.

9. (i) Find the equation of the line on $A(3, -2)$ and $B(-1, 2)$ by stating algebraically that the area of the triangle formed by the points A, B, and $P(x, y)$ is zero.

   (ii) Verify by using the slope-point form of the equation of a line.

10. Two vertices of a triangle are $A(-1, 0)$ and $B(4, 1)$. Find the abscissa of the third vertex if its ordinate is 3 and the area of the triangle is 5.

11. Find the ordinate of the point with abscissa -2 which is collinear with the points $M(3, -5)$ and $N(0, 1)$.

11·21 Discovery of a general expression for the length of a perpendicular from a point to a line (supplementary).

Discovery Exercise 11-20

(B)

Write solutions for the following problems and compare them with those on page 497.

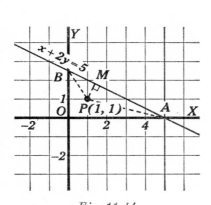

Fig. 11-44

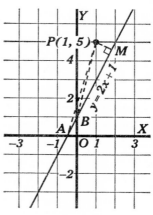

Fig. 11-45

1. In *Fig. 11-44:*
   (i) find the coordinates of A;
   (ii) find the coordinates of B;
   (iii) calculate the area of $\triangle PAB$;
   (iv) calculate AB;
   (v) use $\triangle PAB = \frac{1}{2}bh$ and the result obtained in (iii) to calculate PM.

2. In *Fig. 11-45:*
   (i) find the coordinates of A;
   (ii) find the coordinates of B;
   (iii) calculate the area of $\triangle PAB$;
   (iv) calculate AB;
   (v) calculate PM.

3. In *Fig. 11-46*:
    (i) find the coordinates of D;
    (ii) find the coordinates of E;
    (iii) calculate the area of $\triangle P_1DE$;
    (iv) calculate DE;
    (v) calculate P_1M .

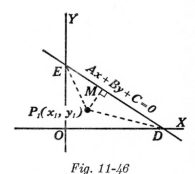

Fig. 11-46

The solution to problem 3 provides the following information:

The general expression for the length of a perpendicular from $P_1(x_1,\ y_1)$ to the line with equation

$$Ax + By + C = 0 \ is$$

$$\frac{|\ Ax_1 + By_1 + C\ |}{\sqrt{A^2 + B^2}}.$$

Example 1. Find the length of the perpendicular d from $R(-1, 4)$ to the line with equation $y = 2x + 1$.

Solution. The equation of the line may be written $2x - y + 1 = 0$.

$$d = \frac{|Ax_1 + By_1 + C|}{\sqrt{A^2 + B^2}}$$

$$= \frac{|2(-1) - 1(4) + 1|}{\sqrt{2^2 + (-1)^2}}$$

$$= \frac{|-5|}{\sqrt{5}}$$

$$= \frac{5}{\sqrt{5}}$$

$$= \sqrt{5}$$

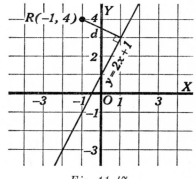

Fig. 11-47

∴ the length of the perpendicular is $\sqrt{5}$.

Example 2. Find the length of the perpendicular from $A(2, -3)$ to the line with equation (i) $x = -2$ (ii) $2y - 3 = 0$.

Solution.
    (i) For the equation $x + 2 = 0$,
$$A = 1, B = 0, C = 2 .$$
$$\therefore \ d_1 = \frac{|1(2) + 0 + 2|}{\sqrt{1^2 + 0^2}} = \frac{|4|}{1} = 4$$
    ∴ the length of the perpendicular is 4 .

(ii) For the equation $2y - 3 = 0$,
$A = 0, B = 2, C = -3$.

$$\therefore d_2 = \frac{|0 + 2(-3) - 3|}{\sqrt{0 + 2^2}}$$

$$= \frac{|-9|}{2}$$

$$= 4\tfrac{1}{2}$$

$\therefore$ the length of the perpendicular is $4\tfrac{1}{2}$.

It should be noted that these results could have been obtained from the diagram by inspection.

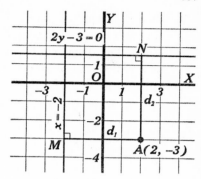

Fig. 11-48

Write solutions for the following problems and compare them with those on page 499.

1. A triangle has vertices $A(-1, 3)$, $B(0, -3)$, and $C(4, 0)$. Find the length of the altitude from A to BC.

2. Find the distance between the parallel lines having equations $x - 3y + 6 = 0$ and $x - 3y - 3 = 0$.

Exercise 11-21

(A)

1. Find the length of a perpendicular from $A(2, 1)$ to the line with equation $3x + 4y = 0$.

2. Find the distance from the origin to the line defined by each of the following equations:

   (i) $6x + 8y - 25 = 0$ (ii) $5x - 12y + 13 = 0$

   (iii) $x - y + 2 = 0$ (iv) $3x - 4y + 10 = 0$

   (v) $3x + y = 0$ (vi) $y = 2x + 5$

(B)

3. Use the general expression for the area of a triangle to calculate the length of a perpendicular from $P(3, -1)$ to the line with equation $3x + 4y + 5 = 0$.

4. Find the length of the perpendicular from the point to the line indicated in each of the following:

   (i) $(-1, 3), 3x - 4y = 0$ (ii) $(0, 2), 5x - 12y - 2 = 0$

   (iii) $(0, 0), 8x + 15y - 17 = 0$ (iv) $(2, 7), 3x - y + 1 = 0$

   (v) $(2, 0), 6x - 8y - 2 = 0$ (vi) $(3, -1), x + 2y + 4 = 0$

   (vii) $(-3, 2), x - 5 = 0$ (viii) $(0, -2), y = -6$

   (ix) $(0, 0), y = mx + b$ (x) $(0, 0), y - y_1 = m(x - x_1)$

5. Find b so that the length of the perpendicular from the origin to the line with equation $y = 2x + b$ is $\sqrt{5}$.

6. Find the distance between the parallel lines having equations $3x - 4y - 12 = 0$ and $6x - 8y - 9 = 0$.

7. For the triangle with vertices $A(1, 4)$, $B(0, -2)$, and $C(5, 0)$, find:
   (i) the length of the altitude from A;
   (ii) the equation of the line of which the altitude is a segment.

8. Find the length of the perpendicular from the point of intersection of the lines having equations $2x - 3y - 7 = 0$ and $x + 2y - 7 = 0$ to the line with equation $5x - 12y - 13 = 0$ and interpret the result.

9. Find the abscissas of the points with ordinate 2 for which the distance to the line having equation $8x - 15y - 11 = 0$ is one unit.

10. Find the radius of a circle with centre $C(-4, 2)$ and touching the line with equation $3x + 4y - 6 = 0$.

11. Calculate the distance between the parallel lines having equations $5x + 12y = 0$ and $10x + 24y - 39 = 0$.

(C)

12. Find the equations that state algebraically that the distance from a point $P(x, y)$ to the line having equation $2x + 3y - 7 = 0$ is $\sqrt{13}$.

13. Find the equation which states algebraically that the point $P(x, y)$ is midway between the parallel lines having equations $2x - 5y - 12 = 0$ and $2x - 5y + 4 = 0$. Describe the position of the line defined by the equation.

11·22 **Geometric relations proved by both analytic and synthetic methods (supplementary).** Analytic methods frequently prove to be less complicated than the methods of synthetic geometry. The algebra of analytic proofs is simplified if coordinate axes are placed judiciously relative to the geometric figures, as illustrated in the following diagrams:

(i) Triangle

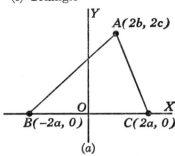

(a)

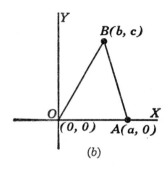

(b)

Fig. 11-49

Fig. 11-49 shows convenient locations of the axes with respect to a triangle. The introduction of $2a$, $2b$, $2c$ avoids fractions if the coordinates of the midpoints of the sides are required.

(ii) Rectangle and square

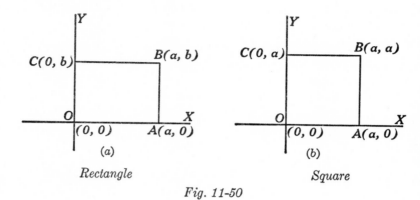

(a)	(b)
Rectangle	Square

Fig. 11-50

(iii) Parallelogram and trapezoid

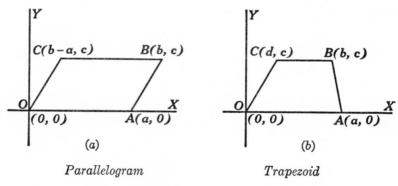

(a)	(b)
Parallelogram	Trapezoid

Fig. 11-51

In *Fig. 11-51*, $CB \parallel OX$; hence C and B have the same ordinate c.

In *Fig. 11-51 (a)*, $OC \parallel AB$. Since the slope of $AB = \dfrac{c}{b-a}$, the slope of $OC = \dfrac{c}{b-a}$. Hence, the abscissa of C must be $b - a$.

In *Fig. 11-51 (b)*, OC is not parallel to AB, so an abscissa different from $b - a$ is used for C.

In the three examples following, both synthetic and analytic proofs are given.

Example 1. A line segment joining the midpoints of two sides of a triangle is parallel to the third side and equal to one-half of it.

Hypothesis: $\triangle ABC$ in which D and E are the midpoints of AB and AC, respectively

Conclusion: $DE \parallel BC$, $DE = \frac{1}{2} BC$

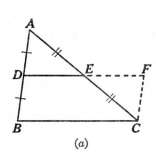 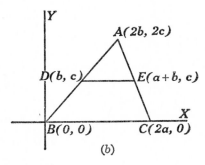

$$(a) \qquad\qquad\qquad\qquad (b)$$

Fig. 11-52

Proof: (a) *Synthetic.*

STATEMENTS	AUTHORITIES
1. F is a point on DE extended, so that $EF = DE$.	1. Existence
2. In $\triangle$'s ADE, CFE $\left\{ \begin{array}{l} AE = CE \\ DE = FE \\ \angle AED = \angle CEF \end{array} \right.$	2. Hypothesis
3.	3. 1
4.	4. Vertical Angle Th.
5. $\triangle ADE \cong \triangle CFE$	5. sas
6. $CF = AD$	6. Definition
7. $AD = DB$	7. Hypothesis
8. $FC = DB$	8. Replacement
9. $\angle ADE = \angle CFE$	9. 5, Definition
10. $ADB \parallel FC$	10. Parallel Line Th.
11. $DF \parallel BC$	11. Quadrilateral-Parallelogram Th.
12. $DF = BC$	12. Quadrilateral-Parallelogram Th.
13. $DE = \frac{1}{2} DF$	13. 1
14. $DE = \frac{1}{2} BC$	14. Replacement

(b) *Analytic.*

In *Fig. 11-52 (b)*, D has coordinates (b, c), and E has coordinates $(a+b, c)$.

$$\text{Slope of } DE = \frac{c - c}{a + b - b} = 0 \qquad \text{Slope of } BC = 0$$

$$\therefore DE \parallel BC$$

$$DE = |a + b - b| = |a| = a \qquad BC = |2a - 0| = 2a$$

$$\therefore DE = \tfrac{1}{2} BC$$

Example 2. The diagonals of a rhombus are perpendicular.

Hypothesis: $ABCD$ is a rhombus with diagonals intersecting on E.

Conclusion: $AC \perp BD$

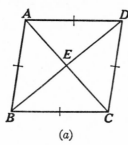 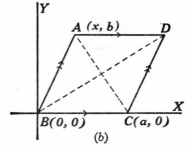

(a) (b)

Fig. 11-53

Proof: (a) *Synthetic.*

STATEMENTS	AUTHORITIES
1. D is equidistant from A and C.	1. Definition
2. D is on the right bisector of AC.	2. Right Bisector Theorem
3. B is on the right bisector of AC.	3. 1 and 2
4. BD is the right bisector of AC.	4. Existence
5. $AC \perp BD$	5. Definition

(b) *Analytic.*

In *Fig. 11-53 (b)*, C has coordinates $(a, 0)$, and A has coordinates (x, b).

Since $AB = BC = a$

$$\therefore \sqrt{x^2 + b^2} = a, \quad \therefore x^2 + b^2 = a^2, \quad \therefore x = \sqrt{a^2 - b^2}$$

$\therefore A$ has coordinates $(\sqrt{a^2 - b^2}, b)$.

$\because AD = a$, D has coordinates $(\sqrt{a^2 - b^2} + a, b)$.

$$\text{Slope of } AC = m_1 = \frac{b}{\sqrt{a^2 - b^2} - a}. \quad \text{Slope of } BD = m_2 = \frac{b}{\sqrt{a^2 - b^2} + a}$$

$$\therefore m_1 m_2 = \frac{b^2}{a^2 - b^2 - a^2} = \frac{b^2}{-b^2} = -1. \quad \therefore AC \perp BD$$

Example 3. If two medians of a triangle are equal, the triangle is isosceles.

Hypothesis: $\triangle ABC$ with medians BD and CE equal in length and intersecting at G

Conclusion: $\triangle ABC$ is isosceles.

Proof: (a) *Synthetic, Fig. 11-54 (a).*

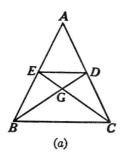

(a)

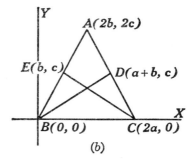

(b)

Fig. 11-54

STATEMENTS	AUTHORITIES
1. $ED \parallel BC$ and $ED = \frac{1}{2} BC$	1. Example 1 (section 11·22)
2. $\angle EDG = \angle CBG$ and $\angle DEG = \angle BCG$	2. Parallel Line Theorem
3. $\triangle EGD \sim \triangle CGB$	3. aaa
4. $\dfrac{DG}{BG} = \dfrac{EG}{CG} = \dfrac{ED}{CB} = \dfrac{1}{2}$	4. Definition, 1
5. $BG = \frac{2}{3} BD$, $CG = \frac{2}{3} CE$	5. Completion
6. $BD = CE$	6. Hypothesis
7. $BG = CG$	7. Replacement
8. $EG = DG$	8. Completion, subtraction
9. In $\triangle$'s EBG, DCG $\Big($ $\quad EG = DG$	9. 8
10. $\qquad\qquad\qquad$ $BG = CG$	10. 7
11. $\qquad\qquad\qquad\Big($ $\angle BGE = \angle CGD$	11. Vertical Angle Th.
12. $\triangle EBG \cong \triangle DCG$	12. sas
13. $BE = CD$	13. Definition
14. $2BE = 2CD$	14. Multiplication
15. $BA = CA$	15. Completion
16. $\triangle ABC$ is isosceles.	16. Definition

(b) *Analytic.*

In *Fig. 11-54 (b)*, D and E have coordinates $(a + b, c)$ and (b, c), respectively. Since
$$BD = CE$$
$$\therefore \quad \sqrt{(a + b)^2 + c^2} = \sqrt{(2a - b)^2 + c^2}$$
$$\therefore \; a^2 + 2ab + b^2 + c^2 = 4a^2 - 4ab + b^2 + c^2$$
$$\therefore \quad 6ab = 3a^2$$
$$\therefore \quad 2b = a$$

Hence $AB = \sqrt{4b^2 + 4c^2} = 2\sqrt{b^2 + c^2}$

$\quad$ and $AC = \sqrt{(2b - 2a)^2 + 4c^2}$
$$= \sqrt{(2b - 4b)^2 + 4c^2} = \sqrt{4b^2 + 4c^2} = 2\sqrt{b^2 + c^2}$$

$\therefore \quad AB = AC$

$\therefore \; \triangle ABC$ is isosceles.

Example 4. Prove the law of cosines for an acute triangle by analytic methods.

Hypothesis: $\triangle ABC$ with BC, CA, and AB having lengths a, b, and c units, respectively, and $\angle ABC = \theta$ units.

Conclusion: $b^2 = c^2 + a^2 - 2ca \cos \theta$

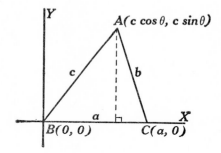

Fig. 11-55

Proof: In *Fig. 11-55*, the coordinates of B, C, and A are $(0, 0)$, $(a, 0)$, and $(c \cos \theta, c \sin \theta)$, respectively.

$\because \; AC = b$
$$\therefore \; b = \sqrt{(c \cos \theta - a)^2 + c^2 \sin^2 \theta}$$
$$= \sqrt{c^2 \cos^2 \theta - 2ca \cos \theta + a^2 + c^2 \sin^2 \theta}$$
$$= \sqrt{c^2(\cos^2 \theta + \sin^2 \theta) + a^2 - 2ca \cos \theta}$$
$$= \sqrt{c^2 + a^2 - 2ca \cos \theta}$$
$$\therefore \; b^2 = c^2 + a^2 - 2ca \cos \theta$$

Exercise 11-22

(B)

Prove the following theorems by both synthetic and analytic methods:

1. The midpoint of the hypotenuse of a right triangle is equidistant from the three vertices.
2. The diagonals of a parallelogram bisect each other.
3. The midpoints of the sides of a rectangle are the vertices of a rhombus.
4. The midpoints of the sides of any quadrilateral are the vertices of a parallelogram.
5. Any two medians of a triangle intersect at a point of trisection of each of the two medians.
6. A line which bisects one side of a triangle and is parallel to a second side bisects the third side.
7. The line segment joining the midpoints of the non-parallel sides of a trapezoid is parallel to the other two sides and has length equal to one-half of their sum.
8. The line segments joining the midpoints of opposite sides of any quadrilateral bisect each other.
9. Lines which are perpendicular to the same line are parallel.
10. If the diagonals of a parallelogram are equal in length, the parallelogram is a rectangle.

Prove the following theorems by analytic methods:

11. If AD is a median of $\triangle ABC$, $AB^2 + AC^2 = 2BD^2 + 2AD^2$.
12. If two sides of a triangle are divided in the same ratio, the line segment joining the points of division is parallel to the third side.
13. If the side BC of $\triangle ABC$ is divided internally at D in the ratio $m : n$, then $mAC^2 + nAB^2 = mDC^2 + nBD^2 + (m + n)AD^2$.
14. For any triangle, the following sets of lines or line segments are concurrent: (i) the altitudes (ii) the medians (iii) the right bisectors of the sides.

Review Exercise 11-23

(A)

1. Find the lengths of the line segments determined by points with the following coordinates:

    (i) $(0, 0)$, $(-4, 3)$ (ii) $(2, 5)$, $(-4, 5)$

    (iii) $(4, -1)$, $(4, -7)$ (iv) $(-2, 4)$, $(10, 9)$

(v) $(7, -1), (-8, 7)$ (vi) $(2, -3), (5, -4)$

2. State the coordinates of the midpoints of line segments for which the end points have the following coordinates:

(i) $(-2, -3), (2, 3)$ (ii) $(-4, 5), (8, -3)$

(iii) $(4, -5), (-4, 3)$ (iv) $(0, 0), (-3, 6)$

(v) $(-\frac{1}{2}, 2), (2\frac{1}{2}, -1)$ (vi) $(2, -3), (2, 8)$

3. Interpret geometrically each of the following:

(i) $\sqrt{x^2 + y^2}$ (ii) $\sqrt{(x-2)^2 + (y-1)^2}$

(iii) $\dfrac{y+2}{x-1}$ (iv) $\left(\dfrac{x-1}{2}, \dfrac{y+3}{2}\right)$

(v) $\left(\dfrac{3x_2 + x_1}{4}, \dfrac{3y_2 + y_1}{4}\right)$ (vi) $\dfrac{y-3}{x-2} = \dfrac{2}{-7}$

4. Find the inclinations of the line:

(i) on $A(2, -3)$ and $B(3, -4)$

(ii) on the origin and $C(2, 2\sqrt{3})$

(iii) having slope $-\dfrac{1}{\sqrt{3}}$

(iv) parallel to the line on $A(6, -2)$ and $B(5, -3)$

(v) having equation $2y - 5 = 0$

(vi) having equation $3x + 2 = 0$

(vii) having equation $x + y + 5 = 0$

(viii) parallel to the line with equation $\sqrt{3}\,x - y + 2 = 0$

(B)

5. $A(-3, -5)$, $B(5, 1)$, and $C(-2, 2)$ are vertices of a triangle. Prove that the triangle is right-angled by using the formula for (i) slope (ii) length of a line segment.

6. Calculate the lengths of the medians of the triangle with vertices $P(1, 4)$, $Q(-5, -2)$, and $R(5, 0)$.

7. The line segment joining $A(3, -1)$ and $B(-4, 2)$ is extended through B to C, so that $BC = 2AB$. Find the coordinates of C.

8. Determine whether or not the points $A(-8, -1)$, $B(1, 1)$, and $C(6, 2)$ are collinear.

9. Find x so that the points $P(x, -2)$, $Q(0, 1)$, and $R(5, 2)$ are collinear.

10. Find the acute angle formed by the lines having slopes 1 and $-\sqrt{3}$, respectively.

11. Find the equation of the line on $A(-2, 3)$ and perpendicular to the line segment joining $P(-6, -1)$ and $Q(5, 2)$.

12. Find the equation of the line which has x-intercept a and y-intercept b.

13. Find the centroid of the triangle with vertices $A(-2, 4)$, $B(6, -1)$, and $C(-1, 3)$. The centroid is a point of trisection of a median.

14. Prove that the lines joining the midpoints of the opposite sides of the quadrilateral with vertices $A(5, 7)$, $B(-3, 5)$, $C(1, -3)$, and $D(7,1)$ bisect each other.

15. Find the coordinates of a point on the y-axis which is equidistant from $A(-2, 6)$ and $B(4, -2)$.

16. A line is on $A(3, -2)$ and the midpoint of the line segment joining $B(-2, 4)$ and $C(6, -7)$. Find its equation.

17. Find y so that the area of the triangle with vertices $A(-3, y)$, $B(2, -4)$, and $C(-1, 5)$ is 12.

18. Compare the area of the quadrilateral with vertices $A(-3, 5)$, $B(1, -3)$, $C(7, 1)$, and $D(5, 7)$ with the area of the quadrilateral having as vertices the midpoints of the sides of $ABCD$.

19. Find the equation of the line having inclination 135° and on the point of intersection of the lines having equations $2x - y - 5 = 0$ and $x + 3y + 1 = 0$.

20. By transforming the equations to the form $y = mx + b$, prove that the lines having equations $2x - 3y + 7 = 0$ and $6x + 4y - 5 = 0$ are perpendicular.

21. Find the length of the altitude from A for a triangle with vertices $A(3, -2)$, $B(-5, -4)$, and $C(0, -8)$.

22. Find the equations which express the condition that the length of a perpendicular from $P(x, y)$ to the line with equation $5x - 12y + 6 = 0$ is 2.

23. Prove that for any parallelogram, the sum of the areas of the squares on the diagonals is equal to the sum of the areas of the squares on the sides.

24. Prove that three times the sum of the areas of the squares on the sides of a triangle is equal to four times the sum of the areas of the squares on the medians.

25. Find the distance between the parallel lines having equations $3x - 4y - 6 = 0$ and $6x - 8y + k = 0$.

26. Find the coordinates of the foot of the perpendicular from $A(1, 5)$ to the line segment joining $B(1, -1)$ and $C(3, 0)$.

27. Prove that the line segment joining $A(-4, 6)$ and $B(8, -3)$ is trisected by the coordinate axes.

28. Prove that the sum of the areas of the squares on two sides of a triangle is equal to twice the area of the square on one-half of the third side plus twice the area of the square on the median to the third side.

29. Find the coordinates of the orthocentre of the triangle with vertices $A(2, 6)$, $B(0, 0)$, and $C(4, 1)$.

DEFINITIONS

In our study of geometry, we made many definitions; this summary is a partial list of these.

Acute angle.   An acute angle is an angle with degree measure less than 90.

Acute triangle.   An acute triangle is a triangle determining three acute angles.

Altitude of a triangle.   The altitude of a triangle is the line segment drawn from a vertex perpendicular to the opposite side and terminating on the opposite side.

Angle.   An angle is the set of all points on two distinct rays with a common end point.

Angle sum of two angles.   The angle sum of two angles is the sum of the measurements of the two angles.

Betweeness on a line.   If A, B, C are three points on a line, B is between A and C if $AC = AB + BC$.

Bisect.   To bisect is to divide into two equal parts.

Centroid.   The centroid of a triangle is the point of intersection of the medians.

Circle.   A circle is a point set such that each member of the set is the same distance (radius) from a fixed point (centre).

Circumcentre.   The circumcentre of a triangle is the point of intersection of the right bisectors of the sides of a triangle.

Circumscribed circle of a triangle.   The circumscribed circle of a triangle is the circle on the three vertices.

Collinear points.   Collinear points are points on the same straight line.

Complementary angles.   Two angles whose angle sum is 90° are complementary angles.

Concave polygon.   A concave polygon is one which has at least one reflex angle.

Concurrent lines.   Concurrent lines are three or more lines on the same point.

417

Congruence of triangles. If a correspondence $ABC \leftrightarrow DEF$ between the vertices of two triangles is such that every pair of corresponding sides is congruent and every pair of corresponding angles is congruent, then this correspondence is a congruence matching and $\triangle ABC \cong \triangle DEF$.

Converse statements. When two conditional statements are so related that the hypothesis and conclusion consist of single statements which are interchanged, then each conditional statement is said to be the converse of the other.

Converse theorem. A converse theorem is a theorem that is formed from a given theorem by interchanging any number of statements in the hypothesis of the given theorem with an equal number of statements in the conclusion.

Convex polygon. A convex polygon is one in which all angles have measurements less than $180°$.

Corollary. A corollary of a theorem is an implication which follows as a direct consequent of the theorem.

Cube. A cube is a prism whose bases and lateral faces are square regions.

Degree. A degree is $\frac{1}{180}$ of a straight angle.

Dihedral angle. A dihedral angle is the point set consisting of the union of a line and two non-coplanar half-planes having the line as a common edge.

Equilateral triangle. An equilateral triangle is a triangle with all sides equal.

Exterior of an angle. The exterior of an angle is the point set not contained in an angle or its interior.

Half-line. A half-line is the point set consisting of all points on a line which are on one side of a given point on the line.

Half-plane. A half-plane is the point set consisting of all points in a given plane which are on one side of a given line.

Hypotenuse. The hypotenuse is the side opposite the right angle in a right triangle.

Interior of an angle. A point D is in the interior of $\angle ABC$ if D is on the same side of line BA as C and on the same side of line BC as A.

Isosceles triangle. An isosceles triangle is a triangle with two sides equal.

Line segment. A line segment is the point set consisting of two distinct points on a line and all the points between them.

Locus. A locus is a set of points.

Median of a triangle. The median of a triangle is the line segment joining any vertex to the midpoint of the opposite side.

Midpoint of a line segment.   If AB is a line segment and C is a point on the segment, then C is the midpoint if $AC = CB$.

Obtuse angle.   An obtuse angle is an angle with degree measure greater than 90 and less than 180.

Obtuse triangle.   An obtuse triangle is a triangle with one angle an obtuse angle.

Orthocentre.   The orthocentre of a triangle is the point of intersection of the altitudes.

Parallel lines.   If two distinct lines lie in the same plane and have no point in common, then the two lines are parallel.

Parallel line segments.   If two distinct line segments are segments of parallel lines, then the two line segments are parallel.

Parallelepiped.   A parallelepiped is a prism whose bases are parallelogram regions.

Parallelogram.   If a quadrilateral has both pairs of opposite sides parallel, then it is a parallelogram.

Parallel planes.   If two distinct planes have no point or line in common, then the two planes are parallel.

Perpendicular distance.   Perpendicular distance is the length of a line segment from a point to a line (or segment) at right angles to the line.

Perpendicular lines.   Perpendicular lines are two lines which intersect at right angles.

Perpendicular line to a plane.   Since a plane is determined by two intersecting lines, if a line is perpendicular to two intersecting lines of a plane on the point of intersection, then the line is perpendicular to the plane.

Perpendicular planes.   If two planes intersect to form a dihedral angle whose measurement is 90°, the two planes are perpendicular.

Polygon.   If the beginning and end of a polygonal path consisting of three or more line segments coincide, then the path is called a polygon.

Polyhedron.   A polyhedron is a closed three-dimensional geometric figure.

Postulate.   A postulate is an assumption.

Proportion.   A proportion is the statement of equality of two ratios.

Prism.   A prism is a polyhedron with two faces that are congruent polygonal regions on parallel planes, and its remaining faces are parallelogram regions with two sides on these parallel planes.

Pyramid.   A pyramid is a polyhedron with one face a polygonal region and the other faces triangular regions with a common vertex not in the plane of the polygonal region.

Quadrilateral.   A quadrilateral is a simple polygon with four sides.

Radius of a circle. The radius of a circle is a line segment whose end points are the centre of the circle and a point on the circle.

Ratio of areas of triangles. The ratio of the areas of triangles is the ratio of the number of square units in the areas of the triangles.

Ratio of line segments. The ratio of line segments is the ratio of the number of units in the lengths of the line segments.

Ray. A ray is the point set consisting of a point on a line and all the points on the line on one side of the given point.

Rectangular parallelepiped. A rectangular parallelepiped is a right prism whose base is a rectangular region.

Reflex angle. Reflex $\angle ABC = 360° - \angle ABC$.

Regular polygon. A regular polygon is one which is equilateral and equiangular.

Regular polyhedron. A regular polyhedron is a polyhedron whose faces are congruent plane figures.

Regular pyramid. A regular pyramid is a pyramid whose base is a regular polygonal region and whose lateral edges have equal lengths.

Right angle. A right angle is an angle whose degree measure is 90.

Right bisector of a line segment. The right bisector of a given line segment is the line which bisects the line segment at right angles.

Right prism. A right prism is a prism whose lateral edges are perpendicular to the bases.

Right triangle. A right triangle is a triangle having one angle a right angle.

Rhombus. A rhombus is a parallelogram with a pair of adjacent sides equal.

Scalene triangle. A scalene triangle is a triangle with no two sides of equal length.

Similar figures. Geometric figures are similar if:

        (i) corresponding angles are equal, and

        (ii) corresponding sides are proportional.

Simple polygon. If the beginning and end of a polygonal path consisting of three or more line segments coincide and no two sides intersect, then the path is called a simple polygon.

Simple polygonal region. A simple polygonal region is the union of triangular regions such that if any two of these intersect, the intersection is a line segment or a point.

Square. A square is a rhombus with one angle a right angle.

Straight angle. A straight angle is an angle whose degree measure is 180.

Supplementary angles. Supplementary angles are angles whose angle sum is 180°.

Transversal. A transversal is a line intersecting two or more lines or line segments at distinct points.

Trapezoid. A trapezoid is a quadrilateral with one pair of opposite sides parallel.

Triangle. A triangle is the set of all points on the line segments determined by three points which are not all on one line.

Triangular region. A triangular region is the union of a triangle and its interior.

Vertical angles. Two angles are vertical angles if their sides form two pairs of opposite rays.

SUMMARY OF POSTULATES

In our study of geometry, we made many assumptions; this summary is a partial list of these.

Existence Postulates.

1. An unlimited number of lines in one plane may lie on one point in the plane.
2. There exists one and only one line which lies on two distinct points.
3. Two distinct lines intersect on, at most, one point.
4. A plane contains at least three non-collinear points.
5. Any three non-collinear points determine a plane.
6. If two distinct planes intersect, they intersect on a line.
7. If two distinct points lie in a plane, then the line containing these points lies in the same plane.
8. Two intersecting straight lines determine a plane.
9. A line intersects a plane not containing the line in, at most, one point.
10. There exists an unlimited number of angles equal to an angle.
11. There exists one and only one ray which bisects an angle.
12. There exists one and only one right bisector of a line segment.
13. There exists one and only one midpoint of a line segment.
14. There exists an unlimited number of line segments equal to a given line segment.

Measurement Postulates.

15. There is a one-to-one correspondence between the points on a line and the real numbers.

16. To every line segment there corresponds a unique positive real number of units called the length of the line segment or the distance between its end points.

17. To each geometric angle there corresponds a unique positive real number of degrees; the degree measure of an angle is greater than zero and equal to or less than 180.

Betweeness Postulates.

18. If three distinct points lie on a line, one and only one of the points is between the other two.

19. Between the two end points on a line segment AB, there is one and only one point C such that $AC = CB$. (C is the midpoint of AB.)

20. Between any two distinct points on a line there exists at least one point.

Completion Postulates.

21. *Line segments.* See page 103.

22. *Angles.* See page 104.

23. *Areas.* See area postulate 30, below.

Congruence Postulates.

24. Equal line segments are congruent; congruent line segments are equal.

25. Equal angles are congruent; congruent angles are equal.

26. If two sides and the contained angle of one triangle are respectively equal to two sides and the contained angle of another triangle, the two triangles are congruent (sas).

27. If two triangles have the three sides of one respectively equal to the three sides of the other, then the triangles are congruent (sss).

28. If two triangles have two angles and the contained side of one respectively equal to two angles and the corresponding side of the other, then the two triangles are congruent (asa).

Parallel Postulate.

29. If l is any line and A is any point not on l, then there is one and only one line on A which is parallel to line l.

Area Postulates.

30. The area of a polygonal region is the sum of the areas of the component regions whose union is the polygonal region.

31. If two polygonal regions are congruent, then they have the same area.

32. Two polygonal regions are equal in area if they can be separated into a finite number of polygons which are congruent in pairs.

33. For every polygonal region, there exists a unique positive real number of units which is called the area of the region.

TEST PAPERS 1-3

Chapters 1-3

TEST PAPER 1

1. In a school, 210 Grade XI students take music and typing, 195 take typing and art, 225 take art and music, and 75 take all three. Use a Venn diagram to determine the number of students taking each subject.

2. If $a = 2$, $b = -3$, $c = -1$, evaluate:
   (i) $|a - b| - |b - c|$
   (ii) $(a + 2b - 3c) - (3a - 5b + c) - (4a + 6b - 2c)$

3. Expand and simplify:
   $(x - y - z)(x - y + z) - (x - y + z)^2$

4. Show that $\left(\dfrac{a}{-b} \times \dfrac{-c}{d}\right) \times \left(-\dfrac{e}{f}\right) = \dfrac{-a}{b}\left[\dfrac{c}{-d} \times \left(-\dfrac{e}{-f}\right)\right]$

5. Express $.325\dot{6}$ as a rational number in the form $\dfrac{a}{b}$.

6. Find:
   (i) $\left\{x \mid \frac{1}{4}(3x - 1) + \frac{1}{3}(2x + 3) - \frac{1}{2}(5x - 2) = 1\right\}$
   (ii) $\left\{y \mid \dfrac{y - 2}{6} < 1 - \dfrac{1 - 2y}{4}\right\}$

7. Draw the graph of:
   $\{y \mid (5 - y)(4 - y) > (2 - y)(6 - y)$ and $(2y - 1)^2 < 5 + 4y^2\}$

8. Solve and verify: $12(3 - x) - x(x + 4) = 0$

9. Simplify:
   (i) $2\sqrt{128} - 3\sqrt{162} - 4\sqrt{147} + \sqrt{300}$
   (ii) $(2\sqrt{2} - 3\sqrt{3})(4\sqrt{2} + 5\sqrt{3}) - (3\sqrt{2} - 2\sqrt{3})^2$
   (iii) $\dfrac{3\sqrt{3} + 2\sqrt{2}}{3\sqrt{3} - 2\sqrt{2}}$

10. Solve: $\dfrac{3}{\sqrt{3 - x}} = \sqrt{3 - x} + \sqrt{2 - x}$

424

TEST PAPER 2

1. If $a = -2, b = -3, c = -1$, evaluate:
$$(a + b + c)(a^2 + b^2 + c^2 - ab - bc - ca)$$

2. In a survey of 100 people, 43 said they watched television program A; 55 watched program B; 45 watched program C. Of these, 15 watched programs A and B, 25 watched programs B and C, and 20 watched programs A and C. This total includes 8 who watched all three programs. How many of these people did not watch any of the three programs?

3. Find: $\{x \mid -2 \leqq x < 5\} \cup \{x \mid 7 > x \geqq 5\}$

4. Expand and simplify:
$$2(x - 2y)(x + 2y) - 3(x - 2y)^2 - (x^2 + xy - 6y^2)$$

5. Show that $.4\dot{9}$ is equivalent to $\frac{1}{2}$.

6. Express in simplest form: $\dfrac{(-2a^2b)(3ab^2c)(-5a^2bc^2)}{(-2b^2)(-10ac)(6bc^3)}$

7. Draw the graph of:
$$\{x \mid 2(x - 2)^2 - 3(x - 4)^2 \neq 8 - x^2, x \in R\}$$

8. Find:
    (i) $\{y \mid 5y(3 - 2y) + 2(3y + 4)^2 \geqq 11y + 4(y + 2)(2y - 1)\}$
    (ii) $\{x \mid (x - a)(x - b) = ab\}$

9. Simplify: (i) $\dfrac{16a^4b^{-4}c^{-3}}{24a^{-3}b^{-3}c^{-3}}$

    (ii) $(2\sqrt{2} - 3\sqrt{3} + 4\sqrt{5})^2 + 6\sqrt{3}(2\sqrt{2} + 4\sqrt{5})$

10. Solve: $\sqrt{4x + 9} - \sqrt{x + 5} = \sqrt{x}$

TEST PAPER 3

1. If $x = -2, y = 1, z = -3$, evaluate:
    (i) $|(x - y)^2| + |(y - z)^2| - |z - x|$
    (ii) $(x + y - z) - (y + z - x) - (z + x - y)$

2. From the sum of $2x - 5y - 6z$ and $3x - 2y + 4z$, subtract the sum of $5x - 7y + 6z$ and $4x - 3y - 2z$.

3. Simplify:
    (i) $(a + 2b)(a^2 - 2ab + 4b^2) - (4a^2 + 2ab + b^2)(2a - b)$

    (ii) $(a + b)^2 - (a - b)^2$ where $a = \dfrac{x + y}{2}$ and $b = \dfrac{x - y}{2}$

4. Arrange the elements of the following set in increasing order of magnitude:

$$\left\{ \frac{-1}{3}, \frac{3}{-8}, \frac{-3}{-2}, \frac{0}{5}, \frac{-4}{-3}, \frac{5}{-6} \right\}$$

5. Express $10.23\dot{2}\dot{7}$ as a rational number in the form $\frac{a}{b}$.

6. Find the solution set of :
   (i) $(a-3)^2 + 30 = 15(a-1) + (a+15)(a-3)$
   (ii) $(2x-1)(x-2) \geqq -x(2-4x) - 2x(x+2)$

7. Solve and verify:
   (i) $2x - 1 = \dfrac{3}{x}$
   (ii) $(2x-3)(x+1) - (2x-3)^2 = 0$

8. Find an expression for the area of a rectangle with sides $(5\sqrt{2} - 2\sqrt{3})$ inches and $(3\sqrt{3} - 2\sqrt{2})$ inches.

9. (i) Solve: $\begin{cases} \sqrt{3}a - b = 2\sqrt{15} \\ \sqrt{5}a + 2b = 3\sqrt{15} \end{cases}$

   (ii) Divide: $31\sqrt{6} + 24\sqrt{5}$ by $7\sqrt{6} + 9\sqrt{5}$

10. Solve: $\sqrt{2x+1} - \sqrt{x} = \sqrt{x-3}$

TEST PAPERS 4-6

Chapters 1-7

TEST PAPER 4

THEOREM

1. State and prove the Pythagorean Theorem.

CALCULATIONS

2. The lengths of the parallel sides of a trapezoid are 10 cm. and 15 cm. If the area is 165 sq. cm., calculate the distance between the parallel sides.

3. The area of $\triangle ABC$ is 45 sq. cm. AD is a median to BC, and G is the centroid. Calculate the area of $\triangle BDG$. (The centroid divides a median in the ratio $2:1$.)

ACCURATE CONSTRUCTIONS

4. (i) Construct a rhombus whose diagonals are 3.0 inches and 4.0 inches, respectively. Measure the length of a side.

(ii) Construct $\triangle ABC$ in which $AB = 3$ inches, $\angle B = 30°$, and $AC = 1\frac{3}{4}$ inches. Show that two different triangles are possible with the given data.

(iii) Construct a square whose area is three times the area of a square whose side is 4.5 cm. Measure the side of the square.

DEDUCTIONS

5. P is any point on BC, the base of an isosceles triangle. If $PY \perp AC$, $PX \perp AB$, and $CZ \perp AB$, prove that $CZ = PX + PY$.

6. On the side AB of $\triangle ABC$, $\triangle PAB$ is described outwardly so that $\angle PBA = 30°$ and $\angle PAB = 90°$. D is a point on AB such that $AD = AP$. E is a point on AC such that $DE \parallel BC$. Prove that $\triangle ADE = \frac{1}{3} \triangle ABC$.

7. In $\triangle ABC$, $\angle B = 90°$. A square $ACDE$ is described outwardly on AC. DF and EG are drawn perpendicular to BC or BC extended. Prove that $EG = AB + DF$.

8. Prove that, if two triangles have two sides of one respectively equal to two sides of the other and the contained angles supplementary, the triangles are equal.

TEST PAPER 5

1. Express $.45\dot{3}$ in the form $\frac{a}{b}$.

2. Find: (i) $\{x \mid (3x - 1)(2x + 3) - 6x(x + 1) = 5 - 3x\}$

(ii) $\{x \mid (2x + 1)(x - 2) - 2x(x + 1) \leq 3,\ x \in I\}$

3. Simplify: (i) $(r^6s^{-4}t^4)^0(5r^7s^{-2}t^5)^2$

(ii) $\left(\dfrac{x^{-3}y^6}{x^{-5}y^8}\right)^{-5}\left(\dfrac{x^{-2}y^{-1}}{x^2\ y^{-3}}\right)^4$

(iii) $\dfrac{36z^5 - 49z^{-3}}{6 - 7z^{-4}}$

4. Rationalize the denominator of each of the following:

(i) $\dfrac{\sqrt{7} + \sqrt{5}}{\sqrt{7} - \sqrt{5}}$

(ii) $\dfrac{2\sqrt{3} + \sqrt{2}}{\sqrt{6} + 2\sqrt{2}}$

5. The sides of a triangle have lengths of 15, 18, and 30 units. If the shortest side of a similar triangle is 10 units long, what are the lengths of the other two sides?

6. State and prove the Triangle Area Ratio Theorem.

7. In $\triangle ABC$, D and E divide AB and AC, respectively, in the same ratio internally. If DC and BE intersect on G, prove that
$$\frac{\triangle DGE}{\triangle BGC} = \frac{\triangle ADE}{\triangle ABC}.$$

8. Prove that the medians of a triangle are concurrent.

9. P is any point on side BC of $\triangle ABC$. $AB = AC$, $PM \perp AB$, $PN \perp AC$, $CR \perp AB$. Prove $PM + PN = CR$.

TEST PAPER 6

1. Express as mixed radicals:

    (i) $\sqrt{147}$ (ii) $\sqrt{a^3 x^2}$ (iii) $\sqrt{(x^2 - y^2)(x + y)}$

2. Solve: $\dfrac{x + 2}{x - 5} = \dfrac{x - 4}{x + 9}$

3. Find: $\{x| -2x < 3 - 3x \text{ and } 3(x - .2) > x + 1.4\}$

4. Calculate the area of a triangle whose sides have lengths 6 inches, 10 inches, and 12 inches.

5. The diagonals of a rhombus are 12 inches and 16 inches, respectively. Calculate:

    (i) the area of the rhombus;

    (ii) the lengths of the sides of the rhombus.

6. Prove the following deduction:

    Hypothesis: $\sim C \to D$, $C \to \sim D$, $\sim E \to \sim C$, $D \to B$, $E \to C$, $\sim E$

    Conclusion: B

7. Construct a square whose area is equal to the difference between the areas of two given squares.

8. Prove that the area of a rhombus is one-half the product of the lengths of its diagonals.

9. $ABCD$ is a trapezoid having $AB \parallel CD$. Prove that the line on the midpoint of CD and on the intersection of the diagonals bisects AB.

10. In $\triangle ABC$, $AB = AC$. D is on the same side of BC as A so that $\triangle ABC = \triangle DBC$. K is on CA extended so that $AC = AK$. Prove that $DK = DB$.

TEST PAPERS 7-9

Chapters 1-11

TEST PAPER 7

1. (i) Find: $\{y \mid y^2 + 2(y + 1)(y - 3) < 3y(y + 2) - 20\}$

   (ii) Solve: $\begin{cases} (a + b)x - (a - b)y = a^2 + b^2 \\ \qquad x - y \qquad\quad = a - b \end{cases}$

2. (i) Express $.23\dot{4}$ as a rational number in the form $\dfrac{a}{b}$.

   (ii) Express $\dfrac{\sqrt{2} + 2\sqrt{5}}{\sqrt{5} - \sqrt{2}}$ with a rational denominator.

3. Solve: (i) $\sqrt{x + 1} + \sqrt{3x} = \sqrt{8x + 1}$

   (ii) $(x - a)(b + c) = x^2 - a^2$

4. State and prove the sas Similar Triangle Theorem.

5. PQR is a triangle having $\angle P = 90°$, $PS \perp QR$, and $ST \parallel PR$. If $PR = 15$ cm., $PQ = 20$ cm., calculate the lengths of PS and ST.

6. In $\parallel^{\mathrm{gm}} ABCD$, P is any point in the interior of $\triangle ABC$. Prove $\triangle APB + \triangle APC = \triangle APD$.

7. Solve the triangle ABC in which $a = 43$, $c = 32$, $\angle A = 46°$.

8. Prove the identity: $\sec^2\theta + \csc^2 \theta = \sec^2 \theta \cdot \csc^2 \theta$.

9. Find the area of the triangle bounded by segments of the lines having equations $x + 11 = 0$, $x + y - 1 = 0$, and $2x - 5y = 23$.

10. Find the centre and the radius of the circle circumscribed about the triangle with vertices $A\ (7, 0)$, $B\ (5, 8)$, and $C\ (-9, -4)$.

TEST PAPER 8

1. Thirty students in a school take German and forty take Biology. If the total number of students taking only one of these subjects is forty, how many of them take both?

2. (i) Find: $\left\{ x \left| \dfrac{3 - 4x}{5} + \dfrac{7x + 11}{15} \neq \dfrac{4 + 5x}{9} \right. \right\}$

   (ii) Solve for x: $(a + x)(b - x) + x^2 = b(a + x) - \dfrac{bc^2}{a}$

3. Solve: $\dfrac{\sqrt{x+16}}{\sqrt{4-x}} + \dfrac{\sqrt{4-x}}{\sqrt{x+16}} = \dfrac{5}{2}$

4. State and prove the Mean Proportional Theorem.

5. The medians AD, BE of $\triangle ABC$ intersect on G. Prove that the line segments AG, BG, and CG separate $\triangle ABC$ into three triangles having equal areas.

6. PQR is a triangle. S and T are points on PQ and PR, respectively, such that $ST \| QR$. If $PS : SQ = 1 : 2$, calculate the ratio of $\triangle PQR$ to $\triangle PST$.

7. (i) Solve for x: $x \cos 0° \sin 30° = \cos 120° \tan 135°$

   (ii) Simplify: $\dfrac{1}{1 - \sin \theta} + \dfrac{1}{1 + \sin \theta} - 2 \sec^2 \theta$

8. Solve the triangle for which $\angle A = 62°$, $\angle B = 48°$, and $c = 44$.

9. Find the coordinates of the point A on the line whose equation is $x + 2y = 4$, such that the slope of the line segment joining A to B $(7, 6)$ is -2.

10. Find the value of b so that the line having equation $y = -2x + b$ lies on: (i) $O(0, 0)$ (ii) $B(-\frac{1}{2}, \frac{3}{4})$

TEST PAPER 9

1. If $x = -2$, $y = -1$, the expression $\left(\dfrac{1}{x^{-1}}\right)^0 + \left(\dfrac{1}{y^{-1}}\right)^0$ is equivalent to:
   (a) 3   (b) $\frac{5}{6}$ (c) 2   (d) 1   (e) none of these

2. The solution set of $\frac{1}{8}x - x + \frac{1}{6}x \neq \frac{5}{6} - \frac{1}{2}x$, $x \in R$ is:
   (a) $\{x \mid x = 4, x \in R\}$ (b) $\{x \mid x = -4, x \in R\}$
   (c) $\{x \mid x \geqq -4, x \in R\}$ (d) $\{x \mid x \neq -4, x \in R\}$
   (e) $\{x \mid x \neq -4, x \in I\}$

3. $\sqrt{18} - \sqrt{27} - \sqrt{12} + \sqrt{162} - \sqrt{98}$ equals:
   (a) $-(\sqrt{3} + \sqrt{2})$ (b) $(\sqrt{3} - \sqrt{2})$ (c) $5(\sqrt{2} - \sqrt{3})$
   (d) $3(\sqrt{3} - \sqrt{2})$ (e) $-5(\sqrt{2} - \sqrt{3})$

4. If $|x + 4| = |-2|$, then x equals:
   (a) -6 (b) 2   (c) -2 or 6   (d) -2 or -6 (e) none of these

5. The number of gallons of water that must be added to 8 gallons of an 80% solution of antifreeze to make a 50% solution is:
   (a) 4.8   (b) 6.4   (c) 4   (d) 2.4   (e) 2

6. P is the midpoint of LM in $\triangle KLM$. $\angle L = 50°, PL = PK = PM$. The measurement of $\angle LKM$ is:

(a) 80°   (b) 90°   (c) 100°   (d) 110°   (e) 120°

7. The lengths of the diagonals of a rhombus are 12 inches and 10 inches. The area of the rhombus is:

(a) 120 sq. in.   (b) 30 sq. in.   (c) 60 sq. in.   (d) 90 sq. in.
(e) 240 sq. in.

8. In $\triangle ABC$, $BC = 20$ in. and the altitude to BC is 10 in. D is any point on BC. E is the midpoint of AD. $\triangle AEC + \triangle BDE$ equals:

(a) 200 sq. in.   (b) 100 sq. in.   (c) 50 sq. in.   (d) 25 sq. in.
(e) 12.5 sq. in.

9. $\triangle ABC \sim \triangle DEF$. If $AB = 6$ in., $BC = 4$ in., $CA = 8$ in., $ED = 12$ in., EF equals:

(a) 6 in.   (b) 8 in.   (c) 9 in.   (d) 16 in.   (e) 18 in.

10. The lengths of the sides of a triangle are 8 inches, 12 inches, and 12 inches. The area of the triangle in square inches is:

(a) $32\sqrt{3}$ (b) 32   (c) $32\sqrt{2}$ (d) 8   (e) $8\sqrt{2}$

11. The coordinates of a point on the terminal arm of an oriented angle are $(-5, -12)$. The sine of this angle is:

(a) $\dfrac{5}{12}$ (b) $\dfrac{12}{13}$ (c) $\dfrac{-5}{13}$ (d) $-\dfrac{12}{13}$ (e) $\dfrac{12}{5}$

12. $\sin 60° \cos 30° + \cos 60° \sin 30°$ equals:

(a) $\dfrac{1}{2}$ (b) 1   (c) $\sqrt{3}$ (d) $\dfrac{1}{\sqrt{3}}$ (e) 2

13. $\tan 0° + \sin 90° - \cos 180° + \csc 90°$ equals:

(a) 0   (b) 1   (c) -1 (d) 2   (e) -2

14. $\dfrac{1 - \sin^2 \theta}{\csc^2 \theta - 1}$ equals:

(a) $\cos \theta$ (b) $\cos^2 \theta$ (c) $\sin \theta$ (d) $\sin^2 \theta$ (e) 1

15. $2 \tan^2 \dfrac{\pi}{6} \sin^2 \dfrac{\pi}{4} + \cos^2 \dfrac{\pi}{3} + \sin^2 \dfrac{\pi}{3} \cos \dfrac{\pi}{2}$ equals:

(a) $\frac{1}{6}$ (b) $\frac{1}{12}$ (c) $\frac{7}{12}$ (d) $\frac{4}{3}$ (e) $\frac{5}{6}$

16. The coordinates of the midpoint of the line segment joining $(7, -3)$ to $(-1, 5)$ are:

(a) $(4, 1)$ (b) $(3, 1)$ (c) $(4, 4)$ (d) $(3, 4)$ (e) $(6, -2)$

17. The slope of the line having equation $2x + 3y = 6$ is:

(a) 2   (b) 3   (c) $\frac{2}{3}$ (d) $-\frac{3}{2}$ (e) $-\frac{2}{3}$

18. The equation of the line on $(3, -2)$ with slope -3 is:

(a) $3x + y + 11 = 0$ (b) $3x + y + 7 = 0$ (c) $3x - y + 11 = 0$
(d) $3x + y - 7 = 0$ (e) $3x - y - 7 = 0$

19. The line segment from $(3, -4)$ to $(-7, 8)$ is divided internally in the ratio $3 : 5$. The coordinates of the point of section are:

(a) $(\frac{9}{2}, \frac{11}{2})$ (b) $(-\frac{13}{4}, \frac{7}{2})$ (c) $(-\frac{3}{4}, \frac{1}{2})$ (d) $(-3, 2)$
(e) $(-13, 14)$

20. The equation of the line on $(5, 7)$ perpendicular to the line having equation $2x - y + 5 = 0$ is:

(a) $x - 2y - 19 = 0$ (b) $x - 2y + 9 = 0$ (c) $x + 2y + 19 = 0$
(d) $x + 2y - 19 = 0$ (e) $x - 2y - 9 = 0$

Trigonometric Tables

DEGREES	RADIANS	SIN	COS	TAN	CSC	SEC	COT
0	.0000	.0000	1.0000	.0000		1.0000	
1	.0175	.0175	.9998	.0175	57.30	1.0002	57.29
2	.0349	.0349	.9994	.0349	28.65	1.0006	28.64
3	.0524	.0523	.9986	.0524	19.11	1.0014	19.08
4	.0698	.0698	.9976	.0699	14.34	1.0024	14.30
5	.0873	.0872	.9962	.0875	11.474	1.0038	11.430
6	.1047	.1045	.9945	.1051	9.5668	1.0055	9.5144
7	.1222	.1219	.9925	.1228	8.2055	1.0075	8.1443
8	.1396	.1392	.9903	.1405	7.1853	1.0098	7.1154
9	.1571	.1564	.9877	.1584	6.3925	1.0125	6.3138
10	.1745	.1736	.9848	.1763	5.7588	1.0154	5.6713
11	.1920	.1908	.9816	.1944	5.2408	1.0187	5.1446
12	.2094	.2079	.9781	.2126	4.8097	1.0223	4.7046
13	.2269	.2250	.9744	.2309	4.4454	1.0263	4.3315
14	.2443	.2419	.9703	.2493	4.1336	1.0306	4.0108
15	.2618	.2588	.9659	.2679	3.8637	1.0353	3.7321
16	.2793	.2756	.9613	.2867	3.6280	1.0403	3.4874
17	.2967	.2924	.9563	.3057	3.4203	1.0457	3.2709
18	.3142	.3090	.9511	.3249	3.2361	1.0515	3.0777
19	.3316	.3256	.9455	.3443	3.0716	1.0576	2.9042
20	.3491	.3420	.9397	.3640	2.9238	1.0642	2.7475
21	.3665	.3584	.9336	.3839	2.7904	1.0711	2.6051
22	.3840	.3746	.9272	.4040	2.6695	1.0785	2.4751
23	.4014	.3907	.9205	.4245	2.5593	1.0864	2.3559
24	.4189	.4067	.9135	.4452	2.4586	1.0946	2.2460
25	.4363	.4226	.9063	.4663	2.3662	1.1034	2.1445
26	.4538	.4384	.8988	.4877	2.2812	1.1126	2.0503
27	.4712	.4540	.8910	.5095	2.2027	1.1223	1.9626
28	.4887	.4695	.8829	.5317	2.1301	1.1326	1.8807
29	.5061	.4848	.8746	.5543	2.0627	1.1434	1.8040

DEGREES	RADIANS	SIN	COS	TAN	CSC	SEC	COT
30	.5236	.5000	.8660	.5774	2.0000	1.1547	1.7321
31	.5411	.5150	.8572	.6009	1.9416	1.1666	1.6643
32	.5585	.5299	.8480	.6249	1.8871	1.1792	1.6003
33	.5760	.5446	.8387	.6494	1.8361	1.1924	1.5399
34	.5934	.5592	.8290	.6745	1.7883	1.2062	1.4826
35	.6109	.5736	.8192	.7002	1.7435	1.2208	1.4281
36	.6283	.5878	.8090	.7265	1.7013	1.2361	1.3764
37	.6458	.6018	.7986	.7536	1.6616	1.2521	1.3270
38	.6632	.6157	.7880	.7813	1.6243	1.2690	1.2799
39	.6807	.6293	.7771	.8098	1.5890	1.2868	1.2349
40	.6981	.6428	.7660	.8391	1.5557	1.3054	1.1918
41	.7156	.6561	.7547	.8693	1.5243	1.3250	1.1504
42	.7330	.6691	.7431	.9004	1.4945	1.3456	1.1106
43	.7505	.6820	.7314	.9325	1.4663	1.3673	1.0724
44	.7679	.6947	.7193	.9657	1.4396	1.3902	1.0355
45	.7854	.7071	.7071	1.0000	1.4142	1.4142	1.0000
46	.8029	.7193	.6947	1.0355	1.3902	1.4396	.9657
47	.8203	.7314	.6820	1.0724	1.3673	1.4663	.9325
48	.8378	.7431	.6691	1.1106	1.3456	1.4945	.9004
49	.8552	.7547	.6561	1.1504	1.3250	1.5243	.8693
50	.8727	.7660	.6428	1.1918	1.3054	1.5557	.8391
51	.8901	.7771	.6293	1.2349	1.2868	1.5890	.8098
52	.9076	.7880	.6157	1.2799	1.2690	1.6243	.7813
53	.9250	.7986	.6018	1.3270	1.2521	1.6616	.7536
54	.9425	.8090	.5878	1.3764	1.2361	1.7013	.7265
55	.9599	.8192	.5736	1.4281	1.2208	1.7435	.7002
56	.9774	.8290	.5592	1.4826	1.2062	1.7883	.6745
57	.9948	.8387	.5446	1.5399	1.1924	1.8361	.6494
58	1.0123	.8480	.5299	1.6003	1.1792	1.8871	.6249
59	1.0297	.8572	.5150	1.6643	1.1666	1.9416	.6009

DEGREES	RADIANS	SIN	COS	TAN	CSC	SEC	COT
60	1.0472	.8660	.5000	1.7321	1.1547	2.0000	.5774
61	1.0647	.8746	.4848	1.8040	1.1434	2.0627	.5543
62	1.0821	.8829	.4695	1.8807	1.1326	2.1301	.5317
63	1.0996	.8910	.4540	1.9626	1.1223	2.2027	.5095
64	1.1170	.8988	.4384	2.0503	1.1126	2.2812	.4877
65	1.1345	.9063	.4226	2.1445	1.1034	2.3662	.4663
66	1.1519	.9135	.4067	2.2460	1.0946	2.4586	.4452
67	1.1694	.9205	.3907	2.3559	1.0864	2.5593	.4245
68	1.1868	.9272	.3746	2.4751	1.0785	2.6695	.4040
69	1.2043	.9336	.3584	2.6051	1.0712	2.7904	.3839
70	1.2217	.9397	.3420	2.7475	1.0642	2.9238	.3640
71	1.2392	.9455	.3256	2.9042	1.0576	3.0716	.3443
72	1.2566	.9511	.3090	3.0777	1.0515	3.2361	.3249
73	1.2741	.9563	.2924	3.2709	1.0457	3.4203	.3057
74	1.2915	.9613	.2756	3.4874	1.0403	3.6280	.2867
75	1.3090	.9659	.2588	3.7321	1.0353	3.8637	.2679
76	1.3265	.9703	.2419	4.0108	1.0306	4.1336	.2493
77	1.3439	.9744	.2250	4.3315	1.0263	4.4454	.2309
78	1.3614	.9781	.2079	4.7046	1.0223	4.8097	.2126
79	1.3788	.9816	.1908	5.1446	1.0187	5.2408	.1944
80	1.3963	.9848	.1736	5.6713	1.0154	5.7588	.1763
81	1.4137	.9877	.1564	6.3138	1.0125	6.3925	.1584
82	1.4312	.9903	.1392	7.1154	1.0098	7.1853	.1405
83	1.4486	.9925	.1219	8.1443	1.0075	8.2055	.1228
84	1.4661	.9945	.1045	9.5144	1.0055	9.5668	.1051
85	1.4835	.9962	.0872	11.43	1.0038	11.474	.0875
86	1.5010	.9976	.0698	14.30	1.0024	14.34	.0699
87	1.5184	.9986	.0523	19.08	1.0014	19.11	.0524
88	1.5359	.9994	.0349	28.64	1.0006	28.65	.0349
89	1.5533	.9998	.0175	57.29	1.0002	57.30	.0175
90	1.5708	1.0000	.0000		1.0000		.0000

SOLUTIONS

Section A.1 (page 1)

1. (i) A is the set of even whole numbers from two to ten inclusive.

(ii) $6 \in A$

2. (i) The set of odd whole numbers from three to nine inclusive.

(ii) The set of fractions with denominators two and numerators the odd whole numbers from one to seven inclusive.

3. (i) 4 members; $\{1, 2, 4, 9\}$ (ii) 4 members; $\{a, b, c, d\}$

(iii) 2 members; $\{1, 2\}$ (iv) 1 member; $\{0\}$

(v) 4 members; $\{0, 2, 3, 4\}$ (vi) 2 members; $\{a, m\}$

Section A.4 (page 5)

1. One member sets: $\{a\}$, $\{b\}$, $\{c\}$, $\{d\}$, $_____$ 4

Two member sets: $\{a, b\}$, $\{a, c\}$, $\{a, d\}$, $\{b, c\}$, $\{b, d\}$, $\{c, d\}$, $_____$ 6

Three member sets: $\{a, b, c\}$, $\{a, b, d\}$, $\{a, c, d\}$, $\{b, c, d\}$, $_____$ 4

Is $\{a, b, c, d\}$ a subset of A? Since every member of $\{a, b, c, d\}$ is also a member of A, the definition allows $\{a, b, c, d\}$ to be considered a subset of A, but it is not a *proper subset* of A. The term *proper subset* is used to refer to a subset which does not contain all the elements of the original set.

The null set $\emptyset$ is considered to be a subset of every set. Thus to complete the list of subsets the following should be added:

no member subsets: $\emptyset$, $_____$ 1

four member subsets: $\{a, b, c, d\}$, $_____$ 1

Total 16

By counting it is observed that the four member set A has 16 or 2^4 subsets including the null set and A itself. It may be shown, in general, that if a set A has n elements, where n represents a counting number, the number of subsets of A is 2^n.

We consider the null set to be a subset of any set for the following two reasons:

(i) Its inclusion does not violate the definition of subset which requires, in this case, that every element of $\emptyset$ belong to A; there are no elements of $\emptyset$ to violate this condition.

(ii) It makes it possible to have a simple formula for the number of subsets which can be formed from a given set.

Section A.5 (page 5)

1. (i) Since some members are common to A and to B, the circles overlap.

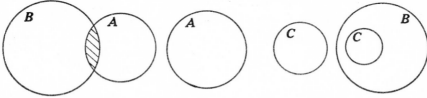

(ii) $A \cap B = \{c, d, e\}$; $c, d,$ and e are the members which belong to both sets A and B.

(iii) Since no members belong to *both* sets, the circles do not overlap.

(iv) The intersection set of A and B.

(v) $B \cap C = \{f, g, h\}$

(vi) $C \subset B$, or C is a proper subset of B, because all the members of C are also members of B, but C does not include all the members of B. Hence, the circle which represents the set C must be entirely inside the circle representing set B.

2. (i), (iii) Since the members 3 and 4 belong to both A and B, the circles overlap.

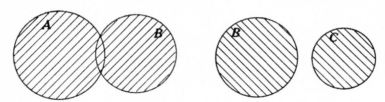

(ii) $A \cup B = \{1, 2, 3, 4, 5, 6\}$; each member of A and each member of B appears once in the list.

(iv) There is no member common to B and C; hence the sets are *disjoint*, and the circles do not overlap.

(v) B or $C = \{3, 4, 5, 6, 7, 8, 9\}$

(vii) $n(B \cup C) = n(B) + n(C)$ if B and C are disjoint sets.

(viii) $n(A \cup B) = 6$

It should be noted that when the intersection of two sets is the null set, the number of members in the union of the sets is equal to the sum of the number of members in each set, but if the intersection of two sets is not the null set, the number of members in the union of the sets is less than the sum of the number of members in each set. In the example in this problem:

$$B \cap C = \emptyset, \quad n(B \cup C) = n(B) + n(C)$$
$$A \cap B \neq \emptyset, \quad n(A \cup B) < n(A) + n(B)$$
$$\text{in fact} \quad n(A \cup B) = n(A) + n(B) - n(A \cap B)$$

3. (i) $A \cap B = \{a, c, e\}$

(ii) $A \cup B = \{a, c, e, g, i, b, d, f\}$

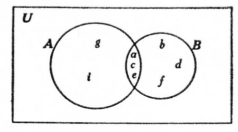

4. (i) (a) $B \subset A$ is true because each of the members of B, that is, 1, 3, 5, 7, 9, is a member of A, but B does not contain all the members of A.

(b) $C \subseteq A$ is true because 2, 4, 6, and 8 are members of A.

(c) $D \subseteq A$ is true because 2, 3, 5, and 7 are members of A.

(d) $\emptyset \subseteq A$ is true by agreement.

(ii) (a) $A \cup B = \{1, 2, 3, 4, 5, 6, 7, 8, 9\}, \quad A \cap B = \{1, 3, 5, 7, 9\}$

(b) $A \cup C = \{1, 2, 3, 4, 5, 6, 7, 8, 9\}, \quad A \cap C = \{2, 4, 6, 8\}$

(c) $B \cup C = \{1, 2, 3, 4, 5, 6, 7, 8, 9\}, \quad B \cap C = \emptyset$

(d) $A \cup D = \{1, 2, 3, 4, 5, 6, 7, 8, 9\}, \quad A \cap D = \{2, 3, 5, 7\}$

(e) $C \cup D = \{2, 3, 4, 5, 6, 7, 8\}, \quad C \cap D = \{2\}$

(f) $(B \cup C) \cup D = \{1, 2, 3, 4, 5, 6, 7, 8, 9\}$

(iii) (a) $2^9 = 512$ (b) $2^5 = 32$

(c) $2^4 = 16$ (d) $2^4 = 16$

Review B

Section B.4 (page 13)

1. The solution set defined by the sentence
$0 \leqq x < 5$, $x \in N_0$ is $\{0, 1, 2, 3, 4\}$.

The graph follows:

2. The sentence $3(4 + y) \geqq 2(y + 7) + 3$ may be written
$$12 + 3y \geqq 2y + 14 + 3$$
or $\qquad y \geqq 5$.

Since $y \in N$, the solution set is $\{5, 6, 7, \ldots\}$.

The graph follows:

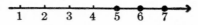

3. Let $A = \{x \mid 3 < x \leqq 5, x \in N\}$.
Then $A = \{4, 5\}$.
Let $B = \{x \mid 9 > x > 6, x \in N\}$.
Then $B = \{8, 7\}$.
Hence $A \cup B = \{4, 5, 7, 8\}$.

4. Let $A = \{x \mid 1 < x \leqq 8, x \in N_0\}$.
Then $A = \{2, 3, 4, 5, 6, 7, 8\}$.
Let $B = \{x \mid 8 > x > 0, x \in N_0\}$.
Then $B = \{7, 6, 5, 4, 3, 2, 1\}$.
Hence $A \cap B = \{2, 3, 4, 5, 6, 7\}$.

Section B.14 (page 25)

1.
$$\begin{array}{r} 7x^2 - x + 2 \\ -10x^2 + 3x - 5 \\ x^2 - 2x + 7 \\ \hline -2x^2 \qquad + 4 \end{array}$$
or
$(7x^2 - x + 2) + (3x - 10x^2 - 5) + (x^2 - 2x + 7)$
$= 7x^2 - x + 2 + 3x - 10x^2 - 5 + x^2 - 2x + 7$
$= -2x^2 + 4$

2.
$$\begin{array}{r} 5x + 3y - 2 \\ 3x - 4y + 3 \\ \hline 8x - y + 1 \\ 6x + 3y - 6 \\ \hline 2x - 4y + 7 \end{array}$$
or
$(5x + 3y - 2) + (3x - 4y + 3) - (6x + 3y - 6)$
$= 5x + 3y - 2 + 3x - 4y + 3 - 6x - 3y + 6$
$= 2x - 4y + 7$

Chapter I

Section 1.1 (page 40)

1. (i) $\qquad$ Let $x = .374999 \ldots$
$$10000x = 3749.99 \ldots$$
$$1000x = 374.99 \ldots$$
$$\therefore 9000x = 3375$$
$$\therefore x = \frac{3375}{9000}$$
$$\therefore x = \frac{375}{1000}$$
$$\therefore .374\dot{9} = \frac{375}{1000} = \frac{3}{8}$$

(ii) $\qquad .375 = \frac{375}{1000} = \frac{3}{8}$ $\qquad \therefore$ both are equivalent to $\frac{3}{8}$.

Chapter II

Section 2.1 (page 53)

1. $(10x + 6) - (11 - 15x) = 20x$ or $(10x + 6) - (11 - 15x) = 20x$
    $\therefore 10x + 6 - 11 + 15x = 20x$ | iff $10x + 6 - 11 + 15x = 20x$
    $\therefore 10x + 15x - 20x = 11 - 6$ | iff $10x + 15x - 20x = 11 - 6$
    $\therefore 5x = 5$ | iff $5x = 5$
    $\therefore x = 1$ | iff $x = 1$

$\therefore$ the root is 1, and the solution set is $\{1\}$.

Verification, by reversing the steps:

$$x = 1$$
$$\therefore 5x = 5$$
$$\therefore 10x + 15x - 20x = 11 - 6$$
$$\therefore 10x + 6 - 11 + 15x = 20x$$
$$\therefore (10x + 6) - (11 - 15x) = 20x$$

$\therefore$ the root is 1,
and the solution set is $\{1\}$.

2. $\{x \mid 8x + (x - 7) + 3 = 2x - (3 + x)\}$
    $8x + (x - 7) + 3 = 2x - (3 + x)$
    $\therefore 8x + x - 7 + 3 = 2x - 3 - x$
    $\therefore 9x - 4 = x - 3$
    $\therefore 9x - x = 4 - 3$
    $\therefore 8x = 1$
    $\therefore x = \dfrac{1}{8}$

$$\{x \mid 8x + (x - 7) + 3 = 2x - (3 + x)\} = \left\{\dfrac{1}{8}\right\}$$

Verification. L.S. $= 8x + (x - 7) + 3$ R.S. $= 2x - (3 + x)$
$$= 1 + (-6\tfrac{7}{8}) + 3 = -2\tfrac{7}{8} \qquad = \dfrac{1}{4} - (3\tfrac{1}{8}) = -2\tfrac{7}{8}$$

3. $3(x - 5) - 2(3 + 4x) = 8 - 6(2x - 1)$
    $\therefore 3x - 15 - 6 - 8x = 8 - 12x + 6$
    $\therefore -5x - 21 = 14 - 12x$
    $\therefore 7x = 35$
    $\therefore x = 5$

The solution set is $\{5\}$.

Verification. L.S. $= 3(x - 5) - 2(3 + 4x)$ R.S. $= 8 - 6(2x - 1)$
$$= 3(0) - 2(23) = -46 \qquad\qquad = 8 - 6(9) = -46$$

Section 2.3 (page 58)

1. $\tfrac{1}{3}(2x - 1) - \tfrac{1}{5}(4x - 6) = \dfrac{7}{15}$

Multiply each term by 15. (L.C.D.)

$$\therefore 15 \times \tfrac{1}{3}(2x - 1) - 15 \times \tfrac{1}{5}(4x - 6) = 15 \times \dfrac{7}{15}$$
$$\therefore 5(2x - 1) - 3(4x - 6) = 7$$
$$\therefore 10x - 5 - 12x + 18 = 7$$
$$\therefore -2x = 7 + 5 - 18$$
$$\therefore -2x = -6$$
$$\therefore x = 3$$

2. $\{x \mid \dfrac{x-2}{2} + \dfrac{x+3}{3} = \dfrac{3x+4}{4} - 2\}$

$$\dfrac{x-2}{2} + \dfrac{x+3}{3} = \dfrac{3x+4}{4} - 2$$

Multiply each term by 12: (L.C.D.)
$\therefore 6(x-2) + 4(x+3) = 3(3x+4) - 24$
$\therefore 6x - 12 + 4x + 12 = 9x + 12 - 24$
$\therefore 6x + 4x - 9x = 12 - 24$
$\therefore x = -12$

$\{x \mid \dfrac{x-2}{2} + \dfrac{x+3}{3} = \dfrac{3x+4}{4} - 2\} = \{-12\}$

Verification. L.S. $= \dfrac{x-2}{2} + \dfrac{x+3}{3}$ R.S. $= \dfrac{3x+4}{4} - 2$

$\qquad = \dfrac{-14}{2} + \dfrac{-9}{3} = -10 \qquad\qquad = \dfrac{-32}{4} - 2 = -10$

Section 2.4 (page 58)

1. $\{x \mid 3(x+2)(x-1) - 2(x-4)^2 = x^2 + 19, x \in I\}$
$\qquad 3(x+2)(x-1) - 2(x-4)^2 = x^2 + 19$
$\therefore 3(x^2 + x - 2) - 2(x^2 - 8x + 16) = x^2 + 19$
$\therefore 3x^2 + 3x - 6 - 2x^2 + 16x - 32 = x^2 + 19$
$\qquad\qquad \therefore 19x = 57$
$\qquad\qquad \therefore x = 3$
$\{x \mid 3(x+2)(x-1) - 2(x-4)^2 = x^2 + 19, x \in I\} = \{3\}$
Verification. L.S. $= 3(x+2)(x-1) - 2(x-4)^2$ R.S. $= x^2 + 19$
$\qquad\qquad = 3(5)(2) - 2(-1)^2 = 28 \qquad\qquad = 9 + 19 = 28$

Section 2.8 (page 66)

1. $\{x \mid 21 - 8x \leqq 9 - 5x, x \in R\}$
$\qquad 21 - 8x \leqq 9 - 5x$
$\therefore -8x + 5x \leqq 9 - 21$
$\therefore -3x \leqq -12$
$\qquad \therefore x \geqq 4$
$\therefore \{x \mid 21 - 8x \leqq 9 - 5x, x \in R\} = \{x \mid x \geqq 4, x \in R\}$

$$\begin{array}{ccccccccccc} & & & & & & \bullet & & & & \\ \hline -2 & -1 & 0 & 1 & 2 & 3 & 4 & 5 & 6 & 7 \end{array}$$

Graph of $\{x \mid x \geqq 4, x \in R\}$

2. $3(-4-y) \geqq 2(2y+3) - 11$
$\therefore -12 - 3y \geqq 4y + 6 - 11$
$\therefore -4y - 3y \geqq 12 + 6 - 11$
$\qquad \therefore -7y \geqq 7$
$\qquad\quad \therefore y \leqq -1$
The solution set is $\{y \mid y \leqq -1, y \in I\}$.

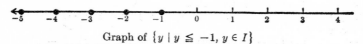

Graph of $\{y \mid y \leqq -1, y \in I\}$

Section 2.9 (page 68)

1. $2x^2 \geqq 2(2x - 3)^2 - 3(2x - 5)(x + 1)$

$\therefore 2x^2 \geqq 2(4x^2 - 12x + 9) - 3(2x^2 - 3x - 5)$

$\therefore 2x^2 \geqq 8x^2 - 24x + 18 - 6x^2 + 9x + 15$

$\therefore 2x^2 - 8x^2 + 24x + 6x^2 - 9x \geqq 18 + 15$

$\therefore 15x \geqq 33$

$\therefore x \geqq 2\frac{1}{5}$

2. $\{x \mid 1 - \dfrac{1 - 2x}{4} > \dfrac{x - 2}{6}, x \in I\}$

$1 - \dfrac{1 - 2x}{4} > \dfrac{x - 2}{6}$

Multiply each side by 12:

$\therefore 12 - 3(1 - 2x) > 2(x - 2)$

$\therefore 12 - 3 + 6x > 2x - 4$

$\therefore 6x - 2x > -4 - 12 + 3$

$\therefore 4x > -13$

$\therefore x > -3\frac{1}{4}$

$\therefore \{x \mid 1 - \dfrac{1 - 2x}{4} > \dfrac{x - 2}{6}, x \in I\} = \{x \mid x > -3\frac{1}{4}, x \in I\}$

Graph of $\{x \mid x > -3\frac{1}{4}, x \in I\}$

Section 2.11 (page 72)

1.

$$2x^2 + 3x - 2 = 0$$

$$\therefore (2x - 1)(x + 2) = 0$$

| $\therefore 2x - 1 = 0$ | or | $x + 2 = 0$ |
| $\therefore x = \dfrac{1}{2}$ | or | $x = -2$ |

The solution set is $\{-2, \frac{1}{2}\}$; the roots are -2, and $\frac{1}{2}$.

Verification.

L.S. $= 2\left(\dfrac{1}{2}\right)^2 + 3\left(\dfrac{1}{2}\right) - 2$ L.S. $= 2(-2)^2 + 3(-2) - 2$

$= \dfrac{1}{2} + \dfrac{3}{2} - 2 = 0$ $= 8 - 6 - 2 = 0$

R.S. $= 0$ R.S. $= 0$

2.

$$x^2 - 6 = x$$

$$\therefore x^2 - x - 6 = 0$$

$$\therefore (x - 3)(x + 2) = 0$$

| $\therefore x - 3 = 0$ | or | $x + 2 = 0$ |
| $\therefore x = 3$ | or | $x = -2$ |

The solution set is $\{-2, 3\}$; the roots are -2 and 3.

Section 2.12 (page 73)

1. $\mid 2x + 1 \mid = +1$, $x \in R$ is equivalent to:

(i) $2x + 1 = +1$ or   (ii) $2x + 1 = -1$

$\therefore x = 0$ $\therefore x = -1$

The solution set is $\{0, -1\}$; the roots of the equation are 0 and -1.

Verification.

If $x = 0$, L.S. $= |0 + 1|$ R.S. $= +1$
$= |+1|$
$= +1$

If $x = -1$, L.S. $= |-2 + 1|$ R.S. $= +1$
$= |-1|$
$= +1$

2. Since the absolute value of a real number cannot be negative, the solution set is $\emptyset$.

Chapter III

Section 3.2 (page 77)

1. $2^2 \cdot 2^4 = 2^{2+4}$
   $= 2^6$
   $= 64$

2. $(-3)^4(-3)^0 = (-3)^{4+0}$
     $= (-3)^4$
     $= 81$

3. $5^3 \times 5^{-2} = 5^{3+(-2)}$
   $= 5^1$
   $= 5$

4. $(-16)^3(-16)^{-3} = (-16)^{3+(-3)}$
     $= (-16)^0$
     $= 1$

5. $x^3 \cdot x^{-4} = x^{3+(-4)}$
   $= x^{-1}$ or $\dfrac{1}{x}$

6. $x^{-2} \cdot x^{-3} = x^{-2+(-3)}$
    $= x^{-5}$ or $\dfrac{1}{x^5}$

Section 3.3 (page 78)

1. $3^5 \div 3^2 = 3^{5-2}$
   $= 3^3$
   $= 27$

2. $(-2)^3 \div (-2)^0 = (-2)^{3-0}$
     $= (-2)^3$
     $= -8$

3. $(-5)^2 \div (-5)^{-3} = (-5)^{2-(-3)}$
    $= (-5)^5$
    $= -3125$

4. $x^0 \div x^{-2} = x^{0-(-2)}$
    $= x^2$

5. $y^{-2} \div y^{-4} = y^{-2-(-4)}$
    $= y^2$

6. $z^0 \div z^0 = z^{0-0}$
    $= z^0$
    $= 1$

Section 3.4 (page 79)

The index laws apply only to factors involving the *same* base.

1. $(a^2b^3c^4)(a^0b^{-2}c^2)$
$= a^{2+0}b^{3-2}c^{4+2}$
$= a^2bc^6$

2. $3m^{-2}p^0q^2 \times 4m^4p^{-3}q^{-4}$
$= 12m^{-2+4}p^{0+(-3)}q^{2+(-4)}$
$= 12m^2p^{-3}q^{-2}$ or $\dfrac{12m}{p^3q^2}$

3. $(x^4y^2z^0) \div (x^2y^4z^3)$
$= x^{4-2}y^{2-4}z^{0-3}$
$= x^2y^{-2}z^{-3}$ or $\dfrac{x^2}{y^2z^3}$

4. $(12r^4s^{-5}) \div (3r^{-2}s^5)$
$= 4r^{4-(-2)}s^{-5-5}$
$= 4r^6s^{-10}$ or $\dfrac{4r^6}{s^{10}}$

Section 3.8 (page 82)

1. $3(a^2)^{10}$
$= 3a^{2\times10}$
$= 3a^{20}$

2. $(3m^2n^3p^4)^3$
$= 3^3m^{2\times3}n^{3\times3}p^{4\times3}$
$= 27m^6n^9p^{12}$

3. $(4x^{-2}z^0y^2)^{-3}$
$= 4^{-3}x^6z^0y^{-6}$
$= \frac{1}{64}x^6y^{-6}$ or $\dfrac{x^6}{64y^6}$

4. $\left(\dfrac{r^2}{t^3}\right)$

$= \dfrac{r^{2\times3}}{t^{3\times3}}$

$= \dfrac{r^6}{t^9}$

5. $\left(\dfrac{6s^3t^{-4}}{3mn^2}\right)^{-1}$

$= \dfrac{3mn^2}{6s^3t^{-4}}$

(the reciprocal of the given expression)

6. $\left(\dfrac{a^0}{b^0}\right)^3$

$= \dfrac{a^0}{b^0}$

$= 1$

Section 3.11 (page 87)

1. $3\sqrt{2} + 4\sqrt{8} - 5\sqrt{18}$
$= 3\sqrt{2} + 4\sqrt{4 \times 2} - 5\sqrt{9 \times 2}$
$= 3\sqrt{2} + 8\sqrt{2} - 15\sqrt{2}$
$= -4\sqrt{2}$ (D)

2. $3\sqrt{8} + 5\sqrt{32} - 2\sqrt{72}$
$= 3\sqrt{4 \times 2} + 5\sqrt{16 \times 2} - 2\sqrt{36 \times 2}$
$= 6\sqrt{2} + 20\sqrt{2} - 12\sqrt{2}$
$= 14\sqrt{2}$ (D)

3. $\sqrt{75} - \sqrt{27} + \sqrt{200} = \sqrt{25 \times 3} - \sqrt{9 \times 3} + \sqrt{100 \times 2}$
$= 5\sqrt{3} - 3\sqrt{3} + 10\sqrt{2}$
$= 2\sqrt{3} + 10\sqrt{2}$ (D)

Section 3.12 (page 88)

1. (i) $\dfrac{\sqrt{3}}{\sqrt{7}} = \sqrt{\dfrac{3}{7}}$

(ii) $\dfrac{\sqrt{5}}{\sqrt{10}} = \sqrt{\dfrac{5}{10}}$
$= \sqrt{\dfrac{1}{2}}$

(iii) $\dfrac{2\sqrt{7}}{\sqrt{3}} = \dfrac{\sqrt{28}}{\sqrt{3}}$
$= \sqrt{\dfrac{28}{3}}$

(iv) $\dfrac{3\sqrt{5}}{2\sqrt{11}} = \dfrac{\sqrt{45}}{\sqrt{44}}$
$= \sqrt{\dfrac{45}{44}}$

2. (i) $\dfrac{\sqrt{12}}{\sqrt{3}} = \sqrt{\dfrac{12}{3}}$
$= \sqrt{4} = 2$

or $\because \sqrt{3} \times \sqrt{4} = \sqrt{12}$
$\therefore \sqrt{12} \div \sqrt{3} = \sqrt{4} = 2$

(ii) $4\sqrt{15} \div 2\sqrt{5} = \dfrac{4\sqrt{15}}{2\sqrt{5}}$
$= 2\sqrt{\dfrac{15}{5}} = 2\sqrt{3}$

or $\because 2\sqrt{5} \times 2\sqrt{3} = 4\sqrt{15}$
$\therefore 4\sqrt{15} \div 2\sqrt{5} = 2\sqrt{3}$

Section 3.14 (page 90)

1. (i) $\sqrt{2}(\sqrt{3} + \sqrt{5})$
$= \sqrt{6} + \sqrt{10}$ (D)

(ii) $3\sqrt{2}(\sqrt{7} + 5\sqrt{11})$
$= 3\sqrt{14} + 15\sqrt{22}$ (D)

2. $(3\sqrt{2} + 5\sqrt{3})^2 = (3\sqrt{2} + 5\sqrt{3})(3\sqrt{2} + 5\sqrt{3})$
$= 3\sqrt{2}(3\sqrt{2} + 5\sqrt{3}) + 5\sqrt{3}(3\sqrt{2} + 5\sqrt{3})$ (D)
$= 18 + 15\sqrt{6} + 15\sqrt{6} + 75$ (D)
$= 93 + 30\sqrt{6}$

3. (i) $(3\sqrt{2} + 5\sqrt{3})^2 = (3\sqrt{2})^2 + 2(3\sqrt{2})(5\sqrt{3}) + (5\sqrt{3})^2$
$= 18 + 30\sqrt{6} + 95$
$= 93 + 30\sqrt{6}$

(ii) $(\sqrt{5} - 2\sqrt{7})^2 = (\sqrt{5})^2 - 2(\sqrt{5})(2\sqrt{7}) + (2\sqrt{7})^2$
$= 5 - 4\sqrt{35} + 28$
$= 33 - 4\sqrt{35}$

4. $\sqrt{2} + \sqrt{3}$

$2\sqrt{2} - \sqrt{3}$

$\overline{}$

$4 + 2\sqrt{6}$

$- \sqrt{6} - 3$ $\Big\}\,D$

$\overline{}$

$4 + \sqrt{6} - 3$

$= 1 + \sqrt{6}$

5. $(\sqrt{2} - \sqrt{3})(\sqrt{2} + \sqrt{3}) = (\sqrt{2} - \sqrt{3})\sqrt{2} + (\sqrt{2} - \sqrt{3})\sqrt{3}$ $\qquad (D)$

$ = 2 - \sqrt{6} + \sqrt{6} - 3 \qquad\qquad (D)$

$ = -1$

6. (i) $\quad (\sqrt{2} - \sqrt{3})(\sqrt{2} + \sqrt{3})$ $\qquad$ (ii) $\quad (3\sqrt{2} + 4\sqrt{5})(3\sqrt{2} - 4\sqrt{5})$

$ = (\sqrt{2})^2 - (\sqrt{3})^2$ $\qquad\qquad\qquad = (3\sqrt{2})^2 - (4\sqrt{5})^2$

$ = 2 - 3 = -1$ $\qquad\qquad\qquad\quad\; = 18 - 80 = -62$

 (iii) $\quad (\sqrt{x} + \sqrt{y})(\sqrt{x} - \sqrt{y})$ $\qquad$ (iv) $\quad (a\sqrt{x} + b\sqrt{y})(a\sqrt{x} - b\sqrt{y})$

$ = x - y$ $\qquad\qquad\qquad\qquad\qquad = a^2x - b^2y$

Section 3.15 (page 92)

1. $\dfrac{\sqrt{2}}{3\sqrt{7} - \sqrt{5}}$

$= \dfrac{\sqrt{2}(3\sqrt{7} + \sqrt{5})}{(3\sqrt{7} - \sqrt{5})(3\sqrt{7} + \sqrt{5})}$

$= \dfrac{3\sqrt{14} + \sqrt{10}}{9\cdot 7 - 5}$

$= \dfrac{3\sqrt{14} + \sqrt{10}}{63 - 5}$

$= \dfrac{3\sqrt{14} + \sqrt{10}}{58}$

2. $\dfrac{3\sqrt{3}}{3\sqrt{5} - 4\sqrt{2}}$

$= \dfrac{3\sqrt{3}(3\sqrt{5} + 4\sqrt{2})}{(3\sqrt{5} - 4\sqrt{2})(3\sqrt{5} + 4\sqrt{2})}$

$= \dfrac{9\sqrt{15} + 12\sqrt{6}}{9\cdot 5 - 16\cdot 2}$

$= \dfrac{9\sqrt{15} + 12\sqrt{6}}{45 - 32}$

$= \dfrac{9\sqrt{15} + 12\sqrt{6}}{13}$

3. $\dfrac{3 + \sqrt{11}}{2\sqrt{7} + 3\sqrt{6}}$

$= \dfrac{(3 + \sqrt{11})(2\sqrt{7} - 3\sqrt{6})}{(2\sqrt{7} + 3\sqrt{6})(2\sqrt{7} - 3\sqrt{6})}$

$= \dfrac{6\sqrt{7} - 9\sqrt{6} + 2\sqrt{77} - 3\sqrt{66}}{4\cdot 7 - 9\cdot 6}$

$= \dfrac{6\sqrt{7} - 9\sqrt{6} + 2\sqrt{77} - 3\sqrt{66}}{-26}$

4. $\dfrac{5\sqrt{2} - 3\sqrt{3}}{2\sqrt{5} + 3\sqrt{2}}$

$= \dfrac{(5\sqrt{2} - 3\sqrt{3})(2\sqrt{5} - 3\sqrt{2})}{(2\sqrt{5} + 3\sqrt{2})(2\sqrt{5} - 3\sqrt{2})}$

$= \dfrac{10\sqrt{10} - 15\cdot 2 - 6\sqrt{15} + 9\sqrt{6}}{4\cdot 5 - 9\cdot 2}$

$= \dfrac{10\sqrt{10} - 6\sqrt{15} + 9\sqrt{6} - 30}{2}$

Section 3.17 (page 95)

1. $\sqrt{b + 5} + \sqrt{b} - \sqrt{4b + 9} = 0$

$ \therefore \; \sqrt{b + 5} + \sqrt{b} = \sqrt{4b + 9}$

$ \therefore \; b + 5 + 2\sqrt{b^2 + 5b} + b = 4b + 9$

$ \therefore \; 2\sqrt{b^2 + 5b} = 2b + 4$

$ \therefore \; \sqrt{b^2 + 5b} = b + 2$

$ \therefore \; b^2 + 5b = b^2 + 4b + 4$

$ \therefore \; b = 4$

Verification. L.S. $= \sqrt{4 + 5} + \sqrt{4} - \sqrt{16 + 9}$ $\qquad$ R.S. $= 0$

$ = 3 + 2 - 5 = 0$

$\therefore$ the root is 4.

2. $\sqrt{x^2 + 7x + 17} - \sqrt{x^2 + 3x + 5} = 2$

$$\therefore \sqrt{x^2 + 7x + 17} = 2 + \sqrt{x^2 + 3x + 5}$$

$$\therefore x^2 + 7x + 17 = 4 + 4\sqrt{x^2 + 3x + 5} + x^2 + 3x + 5$$

$$\therefore 4x + 8 = 4\sqrt{x^2 + 3x + 5}$$

$$\therefore x + 2 = \sqrt{x^2 + 3x + 5}$$

$$\therefore x^2 + 4x + 4 = x^2 + 3x + 5$$

$$\therefore x = 1$$

Verification.   L.S. $= \sqrt{1 + 7 + 17} - \sqrt{1 + 3 + 5}$ R.S. $= 2$

$$= 5 - 3$$
$$= 2$$

$\therefore$ the root is 1.

Chapter IV

Section 4.11 (page 111)

Example 1.

Hypothesis: $R \to \sim S,\ \sim S \to Q,\ T \to R,\ T$

Conclusion: Q

Proof:

STATEMENTS	AUTHORITIES
1. $T \to R$	1. Hypothesis
2. T	2. Hypothesis
3. R	3. Law of Detachment, 1, 2
4. $R \to \sim S$	4. Hypothesis
5. $\sim S$	5. Law of Detachment, 3, 4
6. $\sim S \to Q$	6. Hypothesis
7. Q	7. Law of Detachment, 5, 6

Section 4.12 (page 114)

   (i) A and B are equal angles.

   (ii) no logical consequent

   (iii) $\angle P$ is an acute angle.

   (iv) $\angle A + \angle B + \angle C = 180°$

   (v) $AB = AC$

   (vi) P is on the right bisector of AB.

Section 4.14 (page 119)

Supplementary Angle Theorem

Hypothesis: $\angle ABC = \angle EFG = 180°,\ \angle 2 = \angle 4,$
     $\angle 1$ is the supplement of $\angle 2$,
     $\angle 3$ is the supplement of $\angle 4$.

Conclusion: $\angle 1 = \angle 3$

Proof:

STATEMENTS	AUTHORITIES
1. $\angle ABC = \angle DFG$	1. Hypothesis
2. $\angle 2 = \angle 4$	2. Hypothesis
3. $\angle ABC - \angle 2 = \angle DFG - \angle 4$	3. Subtraction
4. $\angle 1 = \angle 3$	4. Completion

Vertical Angle Theorem

Hypothesis: Lines AB and CD intersect at E, forming vertical angle pairs $\angle 1$, $\angle 3$; $\angle 2$, $\angle 4$.

Conclusion: $\angle 1 = \angle 3$; $\angle 2 = \angle 4$

Proof:

STATEMENTS	AUTHORITIES
1. $\angle CED$ is a straight angle.	1. Hypothesis
2. $\angle 1$ is the supplement of $\angle 2$.	2. Definition
3. $\angle AEB$ is a straight angle.	3. Hypothesis
4. $\angle 3$ is the supplement of $\angle 2$.	4. Definition
5. $\angle 1 = \angle 3$	5. Supplementary Angle Theorem
6. Similarly, $\angle 2$ and $\angle 4$ are each supplements of $\angle 1$.	6. As in 1, 2, 3, 4 above
7. $\angle 2 = \angle 4$	7. Supplementary Angle Theorem

Chapter V

Section 5.2 (page 124)

Example 2.

Proof:

STATEMENTS	AUTHORITIES
1. In $\triangle$'s PAB and QAB $\begin{cases} PA = QA \\ PB = QB \\ AB = AB \end{cases}$	1. Definition (radii)
2.	2. Definition (radii)
3.	3. Reflexive
4. $\triangle PAB \cong \triangle QAB$	4. sss
5. $\angle PAB = \angle QAB$	5. Definition

Example 3.

Analysis:

I CAN PROVE	IF I CAN PROVE
1. $BE = DE$	1. Two triangles congruent with BE and DE corresponding sides.
2. Two triangles congruent with BE and DE corresponding sides	2. $\triangle BEC \cong \triangle DEC$.
3. $\triangle BEC \cong \triangle DEC$	3. $BC = DC$, $EC = EC$, and $\angle BCE = \angle DCE$.
4. $BC = DC$ by hypothesis, $EC = EC$ by reflexive property, $\angle BCE = \angle DCE$	4. Two triangles congruent with $\angle BCE$ and $\angle DCE$ corresponding angles.
5. Two triangles congruent with $\angle BCE$ and $\angle DCE$ corresponding angles	5. $\triangle ABC \cong \triangle ADC$.
6. $\triangle ABC \cong \triangle ADC$	6. $AB = AD$, $BC = DC$, and $AC = AC$.
7. $AB = AD$ by hypothesis, $BC = DC$ by hypothesis, $AC = AC$ by reflexive property.	

Proof:

STATEMENTS		AUTHORITIES
1. In △'s ABC and ADC $AB = AD$		1. Hypothesis
2. $BC = DC$		2. Hypothesis
3. $AC = AC$		3. Reflexive
4. $\triangle ABC \cong \triangle ADC$		4. sss
5. $\angle BCA = \angle DCA$		5. Definition
6. In △'s BEC and DEC $BC = DC$		6. Hypothesis
7. $EC = EC$		7. Reflexive
8. $\angle BCE = \angle DCE$		8. 5
9. $\triangle BEC \cong \triangle DEC$		9. sas
10. $BE = DE$		10. Definition

Section 5.5 (page 131)

Isosceles Triangle Theorem

Two angles of a triangle are equal if and only if the sides opposite the angles are equal.

PART I

Hypothesis: $\triangle ABC$ in which $AC = AB$

Conclusion: $\angle ACB = \angle ABC$

Proof:

STATEMENTS		AUTHORITIES
1. In △'s ABC, ACB $AB = AC$		1. Hypothesis
2. $AC = AB$		2. Hypothesis
3. $\angle BAC = \angle CAB$		3. Reflexive
4. $\triangle ABC \cong \triangle ACB$		4. sas
5. $\angle ABC = \angle ACB$		5. Definition

PART II

Hypothesis: $\triangle ABC$ in which $\angle ABC = \angle ACB$

Conclusion: $AC = AB$

Proof:

STATEMENTS		AUTHORITIES
1. In △'s ABC, ACB $\angle ABC = \angle ACB$		1. Hypothesis
2. $\angle ACB = \angle ABC$		2. Hypothesis
3. $BC = CB$		3. Reflexive
4. $\triangle ABC \cong \triangle ACB$		4. asa
5. $AC = AB$		5. Definition

Section 5.7 (page 135)

The Exterior Angle Theorem

An exterior angle of a triangle is greater than either remote interior angle.

Hypothesis: $\triangle ABC$ in which C is between B and D

Conclusion: $\angle ACD > \angle A$ and $\angle ACD > \angle ABC$

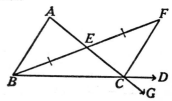

Proof:

STATEMENTS	AUTHORITIES
1. E is the midpoint of AC, and F is a point on ray BE so that $EB = EF$.	1. Existence
2. In $\triangle$'s AEB, CEF $\left\{ \begin{array}{l} AE = CE \\ EB = EF \\ \angle AEB = \angle CEF \end{array} \right.$	2. Definition
3.	3. 1
4.	4. Vertical Angle Theorem
5. $\triangle AEB \cong \triangle CEF$	5. sas
6. $\angle A = \angle ECF$	6. Definition
7. $\angle ACD > \angle ECF$	7. Completion
8. $\angle ACD > \angle A$	8. Replacement
9. $\angle BCG = \angle ACD$	9. Vertical Angle Theorem
10. $\angle BCG > \angle A$	10. Replacement
11. Similarly, $\angle BCG > \angle ABC$, and $\angle ACD > \angle ABC$.	11. Authorities 1 to 10

Angle Side Inequality Theorems

a. If one side of a triangle is greater than another side, then the angle opposite the greater side is greater than the angle opposite the lesser side.

Hypothesis: $\triangle ABC$ in which $AB > AC$

Conclusion: $\angle ACB > \angle ABC$

Proof:

STATEMENTS	AUTHORITIES
1. $AB > AC$	1. Hypothesis
2. D is the point on line segment AB such that $AD = AC$.	2. 1 and Existence
3. $\angle ADC > \angle ABC$	3. Exterior Angle Theorem
4. $\angle ADC = \angle ACD$	4. Isosceles Triangle Theorem
5. $\angle ACD > \angle ABC$	5. Replacement
6. $\angle ACB > \angle ACD$	6. Completion
7. $\angle ACB > \angle ABC$	7. 5, 6, Transitive

b. If one angle of a triangle is greater than another angle, then the side opposite the greater angle is greater than the side opposite the lesser angle.

Hypothesis: $\triangle ABC$ in which $\angle ACB > \angle ABC$

Conclusion: $AB > AC$

Proof:

STATEMENTS	AUTHORITIES
1. (i) $AB > AC$ or (ii) $AB = AC$ or (iii) $AB < AC$	1. Trichotomy
2. $AB = AC$	2. Assumption of (ii)
3. $\angle ACB = \angle ABC$	3. Isosceles Triangle Theorem
4. $AB = AC$ is false.	4. 3 contradicts the hypothesis.
5. $AB \neq AC$	5. Law of Contradiction
6. $AB < AC$	6. Assumption of (iii) in 1
7. $\angle ACB < \angle ABC$	7. Angle Side Inequality Th. (a)
8. $AB < AC$ is false.	8. 7 contradicts the hypothesis.
9. $AB \not< AC$	9. Law of Contradiction
10. $AB > AC$	10. 5, 9

Side Inequality Theorem

The sum of the lengths of two sides of a triangle is greater than the length of the third side.

Hypothesis: $\triangle ABC$

Conclusion: $AB + AC > BC$

Proof:

STATEMENTS	AUTHORITIES
1. D is the point on ray BA such that A is between B and D and $AD = AC$.	1. Existence
2. $\angle ADC = \angle ACD$	2. 1, Isosceles Triangle Theorem
3. $\angle DCB > \angle ACB$	3. 1, Completion
4. $\angle DCB > \angle ADC$	4. 2, 3, Replacement
5. $BD > BC$	5. Angle Side Inequality Th.
6. $BD = BA + AD$	6. Completion
7. $BD = AB + AC$	7. 1
8. $AB + AC > BC$	8. 5, 7, Replacement

Section **5.8** (page 139)

Parallel Line Theorem

If a transversal meets two lines, the two lines are parallel if and only if:
(i) alternate angles are equal, or
(ii) corresponding angles are equal, or
(iii) interior angles on the same side of a transversal are supplementary.

PART I

Hypothesis: Transversal t meeting lines l and m, making

    (i) $\angle 1 = \angle 2$
    (ii) $\angle 1 = \angle 3$
    (iii) $\angle 2 + \angle 4 = 180°$

Conclusion: (i) $l \parallel m$
            (ii) $l \parallel m$
            (iii) $l \parallel m$

(a)   *(b)*

Proof:

STATEMENTS	AUTHORITIES
(i) 1. $l \not\parallel m$	1. Assumption of negation of conclusion
2. l and m have a point in common.	2. Definition
3. $\angle 1 \neq \angle 2$	3. Exterior Angle Theorem
4. $l \not\parallel m$ is false.	4. 3 contradicts the hypothesis.
5. $l \parallel m$	5. Law of Contradiction
(ii) 1. $\angle 1 = \angle 3$	1. Hypothesis
2. $\angle 3 = \angle 2$	2. Vertical Angle Theorem
3. $\angle 1 = \angle 2$	3. Replacement
4. $l \parallel m$	4. Parallel Line Theorem PART I (i)
(iii) 1. $\angle 2 + \angle 4 = 180°$	1. Hypothesis
2. $\angle 1 + \angle 4 = 180°$	2. Definition
3. $\angle 2 + \angle 4 = \angle 1 + \angle 4$	3. Replacement
4. $\angle 2 = \angle 1$	4. Subtraction
5. $l \parallel m$	5. Parallel Line Theorem PART I (i)

PART II

Hypothesis: Transversal t meeting two parallel lines
l and m at A and B, respectively

Conclusion: (i) $\angle 1 = \angle 2$
(ii) $\angle 1 = \angle 3$
(iii) $\angle 2 + \angle 4 = 180°$

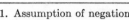

Proof:

STATEMENTS	AUTHORITIES
(i) 1. $\angle 1 \neq \angle 2$	1. Assumption of negation of conclusion
2. Let AG represent the ray such that $\angle GAB = \angle 1$.	2. Existence
3. Ray $AG \parallel m$	3. Parallel Line Theorem PART I
4. $\angle 1 \neq \angle 2$ is false.	4. 3 and hypothesis contradict the Parallel Postulate.
5. $\angle 1 = \angle 2$	5. Law of Contradiction
(ii) 1. $\angle 2 = \angle 3$	1. Vertical Angle Theorem
2. $l \parallel m$	2. Hypothesis
3. $\angle 2 = \angle 1$	3. Parallel Line Theorem PART II (i)
4. $\angle 1 = \angle 3$	4. Replacement
(iii) 1. $l \parallel m$	1. Hypothesis
2. $\angle 2 = \angle 1$	2. Parallel Line Theorem PART II (i)
3. $\angle 1 + \angle 4 = 180°$	3. Definition
4. $\angle 2 + \angle 4 = 180°$	4. Replacement

Quadrilateral-Parallelogram Theorem

If two opposite sides of a quadrilateral are equal and parallel, then the quadrilateral is a parallelogram.

Hypothesis: Quadrilateral $ABCD$ in which $AB = CD$ and $CD \parallel AB$

Conclusion: $ABCD$ is a parallelogram.

Proof:

STATEMENTS	AUTHORITIES
1. In $\triangle$'s ABD, CDB $\Big\{$ $AB = CD$	1. Hypothesis
2. $DB = BD$	2. Reflexive
3. $\angle ABD = \angle CDB$	3. Hypothesis, Parallel Line Theorem
4. $AD = CB$	4. Definition
5. $\angle ADB = \angle CBD$	5. Definition
6. $AD \parallel CB$	6. Parallel Line Theorem
7. $ABCD$ is a parallelogram.	7. Definition

Parallelogram Theorem

In any parallelogram:

(i) the opposite angles are equal; (ii) the opposite sides are equal;
(iii) the diagonals bisect each other.

Hypothesis: Parallelogram $ABCD$ in which AC and BD intersect on E

Conclusion: (i) $\angle ABC = \angle CDA$, $\angle DAB = \angle BCD$
(ii) $AB = CD$, $AD = CB$ (iii) $AE = CE$, $DE = BE$

STATEMENTS	AUTHORITIES
1. $AB \parallel DC$	1. Definition
2. $AD \parallel BC$	2. Definition
3. In $\triangle$'s ABD, CDB $\{$ $\angle ABD = \angle CDB$	3. 1, Parallel Line Theorem
4. $\quad\quad\quad\quad\quad$ $\angle ADB = \angle CBD$	4. 2, Parallel Line Theorem
5. $\quad\quad\quad\quad\quad$ $DB = BD$	5. Reflexive
6. $\triangle ABD \cong \triangle CDB$	6. asa
7. $\angle DAB = \angle BCD$	7. Definition
8. $\angle ABD = \angle CDB$	8. Definition
9. $\angle CBD = \angle ADB$	9. Definition
10. $\angle ABD + \angle CBD = \angle CDB + \angle ADB$	10. Addition, **8, 9**
11. $\angle ABC = \angle CDA$	11. Completion
12. $AB = CD$	12. 6, Definition
13. $AD = CB$	13. 6, Definition
14. In $\triangle$'s AEB, CED $\{$ $AB = DC$	14. 12
15. $\quad\quad\quad\quad\quad$ $\angle ABE = \angle CEB$	15. 3
16. $\quad\quad\quad\quad\quad$ $\angle BAE = \angle DCE$	16. 1, Parallel Line Theorem
17. $\triangle AEB \cong \triangle CED$	17. asa
18. $AE = CE$	18. Definition
19. $EB = ED$	19. Definition

Triangle Angle Sum Theorem

The angle sum of a triangle is 180°.

Hypothesis: $\triangle ABC$

Conclusion: $\angle 1 + \angle 2 + \angle 3 = 180°$

Proof:

STATEMENTS	AUTHORITIES
1. AD is the ray on A parallel to BC.	1. Existence
2. $\angle BAD + \angle ABC = 180°$	2. Parallel Line Theorem
3. $\angle 3 + \angle 4 + \angle 1 = 180°$	3. Replacement
4. $\angle 2 = \angle 4$	4. Parallel Line Theorem
5. $\angle 3 + \angle 2 + \angle 1 = 180°$	5. 3, 4, Replacement

Example 2.

Proof:

STATEMENTS	AUTHORITIES
1. In $\triangle PSQ$, $\angle P + \angle PSQ + \angle PQS$ $= 180°$	1. Triangle Angle Sum Theorem
2. In $\triangle RSQ$, $\angle R + \angle RSQ + \angle RQS$ $= 180°$	2. Triangle Angle Sum Theorem
3. $\angle P + \angle PSQ + \angle PQS + \angle R$ $+ \angle RSQ + \angle RQS = 360°$	3. Addition 1, 2
4. $\angle P + \angle PSR + \angle R + \angle RQP = 360°$	4. Completion
5. $\angle P = \angle PSR, \angle RQP = \angle R$	5. Hypothesis
6. $\angle P + \angle P + \angle RQP + \angle RQP = 360°$	6. Replacement
7. $2\angle P + 2\angle RQP = 360°$	7. Addition
8. $\angle P + \angle RQP = 180°$	8. Division
9. $PS \parallel QR$	9. Parallel Line Theorem

Example 3.

Hypothesis: $\|^{gm} ABCD$, $XA = XD$, $YB = YC$

Conclusion: $BT = DS$

Analysis:

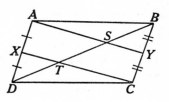

I CAN PROVE	IF I CAN PROVE
1. $BT = DS$	1. $BS + ST = DT + ST.$
2. $BS + ST = DT + ST$	2. $BS = DT.$
3. $BS = DT$	3. $\triangle YSB \cong \triangle XTD.$
4. $\triangle YSB \cong \triangle XTD$	4. (i) $YB = XD,$
	(ii) $\angle YBS = \angle XDT,$
	(iii) $\angle BYS = \angle DXT.$
(i) 5. $YB = XD$	5. $AD = BC$ since $XD = \frac{1}{2}AB$ and $YB = \frac{1}{2}BC.$
6. $AD = BC$ by Parallelogram Theorem.	
(ii) 7. $\angle YBS = \angle XDT$	7. $AD \parallel BC.$
8. $AD \parallel BC$ by Parallelogram Theorem.	
(iii) 9. $\angle BYS = \angle DXT$	9. $\angle DXT = \angle TCY = \angle BYS.$
10. $\angle DXT = \angle TCY = \angle BYS$	10. $AY \parallel XC.$
11. $AY \parallel XC$	11. $AYCX$ is a parallelogram.
12. $AYCX$ is a parallelogram	12. $AX = YC$ and $AX \parallel YC.$
13. $AX = YC$ (see 5 and 6), $AX \parallel YC$ by hypothesis.	

Proof:

STATEMENTS	AUTHORITIES
1. $ABCD$ is a parallelogram.	1. Hypothesis
2. $AD \parallel BC$	2. Definition
3. $AD = BC$	3. Parallelogram Theorem
4. $AX = XD = BY = YC$	4. 3 and Hypothesis
5. $AYCX$ is a parallelogram.	5. 2, 4, Quadrilateral-Parallelogram Theorem
6. $AY \parallel XC$	6. Definition
7. $\angle BYS = \angle BCT$	7. Parallel Line Theorem
8. $\angle BCT = \angle DXT$	8. 2, Parallel Line Theorem
9. $\angle BYS = \angle DXT$	9. Replacement
10. In $\triangle$'s XTD and YSB $\left\{ \begin{array}{l} \angle DXT = \angle BYS \\ \angle TDX = \angle SBY \\ XD = YB \end{array} \right.$	10. 9
11.	11. 2, Parallel Line Theorem
12.	12. 4
13. $\triangle XTD \cong \triangle YSB$	13. asa
14. $TD = SB$	14. Definition
15. $DT + TS = SB + TS$	15. Addition
16. $DS = BT$	16. Completion

Section 5.9 (page 145)

The aas *Congruence Theorem*

If two angles and a side opposite one of them in one triangle are respectively equal to two angles and the corresponding side in a second triangle, then the triangles are congruent.

Hypothesis: $\triangle ABC$ and $\triangle DEF$ such that $\angle A = \angle D$, $\angle B = \angle E$, $BC = EF$

Conclusion: $\triangle ABC \cong \triangle DEF$

Proof:

STATEMENTS		AUTHORITIES
1. In $\triangle$'s ACB, DFE	$\angle A = \angle D$	1. Hypothesis
2.	$\angle B = \angle E$	2. Hypothesis
3.	$\angle C = \angle F$	3. Triangle Angle Sum Theorem
4.	$CB = FE$	4. Hypothesis
5. $\triangle ACB \cong \triangle DFE$		5. asa

Right Triangle Congruence Theorem

If the hypotenuse and one side of a right triangle are respectively equal to the hypotenuse and the corresponding side of a second right triangle, then the triangles are congruent.

Hypothesis: $\triangle ABC$ and $\triangle DEF$ such that $AB = DE$, $AC = DF$, $\angle ACB = \angle DFE$
$= 90°$

Conclusion: $\triangle ABC \cong \triangle DEF$

Proof:

STATEMENTS		AUTHORITIES
1. On the ray opposite FE, G is the point such that $FG = CB$.		1. Existence
2. In $\triangle$'s ABC, DGF	$AC = DF$	2. Hypothesis
3.	$BC = GF$	3. 1
4.	$\angle ACB = \angle DFG = 90°$	4. Definition of opposite ray, Completion
5. $\triangle ABC \cong \triangle DGF$		5. sas
6. $AB = DG$		6. Definition
7. $\angle ABC = \angle DGF$		7. Definition
8. $\angle DEF = \angle DGF$		8. Isosceles Triangle Theorem
9. In $\triangle$'s ABC, DEF	$AB = DE$	9. Hypothesis
10.	$\angle ACB = \angle DFE$	10. Hypothesis
11.	$\angle ABC = \angle DEF$	11. 7, 8, Replacement
12. $\triangle ABC \cong \triangle DEF$		12. aas Congruence Theorem

Section 5.11 (page 148)

The Right Bisector Theorem

A point is equidistant from the end points of a line segment if and only if it is on the right bisector of the line segment.

PART I

Hypothesis: P is any point on XY the right bisector of line segment AB. XY and AB intersect on Q.

Conclusion: $AP = BP$

Analysis:

I CAN PROVE	IF I CAN PROVE
1. $AP = BP$	1. $\triangle AQP \cong \triangle BQP$.
2. $\triangle AQP \cong \triangle BQP$	2. $AQ = BQ$, $PQ = PQ$, $\angle AQP = \angle BQP$.
3. $AQ = BQ$ and $\angle AQP = \angle BQP$ by definition of right bisector, and $PQ = PQ$ by the reflexive property.	

Proof:

STATEMENTS		AUTHORITIES
1. In $\triangle$'s AQP, BQP $\Big\{$	$AQ = BQ$	1. Definition
2.	$\angle AQP = \angle BQP$	2. Definition
3.	$PQ = PQ$	3. Reflexive
4. $\triangle AQP \cong \triangle BQP$		4. sas
5. $AP = BP$		5. Definition

PART II

Hypothesis: A point P and line segment AB such that $PA = PB$

Conclusion: P is on the right bisector of AB.

Analysis:

I CAN PROVE	IF I CAN PROVE
1. P is on the right bisector of AB	1. P and a second position of P, that is, Q, determine the right bisector of AB (since two points determine a line).
2. PQ is the right bisector of AB	2. $AQ = BQ$, $\angle PQA = \angle PQB = 90°$.
3. $AQ = BQ$, $\angle PQA = \angle PQB = 90°$	3. $\triangle PAQ \cong \triangle PBQ$.
4. $\triangle PAQ \cong \triangle PBQ$ by the sss postulate.	

Proof:

STATEMENTS		AUTHORITIES
1. Let Q represent the point on AB equidistant from A and B.		1. Existence
2. In $\triangle$'s PQA, PQB $\Big\{$	$PQ = PQ$	2. Reflexive
3.	$AQ = BQ$	3. 1
4.	$PA = PB$	4. Hypothesis
5. $\triangle PQA \cong \triangle PQB$		5. sss
6. $\angle PQA = \angle PQB$		6. Definition
7. $\angle PQA + \angle PQB = 180°$		7. Completion, Definition
8. $2 \angle PQA = 180°$		8. 6, Replacement, Completion
9. $\angle PQA = 90°$		9. Division
10. PQ is the right bisector of line segment AB.		10. 1, 9, Definition

The Angle Bisector Theorem

A point is equidistant from the sides of an angle if and only if it is on the bisector of the angle.

PART I

Hypothesis: P is any point on the bisector of $\angle ABC$. $PE \perp BC$, $PD \perp AB$

Conclusion: $PE = PD$

Analysis:

I CAN PROVE	IF I CAN PROVE
1. $PE = PD$ 2. $\triangle BDP \cong \triangle BEP$ by the aas Congruence Theorem.	$\triangle BDP \cong \triangle BEP$.

Proof:

STATEMENTS		AUTHORITIES
1. In $\triangle$'s BDP, BEP	$BP = BP$	1. Reflexive
2.	$\angle PDB = \angle PEB$	2. Hypothesis
3.	$\angle DBP = \angle EBP$	3. Hypothesis
4. $\triangle BDP \cong \triangle BEP$		4. aas
5. $PD = PE$		5. Definition

PART II

Hypothesis: P is any point inside $\angle ABC$ such that $PE = PD$ where $PD \perp AB$, $PE \perp BC$.

Conclusion: P is on the bisector of $\angle ABC$.

Analysis:

I CAN PROVE	IF I CAN PROVE
1. P is on the bisector of $\angle ABC$ 2. Ray BP is the bisector of $\angle ABC$ 3. $\angle DBP = \angle EPB$ 4. $\triangle DBP \cong \triangle EBP$ by the Right Triangle Congruence Theorem.	1. Ray BP is the bisector of $\angle ABC$. 2. $\angle DBP = \angle EBP$. 3. $\triangle DBP \cong \triangle EBP$.

Proof:

STATEMENTS		AUTHORITIES
1. In $\triangle$'s DBP, EBP	$BP = BP$	1. Reflexive
2.	$DP = EP$	2. Hypothesis
3.	$\angle BDP = \angle BEP = 90°$	3. Hypothesis, Definition
4. $\triangle DBP \cong \triangle EBP$		4. Right Triangle Congruence Theorem
5. $\angle DBP = \angle EBP$		5. Definition
6. Ray BP is the bisector of $\angle ABC$.		6. Definition
7. P is on the bisector of $\angle ABC$.		7. 6

Section 5.12 (page 151)

Example 1.

  (v) If a geometric figure is not a rhombus, then it is not a square.

  (vi) $D \rightarrow \sim C$

  (vii) $N \rightarrow M$

SOLUTIONS

(viii) If a triangle has two equal angles, then it has two equal sides.

(ix) **Hypothesis:** $\angle AED \neq \angle CEB$

Conclusion: AB and CD are not straight lines intersecting at E.

Section 5.13 (page 153)

Contrapositive proof for the Parallel Line Theorem, PART II

If a transversal meets two parallel lines, then alternate angles are equal.

The contrapositive of this implication is:

If a transversal meets two lines and the alternate angles are not equal, then the lines are not parallel.

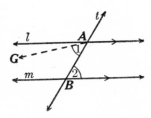

Hypothesis: A transversal t meeting two lines l and m on A and B, respectively, so that
$$\angle 1 \neq \angle 2$$

Conclusion: $l \nparallel m$

Proof:

STATEMENTS	AUTHORITIES
1. $\angle 1 \neq \angle 2$	1. Hypothesis
2. Let AG represent the ray from A so that $\angle GAB = \angle 2$.	2. Existence
3. $AG \parallel m$	3. Parallel Line Theorem
4. $l \nparallel m$	4. Parallel Postulate
5. If $l \parallel m$, then $\angle 1 = \angle 2$.	5. Law of the Contrapositive

Section 5.15 (page 156)

1. (i)

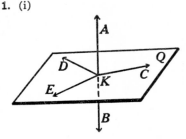

(ii) $\angle$'s AKC, AKD, and AKE are right angles.

Section 5.16 (page 158)

1.

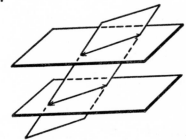

Chapter VI

Section 6.4 (page 170)

Parallelogram Area Theorem

Hypothesis: Parallelograms $ABCD$ and $EFCD$ on the same base and between the same parallel lines ST and XY

Conclusion: $\|^{gm} ABCD = \|^{gm} EFCD$

Proof:

STATEMENTS	AUTHORITIES
1. In $\triangle$'s ADE, BCF $\begin{cases} AD = BC \\ \angle DAE = \angle CBF \\ \angle AED = \angle BFC \end{cases}$	1. Parallelogram Theorem
2.	2. Parallel Line Theorem
3.	3. Parallel Line Theorem
4. $\triangle ADE \cong \triangle BCF$	4. aas
5. $\triangle ADE = \triangle BCF$	5. Area Postulate
6. Fig. $ADCF - \triangle BCF =$ Fig. $ADCF - \triangle ADE$	6. Area Postulate
7. $\|^{gm} ABCD = \|^{gm} EFCD$	7. Completion

Example.

Proof:

STATEMENTS	AUTHORITIES
1. $\|^{gm} AEFD = \|^{gm} AGHD$	1. Parallelogram Area Theorem
2. $\|^{gm} EBCF = \|^{gm} GBCH$	2. Parallelogram Area Theorem
3. $\|^{gm} AEFD + \|^{gm} EBCF = \|^{gm} AGHD + \|^{gm} GBCH$	3. Addition
4. $\|^{gm} ABCD = \|^{gm} AGHD + \|^{gm} GBCH$	4. Area completion

Section 6.5 (page 172)

Parallelogram-Diagonal Theorem

Hypothesis: $\|^{gm} ABCD$

Conclusion: (i) $\triangle ABC = \triangle CDA$
            (ii) $\triangle ABD = \triangle CDB$

Proof:

STATEMENTS	AUTHORITIES
1. In $\triangle$'s ABC, CDA $\begin{cases} AB = CD \\ BC = DA \\ CA = AC \end{cases}$	1. Parallelogram Theorem
2.	2. Parallelogram Theorem
3.	3. Reflexive
4. $\triangle ABC \cong \triangle CDA$	4. sss
5. $\triangle ABC = \triangle CDA$	5. Definition
6. $\triangle ABD = \triangle CDB$	6. As in 1 to 5

Parallelogram-Triangle Area Theorem

Hypothesis: $\triangle ABC$ and $\|^{gm} DGFE$ between the parallel lines VY and ZW such that $BC = GF$

Conclusion: $\triangle ABC = \frac{1}{2} \|^{gm} DGFE$

Proof:

STATEMENTS	AUTHORITIES
1. CX is a line segment terminated on XY such that $CX \parallel AB$.	1. Existence
2. $2 \triangle ABC = \parallel^{gm} ABCX$	2. Parallelogram-Diagonal Theorem
3. $\parallel^{gm} ABCX = \parallel^{gm} DGFE$	3. Parallelogram-Area Theorem
4. $2 \triangle ABC = \parallel^{gm} DGFE$	4. Replacement
5. $\triangle ABC = \frac{1}{2} \parallel^{gm} DGFE$	5. Division

Example.

Proof:

STATEMENTS	AUTHORITIES
1. $BD = DC$	1. Hypothesis
2. $\triangle ABD = \triangle ADC$	2. Parallelogram-Triangle Area Theorem
3. $AE = ED$	3. Hypothesis
4. $\triangle AEB = \triangle EBD$	4. Parallelogram-Triangle Area Theorem
5. $2\triangle AEB = \triangle ABD$	5. Completion
6. $2\triangle ABD = \triangle ABC$	6. Completion
7. $4\triangle AEB = \triangle ABC$	7. Replacement
8. $\triangle AEB = \frac{1}{4}\triangle ABC$	8. Division

Section 6.9 (page 177)

Equal Triangle-Parallel Line Theorem

Hypothesis: $\triangle ABC$ and $\triangle DBC$ on the same side of BC,
$\triangle ABC = \triangle DBC$

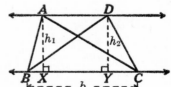

Conclusion: $AD \parallel BC$

Proof:

STATEMENTS	AUTHORITIES
1. The altitude AX of $\triangle ABC$ has length h_1 units.	1. Existence
2. The altitude DY of $\triangle DBC$ has length h_2 units.	2. Existence
3. $BC = b$ units	3. Existence
4. $\triangle ABC = \frac{1}{2} bh_1$	4. Area of a triangle
5. $\triangle DBC = \frac{1}{2} bh_2$	5. Area of a triangle
6. $\triangle ABC = \triangle DBC$	6. Hypothesis
7. $\frac{1}{2} bh_1 = \frac{1}{2} bh_2$	7. Replacement 4, 5, 6
8. $h_1 = h_2$	8. Division
9. $AX \parallel DY$	9. Parallel Line Theorem
10. $AD \parallel BC$	10. Quadrilateral-Parallelogram Theorem

Section 6.11 (page 179)

Example 2.

Proof:

STATEMENTS	AUTHORITIES
1. $z^2 = c^2 + x^2$	1. Pythagorean Theorem
2. $v^2 = y^2 + a^2$	2. Pythagorean Theorem
3. $z^2 + v^2 = c^2 + x^2 + y^2 + a^2$	3. Addition
4. $b^2 = c^2 + a^2$	4. Pythagorean Theorem
5. $w^2 = y^2 + x^2$	5. Pythagorean Theorem
6. $b^2 + w^2 = c^2 + a^2 + y^2 + x^2$	6. Addition
7. $z^2 + v^2 = b^2 + w^2$	7. 3, 6, Replacement

Section 6.12 (page 183)

Example.

Analysis:

I CAN PROVE	IF I CAN PROVE
1. $\triangle ABC$ is right-angled at B	1. $AC^2 = AB^2 + CB^2$.
2. $AC^2 = AB^2 + CB^2$	2. $(n^2 + 1)^2 = (n^2 - 1)^2 + (2n)^2$.
3. $(n^2 + 1)^2 = (n^2 - 1)^2 + (2n)^2$ since $(n^2 - 1)^2 + (2n)^2 = n^4 - 2n^2 + 1 + 4n^2$ $\qquad = n^4 + 2n^2 + 1.$	

Proof:

STATEMENTS	AUTHORITIES
1. $AC^2 = (n^2 + 1)^2$	1. Hypothesis
2. $AC^2 = n^4 + 2n^2 + 1$	2. D
3. $AB^2 + CB^2 = (n^2 - 1)^2 + (2n)^2$	3. Hypothesis
4. $\qquad = n^4 - 2n^2 + 1 + 4n^2$	4. D
5. $\qquad = n^4 + 2n^2 + 1$	5. Number axioms
6. $AC^2 = AB^2 + CB^2$	6. 2 and 5, Replacement
7. $\triangle ABC$ is right-angled at B.	7. Pythagorean Converse

Section 6.13 (page 184)

Example 2.

Description of construction:
1. Draw line segment AD.
2. Construct $EG \parallel AD$ intersecting CD extended on G (Fundamental construction).
3. Draw AG.
4. Draw AC.
5. Construct $BF \parallel AC$ intersecting DC extended on F (Fundamental construction).
6. Draw AF.
7. $\triangle AFG$ is the required triangle.

Example 3.

Description of construction:
1. Construct a right triangle with sides about the right angle a units and b units in length.
2. On the hypotenuse of this triangle, construct a square.
3. The square on the hypotenuse is the required square.

Section 6.18 (page 192)

Example 2. Each of the lateral faces of the pyramid is an isosceles triangular region with base of length 8 inches and altitude of length 15 inches.

The area of one lateral face is $\frac{1}{2} \times 15 \times 8$ square inches = 60 square inches.

Since the base is a square region, there are 4 lateral faces.

$\therefore$ the lateral area is 4×60 square inches = 240 square inches.

Section **6.19** (page 194)

1. (i) 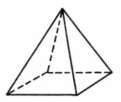   (ii) 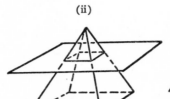   **2.**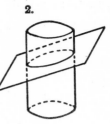

Section **6.20** (page 197)

1. 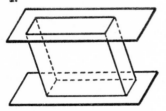   **2.**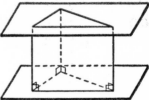

3. 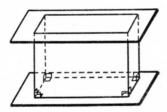   **4.**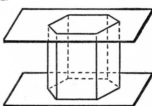

5.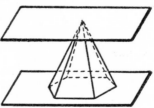

6. 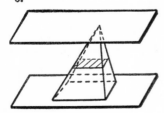   **7.**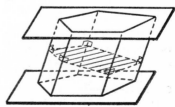

Chapter VII

Section 7.4 (page 213)

Hypothesis: $a, b, c, d \neq 0$ and $\dfrac{a}{b} = \dfrac{c}{d}$

Conclusion: (ii) $\dfrac{a}{c} = \dfrac{b}{d}$ (iii) $\dfrac{b}{a} = \dfrac{d}{c}$ (iv) $\dfrac{a+b}{b} = \dfrac{c+d}{d}$ (v) $\dfrac{a-b}{b} = \dfrac{c-d}{d}$

Proof:

	STATEMENTS	AUTHORITIES
(ii)	1. $\dfrac{a}{b} = \dfrac{c}{d}$	1. Hypothesis
	2. $ad = bc$	2. Cross multiplication
	3. $\dfrac{a}{c} = \dfrac{b}{d}$	3. Division by cd
(iii)	1. $ad = bc$	1. (ii) 2
	2. $\dfrac{d}{c} = \dfrac{b}{a}$	2. Division by ac
	3. $\dfrac{b}{a} = \dfrac{d}{c}$	3. Symmetric
(iv)	1. $\dfrac{a}{b} = \dfrac{c}{d}$	1. Hypothesis
	2. $\dfrac{a}{b} + 1 = \dfrac{c}{d} + 1$	2. Addition
	3. $\dfrac{a+b}{b} = \dfrac{c+d}{d}$	3. Definition
(v)	1. $\dfrac{a}{b} = \dfrac{c}{d}$	1. Hypothesis
	2. $\dfrac{a}{b} - 1 = \dfrac{c}{d} - 1$	2. Subtraction
	3. $\dfrac{a-b}{b} = \dfrac{c-d}{d}$	3. Definition

Section 7.6 (page 220)

Corollary: *Triangle Area Ratio Theorem*

 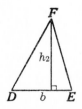

Hypothesis: $\triangle$'s ABC and DEF with altitudes of lengths h_1 units and h_2 units, respectively, and bases of lengths b units

Conclusion: $\dfrac{\triangle ABC}{\triangle DEF} = \dfrac{h_1}{h_2}$

Proof:

STATEMENTS	AUTHORITIES
1. $\triangle ABC = \frac{1}{2}h_1 b$ sq. units	1. Area of a triangle
2. $\triangle DEF = \frac{1}{2}h_2 b$ sq. units	2. Area of a triangle
3. $\dfrac{\triangle ABC}{\triangle DEF} = \dfrac{\frac{1}{2}h_1 b}{\frac{1}{2}h_2 b}$	3. Division
4. $\dfrac{\triangle ABC}{\triangle DEF} = \dfrac{h_1}{h_2}$	4. Principle of equivalent fractions

Section 7.7 (page 223)

Proof for the Triangle Proportionality Theorem, PART I

Proof:

STATEMENTS	AUTHORITIES
1. $BC \parallel DE$	1. Hypothesis
2. $\triangle DEB = \triangle DEC$	2. Parallelogram-Triangle Area Theorem
3. $\dfrac{\triangle AED}{\triangle DEB} = \dfrac{\triangle AED}{\triangle DEC}$	3. Division
4. $\dfrac{AD}{DB} = \dfrac{AE}{EC}$	4. Triangle Area Ratio Theorem

Corollary: *Triangle Proportionality Theorem*

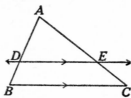

Hypothesis: In the diagram, $DE \parallel BC$.

Conclusion: (i) $\dfrac{AB}{AD} = \dfrac{AC}{AE}$

(ii) $\dfrac{AB}{DB} = \dfrac{AC}{EC}$

Proof:

STATEMENTS	AUTHORITIES
(i) 1. $\dfrac{DB}{AD} = \dfrac{EC}{AE}$	1. Triangle Proportionality Theorem
2. $\dfrac{DB + AD}{AD} = \dfrac{EC + AE}{AE}$	2. Adding unity
3. $\dfrac{AB}{AD} = \dfrac{AC}{AE}$	3. Completion
(ii) 1. $\dfrac{AD}{DB} = \dfrac{AE}{EC}$	1. Triangle Proportionality Theorem
2. $\dfrac{AD + DB}{DB} = \dfrac{AE + EC}{EC}$	2. Adding unity
3. $\dfrac{AB}{AD} = \dfrac{AC}{AC}$	3. Completion

Example.

Proof:

STATEMENTS	AUTHORITIES
1. $ST \parallel QR$	1. Hypothesis
2. $\dfrac{PQ}{QS} = \dfrac{PR}{RT}$	2. Triangle Proportionality Theorem
3. $TV \parallel PQ$	3. Hypothesis
4. $\dfrac{RQ}{RV} = \dfrac{RP}{RT}$	4. Triangle Proportionality Theorem
5. $\dfrac{PQ}{QS} = \dfrac{RQ}{RV}$	5. 2, 4, Replacement

Section 7.8 (page 226)

Proof for the Triangle Proportionality Theorem, PART II

Proof:

STATEMENTS	AUTHORITIES
1. $DE \not\parallel BC$	1. Assumption of negation of conclusion
2. $DF \parallel BC$	2. Existence
3. $\dfrac{AD}{DB} = \dfrac{AF}{FC}$	3. Triangle Proportionality Theorem
4. $DE \not\parallel BC$ is false.	4. By the Line Division Postulate 3 contradicts hypothesis.
5. $DE \parallel BC$	5. Law of Contradiction

Example.

Proof:

STATEMENTS	AUTHORITIES
1. $XY \parallel BC$	1. Hypothesis
2. $\dfrac{AX}{XB} = \dfrac{AY}{YC}$	2. Triangle Proportionality Theorem
3. $YZ \parallel CD$	3. Hypothesis
4. $\dfrac{AZ}{ZD} = \dfrac{AY}{YC}$	4. Triangle Proportionality Theorem
5. $\dfrac{AX}{XB} = \dfrac{AZ}{ZD}$	5. 2, 4, Replacement
6. $XZ \parallel BD$	6. Triangle Proportionality Theorem

Section 7.10 (page 232)

Proof for aaa *Similar Triangle Theorem*, PART I

Proof:

STATEMENTS	AUTHORITIES
(i)	
1. X is a point on AB such that $AX = DE$.	1. Existence
2. Y is a point on AC such that $AY = DF$.	2. Existence

3. In $\triangle$'s AXY and DEF $\left\{ \begin{array}{l} AX = DE \\ AY = DF \\ \angle XAY = \angle EDF \end{array} \right.$

3. 1
4.
4. 2
5.
5. Hypothesis
6. $\triangle AXY \cong \triangle DEF$
6. sas
7. $\angle AXY = \angle DEF$
7. Definition
8. $\angle DEF = \angle ABC$
8. Hypothesis
9. $\angle AXY = \angle ABC$
9. Replacement
10. $XY \parallel BC$
10. Parallel Line Theorem

11. $\dfrac{AB}{AX} = \dfrac{AC}{AY}$
11. Triangle Proportionality Theorem

12. $\dfrac{AB}{DE} = \dfrac{AC}{DF}$
12. 1, 2, Replacement

13. $\dfrac{AB}{DE} = \dfrac{BC}{EF}$
13. Steps similar to 1 to 12

14. $\dfrac{AB}{DE} = \dfrac{AC}{DF} = \dfrac{BC}{EF}$
14. 12, 13

(ii)
15. $\angle A = \angle D, \angle B = \angle E, \angle C = \angle F$
15. Hypothesis
16. $\triangle ABC \sim \triangle DEF$
16. 14, 15, Definition

Corollary: If two angles of one triangle are respectively equal to two angles of another triangle, then the corresponding sides are proportional and hence the triangles are similar.

Hypothesis: $\triangle ABC$ and $\triangle DEF$
such that $\angle A = \angle D, \angle B = \angle E$

Conclusion: (i) $\dfrac{AB}{DE} = \dfrac{BC}{EF} = \dfrac{CA}{FD}$

(ii) $\triangle ABC \sim \triangle DEF$

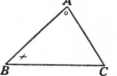

Proof:

STATEMENTS	AUTHORITIES
1. $\angle A = \angle D, \angle B = \angle E$	1. Hypothesis
2. $\angle C = \angle F$	2. Triangle Angle Sum Theorem
3. $\dfrac{AB}{DE} = \dfrac{BC}{EF} = \dfrac{CA}{FD}$	3. aaa Similar Triangle Theorem
4. $\triangle ABC \sim \triangle DEF$	4. aaa Similar Triangle Theorem

Proof for aaa *Similar Triangle Theorem,* PART II

Proof:

STATEMENTS	AUTHORITIES
1. EG and FG are line segments such that $\angle GEF = \angle ABC$, $\angle GFE = \angle ACB$, and G is on the side of EF remote from D.	1. Existence
2. In $\triangle$'s ABC and EGF $\left\{ \begin{array}{l} \angle ABC = \angle GEF \\ \angle ACB = \angle GFE \end{array} \right.$	2. 1
3.	3. 1
4. $\dfrac{AB}{GE} = \dfrac{BC}{EF} = \dfrac{CA}{FG}$	4. aaa

5. $\dfrac{AB}{DE} = \dfrac{BC}{EF} = \dfrac{CA}{FD}$ 5. Hypothesis

6. $GE = DE, FG = FD$ 6. 4, 5

7. In $\triangle$'s EGF and EDF $\begin{cases} EG = ED \\ GF = DF \\ EF = EF \end{cases}$ 7. 6

8.   8. 6

9.   9. Reflexive

10. $\triangle EGF \cong \triangle EDF$ 10. sss

11. $\angle EFG = \angle EFD = \angle ACB$ 11. 1, 10, Definition

12. $\angle FEG = \angle FED = \angle ABC$ 12. 1, 10, Definition

13. $\angle BAC = \angle EDF$ 13. Triangle Angle Sum Theorem

14. $\triangle ABC \sim \triangle DEF$ 14. 11, 12, 13, aaa

Example 1.

Proof:

STATEMENTS	AUTHORITIES
1. In $\triangle$'s MON and POQ $\begin{cases} \angle N = \angle Q \\ \angle MON = \angle QOP \end{cases}$	1. Hypothesis
2.	2. Vertical Angle Theorem
3. $\triangle MON \sim \triangle POQ$	3. aaa

Example 2.

Proof:

STATEMENTS	AUTHORITIES
1. In $\triangle$'s ABX and ACY $\begin{cases} \angle A = \angle A \\ \angle BXA = \angle CYA \end{cases}$	1. Reflexive
2.	2. Definition of altitude
3. $\dfrac{AB}{AC} = \dfrac{AX}{AY}$	3. aaa
4. $AB \cdot AY = AC \cdot AX$	4. Multiplication

Section 7.11 (page 238)

Proof for sas *Similarity Triangle Theorem*

Proof:

STATEMENTS	AUTHORITIES
1. X is the point on AB or AB extended such that $AX = DE$.	1. Existence
2. Y is the point on AC or AC extended such that $AY = DF$.	2. Existence
3. $\triangle AXY \cong \triangle DEF$	3. sas
4. $\dfrac{AB}{DE} = \dfrac{AC}{DF}$	4. Hypothesis
5. $\dfrac{AB}{AX} = \dfrac{AC}{AY}$	5. Replacement
6. $XY \parallel BC$	6. Triangle Proportionality Theorem
7. $\angle ABC = \angle AXY$	7. Parallel Line Theorem
8. $\angle ABC = \angle DEF$	8. 3, 7, Replacement
9. $\angle A = \angle D$	9. Hypothesis
10. $\triangle ABC \sim \triangle DEF$	10. aaa

Example.

Analysis:

I CAN PROVE	IF I CAN PROVE
1. $ML \cdot PR = PM \cdot RS$ (i) 2. $\dfrac{ML}{PM} = \dfrac{RS}{PR}$ (insufficient information).	1. (i) $\dfrac{ML}{PM} = \dfrac{RS}{PR}$ or (ii) $\dfrac{ML}{RS} = \dfrac{PM}{PR}$.
(ii) 3. $\dfrac{ML}{RS} = \dfrac{PM}{PR}$ 4. $\triangle MLP \sim \triangle RSP$ 5. $\angle P = \angle P$ by the reflexive property.	3. $\triangle MLP \sim \triangle RSP$. 4. $\angle P = \angle P$ and $\dfrac{LP}{SP} = \dfrac{PM}{PR}$.
6. $\dfrac{LP}{SP} = \dfrac{PM}{PR}$ 7. $LP \cdot PR = PM \cdot SP$ by hypothesis.	6. $LP \cdot PR = PM \cdot SP$.

Proof:

STATEMENTS	AUTHORITIES
1. $LP \cdot PR = PM \cdot SP$	1. Hypothesis
2. $\dfrac{LP}{SP} = \dfrac{PM}{PR}$	2. Division
3. $\angle P = \angle P$	3. Reflexive
4. $\triangle PLM \sim \triangle PSR$	4. sas Similar Triangle Theorem
5. $\dfrac{ML}{RS} = \dfrac{PM}{PR}$	5. Definition
6. $ML \cdot PR = PM \cdot RS$	6. Multiplication

Section 7.12 (page 241)

Proof for Areas of Similar Triangles Theorem

Proof:

STATEMENTS	AUTHORITIES
1. AG is the altitude from A to BC.	1. Existence
2. DH is the altitude from D to EF.	2. Existence
3. $\triangle ABC = \frac{1}{2}AG \cdot BC$	3. Area of a triangle
4. $\triangle DEF = \frac{1}{2}DH \cdot EF$	4. Area of a triangle
5. $\dfrac{\triangle ABC}{\triangle DEF} = \dfrac{\frac{1}{2}AG \cdot BC}{\frac{1}{2}DH \cdot EF}$	5. Division
6. $\dfrac{\triangle ABC}{\triangle DEF} = \left(\dfrac{AG}{DH}\right) \cdot \left(\dfrac{BC}{EF}\right)$	6. Principle of equivalent fractions
7. In $\triangle$'s ABG and DEH $\begin{cases} \angle B = \angle E \\ \angle AGB = \angle DHE \end{cases}$ 8.	7. Hypothesis, Definition 8. 1, 2, Definition
9. $\dfrac{AG}{DH} = \dfrac{AB}{DE}$	9. aaa
10. $\dfrac{BC}{EF} = \dfrac{AB}{DE}$	10. Hypothesis, Definition
11. $\dfrac{AG}{DH} = \dfrac{BC}{EF}$	11. 9, 10, Replacement

12. $\dfrac{\triangle ABC}{\triangle DEF} = \left(\dfrac{BC}{EF}\right)\left(\dfrac{BC}{EF}\right)$ | 12. 6, 11, Replacement

13. $\dfrac{\triangle ABC}{\triangle DEF} = \dfrac{BC^2}{EF^2} = \dfrac{AB^2}{DE^2} = \dfrac{CA^2}{FD^2}$ | 13. 12, Hypothesis, Definition

Section 7.13 (page 244)
Proof for Mean Proportional Theorem
Proof:

STATEMENTS	AUTHORITIES
1. In $\triangle$'s BCA, BAD $\begin{cases} \angle ABC = \angle DBA \\ \angle BAC = \angle BDA = 90° \end{cases}$	1. Reflexive
2.	2. Hypothesis
3. $\triangle BCA \sim \triangle BAD$	3. aaa
4. $\dfrac{BC}{AB} = \dfrac{AB}{BD}$	4. Definition
5. (i) $\dfrac{a}{c} = \dfrac{c}{x}$	5. Replacement
6. In $\triangle$'s BCA, ACD $\begin{cases} \angle BCA = \angle ACD \\ \angle BAC = \angle ADC = 90° \end{cases}$	6. Reflexive
7.	7. Hypothesis
8. $\triangle BCA \sim \triangle ACD$	8. aaa
9. $\dfrac{BC}{AC} = \dfrac{AC}{DC}$	9. Definition
10. (ii) $\dfrac{a}{b} = \dfrac{b}{y}$	10. Replacement
11. In $\triangle$'s BAD, ACD $\begin{cases} \angle BAD = \angle ACD \\ \angle BDA = \angle ADC = 90° \end{cases}$	11. 1, 2, Triangle Angle Sum Theorem
12.	12. Hypothesis
13. $\triangle BAD \sim \triangle ACD$	13. aaa
14. $\dfrac{BD}{AD} = \dfrac{AD}{CD}$	14. Definition
15. (iii) $\dfrac{x}{h} = \dfrac{h}{y}$	15. Replacement

Section 7.14 (page 246)
Similar Triangles Proof for the Pythagorean Theorem
Proof:

STATEMENTS	AUTHORITIES
1. AM is the altitude from A to BC.	1. Existence
2. Let x units and y units represent the lengths of BM and CM, respectively.	2. Existence
3. $\dfrac{y}{b} = \dfrac{b}{a}$	3. Mean Proportional Theorem
4. $b^2 = ay$	4. Cross multiplication
5. $\dfrac{x}{c} = \dfrac{c}{a}$	5. Mean Proportional Theorem
6. $c^2 = ax$	6. Cross multiplication
7. $b^2 + c^2 = ax + ay$	7. 4, 6, Addition
8. $b^2 + c^2 = a(x + y)$	8. D
9. $b^2 + c^2 = a^2$	9. Replacement

Section 7.15 (page 247)

Example 1.

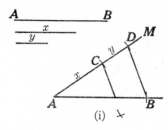 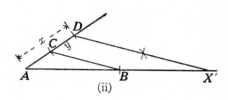

Description of Construction:

(i) 1. Construct a line segment AB equal to the given line segment.
   2. Construct any line segment AM distinct from AB.
   3. Mark C on AM so that $AC = x$ units.
   4. Mark D on AM so that $CD = y$ units and C is between D and A.
   5. Join DB.
   6. Construct a line segment on C parallel to DB intersecting AB at X.
   7. X is the point such that $AX : XB = x : y$, $x, y \in {}^+R$.

(ii) 1. as in (i)   2. as in (i)
   3. Mark D on AM so that $AD = x$ units.
   4. Mark C between A and D so that $DC = y$ units.
   5. Join CB.
   6. Construct a line segment on D parallel to CB intersecting AB at X'.
   7. X' is the point such that $AX' : X'B = x : -y$, $x, y \in {}^+R$, $x > y$.

Example 2.

Given: Three line segments with lengths a units, b units, and c units, respectively

Required: To construct a line segment which is the fourth proportional to the given line segments

RULER-COMPASSES CONSTRUCTION

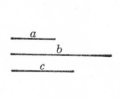 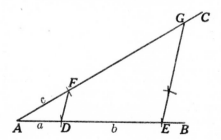

Description of construction:

1. On a line segment AB, mark D and E so that $AD = a$ units, $DE = b$ units.
2. On any line segment AC distinct from AB, mark F so that $AF = c$ units.
3. Join FD.
4. Construct a line segment EG intersecting AC on G so that $EG \parallel DF$ (Fundamental construction).
5. FG is the fourth proportional to AD, DE, and AF, and is the required line segment.

Example 3.

RULER-COMPASSES CONSTRUCTION

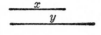

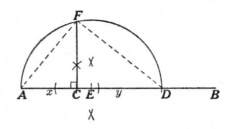

Description of construction:

1. On a line segment AB, mark C and D so that $AC = x$ units and $CD = y$ units.
2. Construct the midpoint E of AD (Fundamental construction).
3. With centre E and radius AE, construct a semi-circle.
4. Construct the perpendicular to AB at C, intersecting the circle at F.
5. CF is the required line segment, since $\triangle AFD$ is right-angled at F.

Chapter VIII

Section 8.1 (page 251)

1.

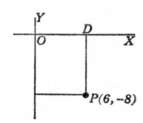

$DP \perp OX$

$\because$ abscissa of P is 6, $\therefore OD = 6$ units.
$\because$ ordinate of P is -8, $\therefore PD = 8$ units.
By the Pythagorean Theorem,
$$OP = \sqrt{6^2 + 8^2} \text{ units}$$
$$= \sqrt{36 + 64} \text{ units}$$
$$= \sqrt{100} \text{ units}$$
$$= 10 \text{ units.}$$
$\therefore$ the distance from O to P is 10 units.

Section 8.2 (page 254)

1. Two positive angles coterminal with an angle of measurement 135° have measurements $(360 + 135)°$ or 495° and $(720 + 135)°$ or 855°.

   Two positive angles coterminal with an angle of measurement $-150°$ have measurements $360° + (-150°)$ or 210° and $720° + (-150°)$ or 570°.

   Two negative angles coterminal with an angle of measurement 135° have measurements $(-360°) + (135°)$ or $-225°$ and $(-720°) + (135°)$ or $-585°$.

   Two negative angles coterminal with an angle of measurement $-150°$ have measurements $(-360°) + (-150°)$ or $-510°$ and $(-720°) + (-150°)$ or $-870°$.

2. $\angle POX$ has measurement $(2 \times 360 + 145)°$ or 865°.

   $\angle QOX$ has measurement $(2 \times 360°) + (-100°)$ or 620°.

   $\angle ROX$ has measurement $(-360°) + (-82°)$ or $-442°$.

3. (i) (a) $150° = (180 - 30)°$ (b) $255° = (180 + 75)°$
   (c) An angle of measurement 225° is coterminal with an angle of measurement $-135°$, and $225° = (180 + 45)°$.
   (d) An angle of measurement 170° is coterminal with an angle of measurement $-190°$, and $170° = (180 - 10)°$.

(ii) (a) An angle of measurement 285° is coterminal with an angle of measurement $-75°$, and $285° = (360 - 75)°$.
   (b) $300° = (360 - 60)°$ (c) $395° = (360 + 35)°$
   (d) An angle of measurement 390° is coterminal with an angle of measurement $-330°$, and $390° = (360 + 30)°$.

4.   (i)   (ii)

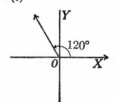

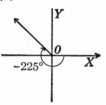

(iii)   (iv)   (v)

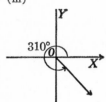

Section 8.3 (page 259)

1. (i) $\angle XOY : \angle XOA = 90 : 180$ (ii) $\angle XOA : \angle XOX = 180 : 360$
      $= 1 : 2$ $= 1 : 2$
   (iii) $\angle XOY : \angle XOX = 90 : 360$
      $= 1 : 4$

2. (i) $\frac{1}{2}\pi : \pi = 1 : 2$ (ii) $\pi : 2\pi = 1 : 2$ (iii) $\frac{1}{2}\pi : 2\pi = 1 : 4$
   In each case, the corresponding ratios are equal.

3. The measurements of central angles are proportional to their arc lengths.

4. (i) $\because \frac{a}{d} = \frac{\pi}{180}$, $\therefore \frac{a}{60} = \frac{\pi}{180}$ and $a = \frac{\pi}{3}$

   An angle of measurement 60° has a radian measure $\frac{\pi}{3}$.

   (ii) $\frac{a}{18} = \frac{\pi}{180}$, $\therefore a = \frac{\pi}{10}$

   An angle of measurement 18° has a radian measure $\frac{\pi}{10}$.

5. (i) $\because \frac{d}{a} = \frac{180}{\pi}$, $\therefore \frac{d}{\frac{3\pi}{4}} = \frac{180}{\pi}$, $d = \frac{3 \times 180}{4} = 135$

   An angle of radian measure $\frac{3\pi}{4}$ has a degree measure of 135.

(ii) $\dfrac{d}{1\frac{2}{3}\pi} = \dfrac{180}{\pi}$, $\therefore d = 1\frac{2}{3} \times 180$

$$= 300$$

An angle of radian measure $1\frac{2}{3}\pi$ has a degree measure of 300.

Section 8.4 (page 262)

1.   (i) Represent the length of OA by r_1 units.

$$r_1 = \sqrt{12^2 + 5^2} = \sqrt{169} = 13$$

$$\sin \propto = \frac{5}{13}, \quad \cos \propto = \frac{-12}{13}, \quad \tan \propto = \frac{-5}{12}$$

    (ii) Represent the length of OB by r_2 units.

$$r_2 = \sqrt{2^2 + 3^2} = \sqrt{13}$$

$$\sin \propto = \frac{-3}{\sqrt{13}}, \quad \cos \propto = \frac{-2}{\sqrt{13}}, \quad \tan \propto = \frac{3}{2}$$

2.   (i) $\sin \propto = \dfrac{b}{1}, \quad \cos \propto = \dfrac{a}{1}, \quad \tan \propto = \dfrac{b}{a}$

    (ii) $\sin^2 \propto + \cos^2 \propto = \left(\dfrac{b}{1}\right)^2 + \left(\dfrac{a}{1}\right)^2$

$$= b^2 + a^2$$

$$= 1 \text{ (since } b^2 + a^2 = 1, \text{ by the Pythagorean Theorem)}$$

Section 8.5 (page 265)

1.

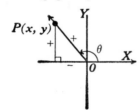

In this quadrant,
sin θ is always a positive real number;
cos θ is always a negative real number;
tan θ is always a negative real number.

2.

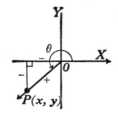

In this quadrant,
sin θ is always a negative real number;
cos θ is always a negative real number;
tan θ is always a positive real number.

3.

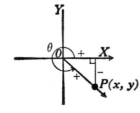

In this quadrant,
sin θ is always a negative real number;
cos θ is always a positive real number;
tan θ is always a negative real number.

Section 8.6 (page 267)

1. (i) Length of $OP = \sqrt{9 + 16} = 5$

$\sin \alpha = \dfrac{4}{5}$, $\cos \alpha = \dfrac{-3}{5}$, $\tan \alpha = -\dfrac{4}{3}$,

$\csc \alpha = \dfrac{5}{4}$, $\sec \alpha = \dfrac{-5}{3}$, $\cot \alpha = \dfrac{-3}{4}$

(ii) Length of $OQ = \sqrt{4 + 25} = \sqrt{29}$

$\sin \beta = \dfrac{-5}{\sqrt{29}}$, $\cos \beta = \dfrac{2}{\sqrt{29}}$, $\tan \beta = \dfrac{-5}{2}$,

$\csc \beta = \dfrac{\sqrt{29}}{-5}$, $\sec \beta = \dfrac{\sqrt{29}}{2}$, $\cot \beta = \dfrac{2}{-5}$

2. (i) $\sin \theta = \dfrac{y}{r}$, $\cos \theta = \dfrac{x}{r}$, $\tan \theta = \dfrac{y}{x}, x \neq 0$,

$\csc \theta = \dfrac{r}{y}, y \neq 0$, $\sec \theta = \dfrac{r}{x}, x \neq 0$, $\cot \theta = \dfrac{x}{y}, y \neq 0$

(ii) $\tan \theta = \dfrac{y}{x}, x \neq 0$ $\dfrac{\sin \theta}{\cos \theta} = \dfrac{\dfrac{y}{r}}{\dfrac{x}{r}} = \dfrac{y}{x}, x \neq 0$

$\therefore \tan \theta = \dfrac{\sin \theta}{\cos \theta}$

$\because \tan \theta \cdot \cot \theta = 1$, $\therefore \cot \theta = \dfrac{\cos \theta}{\sin \theta}$

3. $\because \sin \theta = \dfrac{4}{5}$, $\therefore \csc \theta = \dfrac{5}{4}$

$\because \cos \theta = \dfrac{-3}{5}$, $\therefore \sec \theta = \dfrac{5}{-3}$

$\because \tan \theta = \dfrac{\sin \theta}{\cos \theta}$, $\therefore \tan \theta = \dfrac{\dfrac{4}{5}}{\dfrac{-3}{5}} = \dfrac{4}{-3}$

$\therefore \cot \theta = \dfrac{-3}{4}$

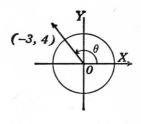

$(-3, 4)$

Section 8.7 (page 270)

1. (i) $\because OD = DP$, $\therefore \angle DOP = \angle DPO$ (Isosceles Triangle Theorem)
$\because \angle ODP = 90°$, $\therefore \angle DOP + \angle DPO = 90°$
(Triangle Angle Sum Theorem)

$\therefore \angle DOP = 45°$ (or $\dfrac{\pi}{4}$ radians)

(ii) $\because OD = DP$, the coordinates of P can be represented as (a, a)
$\therefore a^2 + a^2 = 1^2$ (Pythagorean Theorem)

$\therefore a^2 = \dfrac{1}{2}$ and $a = \dfrac{1}{\sqrt{2}}$

$\therefore$ coordinates of P are $\left(\dfrac{1}{\sqrt{2}}, \dfrac{1}{\sqrt{2}} \right)$.

$$\therefore \sin \frac{\pi}{4} = \frac{1}{\sqrt{2}}, \quad \cos \frac{\pi}{4} = \frac{1}{\sqrt{2}}, \quad \tan \frac{\pi}{4} = \frac{\frac{1}{\sqrt{2}}}{\frac{1}{\sqrt{2}}} = 1$$

$$\csc \frac{\pi}{4} = \sqrt{2}, \quad \sec \frac{\pi}{4} = \sqrt{2}, \quad \cot \frac{\pi}{4} = 1$$

2. (i) $\because OP = OB = BP,$

$\therefore \angle POB = \angle PBO = \angle OPB = 60°$ (or $\frac{\pi}{3}$ radians)

(ii) In $\triangle$'s OPA and BPA,

$OP = BP$	(Hypothesis)
$\angle OAP = \angle BAP = 90°$	(Hypothesis)
$\angle POA = \angle PBA$	(Isosceles Triangle)
$\therefore \triangle OPA \cong \triangle BPA$	(asa)
$\therefore OA = BA$	(Definition)

$\because OB = 1, \therefore OA = \frac{1}{2}$

$AP^2 = OP^2 - OA^2$ (Pythagorean Theorem)

$$= 1^2 - \left(\frac{1}{2}\right)^2 = \frac{3}{4}$$

$\therefore AP = \frac{\sqrt{3}}{2}$

(iii) The coordinates of P are $\left(\frac{1}{2}, \frac{\sqrt{3}}{2}\right)$.

$$\sin \frac{\pi}{3} = \frac{\sqrt{3}}{2}, \quad \cos \frac{\pi}{3} = \frac{1}{2}, \quad \tan \frac{\pi}{3} = \frac{\frac{\sqrt{3}}{2}}{\frac{1}{2}} = \sqrt{3},$$

$$\csc \frac{\pi}{3} = \frac{2}{\sqrt{3}}, \quad \sec \frac{\pi}{3} = 2, \quad \cot \frac{\pi}{3} = \frac{1}{\sqrt{3}}$$

3. (i) In $\triangle$'s OAP and QBO, $OP = QO$ (Hypothesis)

$\angle OAP = \angle QBO = 90°$	(Hypothesis)
$\angle APO = \angle BOQ = 30°$	(Triangle Angle Sum)
$\therefore \triangle OAP \cong \triangle QBO$	(asa)
$\therefore OA = QB, AP = BO$	(Definition)

$\therefore OB = \frac{\sqrt{3}}{2}, BQ = \frac{1}{2}$

$\therefore$ coordinates of Q are $\left(\frac{\sqrt{3}}{2}, \frac{1}{2}\right)$.

(ii) $\sin \frac{\pi}{6} = \frac{1}{2}, \quad \cos \frac{\pi}{6} = \frac{\sqrt{3}}{2}, \quad \tan \frac{\pi}{6} = \frac{\frac{1}{2}}{\frac{\sqrt{3}}{2}} = \frac{1}{\sqrt{3}},$

$$\csc \frac{\pi}{6} = 2, \quad \sec \frac{\pi}{6} = \frac{2}{\sqrt{3}}, \quad \cot \frac{\pi}{6} = \sqrt{3}$$

4. (i) $\angle POP$ has a measurement of $0°$ (or 0 radians).

(ii) The coordinates of P are $(1, 0)$.

$$\sin 0 = \frac{0}{1}, \quad \cos 0 = \frac{1}{1}, \quad \tan 0 = \frac{0}{1}, \quad \sec 0 = 1$$
$$= 0 \qquad\quad = 1 \qquad\quad = 0$$

$\csc 0$ and $\cot 0$ are not equivalent to real numbers.

5. (i) $\angle QOP$ has a measurement of $90°$ or $\frac{\pi}{2}$ radians.

(ii) The coordinates of Q are $(0, 1)$.

$$\sin \frac{\pi}{2} = \frac{1}{1}, \quad \cos \frac{\pi}{2} = \frac{0}{1}, \quad \tan \frac{\pi}{2} = \frac{1}{0}, \quad \csc \frac{\pi}{2} = 1$$
$$= 1 \qquad\quad = 0$$

$\tan \frac{\pi}{2}$ and $\sec \frac{\pi}{2}$ are not equivalent to real numbers.

6.

θ	$\sin \theta$	$\cos \theta$	$\tan \theta$	$\csc \theta$	$\sec \theta$	$\cot \theta$
$\frac{\pi}{4}$	$\frac{1}{\sqrt{2}}$	$\frac{1}{\sqrt{2}}$	1	$\sqrt{2}$	$\sqrt{2}$	1
$\frac{\pi}{3}$	$\frac{\sqrt{3}}{2}$	$\frac{1}{2}$	$\sqrt{3}$	$\frac{2}{\sqrt{3}}$	2	$\frac{1}{\sqrt{3}}$
$\frac{\pi}{6}$	$\frac{1}{2}$	$\frac{\sqrt{3}}{2}$	$\frac{1}{\sqrt{3}}$	2	$\frac{2}{\sqrt{3}}$	$\sqrt{3}$
$\frac{\pi}{2}$	1	0	—	1	—	0
0	0	1	0	—	1	—

Section 8.8 (page 272)

1. (i) $AB = \sqrt{2^2 + 5^2}$ units
$= \sqrt{4 + 25}$ units
$= \sqrt{29}$ units

$$\sin A = \frac{2}{\sqrt{29}}, \quad \sin B = \frac{5}{\sqrt{29}}$$
$$\cos A = \frac{5}{\sqrt{29}}, \quad \cos B = \frac{2}{\sqrt{29}}$$
$$\tan A = \frac{2}{5}, \quad \tan B = \frac{5}{2}$$
$$\csc A = \frac{\sqrt{29}}{2}, \quad \csc B = \frac{\sqrt{29}}{5}$$
$$\sec A = \frac{\sqrt{29}}{5}, \quad \sec B = \frac{\sqrt{29}}{2}$$
$$\cot A = \frac{5}{2}, \quad \cot B = \frac{2}{5}$$

(ii) $\sin A = \cos B, \quad \cos A = \sin B$
$\tan A = \cot B, \quad \cot A = \tan B$
$\sec A = \csc B, \quad \csc A = \sec B$

2. (i) $LM : KM : KL = \frac{1}{2} : 1 : \frac{\sqrt{3}}{2}$
$= 1 : 2 : \sqrt{3}$

(ii) $\sin K = \frac{1}{2}, \quad \sin M = \frac{\sqrt{3}}{2}$
$\cos K = \frac{\sqrt{3}}{2}, \quad \cos M = \frac{1}{2}$
$\tan K = \frac{1}{\sqrt{3}}, \quad \tan M = \sqrt{3}$
$\csc K = 2, \quad \csc M = \frac{2}{\sqrt{3}}$
$\sec K = \frac{2}{\sqrt{3}}, \quad \sec M = 2$
$\cot K = \sqrt{3}, \quad \cot M = \frac{1}{\sqrt{3}}$

3. If A and B are two complementary angles,
then $\sin A = \cos B$, $\cos A = \sin B$
     $\tan A = \cot B$, $\cot A = \tan B$
     $\sec A = \csc B$, $\csc A = \sec B$

4. In $\triangle RST$,

$$\sin R = \frac{r}{s}, \quad \cos R = \frac{t}{s}, \quad \tan R = \frac{r}{t}, \quad \csc R = \frac{s}{r}, \quad \sec R = \frac{s}{t}, \quad \cot R = \frac{t}{r},$$

$$\sin T = \frac{t}{s}, \quad \cos T = \frac{r}{s}, \quad \tan T = \frac{t}{r}, \quad \csc T = \frac{s}{t}, \quad \sec T = \frac{s}{r}, \quad \cot T = \frac{r}{t}.$$

$\therefore \sin R = \cos T$, $\cos R = \sin T$
     $\tan R = \cot T$, $\cot R = \tan T$
     $\sec R = \csc T$, $\csc R = \sec T$

Section 8.9 (page 276)

1.   (i) $\sin 37° = .6018$ (ii) $\sec 80° = 5.7588$
     (iii) $\tan 2° = .0349$ (iv) $\csc 29° = 2.0627$

2.   (i) Since $\tan 63° = 1.9626$
     and $\tan 64° = 2.0503$,
     and since 2.0000 is closer to 1.9626 than to 2.0503
     $\therefore \theta° = 63°$ (to the nearest degree).
   (ii) Since $\cos 36° = .8090$
     and $\cos 37° = .7986$,
     and since 0.8018 is closer to $.7986$ than to $.8090$,
     $\therefore \alpha° = 37°$ (to the nearest degree).

3. As θ increases in measurement from 0 to $\dfrac{\pi}{2}$, the trigonometric ratios $\sin \theta$, $\tan \theta$, and $\sec \theta$ increase, while $\cos \theta$, $\csc \theta$, and $\cot \theta$ decrease.

Section 8.10 (page 278)

1. (i)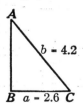

(ii) $c^2 = b^2 - a^2$
      $= (4.2)^2 - (2.6)^2$
      $= 17.64 - 6.76$
      $= 10.88$
   $c = \sqrt{10.88}$
      $= 3.3$ (to one decimal place)

```
        3.29
      ‾‾‾‾‾‾‾‾
      10.88|00
       9
   62 |1.88
      |1.24
  649 |6400
      |5841
```

(iii) $\sin A = \dfrac{a}{b} = \dfrac{2.6}{4.2} = .6190$ (to 4 decimal places)

(iv) $\therefore \angle A = 38°$ (to the nearest degree)
   (v) $\angle C = 180° - (38 + 90)° = 52°$
  (vi) $\tan C = \tan 52° = 1.2799$
(vii) $c = a \tan C = (2.6)(1.2799) = 3.3$ (to one decimal place)
(viii) Since $\tan A = \dfrac{a}{c}$,

     c could be calculated using the relation $c = \dfrac{a}{\tan A}$.

2. (i)

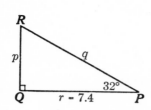

(v) $\angle R = 180° - (90 + 32)°$
$= 58°$

(ii) $\tan P = \tan 32°$
$= .6249$
(iii) $p = r \tan P$
$= (7.4)(.6249)$
$= 4.6$ (to one decimal place)
(iv) $q = r \sec P$
$= (7.4)(\sec 32°)$
$= (7.4)(1.1792)$
$= 8.7$ (to one decimal place)

Section 8.11 (page 280)

1. (i)

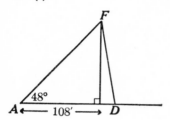

(ii) We are asked to find the height of the flagpole. Represent the height of the flagpole by h ft.

(iii) $\tan A = \dfrac{h}{AD}$ $\therefore \tan 48° = \dfrac{h}{AD}$

(iv) $h = AD \cdot \tan 48°$
$= (108)(1.1106)$
$= 119.94$ (to two decimal places)

(v) The height of the flagpole is 120 ft., to the nearest foot.

2. (i)

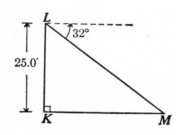

(ii) Represent the distance of the ship from the base of the lighthouse by x ft.

(iii) In $\triangle KLM$, $\angle K = 90°$
$\angle M = 32°$

(iv) $\cot M = \dfrac{KM}{KL}$

$\therefore \cot 32° = \dfrac{x}{250}$

(v) $\therefore x = (250)(1.6003)$
$= 400.075$ (to 4 decimal places)

(vi) $\therefore$ the distance of the ship from the base of the lighthouse is 400.1 ft. (to one decimal place).

3. (i)

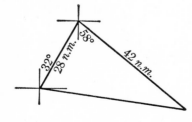

(ii) $\angle PQR = 32° + 58°$
$= 90°$

(iii) Represent the distance of the ship from the starting point by x nautical miles.
$\therefore x^2 = (28)^2 + (42)^2$
$= 784 + 1{,}764$
$= 2{,}548$
$x = 50.4$ (to one decimal place)

(iv) $\therefore$ the distance of the ship from the starting point is 50 n. miles (to the nearest n. mile).

Section 8.12 (page 283)

1. In $\triangle POD$, $OD^2 + DP^2 = OP^2$ (Pythagorean Theorem)
    $\because P$ has coordinates (x, y)
    $\therefore OD = |x| = -x$, $DP = |y| = y$
    $\therefore x^2 + y^2 = 1$

2. $\sin \theta = y$, $\cos \theta = x$

3. $\cos^2 \theta + \sin^2 \theta = 1$
    (or $\sin^2 \theta + \cos^2 \theta = 1$)

4. $\dfrac{\cos^2 \theta}{\cos^2 \theta} + \dfrac{\sin^2 \theta}{\cos^2 \theta} = \dfrac{1}{\cos^2 \theta}$ ($\cos \theta \neq 0$)
    $1 + \tan^2 \theta = \sec^2 \theta$

5. $\dfrac{\cos^2 \theta}{\sin^2 \theta} + \dfrac{\sin^2 \theta}{\sin^2 \theta} = \dfrac{1}{\sin^2 \theta}$ ($\sin \theta \neq 0$)
    $\therefore \cot^2 \theta + 1 = \csc^2 \theta$

Section 8.13 (page 285)

1. L.S. $= 1 + \tan^2 \beta$
    $= \sec^2 \beta$
    $= \dfrac{1}{\cos^2 \beta}$
    $= \dfrac{1}{1 - \sin^2 \beta} =$ R.S.

or L.S. $= 1 + \tan^2 \beta$
    $= \sec^2 \beta$
   R.S. $= \dfrac{1}{1 - \sin^2 \beta}$
    $= \dfrac{1}{\cos^2 \beta} = \sec^2 \beta$

$\therefore 1 + \tan^2 \beta = \dfrac{1}{1 - \sin^2 \beta}$

$\therefore 1 + \tan^2 \beta = \dfrac{1}{1 - \sin^2 \beta}$

Section 8.14 (page 287)

1. $\sin A = \dfrac{h}{b}$, $\sin B = \dfrac{h}{a}$

2. $\therefore h = b \sin A$, $h = a \sin B$
    $\therefore b \sin A = a \sin B$
    $\therefore \dfrac{a}{\sin A} = \dfrac{b}{\sin B}$

3.

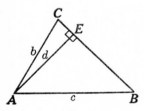

Draw AE perpendicular to BC.
Let $AE = d$ units.

$\sin B = \dfrac{d}{c}$, $\sin C = \dfrac{d}{b}$

$\therefore d = c \sin B$, $d = b \sin C$
$\therefore b \sin C = c \sin B$
$\therefore \dfrac{b}{\sin B} = \dfrac{c}{\sin C}$

4.

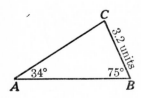

(i) $\angle A + \angle B + \angle C = 180°$
    $\therefore \angle C = 180° - (34 + 75)° = 71°$

(ii) $\dfrac{a}{\sin A} = \dfrac{b}{\sin B}$

    $\dfrac{3.2}{\sin 34°} = \dfrac{b}{\sin 75°}$

    $\therefore b = \dfrac{(3.2)(.9659)}{.5592}$

    $\therefore b = 5.5$ (to one decimal place)

(iii) $\qquad \dfrac{a}{\sin A} = \dfrac{c}{\sin C}$

$\therefore \quad \dfrac{3.2}{\sin 34°} = \dfrac{c}{\sin 71°}$

$c = \dfrac{(3.2)(.9455)}{.5592} = 5.4$ (to one decimal place)

Section 8.15 (page 289)

1. (i) Since $OD = OC$, $DP = CQ$, and $\angle ODP = \angle OCQ$,

$\qquad \triangle ODP \cong \triangle OCQ$ (sas)

$\qquad \therefore \ \angle POD = \angle QOC$

But $\angle XOQ + \angle QOC = 180°$

$\qquad \therefore \ \angle XOQ + \angle XOP = 180°$

$\qquad \therefore \ \angle XOQ$ is the supplement of $\angle XOP$.

(ii) $\sin \angle XOP = \dfrac{b}{\sqrt{a^2 + b^2}}, \qquad \sin \angle XOQ = \dfrac{b}{\sqrt{a^2 + b^2}}$

$\quad \cos \angle XOP = \dfrac{a}{\sqrt{a^2 + b^2}}, \qquad \cos \angle XOQ = \dfrac{-a}{\sqrt{a^2 + b^2}}$

$\quad \tan \angle XOP = \dfrac{b}{a}, \qquad \tan \angle XOQ = \dfrac{b}{-a}$

$\quad \csc \angle XOP = \dfrac{\sqrt{a^2 + b^2}}{b}, \qquad \csc \angle XOQ = \dfrac{\sqrt{a^2 + b^2}}{b}$

$\quad \sec \angle XOP = \dfrac{\sqrt{a^2 + b^2}}{a}, \qquad \sec \angle XOQ = \dfrac{\sqrt{a^2 + b^2}}{-a}$

$\quad \cot \angle XOP = \dfrac{a}{b}, \qquad \cot \angle XOQ = \dfrac{-a}{b}$

$\therefore \sin \angle XOP = \sin \angle XOQ \qquad \cos \angle XOP = -\cos \angle XOQ$

$\quad \csc \angle XOP = \csc \angle XOQ \qquad \sec \angle XOP = -\sec \angle XOQ$

$\qquad \tan \angle XOP = -\tan \angle XOQ$

$\qquad \cot \angle XOP = -\cot \angle XOQ$

Section 8.16 (page 289)

1. $\sin A = \dfrac{h}{b}$ **2.** $\sin \angle CBD = \dfrac{h}{a}$ **3.** $\sin B = \sin \angle CBD = \dfrac{h}{a}$

4. $\therefore h = b \sin A$, $h = a \sin B$

$\qquad \therefore a \sin B = b \sin A$

$\qquad \therefore \dfrac{a}{\sin A} = \dfrac{b}{\sin B}$

5.

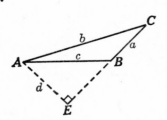

Draw AE perpendicular to line CB.

Let $AE = d$ units.

$\sin C = \dfrac{d}{b}$

$\sin B = \sin \angle ABE = \dfrac{d}{c}$

$\therefore d = b \sin C$, $d = c \sin B$

$\therefore b \sin C = c \sin B$

$\qquad \dfrac{b}{\sin B} = \dfrac{c}{\sin C}$

Section 8.17 (page 291)

1. In $\triangle ACD$, $h^2 = b^2 - p^2$
In $\triangle BCD$, $h^2 = a^2 - (c - p)^2$
$\therefore b^2 - p^2 = a^2 - (c - p)^2$
$\therefore b^2 - p^2 = a^2 - c^2 + 2pc - p^2$
$\therefore a^2 = b^2 + c^2 - 2pc$

2. $p = b \cos A$
$\therefore a^2 = b^2 + c^2 - 2bc \cos A$

3. In $\triangle ACD$, $h^2 = b^2 - p^2$
In $\triangle BCD$, $h^2 = a^2 - (p - c)^2$
$\therefore b^2 - p^2 = a^2 - (p - c)^2$
$\therefore b^2 - p^2 = a^2 - p^2 + 2pc - c^2$
$\therefore a^2 = b^2 + c^2 - 2pc$
$\because p = b \cos A$
$\therefore a^2 = b^2 + c^2 - 2bc \cos A$

Section 8.18 (page 291)

1.
$$\cos A = \frac{b^2 + c^2 - a^2}{2bc}$$
$$= \frac{5^2 + 6^2 - 4^2}{2 \cdot 5 \cdot 6}$$
$$= \frac{25 + 36 - 16}{60}$$
$$= .75$$
$\therefore \angle A = 41°$ (to the nearest degree)

$$\cos B = \frac{a^2 + c^2 - b^2}{2ac}$$
$$= \frac{16 + 36 - 25}{2 \cdot 4 \cdot 6}$$
$$= \frac{27}{48}$$
$$= .5625$$
$\therefore \angle B = 56°$ (to the nearest degree)
$\angle C = 180° - (41 + 56)°$
$= 83°$

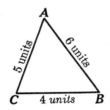

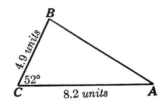

2.   (i) $c^2 = b^2 + a^2 - 2ab \cos C$
         $= (4.9)^2 + (8.2)^2 - 2(4.9)(8.2) \cos 52°$
         $= 24.01 + 67.24 - (80.36)(.6157)$
         $= 41.75$
      $c = 6.5$ (to one decimal place)

   (iii) $\angle B = 180° - (36 + 52)°$
            $= 92°$

(ii)
$$\frac{a}{\sin A} = \frac{c}{\sin C}$$
$$\therefore \frac{4.9}{\sin A} = \frac{6.5}{\sin 52°}$$
$$\sin A = \frac{(4.9)(.7880)}{6.5}$$
$$= .594$$
$$\angle A = 36°$$

Section 8.20 (page 293)

1. (i)

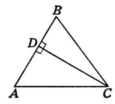

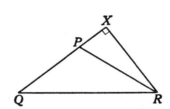

(a) Draw CD perpendicular to AB.
(b) Draw RX perpendicular to line QP.

(ii) (a) In $\triangle ABC$, $b^2 = a^2 + c^2 - 2 \cdot c \cdot BD$.

    (b) In $\triangle PQR$, $p^2 = q^2 + r^2 - 2 \cdot r \cdot PX$.

2.

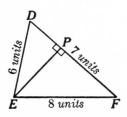

Draw EP perpendicular to DF.
In $\triangle DEF$,

$$DE^2 = EF^2 + DF^2 - 2 \cdot DF \cdot PF$$
$$\therefore 6^2 = 8^2 + 7^2 - 2 \cdot 7 \cdot PF$$
$$\therefore PF = \frac{64 + 49 - 36}{14}$$
$$= \frac{77}{14}$$
$$= \frac{11}{2}$$

The length of the projection of EF on DF is $5\frac{1}{2}$ units.

Section 8.21 (page 296)

1. (i) $BD = 140 \cdot \tan 58°$
    $= (140)(1.6003)$
    $= 224.04$

(ii) $CD = BD \cdot \tan 20°$
    $= (224.04)(.36408)$
    $= 81.55$

(iii) $\therefore$ the height of the tower is 82 ft., to the nearest foot.

2. (i)

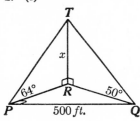

(ii) Let x represent the height of the skyscraper in ft., $x \in R$, $x > 0$.
$PR = x \cot 64°$

(iii) $QR = x \cot 50°$

(iv) $QR^2 = PR^2 + PQ^2$

(v) $\therefore x^2 \cot^2 50° = x^2 \cot^2 64° + (500)^2$
$\therefore x^2(\cot^2 50° - \cot^2 64°) = 500^2$
$\therefore x^2(.8391^2 - .4877^2) = 500^2$
$\therefore x^2(.7041 - .2379) = 250,000$
$\therefore x^2 = \dfrac{250,000}{.4662}$
$\therefore x^2 = 536250.5$
$x = 732.3$

(vi) $\therefore$ the height of the skyscraper is 732 ft., to the nearest foot.

Chapter IX

Section 9.9 (page 310)

1. (i) $R_1 = \{(-1, -3), (0, -1), (1, 1), (2, 3)\}$

(ii) The domain is $\{-1, 0, 1, 2\}$; and the range is $\{-3, -1, 1, 3\}$.

(iii) One element of the range corresponds to each element of the domain.

(iv) See accompanying graph.

(v) A line drawn parallel to the y-axis can meet the graph in at most one point.

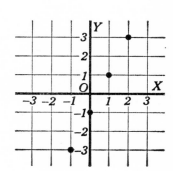

2. (i) $R_2 = \{(4, 4), (1, 2), (0, 0), (1, -2), (4, -4)\}$

   (ii) The domain is $\{0, 1, 4\}$;
and the range is $\{-4, -2, 0, 2, 4\}$.

  (iii) The elements 2 and -2 of the range correspond to the number 1 of the domain.

  (iv) There are two elements of the range for every element of the domain, except for 0.

   (v) See accompanying graph (left below).

  (vi) A line parallel to the y-axis meets the graph in two points or no point.

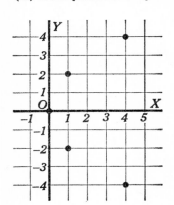 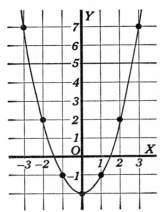

3. (i) $(-3, 7), (-2, 2), (-1, -1), (0, -2), (1, -1), (2, 2)$

   (ii) The x-intercept $= \pm \sqrt{2}$;
the y-intercept $= -2$.

  (iii) See accompanying graph (right above).

  (iv) See accompanying graph.

   (v) The domain is $\{x \mid -3 \le x \le 3, x \in R\}$;
the range is $\{y \mid -2 \le y \le 7, y \in R\}$.

  (vi) There is a unique y in the range for each x in the domain.

 (vii) If a line drawn parallel to the y-axis intersects the graph, it does so in only one point.

4. (i) $R_4 = \{(2, -4), (2, -3), (2, -2), (2, -1),$
$(2, 0), (2, 1), (2, 2), (2, 3), (2, 4)\}$

   (ii) The domain is $\{2\}$;
the range is $\{-4, -3, -2, -1, 0, 1, 2, 3, 4\}$.

  (iii) Nine elements of the range correspond to the element 2 of the domain.

  (iv) If a line drawn parallel to the y-axis intersects the graph, it does so in 9 points.

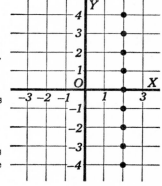

5. (i) R_1 and R_3 are functions.

   (ii) If a line drawn parallel to the y-axis intersects the graph of a function, it does so in only one point.

Chapter X

Section 10.1 (page 330)

1.
$$\begin{cases} x + 2y = 5 & (1) \\ 2x + 3y = 7 & (2) \end{cases}$$

From (1) $\qquad x = 5 - 2y \qquad (3)$

From (2) $\qquad x = \dfrac{7 - 3y}{2} \qquad (4)$

From (3) and (4) $\qquad 5 - 2y = \dfrac{7 - 3y}{2} \qquad (5)$

$$\therefore 10 - 4y = 7 - 3y$$
$$\therefore -y = -3$$
$$\therefore y = 3$$
$$\therefore x = 5 - 6$$
$$\therefore x = -1$$

The solution set is $\{(-1, 3)\}$.

Verification.

L.S. (1) $= -1 + 6$ $\qquad\qquad\qquad$ L.S. (2) $= -2 + 9$
$\qquad\quad = 5$ $\qquad\qquad\qquad\qquad\qquad\qquad = 7$
R.S. (1) $= 5$ $\qquad\qquad\qquad\qquad$ R.S. (2) $= 7$

2.
$$\begin{cases} \frac{1}{2}x - \frac{1}{3}y = 2 & (1) \\ \frac{1}{3}x + \frac{1}{2}y = -\frac{5}{6} & (2) \end{cases}$$

(1) $\times$ 6 $\qquad 3x - 2y = 12 \qquad (3)$
(2) $\times$ 6 $\qquad 2x + 3y = -5 \qquad (4)$

From (3) $\qquad x = \dfrac{12 + 2y}{3} \qquad (5)$

From (4) $\qquad x = \dfrac{-5 - 3y}{2} \qquad (6)$

From (5) and (6) $\qquad \dfrac{12 + 2y}{3} = \dfrac{-5 - 3y}{2}$

$$\therefore 24 + 4y = -15 - 9y$$
$$\therefore 13y = -39$$
$$\therefore y = -3$$

From (5) $\qquad x = \dfrac{12 - 6}{3}$

$$\therefore x = 2$$

The solution set is $\{(2, -3)\}$.

Section 10.3 (page 338)

1.
$$\begin{cases} 4x + 3y = 24 & (1) \\ 3x + 2y = -17 & (2) \end{cases}$$

2 $\times$ (1) $\qquad \begin{cases} 8x + 6y = 48 & (3) \\ 9x + 6y = -51 & (4) \end{cases}$
3 $\times$ (2)

(3) $-$ (4) $\qquad -x = 99$
$$\therefore x = -99 \qquad (5)$$

Substitute in (2) $\qquad -297 + 2y = -17$
$$\therefore 2y = 280$$
$$\therefore y = 140 \qquad (6)$$

The solution set is $\{(-99, 140)\}$.

Verification.

L.S. (1) $= -396 + 420$

       $= 24$

R.S. (1) $= 24$

L.S. (2) $= -297 + 280$

       $= -17$

R.S. (2) $= -17$

2.

$$\begin{cases} \frac{2}{5}x + \frac{3}{8}y = \frac{7}{2} & (1) \\ \frac{1}{5}x - \frac{1}{8}y = \frac{1}{2} & (2) \end{cases}$$

$$\begin{aligned} (1) & & \begin{cases} \frac{2}{5}x + \frac{3}{8}y = \frac{7}{2} & (3) \\ 3 \times (2) & & \frac{3}{5}x - \frac{3}{8}y = \frac{3}{2} & (4) \end{cases} \end{aligned}$$

$(3) + (4)$ $x = 5$ (5)

Substitute in (1) $2 + \frac{3}{8}y = \frac{7}{2}$

$\therefore 16 + 3y = 28$

$\therefore 3y = 12$

$\therefore y = 4$ (6)

$\{(x, y) \mid \frac{2}{5}x + \frac{3}{8}y = \frac{7}{2} \text{ and } \frac{1}{5}x - \frac{1}{8}y = \frac{1}{2}\} = \{(5, 4)\}$

Section 10.4 (page 341)

1.

$$\begin{cases} 4a + 5b + c = 0 & (1) \\ 8a - b + c = 24 & (2) \\ 3a + 2b + 2c = 1 & (3) \end{cases}$$

$$\begin{aligned} & & 8a - b + c = 24 & \quad (2) \\ & & 4a + 5b + c = 0 & \quad (1) \\ \cline{2-2} (2) - (1) & & 4a - 6b = 24 & \\ & & \therefore 2a - 3b = 12 & \quad (4) \end{aligned}$$

$$\begin{aligned} 2 \times (1) & & 8a + 10b + 2c = 0 & \quad (5) \\ & & 3a + 2b + 2c = 1 & \quad (3) \\ \cline{2-2} (5) - (3) & & 5a + 8b = -1 & \quad (6) \\ 5 \times (4) & & 10a - 15b = 60 & \quad (7) \\ 2 \times (6) & & 10a + 16b = -2 & \quad (8) \\ \cline{2-2} (7) - (8) & & -31b = 62 & \\ & & \therefore b = -2 & \quad (9) \end{aligned}$$

Substitute in (4) $2a + 6 = 12$

$\therefore a = 3$ (10)

Substitute in (1) $12 - 10 + c = 0$

$\therefore c = -2$ (11)

The solution set is $\{(3, -2, -2)\}$.

Verification.

L.S. (1) $= 12 - 10 - 2$

       $= 0$

R.S. (1) $= 0$

L.S. (2) $= 24 + 2 - 2$

       $= 24$

R.S. (2) $= 24$

L.S. (3) $= 9 - 4 - 4$

       $= 1$

R.S. (3) $= 1$

2.

$$\begin{cases} m + n = 5 & (1) \\ n + p = 3 & (2) \\ p + q = 7 & (3) \\ m + 5q = 9 & (4) \end{cases}$$

$$\begin{aligned} (1) + (2) + (3) + (4) & & 2m + 2n + 2p + 6q = 24 & \\ & & m + n + p + 3q = 12 & \quad (5) \\ & & m + n = 5 & \quad (1) \\ \cline{2-2} (5) - (1) & & p + 3q = 7 & \quad (6) \\ & & p + q = 7 & \quad (3) \\ \cline{2-2} (6) - (3) & & 2q = 0 & \\ & & \therefore q = 0 & \quad (7) \end{aligned}$$

Substitute in (3) $p = 7$ (8)

Substitute in (2) $n + 7 = 3$

$$\therefore \; n = -4 \quad (9)$$

Substitute in (1) $m - 4 = 5$

$$\therefore \; m = 9 \quad (10)$$

The solution set is $\{(9, -4, 7, 0)\}$.

Section 10.10 (page 359)

1. $3x + 4y = 24$

x-intercept is 8 .

y-intercept is 6 .

The graph (left below) indicates that the only positive integral solution of the equation is $(4, 3)$.

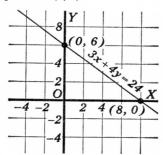 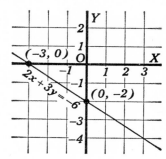

2. (i) $2x + 3y = -6$

x-intercept is -3 .

y-intercept is -2 .

The graph (right above) does not extend into the first quadrant, and hence there is no solution of the equation in positive integers.

(ii) $2x + 3y = -6$

$$2x = -3y - 6$$

$$x = -\tfrac{3}{2}y - 3$$

Thus, x is negative for all positive integral replacements for y. Hence there is no solution of the equation in positive integers.

Section 10.11 (page 363)

Example 2. $79x + 3y = 700$

$$3y = 700 - 79x$$

$$y = 233 + \frac{1}{3} - 26x - \frac{x}{3}$$

$$= 233 - 26x + \frac{1 - x}{3}$$

Since y is an integer, then $\dfrac{1 - x}{3}$ is an integer.

We can now find one integral value of x so that $1 - x$ is divisible by 3 and then find y by substitution. Other values may be obtained by applying the general solution.

If $x = 4$, $y = 128$, but this is not a solution since $x + y + z = 100$.

If $x = 7$, $y = 49$.

General solution of $79x + 3y = 700$ is:
$$x = 7 + 3t, \; y = 49 - 79t$$
if $t = 0$, $\quad x = 7$, $\quad y = 49$, $\qquad \therefore z = 44$;
if $t = -1$, $x = 4$, $\quad y = 128$, $\qquad$ not allowable;
if $t = 1$, $\quad x = 10$, $y = -30$, $\qquad$ not allowable;
if $t = -2$, $x = 1$, $\quad y = 207$, $\qquad$ not allowable;
if $t = 2$, $\quad x = 13$, $y = -109$, $\quad$ not allowable;
and so on.

Therefore there are 7 men, 49 women, and 44 children in the group.

Chapter XI

Section 11.2 Discovery Exercise 11-1 (page 365)

1. (i) PQ is parallel to the x-axis because P and Q have the same ordinate.
    (ii) From the graph, $PQ = 2$.
    (iii) $PQ = |3 - 1|$
    $\quad\quad = |1 - 3|$
    $\quad\quad = +2$

2. (i) Segment AB is parallel to the x-axis.
    (ii) From the graph, $AB = 5$.
    (iii) $AB = |3 - (-2)|$
    $\quad\quad = |-2 - 3|$
    $\quad\quad = +5$

3. (i) RS is parallel to the y-axis.
    (ii) From the graph, $RS = 7$.
    (iii) $RS = |3 - (-4)|$
    $\quad\quad = |-4 - 3|$
    $\quad\quad = +7$

4. (i) P_1P_2 is parallel to the x-axis.
    (ii) $P_1P_2 = |x_2 - x_1|$
    $\quad\quad\quad = |x_1 - x_2|$

5. $P_1P_2 = |y_2 - y_1|$
    $\quad\quad = |y_1 - y_2|$

Section 11.3 (page 367)

1. (i) $AB = |-8 - (-2)|$ $\qquad$ (ii) $PQ = |0 - (-2)|$
    $\quad\quad = +6$ $\qquad\qquad\qquad\qquad = +2$
    (iii) $OA = |-5 - 0|$ $\qquad$ (iv) $RS = |0 - (-2)|$
    $\quad\quad = +5$ $\qquad\qquad\qquad\qquad = +2$
    (v) $MN = |-4 - (-1)|$ $\qquad$ (vi) $WZ = |r - p|$
    $\quad\quad = +3$
    (vii) $AB = |b_2 - b_1|$ $\qquad$ (viii) $CD = |y_2 - y_1|$

Section 11.4 Discovery Exercise 11-2 (page 368)

1. (i) $PR = |5 - 1|$ $\qquad\qquad\qquad RQ = |4 - 1|$
    $\quad\quad = +4$ $\qquad\qquad\qquad\qquad\quad = +3$
    (ii) $PQ = \sqrt{4^2 + 3^2}$
    $\quad\quad = \sqrt{25}$
    $\quad\quad = 5$

2.   (i) The coordinates of M are $(12, 0)$.

(ii) $OM = |12 - 0|$ $AM = |5 - 0|$ $OA = \sqrt{12^2 + 5^2}$

         $= +12$ $= +5$ $= \sqrt{169}$

                                                                                    $= +13$

3.   (i) The coordinates of C are $(-3, 4)$.

(ii) $CB = |5 - (-3)|$ $AC = |4 - (-2)|$ $AB = \sqrt{8^2 + 6^2}$

         $= +8$ $= +6$ $= \sqrt{100}$

                                                                                     $= +10$

4.   (i) $PQ = \sqrt{|3 - (-2)|^2 + |-9 - 3|^2}$ (ii) $AB = \sqrt{|5 - 1|^2 + |3 - 1|^2}$

            $= \sqrt{5^2 + 12^2}$ $= \sqrt{4^2 + 2^2}$

            $= \sqrt{169}$ $= \sqrt{20}$

            $= +13$ $= +2\sqrt{5}$

(iii) $P_1P_2 = \sqrt{|3 - (-3)|^2 + |4 - (-4)|^2}$ (iv) $RS = \sqrt{|-8 - 7|^2 + |7 - (-1)|^2}$

               $= \sqrt{6^2 + 8^2}$ $= \sqrt{15^2 + 8^2}$

               $= \sqrt{100}$ $= \sqrt{289}$

               $= +10$ $= +17$

(v) $MN = \sqrt{|c - a|^2 + |d - b|^2}$ (vi) $P_1P_2 = \sqrt{|x_2 - x_1|^2 + |y_2 - y_1|^2}$

            $= \sqrt{(c - a)^2 + (d - b)^2}$ $= \sqrt{(x_2 - x_1)^2 + (y_2 - y_1)^2}$

Section 11.6 Discovery Exercise 11-4 (page 371)

1.   (i) From the graph, M has coordinates $(1, 2)$.

(ii) $P_1M = |1 - (-1)| = +2$

      $MP_2 = |3 - 1| = +2$

      $P_1P_2 = |3 - (-1)| = +4$

      $P_1M = MP_2 = \frac{1}{2}P_1P_2$

(iii) $1 = \dfrac{3 + (-1)}{2}$; that is, the abscissa of M is one-half the sum of the abscissas of P_1 and P_2.

2.   (i) The coordinates of u are $\left(\dfrac{x_1 + x_2}{2}, y_1\right)$.

(ii) $P_1M = \left|\dfrac{x_1 + x_2}{2} - x_1\right| = \left|\dfrac{x_2 - x_1}{2}\right| = \frac{1}{2}|x_2 - x_1|$

     $MP_2 = \left|x_2 - \dfrac{x_1 + x_2}{2}\right| = \left|\dfrac{x_2 - x_1}{2}\right| = \frac{1}{2}|x_2 - x_1|$

     $P_1P_2 = |x_2 - x_1|$

     $\therefore P_1M = MP_2 = \frac{1}{2}P_1P_2$

3.   (i) The coordinates of M are $(3, -1)$.

(ii) $P_1M = |-1 - 3| = +4$

      $MP_2 = |-5 - (-1)| = +4$

      $\therefore P_1P_2 = |(-5) - 3| = +8$

      $\therefore P_1M = MP_2 = \frac{1}{2}P_1P_2$

(iii) $-1 = \dfrac{(-5) + 3}{2}$; that is, the ordinate of M is one-half the sum of the ordinates of P_1 and P_2.

4.   (i) The coordinates of M are $\left(x_1, \dfrac{y_1 + y_2}{2}\right)$.

    (ii) $P_1M = \left|\dfrac{y_1 + y_2}{2} - y_1\right| = \left|\dfrac{y_2 - y_1}{2}\right| = \tfrac{1}{2}|y_2 - y_1|$

       $MP_2 = \left|y_2 - \dfrac{y_1 + y_2}{2}\right| = \left|\dfrac{y_2 - y_1}{2}\right| = \tfrac{1}{2}|y_2 - y_1|$

       $P_1P_2 = |y_2 - y_1|$

       $\therefore P_1M = MP_2 = \tfrac{1}{2}P_1P_2$

5.   (i) The coordinates of M are $(1, 3)$.

    (ii) $P_1M = \sqrt{(1 + 2)^2 + (3 - 1)^2} = \sqrt{9 + 4} = \sqrt{13}$

       $MP_2 = \sqrt{(4 - 1)^2 + (5 - 3)^2} = \sqrt{9 + 4} = \sqrt{13}$

       $P_1P_2 = \sqrt{(4 + 2)^2 + (5 - 1)^2} = \sqrt{36 + 16} = \sqrt{52} = 2\sqrt{13}$

       $\therefore P_1M = MP_2 = \tfrac{1}{2}P_1P_2$

    (iii) $1 = \dfrac{4 + (-2)}{2}$; hence the abscissa of M is one-half of the sum of the abscissas of P_1 and P_2.

       $3 = \dfrac{5 + 1}{2}$; hence the ordinate of M is one-half the sum of the ordinates of P_1 and P_2.

6.   (i) The coordinates of M are $\left(\dfrac{x_1 + x_2}{2}, \dfrac{y_1 + y_2}{2}\right)$.

    (ii) $P_1M = \sqrt{\left(\dfrac{x_1 + x_2}{2} - x_1\right)^2 + \left(\dfrac{y_1 + y_2}{2} - y_1\right)^2}$

$$= \sqrt{\left(\dfrac{x_1 + x_2 - 2x_1}{2}\right)^2 + \left(\dfrac{y_1 + y_2 - 2y_1}{2}\right)^2}$$

$$= \sqrt{\left(\dfrac{x_2 - x_1}{2}\right)^2 + \left(\dfrac{y_2 - y_1}{2}\right)^2}$$

$$= \tfrac{1}{2}\sqrt{(x_2 - x_1)^2 + (y_2 - y_1)^2}$$

       $MP_2 = \sqrt{\left(x_2 - \dfrac{x_1 + x_2}{2}\right)^2 + \left(y_2 - \dfrac{y_1 + y_2}{2}\right)^2}$

$$= \sqrt{\left(\dfrac{2x_2 - x_1 - x_2}{2}\right)^2 + \left(\dfrac{2y_2 - y_1 - y_2}{2}\right)^2}$$

$$= \sqrt{\left(\dfrac{x_2 - x_1}{2}\right)^2 + \left(\dfrac{y_2 - y_1}{2}\right)^2}$$

$$= \tfrac{1}{2}\sqrt{(x_2 - x_1)^2 + (y_2 - y_1)^2}$$

       $P_1P_2 = \sqrt{(x_2 - x_1)^2 + (y_2 - y_1)^2}$

       $\therefore P_1M = MP_2 = \tfrac{1}{2}P_1P_2$

    (iii) $\dfrac{x_1 + x_2}{2}$ = one-half the sum of the abscissas of P_1 and P_2.

       $\dfrac{y_1 + y_2}{2}$ = one-half the sum of the ordinates of P_1 and P_2.

Section 11.7 (page 373)

1. (i) $\left(\dfrac{-2+4}{2}, \dfrac{-3+2}{2}\right)$ or $\left(1, -\dfrac{1}{2}\right)$

(ii) $\left(\dfrac{2+(-3)}{2}, \dfrac{-5+(-1)}{2}\right)$ or $\left(-\dfrac{1}{2}, -3\right)$

(iii) $\left(\dfrac{-4+(-6)}{2}, \dfrac{-5+(-7)}{2}\right)$ or $(-5, -6)$

(iv) $\left(\dfrac{0+1}{2}, \dfrac{-1+1}{2}\right)$ or $\left(\dfrac{1}{2}, 0\right)$

(v) $\left(\dfrac{-3+3}{2}, \dfrac{-2+2}{2}\right)$ or $(0, 0)$

(vi) $\left(\dfrac{\frac{a}{2}+\frac{c}{2}}{2}, \dfrac{\frac{b}{2}+\frac{d}{2}}{2}\right)$ or $\left(\dfrac{a+c}{4}, \dfrac{b+d}{4}\right)$

Section 11.9 Discovery Exercise 11-6 (page 375)

1. (i) $AM = |x - (-3)| = |x + 3| = x + 3$
   (ii) $PN = |5 - x| = 5 - x$
   (iii) $\dfrac{AM}{PN} = \dfrac{3}{1}$ since $\triangle PAM \sim \triangle BPN$
   (iv) $\dfrac{x+3}{5-x} = \dfrac{3}{1}$
   $\therefore x + 3 = 15 - 3x$
   $\therefore 4x = 12$
   $\therefore x = 3$
   (v) $MP = |y - (-1)| = |y + 1| = y + 1$
   (vi) $NB = |3 - y| = 3 - y$
   (vii) $\dfrac{MP}{NB} = \dfrac{3}{1}$, since $\triangle PAM \sim \triangle BPN$
   (viii) $\dfrac{y+1}{3-y} = \dfrac{3}{1}$
   $\therefore y + 1 = 9 - 3y$
   $\therefore 4y = 8$
   $\therefore y = 2$
   (ix) The coordinates of P are $(3, 2)$.

2. (i) $MR = |x - (-3)| = |x + 3| = x + 3$
   (ii) $NP_2 = |4 - x| = 4 - x$
   (iii) $\dfrac{MR}{NP_2} = \dfrac{4}{3}$ since $\triangle P_1MR \sim \triangle RNP_2$ and $\dfrac{P_1R}{RP_2} = \dfrac{4}{3}$
   (iv) $\dfrac{x+3}{4-x} = \dfrac{4}{3}$
   $\therefore 3x + 9 = 16 - 4x$
   $\therefore 7x = 7$
   $\therefore x = 1$
   (v) $MP_1 = |2 - y| = 2 - y$
   (vi) $NR = |y - (-3)| = |y + 3| = y + 3$

(vii) $\dfrac{MP_1}{NR} = \dfrac{4}{3}$ since $\triangle P_1MR \sim \triangle RNP_2$ and $\dfrac{P_1R}{RP_2} = \dfrac{4}{3}$

(viii) $\quad \dfrac{2-y}{y+3} = \dfrac{4}{3}$

$\qquad \therefore 4y + 12 = 6 - 3y$

$\qquad \therefore 7y = -6$

$\qquad \therefore y = \dfrac{-6}{7}$

(ix) The coordinates of R are $\left(1, -\dfrac{6}{7}\right)$.

3. (i) $P_1S = |x - x_1| = x - x_1$ (ii) $RT = |x_2 - x| = x_2 - x$

(iii) $\dfrac{P_1S}{RT} = \dfrac{m}{n}$, since $\triangle RP_1S \sim \triangle P_2RT$ (vi) $TP_2 = |y_2 - y| = y_2 - y$

(iv) $\qquad \dfrac{x - x_1}{x_2 - x} = \dfrac{m}{n}$ (vii) $\dfrac{SR}{TP_2} = \dfrac{m}{n}$, since $\triangle RP_1S \sim \triangle P_2RT$

$\qquad \therefore nx - nx_1 = mx_2 - mx$

$\qquad \therefore mx + nx = mx_2 + nx_1$ (viii) $\qquad \dfrac{y - y_1}{y_2 - y} = \dfrac{m}{n}$

$\qquad \therefore (m + n)x = mx_2 + nx_1$ $\therefore ny - ny_1 = my_2 - my$

$\qquad\quad \therefore x = \dfrac{mx_2 + nx_1}{m + n}$ $\therefore my + ny = my_2 + ny_1$

                       $\therefore (m + n)y = my_2 + ny_1$

(v) $SR = |y - y_1| = y - y_1$ $\therefore y = \dfrac{my_2 + ny_1}{m + n}$

(ix) The coordinates of R are $\left(\dfrac{mx_2 + nx_1}{m + n}, \dfrac{my_2 + ny_1}{m + n}\right)$.

Section 11.9 (page 375)

1. Let R be the point of division. For this problem, P_1 is $A(-2, 3)$ and P_2 is $B(5, 4)$. Using the general expression for the coordinates of the point of division, R has coordinates:

$$\left(\dfrac{5(5) + 3(-2)}{5 + 3}, \dfrac{5(4) + 3(3)}{5 + 3}\right)$$

or $\left(\dfrac{19}{8}, \dfrac{29}{8}\right)$ or $(2\frac{3}{8}, 3\frac{5}{8})$

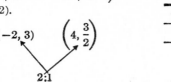

2. Let D be the midpoint of AC. Then, D has coordinates $(4, \frac{3}{2})$. The centroid, G, lies on the median BD and divides the segment BD internally in the ratio 2:1. The coordinates of G are

$$\left(\dfrac{2(4) + 1(-2)}{2 + 1}, \dfrac{2(\frac{3}{2}) + 1(3)}{2 + 1}\right)$$

or $(2, 2)$.

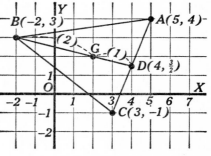

Fig. S 12-1

Section 11.11 Discovery Exercise 11-8 (page 380)

1. (i) The abscissa of B is $\dfrac{3x + 2(-3)}{3 + 2}$ or $\dfrac{3x - 6}{5}$

    (ii) $\dfrac{3x - 6}{5} = 2$

    $\therefore 3x - 6 = 10$
    $\therefore x = 5\frac{1}{3}$

    (iii) The ordinate of B is $\dfrac{3y + 2(-2)}{3 + 2}$ or $\dfrac{3y - 4}{5}$.

    (iv) $\dfrac{3y - 4}{5} = 2$

    $\therefore 3y - 4 = 10$
    $\therefore y = 4\frac{2}{3}$

    (v) $AP : PB = 5 : -2$.

2. (i) $P_1P_2 : P_2R = 4 : 1$

    (ii) The abscissa of P_2 is $\dfrac{4x + 1(3)}{4 + 1}$ or $\dfrac{4x + 3}{5}$.

    (iii) $\dfrac{4x + 3}{5} = -2$

    $\therefore 4x + 3 = -10$
    $\therefore x = -3\frac{1}{4}$

    (iv) The ordinate of P_2 is $\dfrac{4y + 1(-1)}{4 + 1}$ or $\dfrac{4y - 1}{5}$.

    (v) $\dfrac{4y - 1}{5} = 3$

    $\therefore 4y - 1 = 15$
    $\therefore y = 4$

    (vi) R has coordinates $(-3\frac{1}{4}, 4)$.

3. (i) $P_1P_2 : P_2R = m - n : n$

    (ii) The abscissa of P_2 is $\dfrac{(m - n)x + nx_1}{(m - n) + n}$ or $\dfrac{(m - n)x + nx_1}{m}$.

    (iii) $\dfrac{(m - n)x + nx_1}{m} = x_2$

    $\therefore (m - n)x + nx_1 = mx_2$
    $\therefore (m - n)x = mx_2 - nx_1$
    $\therefore x = \dfrac{mx_2 - nx_1}{m - n}$

    (iv) By symmetry, $y = \dfrac{my_2 - ny_1}{m - n}$.

    (v) R has coordinates $\left(\dfrac{mx_2 - nx_1}{m - n}, \dfrac{my_2 - ny_1}{m - n} \right)$.

Section 11.11 (page 380)

1. From the array
   it is seen that the coordinates of the point of section are
   $$\left(\frac{(-2)(1) + 5(-1)}{-2 + 5}, \frac{(-2)(0) + 5(-2)}{-2 + 5} \right)$$
   or $(-2\frac{1}{3}, -3\frac{1}{3})$.

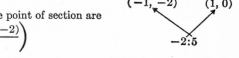

2. Since the diagonals of a parallelogram bisect each other, their point of inter-section is the midpoint of AC: that is, E (0, 1). Then, D divides BE externally in the ratio $2 : -1$.
The coordinates of D are

$$\left(\frac{2(0) + (-1)(-2)}{2 - 1}, \frac{2(1) + (-1)(-2)}{2 - 1}\right)$$

or $(2, 4)$.

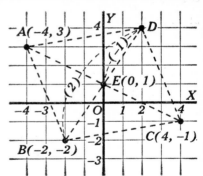

Section 11.12 (page 384)

1. (i) The slope of $P_1P_2 = \dfrac{\triangle y}{\triangle x}$, $x_2 \neq x_1$

$$= \frac{y_2 - y_1}{x_2 - x_1}, \triangle x \neq 0$$

$$= \frac{4 - 1}{5 - (-2)}$$

$$= \frac{3}{7}.$$

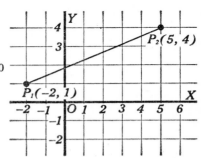

(ii) The slope of a line segment which rises to the right is positive.

2. (i) (a) The slope of $RS = \dfrac{-2 - 2}{4 - (-1)}$

$$= \frac{-4}{5}.$$

(b) The slope of $SR = \dfrac{2 - (-2)}{-1 - 4}$

$$= \frac{4}{-5}.$$

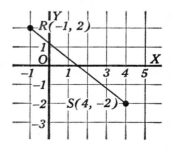

The slopes are equal. The slope of a line segment is independent of the order in which the end points are named.

(ii) The slope of a line segment which rises to the left is negative.

3. (i) The slope of $AB = \dfrac{3 - 3}{3 - (-2)}$ (diagram at the left on page 493)

$$= \frac{0}{5}$$

$$= 0.$$

(ii) The slope of a line segment parallel to the x-axis is 0.

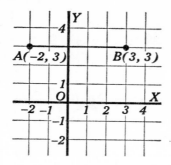
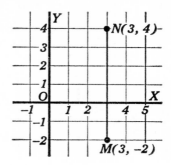

4. (i) The slope of $MN = \dfrac{4 - (-2)}{3 - 3}$ (diagram at the right above)

$$= \frac{6}{0} \text{ (undefined)}.$$

(ii) The slope of a line segment parallel to the y-axis is undefined.

5. (i) The slope of a line segment is independent of the order in which the end points are named.

(ii) The slope of a line segment which rises to the right is positive.

(iii) The slope of a line segment which rises to the left is negative.

(iv) The slope of a line segment parallel to the x-axis is zero.

(v) The slope of a line segment parallel to the y-axis is undefined.

Section 11.13 Discovery Exercise 11-11 (page 388)

1. (i) $AB = \sqrt{1^2 + 2^2} = \sqrt{5}$

$\qquad BC = \sqrt{2^2 + 4^2} = \sqrt{20} = 2\sqrt{5}$

$\qquad AC = \sqrt{3^2 + 6^2} = \sqrt{45} = 3\sqrt{5}$

$\qquad \because AB + BC = AC$

$\qquad \therefore A, B,$ and C are collinear.

(ii) Slope of $AB = \dfrac{0 - (-2)}{1 - 0} = \dfrac{2}{1}$.

$\qquad$ Slope of $BC = \dfrac{4 - 0}{3 - 1} = \dfrac{4}{2} = \dfrac{2}{1}$.

$\qquad \therefore$ the slope of $AB =$ the slope of BC.

(iii) $A, B,$ and C may be proved collinear by showing that the slope of $AB =$ the slope of BC.

2. Slope of $AB = \dfrac{-1 - (-3)}{-1 - 2}$

$= -\dfrac{2}{3}$.

Slope of $BC = \dfrac{1 - (-1)}{-4 - (-1)}$

$= -\dfrac{2}{3}$.

The slope of $AB =$ the slope of BC.

$\therefore$ A, B, and C are collinear.

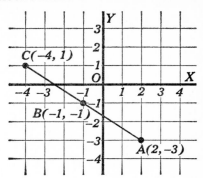

3. Slope of $PQ = \dfrac{3 - 2}{-1 - x}$

$= \dfrac{1}{-1 - x}$.

Slope of $QR = \dfrac{-2 - 3}{3 - (-1)}$

$= \dfrac{-5}{4}$.

P, Q, and R are collinear.

$\therefore$ the slope of $PQ =$ the slope of QR.

$\therefore \dfrac{1}{-1 - x} = \dfrac{-5}{4}$

$\therefore 5 + 5x = 4$

$\therefore 5x = -1$

$\therefore x = -\dfrac{1}{5}$

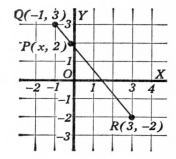

Section 11.14 (page 390)

1. From the tangent tables, tan 75° = 3.7321.
Hence, the slope = 3.732 (correct to 3 decimal places).

2. From the chart, tan 120° = $-\sqrt{3}$.
Hence, the inclination = 120°.

3. The supplement of 140° is 40°.
From the tangent tables, tan 40° = 0.8391.
$\therefore$ tan 140° = -0.8391
Hence, the slope = -0.839 (correct to 3 decimal places).

Section 11.16 (page 394)

1. (i) The equation of a line $\parallel$ y-axis is $y = y_1$.
$\therefore$ the equation is $y = -3$.
(ii) The equation of a line $\parallel$ x-axis is $x = x_1$.
$\therefore$ the equation is $x = 4$.

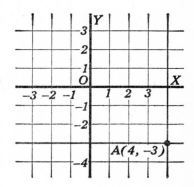

2. The slope of segment $AB = \dfrac{3 - (-1)}{-2 - 4}$

$$= -\dfrac{2}{3}.$$

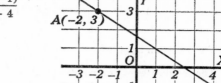

Let $A(-2, 3)$ be $P_1(x_1, y_1)$.
Then the equation is
$y - 3 = -\frac{2}{3}(x + 2)$
or $3y - 9 = -2x - 4$
or $2x + 3y - 5 = 0$.

3. The slope of the line $= \tan 120°$
$$= -\tan 60°$$
$$= -\sqrt{3}.$$

$\therefore$ the equation is $y + 1 = -\sqrt{3}(x - 2)$
or $y + 1 = -\sqrt{3}x + 2\sqrt{3}$
or $\sqrt{3}x + y + 1 - 2\sqrt{3} = 0$.

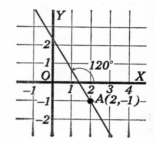

Section 11.17 Discovery Exercise 11-15 (page 396)

1. Using the slope-point form of the equation of a line, the equation of line l is
$$y - 1 = m(x - 0)$$
$$\text{or } y = mx + 1.$$

2. The point B has coordinates $(0, b)$.
The equation of the line is $y - b = m(x - 0)$
$$\text{or } y = mx + b.$$

3. The point A has coordinates $(a, 0)$.
The equation of the line is $y - 0 = m(x - a)$
$$\text{or } y = m(x - a).$$

Section 11.17 (page 396)

1. (i) The slope $= \tan 60°$
$$= \sqrt{3}.$$
Using the form $y = mx + b$, the equation is
$$y = \sqrt{3}x - 2$$
$$\text{or } \sqrt{3}x - y - 2 = 0.$$

(ii) Using the form $y = m(x - a)$, the equation is
$$y = -\tfrac{3}{4}(x - 3)$$
$$\text{or } 4y = -3x + 9$$
$$\text{or } 3x + 4y - 9 = 0.$$

2. The equation $2x - 3y + 6 = 0$ may be written
$$3y = 2x + 6$$
$$\text{or } y = \tfrac{2}{3}x + 2.$$
$$\therefore m = \tfrac{2}{3} \text{ and } b = 2$$

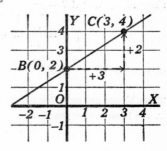

The line passes through $B(0, 2)$. If we use $\triangle x = +3$ and $\triangle y = +2$, a second point $C(3, 4)$ is determined. The graph is shown at the right.

3. The equation $Ax + By + C = 0$ may be written

$$By = -Ax - C$$

$$\text{or} \quad y = -\frac{Ax}{B} - \frac{C}{B}, \ (B \neq 0).$$

This equation has the form $y = mx + b.$ $\therefore$ the slope $= -\dfrac{A}{B}.$

4. The coordinates of two points on the line are $(3, 0)$ and $(0, 4)$.

Slope of the line is $\dfrac{4 - 0}{0 - 3}$ or $-\dfrac{4}{3}.$

The equation of the line is $y - 0 = -\dfrac{4}{3}(x - 3)$

$$\text{or} \quad +x + 3y = 12.$$

5. The coordinates of two points on the line are $(a, 0)$ and $(0, b)$.

The slope of the line is $\dfrac{b - 0}{0 - a}$ or $\dfrac{b}{-a}.$

Hence, the equation of the line is $y - 0 = \dfrac{b}{-a}(x - a)$

$$\text{or} \quad -ay = bx - ab$$

$$\text{or} \quad bx + ay = ab$$

$$\text{or} \quad \frac{x}{a} + \frac{y}{b} = 1. \qquad \text{(Division by } ab\text{)}$$

Section 11.18 (page 399)
Example 1.

The slope of $AD = \dfrac{4 - 3}{5 - (-3)} = \dfrac{1}{8}.$

The slope of $BC = \dfrac{-2 - (-3)}{4 - (-4)} = \dfrac{1}{8}.$

$\therefore \ AD \parallel BC$

The slope of $AB = \dfrac{3 - (-3)}{-3 - (-4)} = \dfrac{6}{1}.$

The slope of $DC = \dfrac{4 - (-2)}{5 - 4} = \dfrac{6}{1}.$

$\therefore \ AB \parallel DC$

$\therefore \ ABCD$ is a parallelogram.

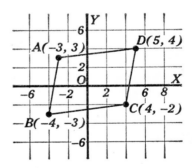

Example 2.

Slope of segment $AB = \dfrac{1 - 3}{7 - (-5)}$

$$= \dfrac{-2}{12} = -\dfrac{1}{6}.$$

Slope of segment $CD = \dfrac{6 - 0}{4 - 3} = \dfrac{6}{1}.$

These slopes are negative reciprocals.

$\therefore$ the lines are perpendicular.

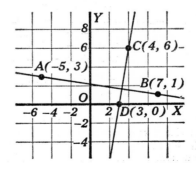

Example 3.

Slope of $AB = \dfrac{6-3}{-1+3} = \dfrac{3}{2}$.

Slope of $AC = \dfrac{6-2}{-1-5} = \dfrac{4}{-6} = -\dfrac{2}{3}$.

These slopes are negative reciprocals.

$\therefore\ AB \perp AC$, and the triangle is right-angled at A.

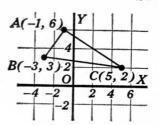

Section 11.19 Discovery Exercise 11-18 (page 401)

1. (i) The coordinates of R, S, and T are $(2, 0)$, $(-3, 0)$, and $(4, 0)$, respectively.

   (ii) Area of trapezoid $ABSR = \frac{1}{2}(2+4)(5) = 15$
   Area of trapezoid $ARTC = \frac{1}{2}(4+1)(2) = 5$
   Area of trapezoid $BSTC = \frac{1}{2}(2+1)(7) = 10.5$

   (iii) Area of $\triangle ABC = 15 + 5 - 10.5 = 9.5$

2. (i) The coordinates of M, N, and R are $(x_1, 0)$, $(x_2, 0)$, and $(x_3, 0)$, respectively.

   (ii) Area of trapezoid $P_1P_2NM = \frac{1}{2}(y_2 + y_1)(x_1 - x_2)$
   Area of trapezoid $P_1MRP_3 = \frac{1}{2}(y_1 + y_3)(x_3 - x_1)$
   Area of trapezoid $P_2NRP_3 = \frac{1}{2}(y_2 + y_3)(x_3 - x_2)$

   (iii) Area of $\triangle P_1P_2P_3 =$ trapezoid $P_1P_2NM +$ trapezoid $P_1MRP_3 -$
   trapezoid P_2NRP_3

   $= \frac{1}{2}(y_2 + y_1)(x_1 - x_2) + \frac{1}{2}(y_1 + y_3)(x_3 - x_1) - \frac{1}{2}(y_2 + y_3)(x_3 - x_2)$
   $= \frac{1}{2}[(x_1y_2 + x_1y_1 - x_2y_2 - x_2y_1) + (x_3y_1 + x_3y_3 - x_1y_1 - x_1y_3)$
   $\qquad - (x_3y_2 + x_3y_3 - x_2y_2 - x_2y_3)]$
   $= \frac{1}{2}[x_1y_2 + x_1y_1 - x_2y_2 - x_2y_1 + x_3y_1 + x_3y_3 - x_1y_1 - x_1y_3$
   $\qquad - x_3y_2 - x_3y_3 + x_2y_2 + x_2y_3]$
   $= \frac{1}{2}[x_1y_2 - x_1y_3 + x_2y_3 - x_2y_1 + x_3y_1 - x_3y_2]$
   $= \frac{1}{2}[x_1(y_2 - y_3) + x_2(y_3 - y_1) + x_3(y_1 - y_2)]$

Section 11.21 Discovery Exercise 11-20 (page 405)

1. (i) A has coordinates $(5, 0)$.

   (ii) B has coordinates $(0, \frac{5}{2})$.

   (iii) Using the array $\begin{vmatrix} 1, & 1 \\ 5, & 0 \\ 0, & \frac{5}{2} \\ 1, & 1 \end{vmatrix}$

   $$\text{Area } \triangle PAB = \frac{1}{2}\left|0 + \frac{25}{2} + 0 - 5 - 0 - \frac{5}{2}\right|$$

   $$= \frac{1}{2}\left|\frac{10}{2}\right|$$

   $$= \frac{5}{2}$$

   (iv) $AB = \sqrt{25 + \dfrac{25}{4}} = \sqrt{\dfrac{125}{4}} = \dfrac{5}{2}\sqrt{5}$

(v) Area $\triangle PAB = \dfrac{1}{2} \cdot \dfrac{5}{2}\sqrt{5} \cdot PM$

But the area $= \dfrac{5}{2}$ ((iii) above).

$\therefore \dfrac{1}{2} \cdot \dfrac{5}{2}\sqrt{5} \cdot PM = \dfrac{5}{2}$

$\therefore PM = \dfrac{2}{\sqrt{5}} = \dfrac{2\sqrt{5}}{5}$

2.   (i) A has coordinates $(-\tfrac{1}{2}, 0)$.

    (ii) B has coordinates $(0, 1)$.

    (iii) Using the array $\begin{vmatrix} 1 & , & 5 \\ -\tfrac{1}{2} & , & 10 \\ 0 & , & 1 \\ 1 & , & 5 \end{vmatrix}$

$$\text{Area } \triangle PAB = \dfrac{1}{2}\left| 0 - \dfrac{1}{2} + 0 + \dfrac{5}{2} - 0 - 1 \right| = \dfrac{1}{2}$$

    (iv) $AB = \sqrt{\dfrac{1}{4} + 1} = \dfrac{\sqrt{5}}{2}$ (v) $\dfrac{1}{2} \cdot \dfrac{\sqrt{5}}{2} \cdot PM = \dfrac{1}{2}$

$$\therefore PM = \dfrac{2}{\sqrt{5}} = \dfrac{2\sqrt{5}}{5}$$

3.   (i) D has coordinates $\left(-\dfrac{C}{A}, 0\right)$.   (ii) E has coordinates $\left(0, -\dfrac{C}{B}\right)$.

    (iii) Using the array $\begin{vmatrix} x_1 & , & y_1 \\ -\dfrac{C}{A}, & & 0 \\ 0, & & -\dfrac{C}{B} \\ x_1 & , & y_1 \end{vmatrix}$

$$\text{Area } \triangle PDE = \dfrac{1}{2}\left| 0 + \dfrac{C^2}{AB} + 0 + \dfrac{C}{A}y_1 + 0 + \dfrac{C}{B}x_1 \right|$$

$$= \dfrac{1}{2}\left| \dfrac{Cx_1}{B} + \dfrac{Cy_1}{A} + \dfrac{C^2}{AB} \right|$$

$$= \dfrac{1}{2}\left| \dfrac{CAx_1 + CBy_1 + C^2}{AB} \right|$$

$$= \dfrac{1}{2}\left| \dfrac{C}{AB}(Ax_1 + By_1 + C) \right|$$

    (iv) $DE = \sqrt{\dfrac{C^2}{A^2} + \dfrac{C^2}{B^2}} = \sqrt{\dfrac{C^2B^2 + C^2A^2}{A^2B^2}} = \sqrt{\dfrac{C^2(B^2 + A^2)}{A^2B^2}}$

$$= \left| \dfrac{C}{AB}\sqrt{A^2 + B^2} \right|$$

    (v) $\dfrac{1}{2}\left| \dfrac{C}{AB}\sqrt{A^2 + B^2} \right| \cdot P_1M = \dfrac{1}{2}\left| \dfrac{C}{AB}(Ax_1 + By_1 + C) \right|$

$$\therefore P_1M = \dfrac{|Ax_1 + By_1 + C|}{\sqrt{A^2 + B^2}}$$

Section **11.21** (page 405)

1. The slope of $BC = \dfrac{3}{4}$.

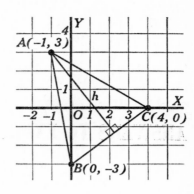

∴ the equation of BC
is $y - 0 = \frac{3}{4}(x - 4)$,
   or $4y = 3x - 12$,
   or $3x - 4y - 12 = 0$.
If the length of the altitude is h units,
then $h = \dfrac{|\, 3(-1) - 4(3) - 12 \,|}{\sqrt{3^2 + 4^2}}$.

∴ $h = \dfrac{|-27|}{5}$

∴ $h = 5\frac{2}{5}$

∴ the altitude is $5\frac{2}{5}$ units.

2. The y-intercept of the line with equation $x - 3y + 6 = 0$ is 2. Hence, B has coordinates $(0, 2)$. If d is the length of the perpendicular from B to the line with equation $x - 3y - 3 = 0$,

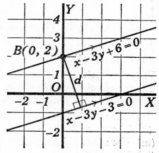

then $d = \dfrac{|\, 0 - 3(2) - 3 \,|}{\sqrt{1^2 + 3^2}}$

$= \dfrac{|-9|}{\sqrt{10}}$

$= \dfrac{9}{10}\sqrt{10}$.

∴ the distance between the parallel
lines is $\dfrac{9}{10}\sqrt{10}$ units.

ANSWERS TO EXERCISES

Exercise A-1 (page 3)

17. (i) B, C, F; D, E, H; A, I
    (ii) A, I
18. $\{2, 3, 5, 7, 11, 13, 17, 19, 23\}$
19. $\{\ \}$
20. $\{1, 2, 3, 4, 5, 6, 10, 12, 15, 20, 30\}$
21. $\left\{\dfrac{3}{4}, \dfrac{3}{7}, \dfrac{3}{11}, \dfrac{4}{7}, \dfrac{4}{11}, \dfrac{7}{11}\right\}$
22. The set of points inside the circle.
    The set of points on the circle.
    The set of points outside the circle.
23. (i) The set of points inside both the circle and the rectangle.
    (ii) The set of points outside both the circle and the rectangle.
    (iii) The set of points inside the rectangle but outside the circle.
    (iv) The set of points outside the rectangle but inside the circle.

Exercise A-2 (page 8)

1. (i)   (ii)   (iii)

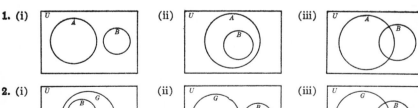

2. (i)   (ii)   (iii)

         (iv)   (v)

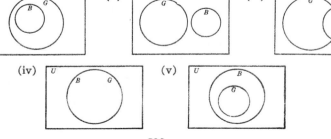

500

3. 21   **4.** 7

5. (i) 332   (ii) 300   **6.** 41

7. 35 sq. ft.

8.

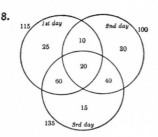

9.

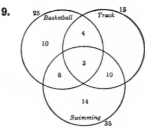

(i) 20   The diagram shows that at least 17 boys
(ii) 30   took part in track. The reporter said
(iii) 15   there were 15.

10. Montreal vs Winnipeg;   Edmonton vs Calgary;   Toronto vs Hamilton;
Ottawa vs B.C. Lions

Exercise B-1 (page 15)

11. $\{6, 7\}$ **12.** $\{3, 4, 5, \ldots\}$

13. $\{1, 2, 3, 4\}$ **14.** $\{1, 2, 3, 4, 8, 9, 10, \ldots\}$

15. $\{3\}$ **16.** $\{0, 2, 3, 4, \ldots\}$

17. $\{6, 7, 8, \ldots\}$ **18.** $\{4\}$

19. $\{1, 2, 3, 4, 5, 7, 8, 9, \ldots\}$

20. $\{0, 1, 2, 3, 6, 7, 8, \ldots\}$

21. $\{4\}$

22. $\{0, 1, 2, 5, 6, 7\}$

23. $\emptyset$

Exercise B-2 (page 20)

5. (i) $5x - 5y$ (ii) $-2a - 2b$ (iii) $3c - 3d$ (iv) $-6m - 6n$
(v) $a - b$ (vi) $3 - 2 = 1$ (vii) $p + q + c$

7.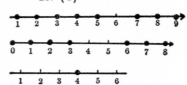

$\{-4\}$

8.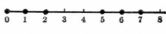

$\{-3\}$

9.

$\{x \mid x \neq 4\}$

10.

$\{0\}$

11.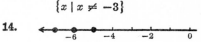

$$\{-7\}$$

12.

$$\{x \mid x \neq -3\}$$

13.

$$\{-4\}$$

14.

$$\{x \mid x < -4\}$$

15.

$$\{x \mid x > -4\}$$

16.

$$\{x \mid x \geqq -2\}$$

17.

18.

19.

20.

Exercise B-3 (page 23)

16. 13	**17.** 11	**18.** 0	**19.** 9	**20.** 3	**21.** 16
22. 7	**23.** 32	**24.** $4x + 3$	**25.** $(x + 1)^2$	**26.** =	**27.** >
28. >	**29.** >	**30.** =	**31.** >	**32.** 0	**33.** −3
34. 12	**35.** 14	**36.** −15			

Exercise B-4 (page 26)

2. $a - b$

3. $2x - 6y$

4. $3x^2 - 3x - 1$

5. $a - 6b + 6c$

6. $4n + 2m + 3p$

7. $-6a + b - 2c$

8. 3

9. 2

10. 1

11. $-2a + 3b$

12. $3x - 9y$

13. 0

14. $-3a + 4b$

15. $x(a + 3b + 3c) + y(a + 2b - 2c)$

16. $x(3p + q - r) + y(r - p - 2q)$ **17.** $x(m - n - p) + y(n - m + p)$

18. $x^3(c - 3) + x^2(b - d) + x(a - 2) + 8$

19. $x^3(1 - k) + x^2(a + p) - x(h + b)$

20. $x^3(m - n + 2) + x^2(p - q) - x(p + 2) + n$

21. $b - d + 1$ **22.** $a - b - 4c$ **23.** $-3a - 2b - 1$

Exercise B-5 (page 28)

6.   (i) $8a - b + 7c$ (ii) $7x - 15y$
      (iii) $-14x + 28y$ (iv) $-4a - 4b + 12c$
      (v) $11m^2 + 5n^2$

7.   (i) equal   (ii) equal

8. −2

9.   (i) $a(a + b)$ (ii) $3(a + 2b - 4c)$
      (iii) $-4p(m + 2 + 3q)$ (iv) $3(-4x + a - 5b)$

10.   (i) $m - nx - ny + 5nz$ (ii) $3ax + 2bx + 3ay + 2by$
      (iii) $4a^2 - 11ab - 3b^2$ (iv) $2x^2 - 5xy + 2y^2$

11.   (i) $6x^2 + 13x + 6$ (ii) $25m^2 + 20m + 4$
      (iii) $81a^2 - 25b^2$ (iv) $6a^2 + ab + 4ac - b^2 + 2bc$
      (v) $6m^2 - 20mn + 7m - 21n + 6n^2$ (vi) $8x^3 + 36x^2 + 54x + 27$

12.   (i) $16a^2 + 4ab$ (ii) $3m^3 - 2m^2 - m + 10$

Exercise B-6 (page 33)

6. (i) $\dfrac{p + 3q}{-2}$ (ii) $\dfrac{12ab^2}{5r}$ (iii) $\dfrac{2 - 5a + 3a^2}{4a^2}$ (iv) $\dfrac{-3x^3}{y^2}$ (v) $-\dfrac{2}{a + 2}$

7. (i) $-b$ (ii) $\dfrac{-6y}{xz}$ (iii) $\dfrac{-2}{3a}$ (iv) $\dfrac{5c}{-2}$

   (v) $\dfrac{-3(1 + 3b)}{4a}$ (vi) $\dfrac{2}{a}$

8. (i) $\dfrac{-3t}{5s}, t \neq 0$ (ii) $\dfrac{-c}{ab}$ (iii) $\dfrac{-25}{2a^2}$ (iv) $\dfrac{-c^3}{12d^2}$

   (v) $\dfrac{-2y}{3x^2}, x \neq 0$ (vi) $-\dfrac{7ab}{2c}$ (vii) $\dfrac{+1}{y}$

9. (i) $\dfrac{3}{2}$ (ii) 1 (iii) $\dfrac{27}{8}$

10. (i) $\dfrac{2b}{a}$ (ii) $\dfrac{4}{3}$ (iii) $-\dfrac{1}{3}$ (iv) no reciprocal

Exercise B-7 (page 38)

13. $-\dfrac{5}{18}$ 14. 0 15. $-\dfrac{3}{2xy}$

16. $\dfrac{x^4 - 2y^4 + 3z^4}{x^2y^2z^2}$ 17. $\dfrac{5p^2 - 2qr}{3pqr}$

18. $\dfrac{b + c - 2}{b + c}$ 19. $\dfrac{3 - 2x - 2y}{x + y}$

20. $\dfrac{m^2n + m + n^2m + n}{mn}$ 21. $\dfrac{2x^2 + 2y^2 - xy}{2xy}$

22. $\dfrac{5x - y}{(x - y)(x + y)}$ 23. $\dfrac{r_2r_3 + r_1r_3 + r_1r_2}{r_1r_2r_3}$

24. 5 25. $\left\{\dfrac{-3}{7}, \dfrac{2}{-7}, \dfrac{-2}{-7}, \dfrac{-3}{-7}\right\}$

26. $\left\{\dfrac{-5}{4}, -\dfrac{-5}{-8}, -\dfrac{5}{-8}, \dfrac{-5}{-4}\right\}$ 27. $\left\{\dfrac{5}{-6}, -\dfrac{1}{3}, \dfrac{1}{-4}, \dfrac{-7}{-12}, -\dfrac{-2}{3}\right\}$

28. $\left\{-\dfrac{2}{7}, \dfrac{4}{-15}, -\dfrac{-9}{-35}\right\}$ 29. $-\dfrac{7xy}{6}$

30. $\dfrac{-2q + 15p^2}{3p^2q^2}$ 31. $-\dfrac{5}{ab}$

Exercise 1-1 (page 43)

5. $3.2\dot{0}$ 6. $6.\dot{6}$ 7. $.0\dot{9}$ 8. $.40\dot{7}$

9. $2.\dot{1}$ 10. $13.\dot{5}7142\dot{8}$ 11. -11.1 12. $-0.\dot{4}1935483870967\dot{7}$

13. $\dfrac{5}{9}$ 14. $\dfrac{5}{33}$ 15. $\dfrac{7}{3}$ 16. $\dfrac{707}{500}$

17. $\dfrac{37822}{9999}$ 18. $\dfrac{64}{275}$ 19. $\dfrac{32707}{90000}$ 20. $\dfrac{1434}{555}$

Exercise 1-2 (page 51)

10. 3.14, 3.142, 3.1416
12. 15.35, 15.346, 15.3457
14. 2.16, 2.156, 2.1556
16. 15.24, 15.235, 15.2354
18. 2.72, 2.718, 2.7183

11. 1.41, 1.414, 1.4143
13. 17.43, 17.433, 17.4328
15. 18.23, 18.232, 18.2323
17. 3.67, 3.673, 3.6726

19.

PROPERTY		N_0	I	Q	R
Addition:	(1) Closed	✓	✓	✓	✓
	(2) Commutative	✓	✓	✓	✓
	(3) Associative	✓	✓	✓	✓
	(4) Identity	✓	✓	✓	✓
	(5) Inverse		✓	✓	✓
Multiplication:	(6) Closed	✓	✓	✓	✓
	(7) Commutative	✓	✓	✓	✓
	(8) Associative	✓	✓	✓	✓
	(9) Identity	✓	✓	✓	✓
	(10) Inverse			✓*	✓*
	(11) Distributive	✓	✓	✓	✓
*except 0					

Exercise 2-1 (page 57)

20. 4	**21.** 2	**22.** 4	**23.** −4	**24.** 4
25. −15	**26.** 2	**27.** $-\frac{7}{2}$	**28.** 2	**29.** 2
30. $\{8\}$	**31.** $\{1\}$	**32.** $\{0\}$	**33.** $\{33\}$	

Exercise 2-2 (page 58)

10. 12	**11.** −6	**12.** −11	**13.** 7	**14.** 8
15. −7	**16.** 1	**17.** −1	**18.** −25	**19.** 1
20. 3	**21.** −1	**22.** 20	**23.** 50	**24.** −1
25. 8	**26.** −1	**27.** $\{1\frac{1}{2}\}$	**28.** $\{7\}$	**29.** $\{\frac{7}{11}\}$
30. $\{6\}$	**31.** $\{0\}$	**32.** $\{-\frac{3}{2}\}$		

Exercise 2-3 (page 61)

9. $\left\{\frac{1}{4}\right\}$ **10.** $\{6\}$

11. $\{. . ., -5, -4, -2, -1, 0, . . .\}$

12. $\{3\frac{3}{4}\}$

13. $\{. . ., -4, -3, -1, 0, 1, . . .\}$

14. $\{. . ., 6, 7, 9, 10, 11, . . .\}$

15. $\{x \mid x \neq -4, x \in R\}$

16. $\{1, 2, 4, 5, 6, . . .\}$

17. $\{1, 2, 3, 4, . . .\}$

18. (i) $\{x \mid x \neq 3, x \in R\}$

  (ii) $\{. . ., 0, 1, 2, 4, 5, 6, . . .\}$

  (iii) $\{1, 2, 4, 5, 6, . . .\}$

Exercise 2-4 (page 67)

19. $x \leqq 13$

20. $x = 1$

21. $x < 1$

22. $x > 2$

23. $y = 0.6$

24. $x \leqq -2$

25. $x \leqq 5$

26. $x < 2$

27. $y \geqq 0$

28. $x < -6\frac{1}{2}$

29. $x < -1\frac{3}{4}$

30. $\{x \mid x \geqq 2, x \in I\}$

31. $\{x \mid x \leqq -3, x \in I\}$

32. $\{y \mid y < -19, y \in R\}$

33. $\{x \mid x \geqq -2, x \in R\}$

34. $\{x \mid x \leqq 2\frac{1}{2}, x \in R\}$

35. $\{x \mid x > 1\frac{1}{3}, x \in R\}$

36. $\{x \mid x > 0, x \in I\}$

37. $\{x \mid x \leqq -4\frac{1}{4}, x \in R\}$

38. $\{y \mid y \geqq 7, y \in N\}$

39. $\{x \mid x < 14, x \in R\}$

40. $\{x \mid x \geqq 5, x \in R\}$

41. $\{x \mid x \leqq 7, x \in R\}$ 42. $\{x \mid x \geqq \frac{1}{2}, x \in R\}$ 43. $\{y \mid y \geqq -2, y \in R\}$

Exercise 2-5 (page 68)

1. $x < 2$ **2.** $y < 3$ **3.** $x > \frac{2}{3}$ **4.** $x \geqq -1$

5. $\{y \mid y > -2\frac{3}{4}, y \in R\}$

6. $\{y \mid y > 1, y \in I\}$

7. $\{x \mid x < 7, x \in N\}$

8. $\{y \mid y \leqq -4, y \in I\}$

9. $\{x \mid x < 2\frac{3}{4}, x \in R\}$

10. $\{x \mid x \neq -1, x \in I\}$

11. $\{y \mid y \leqq 1\frac{1}{2}, y \in R\}$ **12.** $\{x \mid x > 3\frac{1}{4}, x \in R\}$

13. $\{x \mid x \leqq 12, x \in R\}$ **14.** $\{a \mid a > 1\frac{2}{5}, a \in R\}$

Exercise 2-6 (page 71)

9.   **10.**

11.   **12.**

13.   **14.**

15.   **16.**

17.   **18.**

19.   **20.**

21.   **22.**

Exercise 2-7 (page 73)

7. $5, -4$ **8.** $5, 3$ **9.** $5, -2$ **10.** $10, -10$

11. $\frac{3}{4}, -\frac{3}{4}$ **12.** $0, 9$ **13.** $-\frac{5}{2}, 1$ **14.** $8, 8$

15. $8, -7$ **16.** $\frac{7}{3}, -2$ **17.** $7, -7$ **18.** $-\frac{1}{7}, -5$

19. $\frac{3}{2}, -\frac{2}{3}$ **20.** $\frac{1}{3}, -5$ **21.** $1\frac{2}{3}, -\frac{1}{2}$ **22.** $-\frac{2}{7}, \frac{2}{3}$

23. $-\frac{2}{3}, 3$ **24.** $\frac{2}{3}, 1\frac{1}{2}$ **25.** $-4\frac{1}{2}, 1\frac{1}{2}$ **26.** $-\frac{2}{3}, -6$

27. $-18, 2$ **28.** $-7c, 3c$ **29.** $\frac{4b}{7}, \frac{-b}{2}$ **30.** a, b

31. $-\frac{1}{2}, \frac{1}{m}$ **32.** $0, p + q$ **33.** $-2c, -2d$

Exercise 2-8 (page 74)

10. $\{4, -3\}$ **11.** $\left\{\dfrac{2}{3}, -2\right\}$ **12.** $\varnothing$ **13.** $\left\{2, -\dfrac{2}{3}\right\}$

14. $\varnothing$ **15.** $\left\{\dfrac{1}{2}, -2\right\}$ **16.** $\left\{\dfrac{5}{2}, -\dfrac{7}{2}\right\}$ **17.** $\left\{\dfrac{3}{2}, -\dfrac{5}{2}\right\}$

18. $\{-2, -6\}$ **19.** $\left\{\dfrac{21}{4}, -\dfrac{21}{4}\right\}$ **20.** $\left\{1, -\dfrac{5}{3}\right\}$ **21.** $\left\{\dfrac{5}{3}, -1\right\}$

22. $\left\{\dfrac{3}{4}, -\dfrac{3}{4}\right\}$ **23.** $\{-1, 1\}$

24. $\{3, 1\}$ **25.** $\{-1, 3\}$

26. $\left\{\dfrac{3}{2}, -\dfrac{9}{2}\right\}$ **27.** $\{-1, 2\}$

28. $\left\{\dfrac{5}{3}, 1\right\}$ **29.** $\left\{\dfrac{11}{6}, \dfrac{5}{6}\right\}$

30. $\varnothing$

Review Exercise 2-9 (page 75)

15. $\{x \mid x > 3, x \in I\}$

16.

17. (i)   (ii)

18. (i) $\{y \mid y > 6 \text{ or } y < -2, y \in R\}$

(ii) $\{x \mid -2 \leqq x \leqq 1, x \in R\}$

19.   **20.** $\{-8\}$

21. -5 **22.** $4a - 12b$

23. -51 **24.** $3b - 4c$

25.   **26.**

27.   **28.**

30. $\{-0.25, 0.25\}$ **31.** $\left\{-\dfrac{3}{4}, \dfrac{5}{2}\right\}$

32. $\left\{0, \dfrac{19}{7}\right\}$ **33.** $\left\{\dfrac{9}{2}, -\dfrac{2}{3}\right\}$

Exercise 3-3 (page 85)

71. $|x + 3|$ **72.** $|x - 3|$ **73.** $|2x + 1|$

74. $|3x + 2|$ **75.** $|2x - 5|$ **76.** $\left|\dfrac{x}{2} - \dfrac{1}{4}\right|$

77. $|5 + 3x|$ **78.** $|7x - 1|$ **79.** $|8x + 3|$

80. $\sqrt{a^2 b}$ **81.** $\sqrt{9c}$ **82.** $\sqrt{27x^2 y}$

83. $\sqrt{3(a - b)^2}$ **84.** $\sqrt{2(a + b)^2}$ **85.** $\sqrt{(x + 3)^2 y}$

86. $\sqrt{(a - b)^2 (a + b)}$ **87.** $\sqrt{5(2x + 4)^2}$ **88.** $\sqrt{z(3x + y)^2}$

89. $3\sqrt{11}$ **90.** $|a|\sqrt{3}$ **91.** $|x-1|\sqrt{2}$

92. $|x+8|\sqrt{3}$ **93.** $|x+1|\sqrt{5}$ **94.** $|b-4|\sqrt{a}$

95. $\left|\dfrac{a-b}{a+b}\right|$ **96.** $2|a+ab|\sqrt{3}$ **97.** $|x+1|\sqrt{3}$

98. $|xy|\sqrt{6}$ **99.** $x^2\sqrt{x}$ **100.** $12\sqrt{3}$

101. 24 **102.** $|b|\sqrt{3}$ **103.** 60

104. 12 **105.** 12 **106.** $2\sqrt{10}$

107. $450\sqrt{2}$ **108.** $84\sqrt{2}$ **109.** $1,000$

110. $\dfrac{2\sqrt{2}}{9}$ **111.** $\dfrac{4\sqrt{5}}{3}$ **112.** $\sqrt{2}$

Exercise 3-4 (page 88)

16. $2\sqrt{2}$ **17.** $11\sqrt{2}$ **18.** $22\sqrt{2}$

19. $10\sqrt{3}$ **20.** $-4\sqrt{5}$ **21.** $4\sqrt{3}$

22. $4\sqrt{7}$ **23.** $x(\sqrt{2}-1)$ **24.** $17\sqrt{2}$

25. $\dfrac{6}{\sqrt{5}}$ **26.** $\dfrac{19}{12}\sqrt{5}$ **27.** $-\sqrt{10}$

28. $\dfrac{5}{2}\sqrt{2}$ **29.** $3\sqrt{b}$ **30.** $3|a|\sqrt{2}$

31. $2\sqrt{6}$ **32.** $12\sqrt{6}-9\sqrt{2}$ **33.** $4\sqrt{2}$

34. $14\sqrt{2}$ **35.** $25\sqrt{2}$ **36.** $4\sqrt{2}$

37. $9\sqrt{6}$ **38.** $2\sqrt{5}+4\sqrt{2}$ **39.** $38\sqrt{2}$ **40.** $1+\dfrac{4\sqrt{3}}{3}$

Exercise 3-5 (page 89)

29. $\sqrt{2}$ **30.** $\dfrac{\sqrt{15}}{3}$ **31.** $\dfrac{\sqrt{6}}{3}$ **32.** $\sqrt{b}$ **33.** $\dfrac{\sqrt{6}}{5}$ **34.** $8\sqrt{x}$

35. $\dfrac{2\sqrt{5}}{5}$ **36.** $\dfrac{\sqrt{77}}{7}$ **37.** $\sqrt{2}$ **38.** $\dfrac{\sqrt{15}}{2}$ **39.** $\dfrac{\sqrt{15}}{50}$ **40.** $\dfrac{\sqrt{70}}{14}$

41. $\dfrac{3\sqrt{2}}{2}$ **42.** $\dfrac{\sqrt{2}}{2}$ **43.** $\sqrt{10}$ **44.** $\dfrac{6\sqrt{2}}{5}$ **45.** 0.71 **46.** 0.89

47. 0.28 **48.** 2.24 **49.** 1.06

Exercise 3-6 (page 91)

1. $2+2\sqrt{2}$ **2.** $6-2\sqrt{3}$ **3.** $\sqrt{5}+10$ **4.** $5\sqrt{2}+2$

5. $2\sqrt{6}+2\sqrt{15}$ **6.** $2\sqrt{10}-12$ **7.** $2\sqrt{15}+5$ **8.** 1

9. 1 **10.** $11+6\sqrt{2}$ **11.** $5-2\sqrt{6}$ **12.** -2

13. $7+4\sqrt{3}$ **14.** $8+4\sqrt{3}$ **15.** 3 **16.** 1

17. $\dfrac{12+2\sqrt{11}}{4}$ **18.** $\dfrac{7-4\sqrt{3}}{4}$ **19.** -22 **20.** $10\sqrt{6}$

21. $66-24\sqrt{6}$ **22.** $9x+y-6\sqrt{xy}$ **23.** $93-30\sqrt{6}$ **24.** $2\sqrt{7}-28$

25. $x-1$ **26.** 44 **27.** $x+y-2\sqrt{xy}$ **28.** $a+b+2\sqrt{ab}$

29. $\sqrt{7}$ **30.** $\dfrac{7}{3}$ **31.** $19+5\sqrt{10}$ **32.** $6x-3y+7\sqrt{xy}$

33. $74 - 10\sqrt{35}$

34. $\sqrt{ac} + \sqrt{ad} + \sqrt{bc} + \sqrt{bd}$

35. $7\sqrt{55} - 3$

36. $22 + 10\sqrt{5}$

Exercise 3-7 (page 93)

1. $\sqrt{2} - 1$

2. $\dfrac{3 + \sqrt{3}}{2}$

3. $6\sqrt{5} - 12$

4. $\dfrac{15 + 5\sqrt{7}}{2}$

5. $\dfrac{2x + 2\sqrt{y}}{x^2 - y}$

6. $\dfrac{2\sqrt{5} + \sqrt{30}}{-2}$

7. $\dfrac{\sqrt{35} + 3\sqrt{7}}{-4}$

8. $\dfrac{2\sqrt{21} - 4\sqrt{3}}{3}$

9. $\dfrac{2\sqrt{2} + 3}{-1}$

10. $3\sqrt{3} - 3\sqrt{2}$

11. $\dfrac{5 - \sqrt{10}}{3}$

12. $2\sqrt{6} + \sqrt{21}$

13. $\dfrac{5 + 2\sqrt{6}}{-1}$

14. $\dfrac{21 - 8\sqrt{5}}{11}$

15. $4 + \sqrt{15}$

16. $\dfrac{11 - 4\sqrt{6}}{-5}$

17. -1

18. $\dfrac{15 - 2\sqrt{10} + 2\sqrt{14} - 3\sqrt{35}}{2}$

19. $\dfrac{187 - 40\sqrt{21}}{37}$

20. $\dfrac{12\sqrt{6} - 35}{19}$

21. $\dfrac{7\sqrt{15} - 27}{2}$

22. $\dfrac{x^2 + y^2z + 2xy\sqrt{z}}{x^2 - y^2z}$

23. $\dfrac{a^2 + 7 - 4\sqrt{a^2 + 3}}{a^2 - 1}$

24. $\dfrac{a + b - 2\sqrt{ab}}{a - b}$

25. $x + \sqrt{x^2 - 1}$

26. $y\sqrt{a} - y\sqrt{b}\ (a \neq b)$

27. $\dfrac{(a - 3\sqrt{b})\ \sqrt{b + a}}{b + a}$

28. $\dfrac{2 + 3\sqrt{2} + 2\sqrt{3} + \sqrt{6}}{2}$

Exercise 3-8 (page 95)

1. 18   **2.** no roots   **3.** 22   **4.** $\dfrac{55}{9}$ **5.** 5   **6.** 4

7. no roots   **8.** 11   **9.** no roots   **10.** 2   **11.** 9   **12.** 1

Exercise 3-9 (page 96)

1. 8   **2.** no roots   **3.** no roots   **4.** 1   **5.** 0   **6.** 4

7. 6   **8.** 9   **9.** 12   **10.** 2   **11.** $\dfrac{6}{5}$ **12.** 4

13. 6   **14.** $\dfrac{ab}{a + b}$

Discovery Exercise 4-1 (page 100)

1. (i) half-lines AX, BX, BY, CY, CZ, AZ
(ii) rays AX, BX, BY, CY, CZ, AZ
(iii) line segments AB, BC, CA
(iv) half-lines BX, AX, ray BX, line segment AB

2. (i) $\triangle XYZ, \triangle ZWT, \triangle TYS, \triangle XWS$
(ii) (a) $\{T\}$ (b) $\{S\}$ (c) $\emptyset$ (d) $\{T, W\}$
(e) line segment TY (f) line segments ZW and ZT (g) $\{T\}$

3.

(i) 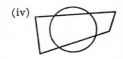   (ii) 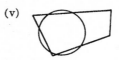   (iii)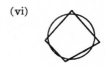

(iv) 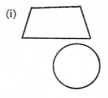   (v)   (vi)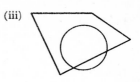

5. (i) parallel

6. (i) l_1 and l_2, l_1 and l_3, l_1 and l_4, l_2 and l_3, l_2 and l_4, l_3 and l_4

7. (i) A, B; A, C; A, D; A, E; B, C; B, D; B, E; C, D; C, E; D, E

8. (i) A, D, C; A, G, K, F; D, I, F; C, I, K, E; C, F, B; A, E, B; D, G, E; E, H, F; D, H, K, B

  (ii) AB, AF, AD; EB, EF, EC, ED; BA, BD, BC; FB, FE, FA, FD; CB, CE, CA; DC, DF, DB, DE; KA, KD, KC; GA, GD; ID, IK; HE, HB

Discovery Exercise 4-2 (page 104)

1. (a) (i) triangle   (ii) two equal sides
    (b) (i) triangle   (ii) no two sides equal
    (c) (i) triangle   (ii) three equal sides

2. (i) $MN + NP = MP$ $NM + MP = NP$

3. (i) 180°   (ii) supplementary angles
    (iii) (c), (e)   (iv) 145°, 108°, 75°, 96°, 88°, 65°, 50°

4. (i) one   (ii) 90°

5. (i) 90°   (ii) complementary angles
    (iii) (a), (b), (e)   (iv) 20°, 28°, 36°, 48°, 18°, 54°, 72°

6. (i) right bisector   (iii) one

7. (a) (ii) triangle   (iii) All angles are acute.
    (b) (ii) triangle   (iii) One angle is a right angle.
    (c) (ii) triangle   (iii) One angle is an obtuse angle.

Exercise 4-3 (page 108)

15. and; P and Q **16.** or; P or Q

17. not; $\sim P$ **18.** if . . . then . . .; $P \rightarrow Q$

19. if . . . then . . .; $P \rightarrow Q$ **20.** simple sentence; P

21. and; P and Q **22.** and; if . . . then . . .; $(P \text{ and } Q \text{ and } R) \rightarrow S$

23. if . . . then . . .; $P \rightarrow Q$

24. If a triangle is isosceles, then it has two equal sides.

25. An angle is acute, and it is obtuse.

26. A triangle is not a quadrilateral.

27. If a figure has four equal sides, then it is a square or it is a rhombus.

Exercise 4-6 (page 115)

13. $\angle ABC = \angle PQR$

15. $\angle A$ has a measurement greater than 90°.

17. $PQRS$ has both pairs of opposite sides parallel.

19. P, Q, R, and S are in the same plane.

21. no logical consequent

23. Lines MN and ST intersect to form a right angle.

14. no logical consequent

16. no logical consequent

18. $\triangle RST$ has all sides equal.

20. X, Y, and Z are coplanar.

22. no logical consequent

24. $\angle 1 = \angle 2$

Exercise 5-7 (page 157)

2. (i) Line RT must be perpendicular to all lines through S contained in plane P.
(ii) 2

3. 2

6.

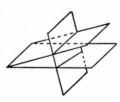

8.

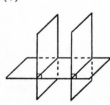

Exercise 5-8 (page 160)

2. (i)

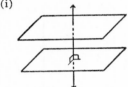

(ii)

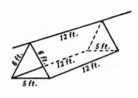

(iii)   (iv)   (v)

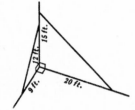 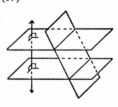 

(vi)   (vii)   (viii)

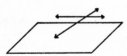  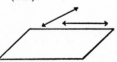

3. 120°

Exercise 5-9 (page 161)

1. 120°, 240°   **2.** 120°   **3.** 7 cm.   **4.** 35°   **5.** 70°, 60°, 50°   **6.** 40°   **7.** 73°, 49°

8. 6 cm., 6 cm., 4 cm., 4 cm.   **9.** 90°   **10.** 60°, 60°, 60°   **11.** 92°   **12.** 30°

13. 140°, 140°   **14.** 180°   **15.** 60°   **16.** 5 cm.   **17.** 150°

Exercise 6-1 (page 166)

1.

Polygon with diagonals drawn from one vertex	Number of sides	Number of triangles	Angle sum of polygon in straight angles	Angle sum of polygon in degrees
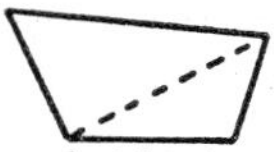 Quadrilateral	4	2	2	360
 Pentagon	5	3	3	540
 Hexagon	6	4	4	720
 Septagon	7	5	5	900
 Octagon	8	6	6	1,080
 Decagon	10	8	8	1,440
	50	48	48	8,640
	90	88	88	15,840
	200	198	198	35,640
	1,002	1,000	1,000	180,000
n-gon	n	$n-2$	$n-2$	$180(n-2)$

2. 720° **3.** 900° **6.** (i) 1,440 (ii) 9,000 (iii) 180
7. (i) 120 (ii) 150 (iii) 170

Exercise 6-4 (page 177)

6. 4,800 sq. cm. **7.** 80 sq. cm. **8.** 20 in. **9.** 50 sq. in. **10.** 16 in.

Exercise 6-6 (page 181)

6. 30 in. **7.** 5 cm. **8.** 8 sq. in. **9.** 3.92 in. **10.** $4\sqrt{3}$ mm.
11. 51.6 in. **12.** 1.77 in. **13.** 16 ft.

Exercise 6-9 (page 188)

1. (i) 84 sq. ft. (ii) 283 sq. cm. (iii) 277 sq. in. (iv) 150 sq. mm.
(v) 16 sq. cm. (vi) 84 sq. ft. (vii) 3 sq. cm. (viii) 7 sq. cm.
2. 126 sq. cm. **3.** $6\frac{6}{13}$ in., 6 in., $5\frac{3}{5}$ in.

Exercise 6-11 (page 193)

1. (i) $h(a + b + c)$ sq. units (ii) $h(a + b + c + d)$ sq. units
2. 288 sq. in.

3. (i) $\frac{1}{2} \cdot 3a \cdot l$ sq. units (ii) $2s \cdot l$ sq. units (iii) $\frac{1}{2} \cdot 5p \cdot l$ sq. units

4. 319 sq. cm. **5.** 240 sq. in. **6.** (i) 2,400 sq. in. (ii) 3,936 sq. in. **7.** 576 sq. cm.

Exercise 6-12 (page 196)

3. (i)   (ii)   (iii)

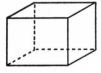

(iv)   (v)   (vi)

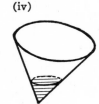

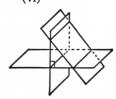

4. (i)   **5.**

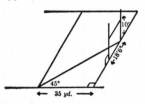
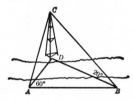

(ii) $63\frac{5}{6}$ yds.

6.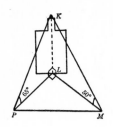

7.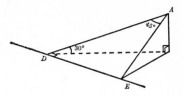

Exercise 6-13 (page 198)

1.

2.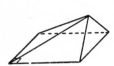

3.

4.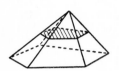

5. (i) 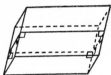   (ii)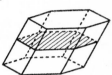

(iii) 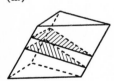   (iv) 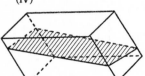   **6.**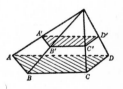

Discovery Exercise 6-14 (page 199)

1.

DIAGRAM	NAME OF POLYHEDRON	F	E	V	F + V	E + 2
(i)	Heptahedron	7	15	10	17	17
(ii)	Hexahedron	6	10	6	12	12
(iii)	Tetrahedron	4	6	4	8	8
(iv)	Hexahedron	6	12	8	14	14
(v)	Decahedron	10	24	16	26	26
(vi)	Pentahedron	5	8	5	10	10
(vii)	Pentahedron	5	9	6	11	11
(viii)	Octahedron	8	15	9	17	17
(ix)	Decahedron	10	15	7	17	17
(x)	Nonahedron	9	21	14	23	23
(xi)	Nonahedron	9	16	9	18	18
(xii)	Dodecahedron	12	18	8	20	20

2. The probable relationship among the faces, edges, and vertices of a polyhedron is
$$F + V = E + 2.$$

Exercise 6-15 (page 204)

1.

	F	E	V	F + V	E + 2
Regular Tetrahedron	4	6	4	8	8
Cube	6	12	8	14	14
Regular Octahedron	8	12	6	14	14
Regular Dodecahedron	12	30	20	32	32
Regular Icosahedron	20	30	12	32	32

Exercise 6-16 (page 206)

1. 24 in. **2.** 60 sq. cm. **3.** 8 sq. in. **4.** 2 sq. in., 4 sq. in.
5. 50 sq. in. **6.** 64 sq. in. **7.** 7 sq. in. **8.** 16 in.
9. 50 sq. in. **10.** 8 sq. in. **11.** 64 sq. mm. **12.** 40 sq. in.
13. 36 ft. **14.** 19.8 in. **15.** 14.1 in. **16.** 140 sq. in.
17. 120 sq. in.

Review Exercise 6-17 (page 207)

2. (i) (a) 16 sq. in. (b) 96 sq. in. (ii) 9.6 in.
3. 53 cm. **4.** 50 sq. in.
5. 88 sq. in. **6.** 13 in.
7. 14 in. **16.** 840 sq. in.
17. $6\sqrt{2}$ in., $72\sqrt{2}$ sq. in.

Exercise 7-1 (page 212)

6. (i) $5 : -7 : 9 = -\dfrac{10}{3} : \dfrac{14}{3} : -6;$ $12 : 18 : 24 = 2 : 3 : 4$

  (ii) $-\dfrac{3}{2},\ 6$

7. $4 : 5$ **8.** 18 in., 12 in.   **9.** $5 : 3$ **10.** (i) $2 : 3$ (ii) $4 : 9$

Exercise 7-2 (page 215)

14. (i) 7 (ii) y^2 (iii) $x^2 - y^2$ (iv) $\dfrac{a + b}{a}$

15. (i) 27 (ii) $\dfrac{4}{3}$ (iii) ar^2 (iv) y^2

16. (i) ± 12 (ii) $\pm\dfrac{3}{2}$ (iii) ± 1 (iv) $\pm ar$

17. (i) $7 : 5$ $3 : 2$ $-2 : 1$ $b : a$
  (ii) $\dfrac{12}{5}, \dfrac{5}{2}, -1, \dfrac{b + a}{a}$ (iii) $\dfrac{2}{5}, \dfrac{1}{2}, -3, \dfrac{b - a}{a}$

18. (i) $3 : 2$ (ii) $5 : 3$ (iii) $2 : 5$ **19.** 42 cm.

20. (i) $\dfrac{2}{5}$ (ii) $\dfrac{3}{5}$ **21.** (i) $\dfrac{1}{5}$ (ii) $\dfrac{4}{5}$ **22.** (i) $\dfrac{2m}{2m + 3s}$ (ii) $\dfrac{3s}{2m + 3s}$

23. (i) $\dfrac{a + b}{2a}$ (ii) $\dfrac{a - b}{2a}$

Exercise 7-3 (page 216)

1. $3 : 4$ **2.** $2\frac{5}{8}$ in.   **3.** \$3,200, \$2,400, \$1,000
4. 2 ft. 6 in.   **5.** 95   **6.** $9 : 1$
7. $33\frac{1}{3}\%$ **8.** 80% **9.** 352 ft.
10. 75

Exercise 7-4 (page 219)

5. (i) $3 : 5$ (ii) $5 : 3$ (iii) $8 : -5$ (iv) $8 : -3$
6. (i) $9 : 7$ (ii) $2 : 7$ **7.** (i) $3 : 4$ (ii) $7 : -4$
8. (i) $\dfrac{m}{m+n}$ (ii) $\dfrac{n}{m+n}$ **9.** (i) $\dfrac{a}{a-b}$ (ii) $\dfrac{a}{b-a}$

Exercise 7-8 (page 231)

4.   (i) $AB : ED = BC : DF = AC : EF$ (ii) $BC : AC = CD : CB = BD : AB$
(iii) $PQ : PS : QS = QR : SQ : SR = PR : PQ : QR$

Exercise 7-11 (page 242)

1. $1 : 2$ **2.** $1 : 3$ **3.** (i) $9 : 25$ (ii) $16 : 25$ **4.** $1 : 2$

Exercise 7-12 (page 243)

1. 28°   **2.** 15 cm.   **3.** 24   **4.** 7 cm.   **5.** 18 in.
6. 90°   **7.** 12 cm.   **8.** 36°   **9.** 14 cm.   **10.** 12 in.
11. $7\frac{1}{5}$ cm., 12 cm.   **12.** 1.5 sq. cm.   **13.** 24 sq. cm.   **14.** 100 sq. in.   **15.** 16 in.

Exercise 7-13 (page 245)

4. 2.7 cm., 4.8 cm., 3.6 cm.   **5.** 9 in., 4 in.

Exercise 8-1 (page 253)

2. $A(2, 3)$, $B(-3, 3)$, $C(-2, -1)$, $D(4, -3)$, $E(3, 0)$, $F(0, 2)$, $G(-4, -3)$, $H(0, -3)$, $I(4, 2)$, $J(-5, 3)$, $K(-1, 0)$, $L(3, -2)$, $M(1\frac{1}{2}, 1\frac{1}{2})$, $N(-2\frac{1}{2}, 1)$, $Q(-4, -1\frac{1}{2})$

3.

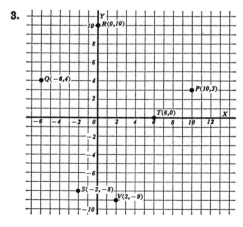

4. 10, 8   **5.** $(-3, -3)$, $(2, 5)$, $(7, 1)$
6. 5   **7.** 5

Exercise 8-2 (page 257)

4. (i) +475°   (ii) +320°   (iii) +918°
    (iv) +435°   (v) −834°   (vi) −188°

5. (i) −240°   (ii) 480°   (iii) 840°
    (iv) −600°   (v) 1200°   (vi) −960°

6. (i) (a) (180 + 47)°   (b) (180 − 70)°   (c) (360 − 70)°
        (d) (180 + 48)°   (e) (360 − 55)°   (f) (180 − 25)°
        (g) (360 + 22)°   (h) (360 + 60)°

(ii) (a)   (b)   (c)   (d)   (e)

(f)   (g)   (h)

7. (i) (a) 330°, 690°, −430°, −790°   (b) 702°, 1,062°, −18°, −378°
       (c) 198°, 558°, −522°, −882°   (d) 170°, 530°, −190°, −910°
       (e) 285°, 645°, −75°, −795°   (f) 125°, 845°, −235°, −595°
       (g) 365°, 725°, −355°, −715°   (h) 60°, 420°, −300°, −660°

(ii) (a)   (b)   (c)   (d)   (e)

(f)   (g)   (h)

8.   (i)   (ii)   (iii)   (iv)

     3rd quadrant   3rd quadrant   4th quadrant   4th quadrant

(v)   (vi)   (vii)   (viii)

2nd quadrant   3rd quadrant   2nd quadrant   1st quadrant

Exercise 8-3 (page 262)

1.

Degree measure	30	45	60	90	120	135	150	180
Radian measure	$\dfrac{\pi}{6}$	$\dfrac{\pi}{4}$	$\dfrac{\pi}{3}$	$\dfrac{\pi}{2}$	$\dfrac{2\pi}{3}$	$\dfrac{3\pi}{4}$	$\dfrac{5\pi}{6}$	π

2. (i) 6°   (ii) $-135°$ (iii) 225°   (iv) 1,830°
   (v) $-450°$ (vi) $247\frac{1}{2}°$ (vii) 18°   (viii) 300°

3. (i) $\dfrac{3\pi}{2}$ (ii) $-\dfrac{5\pi}{6}$ (iii) $-1\frac{3}{4}\pi$ (iv) $\dfrac{\pi}{18}$

   (v) $-4\frac{2}{3}\pi$ (vi) $2\frac{1}{2}\pi$ (vii) $\dfrac{\pi}{180}$ (viii) 6π **4.** $5\frac{1}{2}\pi$

Exercise 8-4 (page 266)

2. (i)   (ii)   (iii)   (iv)

(i)
$$\sin\theta = \frac{-5}{13}$$
$$\cos\theta = \frac{12}{13}$$
$$\tan\theta = \frac{-5}{12}$$

(ii)
$$\sin\theta = \frac{-4}{5}$$
$$\cos\theta = \frac{-3}{5}$$
$$\tan\theta = \frac{4}{3}$$

(iii)
$$\sin\theta = \frac{-1}{\sqrt{5}}$$
$$\cos\theta = \frac{2}{\sqrt{5}}$$
$$\tan\theta = \frac{-1}{2}$$

(iv)
$$\sin\theta = 0$$
$$\cos\theta = -1$$
$$\tan\theta = 0$$

(v)   (vi)   (vii)   (viii)

(v)
$$\sin\theta = \frac{-5}{\sqrt{26}}$$
$$\cos\theta = \frac{1}{\sqrt{26}}$$
$$\tan\theta = -5$$

(vi)
$$\sin\theta = \frac{1}{\sqrt{17}}$$
$$\cos\theta = \frac{4}{\sqrt{17}}$$
$$\tan\theta = \frac{1}{4}$$

(vii)
$$\sin\theta = 0$$
$$\cos\theta = 1$$
$$\tan\theta = 0$$

(viii)
$$\sin\theta = \frac{-3}{\sqrt{13}}$$
$$\cos\theta = \frac{-2}{\sqrt{13}}$$
$$\tan\theta = \frac{3}{2}$$

3. (i) sin 0° = 0   (ii) sin 90° = 1   (iii) sin 180° = 0   (iv) sin 270° = −1
   cos 0° = 1   cos 90° = 0   cos 180° = −1   cos 270° = 0

4. (i) (a) 1   (b) $\dfrac{-2}{5}$ (c) $\dfrac{-2}{5}$ (ii) (a) 1   (b) $\dfrac{2}{3}$ (c) $\dfrac{2}{3}$

   (iii) (a) $\sin^2\theta + \cos^2\theta = 1$ (b) $\dfrac{\sin\theta}{\cos\theta} = \tan\theta$

5. $\cos\theta = \dfrac{-4}{5}$, $\tan\theta = \dfrac{3}{4}$ 6. (i) $\sin\theta = \pm\dfrac{5}{13}$ (ii) $\cos\theta = \pm\dfrac{12}{13}$

7.

$$\sin\alpha = \frac{3}{\sqrt{34}}$$

$$\tan\alpha = \frac{-3}{5}$$

$$\sin\beta = \frac{-3}{\sqrt{34}}$$

$$\tan\beta = \frac{3}{5}$$

Exercise 8-5 (page 269)

2.   (i)   (ii)   (iii)   (iv)

	(i)	(ii)	(iii)	(iv)
$\sin\theta$	$\dfrac{-5}{13}$	$\dfrac{3}{5}$	$\dfrac{-1}{\sqrt{5}}$	0
$\cos\theta$	$\dfrac{-12}{13}$	$\dfrac{-4}{5}$	$\dfrac{2}{\sqrt{5}}$	−1
$\tan\theta$	$\dfrac{5}{12}$	$\dfrac{-3}{4}$	$\dfrac{-1}{2}$	0
$\csc\theta$	$\dfrac{-13}{5}$	$\dfrac{5}{3}$	$-\sqrt{5}$	not equivalent to a real number
$\sec\theta$	$\dfrac{-13}{12}$	$\dfrac{-5}{4}$	$\dfrac{\sqrt{5}}{2}$	−1
$\cot\theta$	$\dfrac{12}{5}$	$\dfrac{-4}{3}$	-2	not equivalent to a real number

2.

	(v)	(vi)	(vii)	(viii)

	(v)	(vi)	(vii)	(viii)
$\sin \theta$	-1	$\dfrac{4}{\sqrt{17}}$	0	$\dfrac{-3}{\sqrt{13}}$
$\cos \theta$	0	$\dfrac{1}{\sqrt{17}}$	1	$\dfrac{-2}{\sqrt{13}}$
$\tan \theta$	not equivalent to a real number	4	0	$\dfrac{3}{2}$
$\csc \theta$	-1	$\dfrac{\sqrt{17}}{4}$	not equivalent to a real number	$\dfrac{-\sqrt{13}}{3}$
$\sec \theta$	not equivalent to a real number	$\sqrt{17}$	1	$\dfrac{-\sqrt{13}}{2}$
$\cot \theta$	0	$\dfrac{1}{4}$	not equivalent to a real number	$\dfrac{2}{3}$

3. (i) csc 0° is not equivalent to a real number.
      sec 0° = 1
      cot 0° is not equivalent to a real number.

   (ii) csc 90° = 1
       sec 90° is not equivalent to a real number.
       cot 90° = 0

   (iii) csc 180° is not equivalent to a real number.
       sec 180° = −1
       cot 180° is not equivalent to a real number.

   (iv) csc 270° = −1
       sec 270° is not equivalent to a real number.
       cot 270° = 0

4. (i)

In each case, (a) $\sec^2 \theta - \tan^2 \theta = 1$ (b) $\csc^2 \theta - \cot^2 \theta = 1$.

   (ii) For any angle θ, $\sec^2 \theta - \tan^2 \theta = 1$, and $\csc^2 \theta - \cot^2 \theta = 1$ where each of these ratios is equivalent to a real number.

5. $\tan \beta = -\dfrac{1}{3}$, $\csc \beta = \sqrt{10}$, $\sec \beta = -\dfrac{\sqrt{10}}{3}$, $\cot \beta = -3$

6. $\sin \alpha = \dfrac{-12}{13}$, $\cos \alpha = \dfrac{-5}{13}$, $\csc \alpha = \dfrac{-13}{12}$, $\cot \alpha = \dfrac{5}{12}$

Exercise 8-6 (page 271)

4. (i) 1   (ii) $\frac{1}{4}$ (iii) -5 (iv) 6

     (v) **5**   (vi) $1\frac{1}{2}$ (vii) $\frac{1}{2}$ (viii) 2

Exercise 8-7 (page 275)

2. (i)
$$\sin A = \frac{2}{\sqrt{13}}, \quad \sin C = \frac{3}{\sqrt{13}}$$
$$\cos A = \frac{3}{\sqrt{13}}, \quad \cos C = \frac{2}{\sqrt{13}}$$
$$\tan A = \frac{2}{3}, \quad \tan C = \frac{3}{2}$$
$$\csc A = \frac{\sqrt{13}}{2}, \quad \csc C = \frac{\sqrt{13}}{3}$$
$$\sec A = \frac{\sqrt{13}}{3}, \quad \sec C = \frac{\sqrt{13}}{2}$$
$$\cot A = \frac{3}{2}, \quad \cot C = \frac{2}{3}$$

(ii)
$$\sin B = \frac{2}{\sqrt{29}}, \quad \sin C = \frac{5}{\sqrt{29}}$$
$$\cos B = \frac{5}{\sqrt{29}}, \quad \cos C = \frac{2}{\sqrt{29}}$$
$$\tan B = \frac{2}{5}, \quad \tan C = \frac{5}{2}$$
$$\csc B = \frac{\sqrt{29}}{2}, \quad \csc C = \frac{\sqrt{29}}{5}$$
$$\sec B = \frac{\sqrt{29}}{5}, \quad \sec C = \frac{\sqrt{29}}{2}$$
$$\cot B = \frac{5}{2}, \quad \cot C = \frac{2}{5}$$

(iii)
$$\sin A = \frac{4}{5}, \quad \sin B = \frac{3}{5}$$
$$\cos A = \frac{3}{5}, \quad \cos B = \frac{4}{5}$$
$$\tan A = \frac{4}{3}, \quad \tan B = \frac{3}{4}$$
$$\csc A = \frac{5}{4}, \quad \csc B = \frac{5}{3}$$
$$\sec A = \frac{5}{3}, \quad \sec B = \frac{5}{4}$$
$$\cot A = \frac{3}{4}, \quad \cot B = \frac{4}{3}$$

(iv)
$$\sin A = \frac{1}{\sqrt{2}}, \quad \sin B = \frac{1}{\sqrt{2}}$$
$$\cos A = \frac{1}{\sqrt{2}}, \quad \cos B = \frac{1}{\sqrt{2}}$$
$$\tan A = 1, \quad \tan B = 1$$
$$\csc A = \sqrt{2}, \quad \csc B = \sqrt{2}$$
$$\sec A = \sqrt{2}, \quad \sec B = \sqrt{2}$$
$$\cot A = 1, \quad \cot B = 1$$

3. (i)
$$\sin \angle PQT = \frac{\sqrt{3}}{2}, \quad \csc \angle PQT = \frac{2}{\sqrt{3}}$$
$$\cos \angle PQT = \frac{1}{2}, \quad \sec \angle PQT = 2$$
$$\tan \angle PQT = \sqrt{3}, \quad \cot \angle PQT = \frac{1}{\sqrt{3}}$$

(ii)
$$\sin \angle QPT = \frac{1}{2}, \quad \cos \angle QPT = \frac{\sqrt{3}}{2}, \quad \tan \angle QPT = \frac{1}{\sqrt{3}},$$
$$\csc \angle QPT = 2, \quad \sec \angle QPT = \frac{2}{\sqrt{3}}, \quad \cot \angle QPT = \sqrt{3}$$

4. (i) $\sin A = \dfrac{BC}{AB}$, $\csc A = \dfrac{AB}{BC}$ (ii) $\sin A = \dfrac{DC}{AC}$, $\csc A = \dfrac{AC}{DC}$

      $\cos A = \dfrac{AC}{AB}$, $\sec A = \dfrac{AB}{AC}$ $\cos A = \dfrac{AD}{AC}$, $\sec A = \dfrac{AC}{AD}$

      $\tan A = \dfrac{BC}{AC}$, $\cot A = \dfrac{AC}{BC}$ $\tan A = \dfrac{DC}{AD}$, $\cot A = \dfrac{AD}{DC}$

5. (i) $\sin \angle ACB = \dfrac{AB}{BC} = \dfrac{AD}{AC}$ (ii) $\sin \angle AEB = \dfrac{AB}{AE} = \dfrac{BD}{BE}$

      $\cos \angle ACB = \dfrac{AC}{BC} = \dfrac{DC}{AC}$ $\cos \angle AEB = \dfrac{BE}{AE} = \dfrac{DE}{BE}$

      $\tan \angle ACB = \dfrac{AB}{AC} = \dfrac{AD}{DC}$ $\tan \angle AEB = \dfrac{AB}{BE} = \dfrac{BD}{DE}$

      $\csc \angle ACB = \dfrac{BC}{AB} = \dfrac{AC}{AD}$ $\csc \angle AEB = \dfrac{AE}{AB} = \dfrac{BE}{BD}$

      $\sec \angle ACB = \dfrac{BC}{AC} = \dfrac{AC}{DC}$ $\sec \angle AEB = \dfrac{AE}{BE} = \dfrac{BE}{DE}$

      $\cot \angle ACB = \dfrac{AC}{AB} = \dfrac{DC}{AD}$ $\cot \angle AEB = \dfrac{BE}{AB} = \dfrac{DE}{BD}$

  (iii) $\sin \angle BAE = \dfrac{BE}{AE} = \dfrac{BD}{AB}$ $\csc \angle BAE = \dfrac{AE}{BE} = \dfrac{AB}{BD}$

      $\cos \angle BAE = \dfrac{AB}{AE} = \dfrac{AD}{AB}$ $\sec \angle BAE = \dfrac{AE}{AB} = \dfrac{AB}{AD}$

      $\tan \angle BAE = \dfrac{BE}{AB} = \dfrac{BD}{AD}$ $\cot \angle BAE = \dfrac{AB}{BE} = \dfrac{AD}{BD}$

6. (i) $\csc 40°$ (ii) $\sin 15°$ (iii) $\cot 42°$
   (iv) $\cos 33°$ (v) $\sec 30°$ (vi) $\tan 24°$

7. $\sin \angle ABD = \dfrac{1}{\sqrt{2}}$ $\csc \angle ABD = \sqrt{2}$

    $\cos \angle ABD = \dfrac{1}{\sqrt{2}}$ $\sec \angle ABD = \sqrt{2}$

    $\tan \angle ABD = 1$ $\cot \angle ABD = 1$

8. (i) $\sin A = \dfrac{3}{5}$, $\sin C = \dfrac{4}{5}$ (ii) $\sin A = \dfrac{2}{\sqrt{5}}$, $\sin C = \dfrac{1}{\sqrt{5}}$

      $\cos A = \dfrac{4}{5}$, $\cos C = \dfrac{3}{5}$ $\cos A = \dfrac{1}{\sqrt{5}}$, $\cos C = \dfrac{2}{\sqrt{5}}$

      $\tan A = \dfrac{3}{4}$, $\tan C = \dfrac{4}{3}$ $\tan A = 2$, $\tan C = \dfrac{1}{2}$

      $\csc A = \dfrac{5}{3}$, $\csc C = \dfrac{5}{4}$ $\csc A = \dfrac{\sqrt{5}}{2}$, $\csc C = \sqrt{5}$

      $\sec A = \dfrac{5}{4}$, $\sec C = \dfrac{5}{3}$ $\sec A = \sqrt{5}$, $\sec C = \dfrac{\sqrt{5}}{2}$

      $\cot A = \dfrac{4}{3}$, $\cot C = \dfrac{3}{4}$ $\cot A = \dfrac{1}{2}$, $\cot C = 2$

(iii) $\sin A = \dfrac{8}{17}$, $\sin C = \dfrac{15}{17}$ (iv) $\sin A = \dfrac{21}{29}$, $\sin C = \dfrac{20}{29}$

$\cos A = \dfrac{15}{17}$, $\cos C = \dfrac{8}{17}$ $\cos A = \dfrac{20}{29}$, $\cos C = \dfrac{21}{29}$

$\tan A = \dfrac{8}{15}$, $\tan C = \dfrac{15}{8}$ $\tan A = \dfrac{21}{20}$, $\tan C = \dfrac{20}{21}$

$\csc A = \dfrac{17}{8}$, $\csc C = \dfrac{17}{15}$ $\csc A = \dfrac{29}{21}$, $\csc C = \dfrac{29}{20}$

$\sec A = \dfrac{17}{15}$, $\sec C = \dfrac{17}{8}$ $\sec A = \dfrac{29}{20}$, $\sec C = \dfrac{29}{21}$

$\cot A = \dfrac{15}{8}$, $\cot C = \dfrac{8}{15}$ $\cot A = \dfrac{20}{21}$, $\cot C = \dfrac{21}{20}$

Exercise 8-8 (page 277)

16. .8746   **17.** 3.7321   **18.**   .8480   **19.** 2.790
20. .5095   **21.**   .0872   **22.** 1.2868   **23.**   .9004
24. .1736   **25.** 1.2690   **26.** 28.654   **27.** 1.0000
28. 49°   **29.** 65°   **30.** 27°   **31.** 68°
32. 35°   **33.** 84°   **34.** 53°   **35.** 21°
36. 5°   **37.** 78°

Exercise 8-9 (page 279)

3. (i) $c = 5$, $\angle B = 67°$, $\angle C = 23°$ (ii) $b = 2.9$, $\angle A = 59°$, $\angle C = 31°$
(iii) $a = 16.0$, $b = 18.9$, $\angle C = 32°$ (iv) $a = 10.1$, $c = 11.6$, $\angle A = 61°$
(v) $a = 69.4$, $\angle A = 66°$, $\angle C = 24°$ (vi) $b = 11.8$, $c = 12.8$, $\angle B = 67°$
(vii) $b = 6.1$, $c = 5.1$, $\angle B = 50°$ (viii) $b = 33.2$, $\angle A = 44°$, $\angle C = 46°$
(ix) $a = 2.6$, $b = 8.0$, $\angle A = 18°$ (x) $a = 20.7$, $c = 5.4$, $\angle B = 75°$
4. 8.6 in.

Exercise 8-10 (page 282)

1. 700 ft.   **2.** 321 ft.   **3.** 56 ft.   **4.** 480 ft.   **5.** 56 ft.
6. 37 mi.   **7.** 163 mi.   **8.** 70 ft.   **9.** 1,225 ft.   **10.** 520 ft.
11. 190 ft.   **12.** 432 yd.   **13.** 1,963 yd.   **14.** 3,565 ft.

Exercise 8-13 (page 288)

3. $b = 4.8$, $c = 8.0$, $\angle C = 68°$ **4.** $a = 7.3$, $c = 5.3$, $\angle B = 76°$
5. $a = 3.3$, $b = 3.9$, $\angle B = 78°$ **6.** $a = 10.7$, $c = 4.9$, $\angle B = 68°$
7. 5.7 units, 7.9 units   **8.** $BC = 5.4$ mi., $AC = 4.4$ mi.
9. $AB = 22.6$ ft., $AC = 10.2$ ft.   **10.** $IA = 932$ yd., $IB = 1,314$ yd.

Exercise 8-14 (page 290)

1. (i) -0.5736 (ii) -2.7475 (iii) .9962
(iv) -0.6249 (v) -1.0154 (vi) 1.3456
2. $b = 21.7$, $c = 32.3$, $\angle A = 12°$ **3.** $a = 3.5$, $b = 3.3$, $\angle B = 38°$
4. $a = 6.7$, $c = 4.3$, $\angle C = 20°$ **5.** 4.3 in.   **6.** 263 ft., 250 ft.

Exercise 8-15 (page 292)

3. $\angle A = 83°$, $\angle B = 41°$, $\angle C = 56°$ **4.** $a = 5.9$, $\angle B = 73°$, $\angle C = 45°$
5. $b = 42.8$, $\angle A = 45°$, $\angle C = 63°$ **6.** $\angle A = 61°$, $\angle B = 53°$, $\angle C = 66°$
7. S 3° W   **8.** 6°
9. 49 rods   **10.** 102°, 78°

Exercise 8-16 (page 295)

3. (i) 6.1 units   (ii) 7.5 units   (iii) 14.0 units
6. 9.2   **7.** 21   **8.** 17.3 in.   **9.** 16 in., 12 in.

Exercise 8-17 (page 297)

1. (i) 271 ft.   (ii) 132 ft.   **2.** 868 ft.   **3.** 616 ft.
4. 1,155 ft., 3,173 ft.   **5.** 211 ft.   **6.** 67 ft.
7. 19°   **8.** 54°   **9.** 203 ft.

Practice Exercise 8-18 (page 299)

4. $5 + \sqrt{3}$ **5.** 6   **6.** $\dfrac{1}{2}$ **7.** 1

8. $\dfrac{1}{3}$ **9.** (i) $\pm\dfrac{\sqrt{5}}{2}$ (ii) $\pm\dfrac{3}{\sqrt{5}}$

15. 703 ft.   **16.** 167 ft.   **17.** 155 ft.   **18.** 0.2 ft.

Exercise 9-1 (page 303)

1.   (i) $R_1 = \{(0, 0), (2, 6)\}$
      (ii) $R_2 = \{(-2, -2), (0, 0), (2, 2), (4, 4), (6, 6), (8, 8)\}$
     (iii) $R_3 = \{(-2, 4), (0, 0), (2, 4)\}$
     (iv) $R_4 = \{(-2, 0), (0, 2), (2, 4), (4, 6), (6, 8)\}$
     (v) $R_5 = \{(-2, 0), (-2, 2), (-2, 4), (-2, 6), (-2, 8), (0, 2), (0, 4), (0, 6),$
                $(0, 8), (2, 4), (2, 6), (2, 8), (4, 6), (4, 8), (6, 8)\}$
     (vi) $R_6 = \{(4, -2), (0, 0), (4, 2)\}$

2.   (i) $B_1 = \left\{ \left(\dfrac{3}{1}, \dfrac{5}{3}\right), \left(\dfrac{3}{1}, \dfrac{1}{1}\right), \left(\dfrac{3}{1}, \dfrac{7}{8}\right), \left(\dfrac{3}{1}, \dfrac{3}{5}\right), \left(\dfrac{3}{1}, \dfrac{1}{2}\right), \left(\dfrac{3}{1}, \dfrac{1}{3}\right), \left(\dfrac{5}{3}, \dfrac{1}{1}\right), \left(\dfrac{5}{3}, \dfrac{7}{8}\right), \right.$
             $\left(\dfrac{5}{3}, \dfrac{3}{5}\right), \left(\dfrac{5}{3}, \dfrac{1}{2}\right), \left(\dfrac{5}{3}, \dfrac{1}{3}\right), \left(\dfrac{1}{1}, \dfrac{7}{8}\right), \left(\dfrac{1}{1}, \dfrac{3}{5}\right), \left(\dfrac{1}{1}, \dfrac{1}{2}\right), \left(\dfrac{1}{1}, \dfrac{1}{3}\right), \left(\dfrac{7}{8}, \dfrac{3}{5}\right),$
             $\left. \left(\dfrac{7}{8}, \dfrac{1}{2}\right), \left(\dfrac{7}{8}, \dfrac{1}{3}\right), \left(\dfrac{3}{5}, \dfrac{1}{2}\right), \left(\dfrac{3}{5}, \dfrac{1}{3}\right), \left(\dfrac{1}{2}, \dfrac{1}{3}\right) \right\}$

     (ii) $B_2 = \left\{ \left(\dfrac{1}{3}, \dfrac{1}{2}\right), \left(\dfrac{1}{3}, \dfrac{3}{5}\right), \left(\dfrac{1}{3}, \dfrac{7}{8}\right), \left(\dfrac{1}{3}, \dfrac{1}{1}\right), \left(\dfrac{1}{3}, \dfrac{5}{3}\right), \left(\dfrac{1}{3}, \dfrac{3}{1}\right), \left(\dfrac{1}{2}, \dfrac{5}{3}\right), \left(\dfrac{1}{2}, \dfrac{7}{8}\right), \right.$
             $\left(\dfrac{1}{2}, \dfrac{1}{1}\right), \left(\dfrac{1}{2}, \dfrac{5}{3}\right), \left(\dfrac{1}{2}, \dfrac{3}{1}\right), \left(\dfrac{3}{5}, \dfrac{7}{8}\right), \left(\dfrac{3}{5}, \dfrac{1}{1}\right), \left(\dfrac{3}{5}, \dfrac{5}{3}\right), \left(\dfrac{3}{5}, \dfrac{3}{1}\right), \left(\dfrac{7}{8}, \dfrac{1}{1}\right),$
             $\left. \left(\dfrac{7}{8}, \dfrac{5}{3}\right), \left(\dfrac{7}{8}, \dfrac{3}{1}\right), \left(\dfrac{1}{1}, \dfrac{5}{3}\right), \left(\dfrac{1}{1}, \dfrac{3}{1}\right), \left(\dfrac{5}{3}, \dfrac{3}{1}\right) \right\}$

     (iii) $B_3 = \left\{ \left(\dfrac{1}{1}, \dfrac{1}{1}\right), \left(\dfrac{1}{3}, \dfrac{3}{1}\right), \left(\dfrac{3}{1}, \dfrac{1}{3}\right), \left(\dfrac{3}{5}, \dfrac{5}{3}\right), \left(\dfrac{5}{3}, \dfrac{3}{5}\right) \right\}$

(iv) $B_4 = \left\{ \left(\frac{1}{3}, \frac{7}{8}\right), \left(\frac{1}{3}, \frac{1}{1}\right), \left(\frac{1}{3}, \frac{5}{3}\right), \left(\frac{1}{3}, \frac{3}{1}\right), \left(\frac{1}{2}, \frac{5}{3}\right), \left(\frac{1}{2}, \frac{3}{1}\right), \left(\frac{3}{5}, \frac{5}{3}\right), \left(\frac{3}{5}, \frac{3}{1}\right), \right.$
$\left. \left(\frac{7}{8}, \frac{3}{1}\right), \left(\frac{1}{1}, \frac{3}{1}\right) \right\}$

3. (i) 20; 20; 25   (ii) 0, 2, 4, 6, 8; 1, 3, 5, 9   (iii) 4

4. $\{(-2, -2), (-2, 0), (-2, 2), (0, -2), (0, 0), (0, 2), (2, -2), (2, 0), (2, 2)\}$

5.

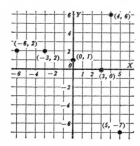 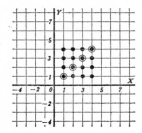

6. (i) $A \times A = \{(1, 1), (1, 2), (1, 3), (1, 4),$
$(2, 1), (2, 2), (2, 3), (2, 4),$
$(3, 1), (3, 2), (3, 3), (3, 4),$
$(4, 1), (4, 2), (4, 3), (4, 4)\}$

(ii) See accompanying graph (right above).

(iii) All the points above those circled in (ii);
all the points below those circled in (ii).

7. (i) $M \times N = \{(-1, -4), (-1, 0), (-1, 5), (1, -4), (1, 0), (1, 5), (3, -4),$
$(3, 0), (3, 5)\}$
$N \times M = \{(-4, -1), (-4, 1), (-4, 3), (0, -1), (0, 1), (0, 3), (5, -1),$
$(5, 1), (5, 3)\}$

(ii)

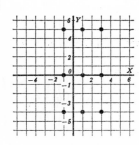 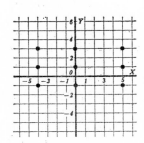

Graph of $M \times N$ Graph of $N \times M$

8. (i) $D \times D = \{(-2, -2), (-2, 0), (-2, 2), (-2, 4),$
$(0, -2), (0, 0), (0, 2), (0, 4),$
$(2, -2), (2, 0), (2, 2), (2, 4),$
$(4, -2), (4, 0), (4, 2), (4, 4)\}$

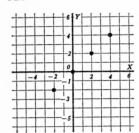 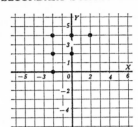 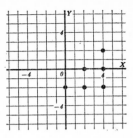

(ii) $D_1 = \{(-2, -2), (0, 0), (2, 2), (4, 4)\}$; graph left above.

(iii) $D_2 = \{(-2, 0), (-2, 2), (-2, 4), (0, 2), (0, 4), (2, 4)\}$; graph centre above.

(iv) $D_3 = \{(4, 2), (4, 0), (4, -2), (2, 0), (2, -2), (0, -2)\}$; graph right above.

Exercise 9-2 (page 306)

1. $\{(-1, -1), (0, 0), (1, 1), (2, 2), (3, 3), (4, 4)\}$
Domain is $\{x \mid x \in U\}$.   Range is $\{y \mid y \in U\}$.

2. $\{(0, 0), (1, 2), (2, 4)\}$
Domain is $\{0, 1, 2\}$.   Range is $\{0, 2, 4\}$.

3. $\{(-1, 0), (-1, 1), (-1, 2), (-1, 3), (-1, 4), (0, 1), (0, 2), (0, 3), (0, 4), (1, 2),$
$(1, 3), (1, 4), (2, 3), (2, 4), (3, 4), (1, 1), (2, 2), (3, 3), (4, 4)\}$
Domain is $\{x \mid x \in U\}$.   Range is $\{y \mid y \in U\}$.

4. $\{(-1, 4), (0, 4), (1, 4), (2, 4), (3, 4), (4, 4)\}$
Domain is $\{x \mid x \in U\}$.   Range is $\{4\}$.

5. $\{(-1, 0), (0, 1), (1, 2), (2, 3), (3, 4)\}$
Domain is $\{-1, 0, 1, 2, 3\}$.   Range is $\{0, 1, 2, 3, 4\}$.

6. $\{(-1, -1), (-1, 0), (-1, 1), (-1, 2), (-1, 3), (-1, 4)\}$
Domain is $\{-1\}$.   Range is $\{y \mid y \in U\}$.

7. $(-3, -3), (-3, -2), (-3, -1), (-3, 0)$, etc.
Domain is $\{-3\}$.   Range is $\{y \mid y \in I\}$.

8. $(0, 2), (1, 2), (2, 2), (3, 2)$, etc.
Domain is $\{x \mid x \in I\}$.   Range is $\{2\}$.

9. $(1, 0), (2, 1), (3, 2), (4, 3)$, etc.
Domain is $\{1, 2, 3, 4, 5, 6, 7, 8, 9\}$.   Range is $\{0, 1, 2, 3, 4, 5, 6, 7, 8\}$.

10. $(0, 0), (1, 1), (4, 2), (9, 3)$, etc.
Domain is $\{0, 1, 4, 9, 16, \ldots\}$.   Range is $\{y \mid y \in I\}$.

11. $(-2, 4), (-1, 2), (0, 0), (1, 2)$, etc.
Domain is $\{-3, -2, -1, 0, 1, 2\}$.   Range is $\{0, 2, 4, 6\}$.

12. $(-2, 6), (0, 3), (2, 0), (4, -3)$, etc.
Domain is $\{\ldots, -4, -2, 0, 2, 4, \ldots\}$.
Range is $\{\ldots, -6, -3, 0, 3, 6, \ldots\}$.

13. $(-2, 0), (-1, 0), (0, 0), (1, 0)$, etc.
Domain is $\{x \mid x \in I\}$.   Range is $\{0\}$.

14. $(0, -1), (0, 0), (0, 1), (0, 2)$, etc.
Domain is $\{0\}$.   Range is $\{y \mid y \in I\}$.

15.

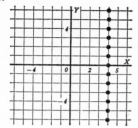

Domain is $\{4\}$.
Range is $\{y \mid y \in I\}$.

16.

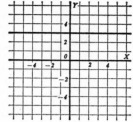

Domain is $\{x \mid x \in R\}$.
Range is $\{3\}$.

17.

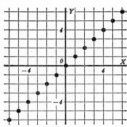

Domain is $\{x \mid x \in I\}$.
Range is $\{y \mid y \in I\}$.

18.

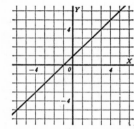

Domain is $\{x \mid x \in R\}$.
Range is $\{y \mid y \in R\}$.

19.

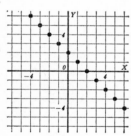

Domain is $\{x \mid x \in I\}$.
Range is $\{y \mid y \in I\}$.

20.

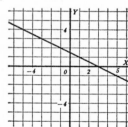

Domain is $\{x \mid x \in R\}$.
Range is $\{y \mid y \in R\}$.

21.

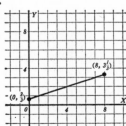

Domain is $\{x \mid 0 \leqq x \leqq 8, x \in R\}$.
Range is $\{y \mid \frac{2}{3} \leqq y \leqq 3\frac{1}{3}, y \in R\}$.

22.

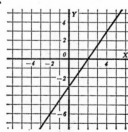

Domain is $\{x \mid x \in R\}$.
Range is $\{y \mid y \in R\}$.

23.

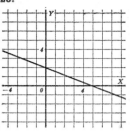

Domain is $\{x \mid x \in R\}$.
Range is $\{y \mid y \in R\}$.

Exercise 9-3 (page 309)

1.

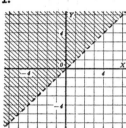

2.

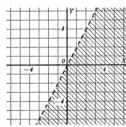

3.

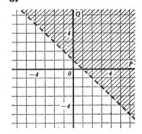

4.

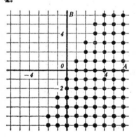

5.

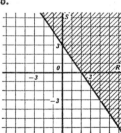

6.

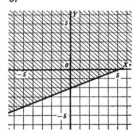

7.

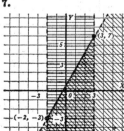

8.

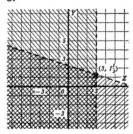

9.

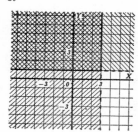

10.

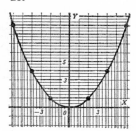

Exercise 9-4 (page 311)

19.

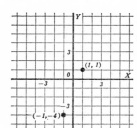

20. $F = \{(-2, 5), (-1, 2), (0, 1), (1, 2), (2, 5)\}$

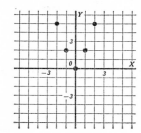

21. $y = x + 1, -2 \leqq x \leqq 1, x, y \in I$

22. (i) Domain is $\{-3, -2, -1, 0, 1, 2, 3\}$.
Range is $\{0, 1, 4, 9\}$.

  (ii) $y = x^2, |x| \leqq 3, x, y \in I$

23. (i) $\{(x, y) \mid y = 5x, 0 < x \leqq 5, x, y \in R\}$

  (ii) The relation is a function.

  (iii) Domain is $\{x \mid 0 < x \leqq 5, x \in R\}$.
Range is $\{y \mid 0 < y \leqq 25, y \in R\}$.

24. (i) $\{(r, A) \mid A = \pi r^2, r > 0, r \in R\}$

  (ii) Domain is $\{r \mid r > 0, r \in R\}$.
Range is $\{A \mid A > 0, A \in R\}$.

  (iii) The relation is a function.

25. (i) $\{(t, d) \mid d = 600t, 0 \leqq t \leqq 6, t \in R\}$

  (ii) Domain is $\{t \mid 0 \leqq t \leqq 6, t \in R\}$.
Range is $\{d \mid 0 \leqq d \leqq 3,600, d \in R\}$.

  (iii) The relation is a function.

26. (i) $\{(n, d) \mid d = 25n, 0 \leqq n \leqq 8, n \in I\}$

  (ii) Domain is $\{n \mid 0 \leqq n \leqq 8, n \in I\}$.
Range is $\{0, 25, 50, 75, 100, 125, 150, 175, 200\}$.

  (iii) The relation is a function.

Exercise 9-5 (page 314)

5. (i)

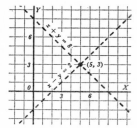

$A = \{(5, 3)\}$
Domain is $\{5\}$.
Range is $\{3\}$.

(ii)

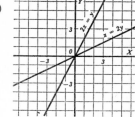

Domain is $\{x \mid x \in R\}$.
Range is $\{y \mid y \in R\}$.

(iii)

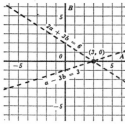

$C = \{(3, 0)\}$
Domain is $\{3\}$.
Range is $\{0\}$.

(iv)

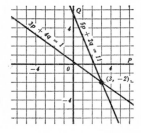

Domain is $\{x \mid x \in R\}$.
Range is $\{y \mid y \in R\}$.

6.

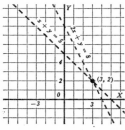

The relation is $\{(3, 2)\}$.

7.

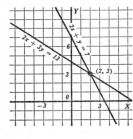

8.

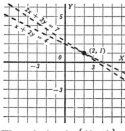

The relation is $\{(2, 1)\}$.

9.

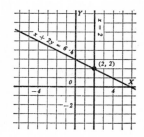

Exercise 9-6 (page 319)

1.

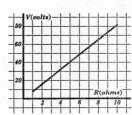

2. (i)

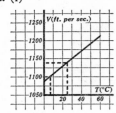

(ii) (a) 1141 ft. per sec.
(b) 6°C

3. (i)

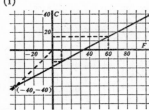

(ii) (a) 60°F
(b) −12°C
(c) −40°C

4.

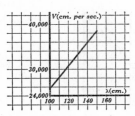

5. (i) $\{(t, v) \mid v = 32t, v, t \in {}^+R\}$

(ii) $\{(t, v) \mid v = 10 + 20t, v, t \in {}^+R\}$

6.

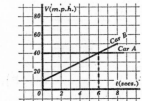

(i) 6 sec.
(ii) For car A:
$\{(t, v) \mid v = 40, t \geqq 0, t \in R\}$
For car B:
$\{(t, v) \mid v = 10 + 5t, t \geqq 0, t, v \in R\}$

Exercise 9-7 (page 322)

1.

Domain is $\{x \mid x \in R\}$.
Range is $\{y \mid y \in R\}$.

2.

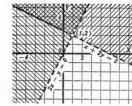

Domain is $\{x \mid x \in R\}$.
Range is $\{y \mid y > 2, y \in R\}$.

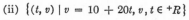

3.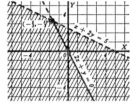

Domain is $\{x \mid x \geqq -\dfrac{5}{3}, x \in R\}$.

Range is $\{y \mid y \leqq \dfrac{10}{3}, y \in R\}$.

4.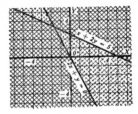

Domain is $\{x \mid x \in R\}$.

Range is $\{y \mid y \in R\}$.

5.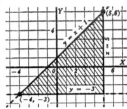

Domain is $\{x \mid -4 \leqq x \leqq 5, x \in R\}$.
Range is $\{y \mid -3 \leqq y \leqq 6, y \in R\}$.

6.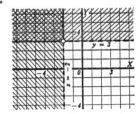

Domain is $\{x \mid x \in R\}$.
Range is $\{y \mid y \in R\}$.

7.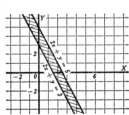

Domain is $\{x \mid x \in R\}$.
Range is $\{y \mid y \in R\}$.

8.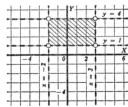

Domain is $\{x \mid -2 < x < 3, x \in R\}$.
Range is $\{y \mid 1 < y < 4, y \in R\}$.

9. (i)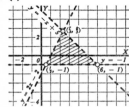

Domain is $\{x \mid \dfrac{1}{2} < x < 6, x \in R\}$.

Range is $\{y \mid -1 < y < \dfrac{8}{3}, y \in R\}$.

(ii)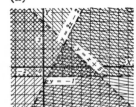

Domain is $\{x \mid x \in R\}$.

Range is $\{y \mid y \in R\}$.

10.

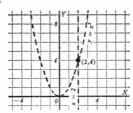

Domain is $\{2\}$.
Range is $\{4\}$.

11.

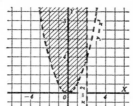

Domain is $\{x \mid x < 2, x \in R\}$.
Range is $\{y \mid y > 0, y \in R\}$.

12.

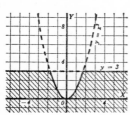

Domain is $\{x \mid x \in R\}$.
Range is $\{y \mid y \leqq 3, y \in R\}$.

13.

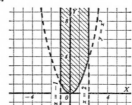

Domain is $\{x \mid -1 \leqq x \leqq 2, x \in R\}$.
Range is $\{y \mid y \geqq 0, y \in R\}$.

14. $\{(x, y) \mid y \leqq x + 2 \text{ and } y \leqq 2 \text{ and } y \geqq x - 1 \text{ and } y \geqq -1, x, y \in R\}$

15. $\{(x, y) \mid y \leqq 3x \text{ and } y \geqq 0 \text{ and } y \leqq -3x + 12, x, y \in R\}$

16. $\{(x, y) \mid x \geqq 0 \text{ and } y \geqq 0 \text{ and } y < \dfrac{12 - 3x}{4}, x, y \in R\}$ or, alternatively,

$\{(x, y) \mid x \geqq 0 \text{ and } y \geqq 0 \text{ and } 4y + 3x - 12 < 0, x, y \in R\}$

17. $\{(x, y) \mid x^2 + y^2 \leqq 9 \text{ and } y \geqq x + 2, x, y \in R\}$

18. $\{(x, y) \mid y \leqq \dfrac{3x + 6}{2} \text{ and } y \geqq \dfrac{3x}{2}, x, y \in R\}$ or, alternatively,

$\{(x, y) \mid 3x - 2y + 6 \geqq 0 \text{ and } 3x - 2y \leqq 0, x, y \in R\}$

19. $\{(x, y) \mid y \leqq \dfrac{6 - 3x}{2} \text{ and } y < 2x + 2 \text{ and } y > 1 - x, x, y \in R\}$ or, alternatively,

$\{(x, y) \mid 3x + 2y - 6 \leqq 0 \text{ and } 2x - y + 2 > 0 \text{ and } x + y - 1 > 0, x, y \in R\}$

Exercise 9-8 (page 326)

1. Maximum value of C occurs when C-line passes through $A(6, 1)$. Hence the maximum value of $C = 7$.

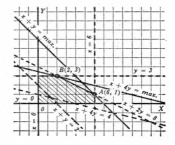

2. See the diagram for question 1.
Maximum value of K occurs when K-line passes through $B(2, 3)$. Hence the maximum value of $K = 2 + 4(3)$, or 14.

3.

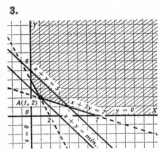

Minimum value of Q occurs when Q-line passes through $A(1, 2)$. Hence the minimum value of $Q = 3$.

4.

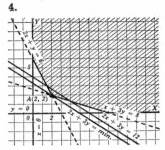

Minimum value of C occurs when the C-line passes through $A(2, 2)$. Hence the minimum value of $C = 2(2) + 3(2)$, or 10.

5.

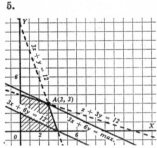

Maximum value of P occurs when P-line passes through $A(3, 3)$. Hence maximum value of $P = 3(3) + 6(3)$ or 27: that is, maximum profit occurs when 3 radios of each type are manufactured.

6.

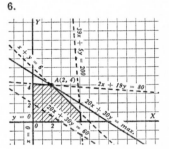

Maximum value of P occurs when P-line passes through $A(2, 4)$. Hence the maximum value of $P = 20(2) + 30(4)$, or 160: that is, maximum profit occurs when 2 standard models and 4 deluxe models are manufactured.

7.

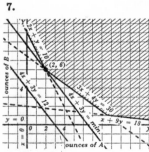

Protein: $10x + 5y \geqq 50$ or $2x + y \geqq 10$
Fat: $0.1x + 0.9y \geqq 1.8$ or $x + 9y \geqq 18$
Carbohydrate: $15x + 20y \geqq 150$ or $3x + 4y \geqq 30$
Cost: $4x + 3y$
From graph, cost is a minimum if 2 ounces of A and 6 ounces of B are purchased.

8.

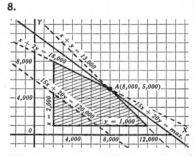

Maximum value of P occurs when the P-line passes through $A(8,000, 5,000)$. Hence the maximum value of $P = 15(8,000) + 20(5,000)$, or 220,000: that is, the maximum profit occurs when 8,000 barrels of standard gasoline and 5,000 barrels of premium gasoline are produced.

9.

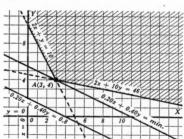

10.

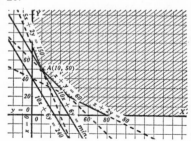

Minimum value of C occurs when the C-line passes through $A(3, 4)$. Hence the minimum value of $C = 0.20(3) + 0.40(4)$ or 2.2: that is, the minimum cost occurs when 3 ounces of alpha and 4 ounces of beta are produced.

Minimum value of C occurs when the C-line passes through $A(10, 50)$. Hence the minimum value of $C = 10(10) + 6(50)$, or 400 (cents): i.e. \$4.00 is the minimum cost. This occurs when 10 lbs. of Tops-N-Turf and 50 lbs of Lush-S-Lawn are purchased.

Review Exercise 9-9 (page 328)

1. (i) 24; 24; 16

    (ii) $(2, -3), (2, -1), (2, 0), (2, 1), (2, 3), (2, 5)$

    (iii) $(-1, -3), (-1, -1), (-1, 0), (-1, 1), (-1, 3), (-1, 5)$

2.

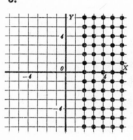

3.

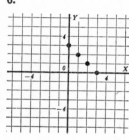

4.

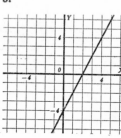

5.

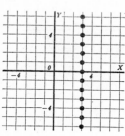

6.

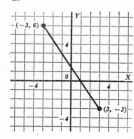

7.

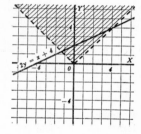

8.

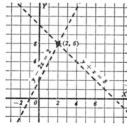

Domain is $\{2\}$.
Range is $\{6\}$.

9.

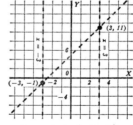

Domain is $\{-3, 3\}$.
Range is $\{-1, 11\}$.

10.

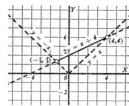

Domain is $\left\{x \mid -\dfrac{4}{3} < x < 4, x \in R\right\}$.

Range is $\left\{y \mid \dfrac{4}{3} < y < 4, y \in R\right\}$.

11.

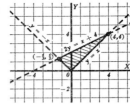

Domain is $\left\{x \mid -\dfrac{4}{3} \leqq x \leqq 4, x \in R\right\}$.

Range is $\{y \mid 0 \leqq y \leqq 4, y \in R\}$.

12.

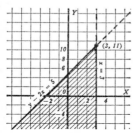

Domain is $\{x \mid x \leqq 3, x \in R\}$.
Range is $\{y \mid y \leqq 11, y \in R\}$.

13.

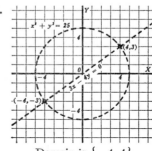

Domain is $\{-4, 4\}$,
Range is $\{-3, 3\}$.

14.

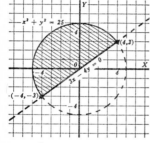

Domain is $\{x \mid -5 \leqq x \leqq 4, x \in R\}$.
Range is $\{y \mid -3 \leqq y \leqq 5, y \in R\}$.

15.

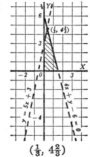

$\left(\dfrac{1}{3}, 4\dfrac{2}{3}\right)$

Exercise 10-1 (page 334)

9. $\{(-4,\,6)\}$ **10.** $\{(5,\,9)\}$ **11.** $\{(1\frac{1}{4},\,-1\frac{1}{8})\}$ **12.** $\{(-1,\,-2)\}$
13. $\{(2,\,2)\}$ **14.** $\{(2,\,1)\}$ **15.** $\{(1\frac{1}{4},\,2\frac{3}{4})\}$ **16.** $x=6,\ y=-2$
17. $x=7\frac{1}{7},\ y=-1\frac{4}{7}$ **18.** $x=12,\,y=8$

Exercise 10-2 (page 337)

4. 1, 2 **5.** 8, 3 **6.** 4, 6 **7.** .1, .4
8. 2, 5 **9.** -2, 7 **10.** $\{(-1,\,-2)\}$ **11.** $\{(12,\,18)\}$
12. (i) $\{(2,\,-1)\}$ **13.** $\{(4,5)\}$ **14.** $\{(5,\,2)\}$ **15.** $\{(3,\,4)\}$ **16.** $\{(\frac{1}{2},\,\frac{1}{3})\}$

Exercise 10-3 (page 340)

7. $\{(-3,\,1)\}$ **8.** $\{(6,\,2)\}$ **9.** $\{(7,\,8)\}$ **10.** $\left\{\left(-\dfrac{4}{3},\,\dfrac{17}{3}\right)\right\}$ **11.** $\{(-1,\,2)\}$
12. $\{(10,\,6)\}$ **13.** $\{(18,27)\}$ **14.** $\{(282,145)\}$ **15.** $\{(6,\,-8)\}$ **16.** $\{(7,\,-5)\}$
17. $\left\{\left(\dfrac{7}{3},\,-\dfrac{3}{2}\right)\right\}$ **18.** $\{(-4,\,3)\}$ **19.** $\{(-7,\,-5)\}$ **20.** $\{(-2,\,7)\}$

Exercise 10-4 (page 344)

1. $(2,\,1,\,-1)$ **2.** $(1,\,-1,\,1)$ **3.** $(3,\,-2,\,1)$ **4.** $(2,\,-3,\,-1)$
5. $(1,\,-3,\,3)$ **6.** $(\frac{2}{3},\,-3,\,3)$ **7.** $(2,\,\frac{1}{2},\,-2)$ **8.** $(2,\,-1,\,0)$
9. $(5,\,2,\,1)$ **10.** $(10,\,15,\,60)$ **11.** $(2\frac{1}{2},\,\frac{1}{2},\,0,\,4\frac{1}{2})$ **12.** $(2,\,-1,\,-3,\,1)$

Exercise 10-5 (page 348)

1. 7 cm., 5 cm.
2. 16, 11
3. \$6,000 at 5%, \$4,000 at 6%
4. 60 m.p.h.
5. 12 years
6. 57
7. 18, 14, 27
8. 513, 211
9. 18
10. 2,500, 1,500
11. \$4,000, \$16,000
12. 500 m.p.h., 20 m.p.h.
13. $\dfrac{13}{24}$
14. 25 in., 24 in., 7 in.
15. \$1.95, \$0.39
16. 100 c.c.
17. 6 bull's eyes, 4 inners
18. 4 m.p.h., $2\frac{1}{2}$ m.p.h.
19. 20
20. \$260, \$220
21. 627
22. 61, 29, 6

Exercise 10-6 (page 351)

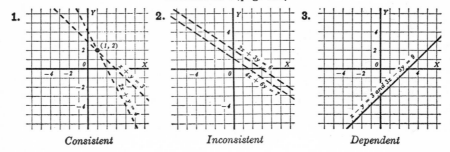

1. *Consistent* **2.** *Inconsistent* **3.** *Dependent*

Exercise 10-7 (page 353)

1. (r, s)

2. $\left(\dfrac{c(a + b)}{a + 2b}, \dfrac{c}{a + 2b} \right)$

3. $(2n, 2m)$

4. $(a + b, a - b)$

5. (k, h)

6. $\left(\dfrac{c(a - b)}{a^2 + b^2}, \dfrac{c(a + b)}{a^2 + b^2} \right)$

7. $\left(\dfrac{c_1 - b_1}{a_1 - b_1}, \dfrac{a_1 - c_1}{a_1 - b_1} \right)$

8. $\dfrac{1}{a}, \dfrac{1}{b}$

9. (b, a)

10. (a, b)

Exercise 10-8 (page 358)

13. $\dfrac{1}{1}, \dfrac{1}{1}, \dfrac{5}{3}$; none; no graph

14. $\dfrac{3}{2}, \dfrac{-1}{1}, \dfrac{5}{4}$; one; a point

15. $\dfrac{1}{1}, \dfrac{1}{1}, \dfrac{1}{1}$; unlimited; a line

16. $\dfrac{1}{1}, \dfrac{1}{1}, \dfrac{2}{1}$; none; no graph

17. $\dfrac{1}{2}, \dfrac{1}{2}, \dfrac{1}{2}$; unlimited; a line

18. $\dfrac{2}{3}, \dfrac{1}{-2}, \dfrac{5}{4}$; one; a point

19. $\dfrac{1}{2}, \dfrac{-1}{2}, \dfrac{1}{2}$; one; a point

20. $\dfrac{1}{2}, \dfrac{1}{2}, \dfrac{1}{5}$; none; no graph

21. $\dfrac{1}{1}, \dfrac{1}{1}, \dfrac{1}{1}$; unlimited; a line

22. $\dfrac{3}{1}, \dfrac{3}{1}, \dfrac{3}{1}$; unlimited

23. $\dfrac{4}{3}, \dfrac{3}{4}, \dfrac{0}{-28}$; one

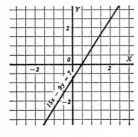

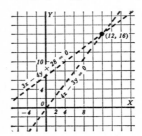

24. $\dfrac{1}{1}, \dfrac{1}{1}, \dfrac{1}{4}$; none

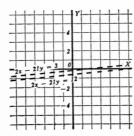

25. $(3, 0)$ **26.** $(2, 1)$ **27.** $(6, 2)$ **28.** $\left(-\dfrac{1}{2}, -\dfrac{1}{4} \right)$

29. $(8, 10)$ **30.** $(0.1, 0.4)$ **31.** $\left\{ \left(\dfrac{3}{4}, \dfrac{5}{3} \right) \right\}$ **32.** $\{(2, 5)\}$

33. $\{(x, y) \mid y = 3x + 1, x, y \in R\}$ **34.** $\{(4, 6)\}$

Exercise 10-9 (page 364)

1. $(4, 4)$
2. $(10, 20)$, $(5, 23)$, $(15, 17)$, $(20, 14)$, $(25, 11)$, $(30, 8)$, $(35, 5)$, $(40, 2)$
3. no solution   4. $(1, 24)$, $(3, 19)$, $(5, 14)$, $(7, 9)$, $(9, 4)$ 5. $(3, 7)$
6. $(9, 3)$ 7. $(7, 3)$, $(2, 6)$ 8. $(56, 25)$, $(16, 65)$
9. $(15, 22)$ 10. 11 12. $(1, 2, 3)$
13. $(4, 37, 2)$, $(7, 29, 7)$, $(10, 21, 12)$, $(13, 13, 17)$, $(16, 5, 22)$
14. $(4, 41, 5)$, $(8, 32, 10)$, $(12, 23, 15)$, $(16, 14, 20)$, $(20, 5, 25)$
15. $1{,}147$ 16. 23

Exercise 11-3 (page 370)

2. (i) 5 (ii) $\sqrt{130}$ (iii) $5\sqrt{5}$ (iv) $4\sqrt{2}$ (v) 8 (vi) 2
3. ± 6 4. (i) 18 (ii) 28
5. (i) right-angled   (ii) isosceles   7. -5
8. (i) $(1, 0)$ (ii) $(0, -1)$ 11. $x^2 + y^2 + 4x - 8y - 5 = 0$
12. $2 : 1$ 14. not collinear
15. 7

Exercise 11-5 (page 374)

2. $\sqrt{97}$, $\sqrt{61}$, $\sqrt{10}$ 3. $(3, 2)$

6. $\left(\dfrac{3}{2}, -\dfrac{5}{2}\right)$ 7. yes

Exercise 11-7 (page 378)

3. (i) $(-2\frac{4}{7}, 2\frac{3}{7})$ (ii) $\left(-3\frac{1}{9}, \dfrac{2}{3}\right)$ (iii) $(-1\frac{2}{3}, -1\frac{1}{3})$ (iv) $\left(1\frac{3}{7}, -\dfrac{2}{7}\right)$
4. $(0, -4)$; $(1, -5)$ 5. $(2, 0)$
6. $(-2, -6)$; $(0, -4)$; $(2, -2)$ 7. -1
8. $(2, -17)$ 9. $\left(\dfrac{x_1 + x_2 + x_3}{3}, \dfrac{y_1 + y_2 + y_3}{3}\right)$

Exercise 11-9 (page 383)

4. (i) $(11, 9)$ (ii) $(-2, 1)$ (iii) $(11, 34)$ (iv) $(4\frac{1}{2}, -7\frac{1}{2})$
5. -4 6. $(-2, -3)$ 7. $(11, -6)$
8. $(5\frac{3}{5}, 1\frac{1}{5})$ 9. $4 : -1$ 10. $(11, -8)$

Exercise 11-10 (page 386)

16. 1 17. -1 18. 0 19. undefined
20. $\frac{1}{2}, a \neq 0$ 21. undefined   22. $-\frac{3}{2}$ 23. 0
24. $\dfrac{b}{a}$ 25. 4 26. $\frac{4}{3}$ 27. $-5\frac{1}{2}$
28. $10x + 7y - 19 = 0$

Exercise 11-12 (page 389)

8. Yes.   9. No.   10. No.   11. Yes.
12. No.   13. Yes.   14. Yes.   15. No.
16. 2 17. Yes.   18. $6x + 7y + 9 = 0$ 19. $\frac{3}{2}$

Exercise 11-13 (page 392)

3. (i) 72°   (ii) 45°   (iii) 60°   (iv) 90°   (v) 159°   (vi) 81°
4. (i) 0.58 (ii) −1.00   (iii) 2.41 (iv) −0.47   (v) −1.73 (vi) −57.29
5. 90°   **6.** (i) 60°   (ii) 75°   (iii) 90°   (iv) 20°   (v) 75° (vi) 40°
7. −5   **8.** 8°

Exercise 11-14 (page 395)

19.   (i) $4x - 5y + 43 = 0$ (ii) $x - y = 0$
      (iii) $y = 4$ (iv) $x + y - 4 = 0$
      (v) $x + y - 1 = 0$ (vi) $y = -4$
      (vii) $x = 1$ (viii) $6x + 4y + 1 = 0$
      (ix) $8x - 9y - 12 = 0$ (x) $4x + 6y + 1 = 0$
20. $y = -4$ **21.** $y = 0$
22. $x = 3$ **23.** $x = 0$ **24.** $bx - ay = 0$; no absolute term; yes

Exercise 11-16 (page 398)

2. $2x - 2\sqrt{3}y - 7 = 0$ **3.** $3x - 2y + 6 = 0$
4. $x = -3; y = -1; x = 4; y = 2$ **5.** (i) 4   (ii) $x + \sqrt{3}y - 4\sqrt{3} = 0$
6. $-\dfrac{1}{2}; \dfrac{5}{2}$ **7.** $x = -1$ **8.** (i) 3   (ii) −5
9. (i) $(-4, 3)$ (ii) $\sqrt{3}$, $\sqrt{3}x - y + 4\sqrt{3} + 3 = 0$
10. (i) $y = -2x + b$ (ii) $b = 6; 2x + y - 6 = 0$

Exercise 11-17 (page 400)

4. $(0, \frac{1}{2})$ **5.** Yes.
6. $5x - 6y - 18 = 0$ **7.** $4x + 3y + 6 = 0$ **8.** 6
9. $5x + 4y + 11 = 0$; $x + y + 4 = 0$ **10.** $\dfrac{3}{4}$ **11.** $\dfrac{B}{A}$
12. $x - 3y + 19 = 0$; $4x + 3y - 29 = 0$ **13.** $2x + 5y - 9 = 0$ **14.** $(\frac{1}{2}, 0)$

Exercise 11-19 (page 404)

3. 20   **4.** (i) 30 (ii) 27 (iii) 11 (iv) 9 (v) 0
5. not collinear   **6.** −7
7. (i) 14.5 (ii) 5.8
8. $2x + 7y - 14 = 0$ or $2x + 7y + 6 = 0$ **9.** (i) $x + y - 1 = 0$
10. 4 or 24   **11.** $6\frac{2}{3}$

Exercise 11-21 (page 407)

3. 2
4.   (i) 3   (ii) 2   (iii) 1   (iv) 0   **(v)** 1
     (vi) $\sqrt{5}$ (vii) 8   (viii) 4   (ix) $\dfrac{|b|}{\sqrt{m^2 + 1}}$ (x) $\dfrac{|y_1 - mx_1|}{\sqrt{m^2 + 1}}$
5. ±5   **6.** $1\frac{1}{2}$
7. (i) $\dfrac{28\sqrt{29}}{29}$ (ii) $5x + 2y - 13 = 0$ **8.** The lines are concurrent.
9. 3, $7\frac{1}{4}$ **10.** 2
11. $1\frac{1}{2}$ **12.** $2x + 3y - 20 = 0$, $2x + 3y + 6 = 0$
13. $2x - 5y - 4 = 0$. Parallel to and midway between the given lines.

Review Exercise 11-23 (page 414)

6. $\sqrt{26}$, $4\sqrt{5}$, $5\sqrt{2}$ **7.** $(-18, 8)$

8. No.   **9.** -15

10. $75°$ **11.** $11x + 3y + 13 = 0$

12. $bx + ay - ab = 0$ **13.** $(1, 2)$

15. $(0, 1\frac{1}{4})$ **16.** $x + 2y + 1 = 0$

17. 3 or 19   **18.** double

19. $x + y - 1 = 0$ **21.** $\dfrac{42\sqrt{11}}{41}$

22. $5x - 12y - 20 = 0$, $5x - 12y + 32 = 0$

25. $\dfrac{|12 + k|}{10}$ **26.** $(3\frac{2}{5}, \frac{1}{5})$

29. $(3\frac{2}{11}, 1\frac{3}{11})$

Test Paper 1 (page 424)

1. music 360,   typing 330,   art 345

2. (i) 3   (ii) -13 **3.** $2z(y - z - x)$

5. $\dfrac{806}{2475}$ **6.** (i) $\{3\}$ (ii) $\left\{y \mid y > -\dfrac{13}{4}\right\}$

7.   **8.** $-18, 2$

9. (i) $-11\sqrt{2} - 18\sqrt{3}$ (ii) $-59 + 10\sqrt{6}$ (iii) $\dfrac{35 + 12\sqrt{6}}{19}$

10. $\dfrac{6}{5}$

Test Paper 2 (page 425)

1. -18 **2.** 9   **3.** $\{x \mid -2 \leqq x < 7\}$

4. $-2x^2 + 11xy - 14y^2$ **6.** $\dfrac{a^4b}{4c}$

7.

8. (i) $\{y \mid y \geqq -1\}$ (ii) $\{0, a + b\}$

9. (i) $\dfrac{2a^7}{3b}$ (ii) $115 + 16\sqrt{10}$ **10.** 4

Test Paper 3 (page 425)

1. (i) 24   (ii) 8   **2.** $-4x + 3y - 6z$

3. (i) $-7a^3 + 9b^3$ (ii) $x^2 - y^2$

4. $\left\{\dfrac{5}{-6}, \dfrac{3}{-8}, \dfrac{-1}{3}, \dfrac{0}{5}, \dfrac{-4}{-3}, \dfrac{-3}{-2}\right\}$ **5.** $\dfrac{2814}{275}$

6. (i) $\{3\}$ (ii) $\{x \mid x \geqq -2\}$

7. (i) $-1, \frac{3}{2}$ (ii) $\frac{3}{2}, 4$ **8.** $(19\sqrt{6} - 38)$ sq. in.

9. (i) $(6\sqrt{5} - 5\sqrt{3}, 4\sqrt{15} - 15)$ (ii) $\sqrt{30} - 2$ **10.** 4

Test Paper 4 (page 426)

2. 13.2 cm.   **3.** 7.5 sq. cm.   **4.** (i) 2.5 in.   (iii) 7.8 cm.

Test Paper 5 (page 427)

1. $\frac{449}{990}$ **2.** (i) $\{2\}$ (ii) $\{x \mid x \leqq -1,\ x \in I\}$

3. (i) $\dfrac{25r^{14}t^{10}}{s^4}$ (ii) $\dfrac{y^{18}}{x^{26}}$ (iii) $6z^5 + 7z$

4. (i) $6 + \sqrt{35}$ (ii) $-3\sqrt{2} + 2\sqrt{6} - \sqrt{3} + 2$ **5.** 12 units, 20 units

Test Paper 6 (page 428)

1. (i) $7\sqrt{3}$ (ii) $\mid ax \mid \sqrt{a}$ (iii) $\mid x + y \mid \sqrt{x} - y$

2. $\frac{1}{10}$ **3.** $\{x \mid 1 < x < 3\}$ **4.** $8\sqrt{14}$ sq. in.

5. (i) 96 sq. in. (ii) 10 in.

Test Paper 7 (page 429)

1. (i) $\{y \mid y > \frac{7}{5}\}$ (ii) (a, b)

2. (i) $\frac{116}{495}$ (ii) $4 + \sqrt{10}$

3. (i) $0, 3$ (ii) $a, b + c - a$

5. $12, 8\sqrt{3}$ **7.** $b = 59,\ \angle C = 32°,\ \angle B = 102°$

9. $157\frac{1}{2}$ **10.** $(-2, 2),\ \sqrt{85}$

Test Paper 8 (page 429)

1. 15   **2.** (i) $\{x \mid x \neq 1,\ x \in R\}$ (ii) $\dfrac{bc^2}{a^2}$

3. $0, -12$ **7.** (i) 1 (ii) 0

8. $a = 41,\ b = 35,\ \angle C = 70°$ **9.** $(12, -4)$

10. (i) 0 (ii) $-\frac{1}{4}$

Test Paper 9 (page 430)

1. (c)   **2.** (d)   **3.** (c)   **4.** (d)   **5.** (a)

6. (b)   **7.** (c)   **8.** (c)   **9.** (d)   **10.** (c)

11. (d)   **12.** (b)   **13.** (b)   **14.** (d)   **15.** (c)

16. (b)   **17.** (e)   **18.** (d)   **19.** (c)   **20.** (d)

INDEX

GLENFOREST SEP 1971